FUNDAMENTALS OF CIRCUITS, ELECTRONICS, AND SIGNAL ANALYSIS

FUNDAMENTALS OF CIRCUITS, ELECTRONICS, AND SIGNAL ANALYSIS

Kendall L. Su
Georgia Institute of Technology

Printed in the U.S.A.

Library of Congress Catalog Card Number: 77-074147

ISBN: 0-395-25038-2

D
621.3815'3
su

CONTENTS

PREFACE

This text is primarily intended to be used in an introductory course for electrical engineering majors. It is designed to serve as a text for a preparatory course for other, higher-level courses in several areas. It begins with a treatment of simple circuits. Then it presents general techniques of network analysis. It then uses these techniques to introduce the student to basic electronics. These analyses of electronic circuits also serve, at the same time, as exercises for the study of circuit analysis. After that, we turn our attention to the analysis of signals, both in the time domain and in the frequency domain, as well as their interrelationship in these two domains. These ideas are further generalized into the systems concept, using networks as examples. To some extent, this approach unifies several basic topics — some of which are common or overlapping — in circuits, electronics, transforms, signal analysis, and systems.

Because of this unified approach, the student will not have to repeat the same topics that used to appear in several texts in the same curriculum. These topics are instead viewed as the same background material for several areas, such as networks, system theory, devices, electronics, communication, power, control engineering, instrumentation, digital systems, and computers. It is particularly suited for curriculums in which students are not required to take higher-level courses in all the aforementioned areas. In these curriculums, the course in which this text is used will be the terminal course for those students whose programs do not indicate further courses in areas in which they are not specializing.

The text can also be used for an introductory course in electrical engineering for students in allied fields whose interest in electrical engineering requires a more definitive treatment than can be found in a general superficial survey of all topics in electrical engineering. It is particularly suited to students whose future careers will be benefited if they understand the basic principles and terminology in certain areas in electronics and electrical engineering. These students include those in many branches of engineering and technology, physics, chemistry, mathematics, computer science, biological sciences, medicine, behavioral science, and so forth.

The fields of electrical and computer engineering have broadened so much in the last few decades that it is no longer possible to cover every subarea in the same depth as used to be possible in a four-year curriculum in these fields. Yet these subareas are all somewhat interrelated. Hence some tradeoff between depth and breadth is necessary. One option in designing an electrical-engineering curriculum is to have a broad requirement at the basic level and to allow the student to choose — and pursue in depth — only a few of the many subareas. Also this approach makes it possible to present some of the overlapping topics more efficiently. This text is designed to accomplish some of these goals.

Another important need that this text is designed to meet is the need of many engineers and scientists whose specialties are not in traditional electrical engineering. These people often find that they are working more and more closely with electronics. A basic text that would enable them to become somewhat conversant with areas such as circuits, electronics, instrumentation, computers, and so forth, would be extremely helpful in their careers.

On the basis of the foregoing reasons, we have adopted the following editorial practices.

1 The treatment of devices is confined to qualitative descriptions and terminal characteristics. We believe that the best place to treat devices in detail is in a separate course dealing with the physics of materials and devices.

2 Although considerations of aspects of engineering design are occasionally touched on, the emphasis in this volume is primarily on basic principles and methods of analysis.

3 We assume that the student has had only basic courses in calculus and physics. Beyond that there is no real body of knowledge in mathematics that is absolutely needed for this text. There is an appendix on matrices, which is organized as if it were a chapter.

4 The chapter on state variables is quite independent of the rest of the text, and may be omitted from a course if the instructor so desires. Some instructors regard this topic as very basic. Others argue that it is best introduced where this method is most useful — in system theory, computer-aided analysis or design, nonlinear systems, time-varying systems — but not as a basic tool. We feel that it should be taught in a basic course, but not as a prerequisite for the bulk of the material.

5 The chapter on digital circuits is also organized as a self-contained entity. This level of treatment is adequate for a survey course.

6 The style of presentation emphasizes conciseness and brevity. This is done for two reasons. Since we are assuming that the instructor will maintain a fairly rapid pace in covering the material in the text, a more detailed and wordy exposition would tend to distract the mainstream of thought. The other reason is a practical one: A detailed treatment of every topic would lead to a book that was just too voluminous. But we believe that the extent and thoroughness of our coverage is quite adequate for the purposes for which it is intended.

7 For similar reasons, we choose to emphasize plausibility, rather than rigor. We believe that most engineering students benefit more from practical aspects of engineering, correctly handled, than from abstractions and over-exacting treatment of the subject matter. Occasionally, we rely on examples to illustrate certain points.

Chapter 1 gives basic definitions of terms and symbols used in the text, and terminal characteristics of resistance, inductance, capacitance, and controlled sources. The descriptions of these elements are not confined to linear time-invariant aspects, but are general in their applications.

Chapter 2 introduces Kirchhoff's voltage and current laws, and develops several simple relationships and techniques of analysis based on these laws, using simple memoryless circuits to illustrate them. In order to save time, topological considerations of networks are implemented right on the network diagrams rather than on separately constructed graphs.

The concept of linear networks is first defined in Chapter 3, which describes several special properties of linear networks in the form of network theorems. We introduced Tellegen's theorem here, though its validity is not restricted to linear networks, because there is really no other logical place for it in this volume.

Energy-storing elements begin to appear in circuits in Chapter 4. Here we treat some simple circuits involving memory elements, more to illustrate how complicated these circuit problems can be than to attempt to develop any general method of treating complicated memory networks. These examples also serve to show the roles of a certain special class of differential equations in memory networks and lead to the formulation of ac-circuit problems and the introduction of the complex frequency variable in Chapter 5.

We approach the notion of ac circuit analysis from the viewpoint of the solution for the steady-state response of a network with exponential excitations. We then extend the analysis techniques developed for memoryless networks in Chapters 2 and 3 to circuits with complex-number elements and source strengths. Several aspects of ac power, including the maximum-power theorem, are then examined.

Chapter 6 treats circuits with nonlinear and linear memoryless elements, with particular attention being paid to circuits with diodes as nonlinear elements. We give qualitative descriptions of some diodes, but the emphasis is on their terminal characteristics. We also give some applications of these circuits.

Up until this point, we have been concerned only with two-terminal elements. Before delving into electronic circuits, Chapter 7 presents some basic rules and techniques for handling multi-terminal or multi-port devices. It emphasizes how networks with two ports are analyzed when they are unterminated, terminated in an impedance, or interconnected. Amplifiers, magnetically coupled inductors, and ideal transformers appear as two-ports in networks and systems. Chapter 7 also gives examples on how to handle three-terminal devices, such as transistors.

Chapters 8, 9, and 10 treat the basics in electronics: the field-effect transistor, the bipolar transistor, the vacuum tube, integrated circuits, and the operational amplifier. When appropriate, three types of problems are treated — the dc, the slow-varying large-signal, and the small-signal ac. Here the emphasis is on acquiring a facility in analyzing a given circuit and an understanding of the underlying principles rather than on considerations of design, formulas for specific circuits, or specialty circuits. Up to this point, all electrical quantities are either dc, single-frequency sinusoidal, or some special functions of time.

In Chapter 11, we begin to look into methods of determining the performance of networks when the frequency is varied. In Chapter 12, we carry out network analysis in the time domain.

Our exposition of the concept of transforms begins with the idea of Fourier series expansion of periodic quantities in Chapter 13. This admittedly is a purely mathematical topic. However, by identifying these series with electrical quantities in circuits, we are able to give some physical significance to the connection between the time domain and the frequency domain. We then extend this concept to nonperiodic quantities in Chapter 14, which deals with the Fourier integral. In Chapter 15, we treat the two-sided Laplace transform as a generalization of the Fourier transform by replacing $j\omega$ by s and interposing the regions of convergence. Then we specialize the two-sided transform to the one-sided transform. Thus we do not emphasize the Laplace transform as being a tool for solving network problems, although we do include this application. On the whole, Laplace transform is treated from the standpoint of both circuit-analysis and signal-analysis techniques.

Chapter 16 gives an account of the state-variable method as it applies to linear networks. Perhaps this is not the best way to show the versatility and outstanding features of this method. But to do it any other way would be impractical in this volume.

The last chapter gives a survey of the fundamentals of digital circuits. It defines basic binary operations and gates, then gives examples of what they do, how they work, and how they can be constructed.

Three appendixes are included. Appendix A gives proofs of several theorems stated in Chapter 3. Appendix B presents pertinent topics in matrix algebra. The instructor can use this appendix as a regular chapter, if a curriculum is so designed that this topic is taught — or should be reviewed — in the course sequence covering the material of this text. (A logical place to use it would be between Chapters 6 and 7.) Appendix C gives answers to selected homework problems.

The text is ideally suited for a three-semester or a four-quarter sequence if all topics included are to be covered adequately. Of course, the number of hours in each term depend somewhat on the overall curriculum. Our estimate is that nine semester-hours or twelve quarter-hours would be typical.

The instructor can also adapt this text to suit many other curriculum needs by selecting only certain appropriate topics. For example, a three-quarter course for E.E. majors may cover only the first 15 chapters. Or a two-quarter survey course in electronics may include only Chapters 1, 2, 3, 4, 5, 6, 8, 9, 10, and 17, plus part of Chapter 7, with possible omissions of topics such as Tellegen's theorem, indefinite admittance matrix, and the like. Another possibility would be to leave out the electronics part of this volume (Chapters 8, 9, 10 and 17) and use the text in a course in circuits and signal analysis. All these combinations are feasible without disruption or discontinuity in the presentation of the course material.

This book is the outgrowth of a set of class notes prepared for several basic courses at Georgia Tech in the last five years. While the manuscript of this book was being prepared and class-tested, many of my colleagues and students have been inconvenienced. They had to put up with the various forms of reproduction of early versions of the manuscript. I don't feel that an apology to them would be appropriate, although I do appreciate their patience and support. Rather, I wish to say that I sincerely feel that they all had a part in the preparation of the manuscript. To those who offered suggestions and comments, I am deeply grateful. I want especially to thank my dear friend and colleague, Professor Thomas M. White, for his careful reading of the final manuscript. I am also indebted to Professor John Carr, of the University of Pennsylvania, Professor Harvey Doemland, of the University of Kansas, Professor Ward J. Helms, of the University of Washington, and Professor R.P. Santoro, of the U.S. Naval Academy, for their constructive comments on the book during its various stages of development.

I owe a special debt of gratitude to my life partner, Jennifer, for her patience and understanding during the preparation of this book.

K. L. S.

1 | PRELIMINARIES AND CIRCUIT ELEMENTS

1.1   Introduction

We live in an age of highly developed technology: instant communication, extremely high mobility, extensive computerization, and space explorations. We can safely state that these feats would not have been possible without the advent of electrical and electronics engineering. The four major areas of this engineering field are: analog systems, digital systems, electromagnetic field theory, and properties of materials. This volume deals with the basic tools and concepts in two of these areas: *analog systems* and *digital systems*.

The mathematical tools used in this area are, to a great extent, common to a large variety of systems, such as mechanical, acoustical, hydraulic, commodity flow, and of course electrical systems. You should keep in mind that most of the techniques you are going to learn here are directly applicable to many other systems.

In an analog system, electrical quantities may assume any values, sometimes within a certain range. In a digital system, the quantities can assume only certain discrete values, or ranges of values. In a binary system, a quantity may assume one of two values, say, either 1 or 0. In a trinary system, a quantity may assume only one of three values, say, 2, 1, or 0. And so on.

An interconnection of a number of electrical *elements* is called an electric *circuit*, *network*, or *system*. Usually a relatively simple interconnection is known as a *circuit*. A more complex interconnection is known as a *network*. The term *system* usually connotes an interconnection of components each of which is a circuit, a network, or another system. There is no clearly definable line of demarcation among these three terms. They are strictly subjective. Thus, for our purposes, these three terms may be used interchangeably.

A circuit can be used to deliver power, to process or transmit signals, to measure a physical quantity, or to store information. Whatever the purpose, the function of a circuit is usually manifested in the magnitude or time variation of either a *voltage* or a *current*. An *input* of a circuit is the locality at which a voltage or current is applied. An *output* is the locality at which a voltage or current is observed. The electric quantity (voltage or current) applied at the input is called the *excitation, input,* or *stimulus*. The quantity at the output is known as the *response*, or, more simply, the *output*. Generally both the excitation and the response—as well as all internal quantities of a circuit—are functions of time. If these functions of time are specified for *all* time, then we have a *continuous-time system*. If the values of these functions at only certain fixed instants are of interest, then the system is a *discrete-time system*. Figure 1.1 illustrates how a system quantity may be analog or digital, and may be either a continuous-time or a discrete-time system.

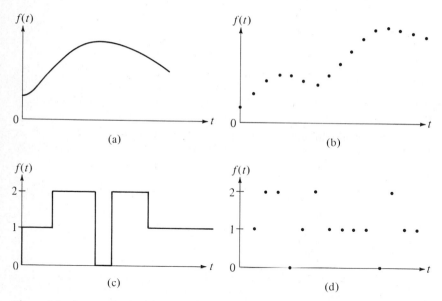

Figure 1.1 A quantity in (a) a continuous-time analog system, (b) a discrete-time analog system, (c) a continuous-time digital (trinary) system, and (d) a discrete-time digital (trinary) system.

In this volume, we shall deal exclusively with the *analysis* of electrical systems. In an analysis problem, a circuit and one or several inputs are given, and the output or outputs are to be found. In a more difficult type of problem—the *synthesis* or *design*—one or several inputs and their corresponding desired output(s) are given, and a circuit is to be found or designed.

1.2 Basic symbols and notation

A circuit *element* is usually a mathematical model of a physical device. It represents the external electrical behavior of the device in mathematical terms. In representing a physical device by a circuit element, we almost always need some approximation. Hence it is extremely important to keep in mind the limited ability of the circuit element to represent its real-world counterpart accurately. Within these limitations, however, we shall regard these models as the *exact* representation of the corresponding device and apply all facilities and finesses at our disposal to attack the problem at hand. But we must exercise due precautions in interpreting our results.

We shall assume that you are sufficiently familiar, from physics courses, with the basic electromagnetic quantities listed in Table 1.1. Certain frequently used prefixes that indicate multiples or submultiples are given in Table 1.2 for your reference.

Table **1.1** Some basic physical quantities

Quantity	Unit	Abbreviation
Time	second	s
Electric charge	coulomb	C
Electric current	ampere	A
Voltage (potential difference)	volt	V
Magnetic flux	weber	Wb
Energy	joule	J
Power	watt	W

Table **1.2** Prefixes and abbreviations for multiples and submultiples

Multiple or submultiple	Prefix	Abbreviation
10^{12}	tera	T
10^{9}	giga	G
10^{6}	mega	M
10^{3}	kilo	k
10^{-3}	milli	m
10^{-6}	micro	μ
10^{-9}	nano	n
10^{-12}	pico	p

A *terminal* is simply a connecting point or junction in a network. The physical counterpart of a terminal may be either a *terminal post* or a *soldered joint*. It is represented by a small dot—solid or hollow—as shown in Figure 1.2(a).

A *short circuit* (or simply *short*) is a path along which an electric current is free to flow. A short circuit may represent a highly conducting wire. It is also frequently used to connect points in a network that have the same potential. It is represented symbolically by a solid line, as shown in Figure 1.2(b).

An *open circuit* is a condition in which no electric current can flow between two points. This situation is represented by the lack of a path, as illustrated in Figure 1.2(c).

A *switch* connected between two terminals places a short circuit between the two terminals when it is *closed*, and an open circuit when it is *opened*. The latter status is shown in Figure 1.2(d).

A *grounded terminal* or *ground* is one whose absolute potential is assumed to be zero. A grounded terminal may be merely one whose potential is used for reference purposes. Or else it may be the representation of an actual grounding, achieved by physically connecting that point to earth. The symbol for a ground is shown in Figure 1.2(e).

In electrical engineering, an *electric potential* is more commonly known as a *voltage*. The absolute potential at a point is the voltage of that point (above ground). The relative potential between two points is the voltage difference between those points. There are two ways to describe the voltage difference between two points: (1) The *voltage rise* from A to B is the amount of voltage by which B exceeds A. (2) The *voltage drop* from C to D is the

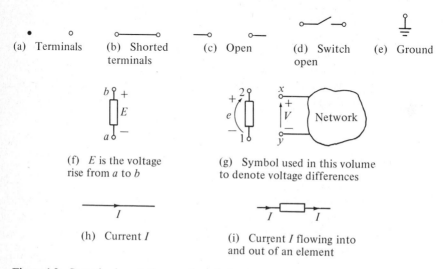

(a) Terminals (b) Shorted terminals (c) Open (d) Switch open (e) Ground

(f) E is the voltage rise from a to b

(g) Symbol used in this volume to denote voltage differences

(h) Current I

(i) Current I flowing into and out of an element

Figure 1.2 Some basic notations and symbols.

amount of voltage by which C exceeds D. Hence, if point 1 is at 10 V and point 2 is at 6 V, we may describe the potential difference between these two points in any of the following ways.

The voltage rise from 2 to 1 is 4 V.
The voltage rise from 1 to 2 is -4 V.
The voltage drop from 1 to 2 is 4 V.
The voltage drop from 2 to 1 is -4 V.

These four statements are all equivalent.

In electrical engineering literature, two types of symbols are used to denote voltage differences—plus and minus signs and arrows. In the plus-and-minus convention, the terminal on the plus side of a voltage is *assumed* to have the higher voltage. Thus, in Figure 1.2(f), E denotes the voltage rise from a to b or, equivalently, the voltage drop from b to a. (Of course, E itself may actually have a negative numerical value.)

An arrow is used by most authors to denote the direction of a voltage rise. Unfortunately, some authors use an arrow to indicate a voltage drop. Then there are those who use two-headed arrows to indicate the two points between which a voltage difference is assumed. A pair of plus and minus signs is then added to indicate the direction of the assumed relative voltage, according to the convention described in the previous paragraph.

In this volume, we shall use an arrow to indicate the direction of an assumed voltage rise, adding a pair of plus and minus signs to minimize any possible ambiguity. For example, in Figure 1.2(g), e denotes the voltage rise from 1 to 2 and V denotes the voltage rise from y to x.

It is sometimes convenient to use a double-subscript notation for voltages. Thus E_{xy} or V_{xy} denotes the voltage of point x with reference to point y. In this convention, E_{xy} or V_{xy} is either the voltage rise from y to x or the voltage drop from x to y. In Figure 1.2(f), $E = E_{ba}$. And in Figure 1.2(g), $E_{21} = e$ and $E_{xy} = V$. In general, $E_{xy} = E_x - E_y$.

The direction of a *current* is the direction of the *positive charge flow*. (This is exactly opposite to the direction of the electron flow.) A current is denoted by an arrow in the short circuit, as shown in Figure 1.2, parts (h) and (i).

1.3 The resistor

A *resistor* is a power-consuming device whose electric behavior can be completely characterized by its voltage–current (*v-i*) curve. The simplest resistor is the *linear time-invariant* (LTI) type. An LTI resistor has a linear *v-i* curve, as shown in Figure 1.3; this curve does not vary with time.

Such a resistor can be characterized by either of the two simple equations

$$v(t) = Ri(t) \tag{1.1}$$

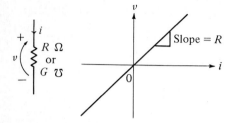

Figure 1.3 The symbol and the *v-i* curve of an LTI resistor.

or

$$i(t) = Gv(t) \tag{1.2}$$

where R is the *resistance*, which is equal to the slope of the *v-i* line, and G is the *conductance* of the device. Obviously

$$RG = 1 \tag{1.3}$$

When v is expressed in volts and i is expressed in amperes, R has a unit of *ohms* (frequently represented by the Greek letter omega, Ω) and G a unit of *mhos** (frequently represented by an inverted omega, $\mho$). An LTI resistor is represented by the symbols in Figure 1.3, with its resistance or conductance shown alongside. Equation (1.1) or (1.2) is known as the *Ohm's law* equation and is a good approximation of many physical resistors over practical ranges of voltages and currents.

A *linear time-varying* (LTV) *resistor* is the mathematical model of devices whose *v-i* curve is always a straight line, and the slope of this line varies with time. Thus the resistance (or conductance) of such a device is a function of time $R(t)$ [or $G(t)$] and the correct relationship of its voltage and current should read

$$v(t) = R(t)i(t) \tag{1.4}$$

or

$$i(t) = G(t)v(t) \tag{1.5}$$

The change in resistance of an LTV resistor may be either abrupt (discontinuous) or gradual (continuous). For example, abrupt changes of resistance may be simulated by switching (commutating) from one LTI resistor to another, as shown in Figure 1.4, in which the switch has a set of fixed segments of metal and a rotating contact. The $R(t)$ of such an arrangement may be represented by the stepped curve of Figure 1.4. In a similar way, a gradual change of the resistance of an LTV resistor may be effected by rotating the shaft of a potentiometer (variable resistor).

---

* The international unit for conductance is the *siemen*, represented by S. A siemen is equal to a mho.

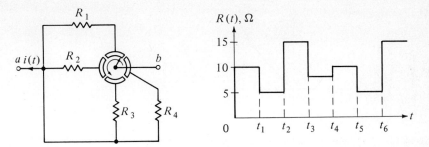

Figure 1.4 The simulation of a stepped LTV resistor and its resistance as a function of time.

For example, in Figure 1.4, $R_1 = 10 \, \Omega$, $R_2 = 5 \, \Omega$, $R_3 = 15 \, \Omega$, $R_4 = 8 \, \Omega$, $t_1 = \pi/2$ s, $t_2 = \pi$ s, $t_3 = 3\pi/2$ s, $t_4 = 2\pi$ s, and $e_b - e_a = 100 \sin(t)$ V. Then $i(t)$ will be that given in Figure 1.5.

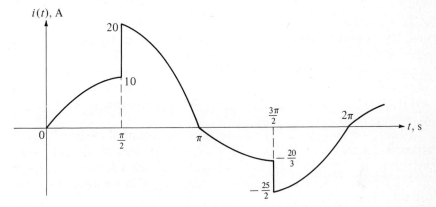

Figure 1.5 The $i(t)$ of the resistor in Figure 1.4.

A *nonlinear time-invariant resistor* is one whose *v-i* curve is not a straight line, and the slope of this line does *not* change as time goes on. Generally, this class of resistors is known simply as *nonlinear (NL) resistors*. An example of a nonlinear resistor is an incandescent lamp, whose typical *v-i* curve is shown in Figure 1.6, as well as the circuit symbol of an NL resistor.

Another example of a nonlinear resistor is a *semiconductor diode*, whose *v-i* characteristic is given by

$$i = i_o(\epsilon^{v/V_T} - 1) \tag{1.6}$$

where V_T is a function of the material and i_o is *reverse saturation current*, which is approached as v becomes negative and very large compared with V_T. A typical semiconductor diode characteristic, along with its circuit symbol, is shown in Figure 1.7.

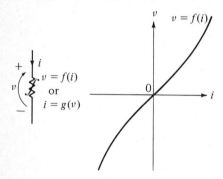

Figure 1.6 The symbol and a typical v-i curve of an NL resistor.

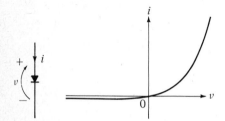

Figure 1.7 The symbol and a typical i-v curve of a diode.

EXAMPLE 1   A semiconductor diode has a reverse saturation current of 10^{-12} A and a V_T of 0.026 V. Find $i(t)$ if

$$v(t) = 0.5 \sin (t) \text{ V} \tag{1.7}$$

From (1.6), we have

$$i(t) = 10^{-12}(\epsilon^{19.23 \sin t} - 1) \tag{1.8}$$

We can choose a few points along the time axis and calculate $i(t)$ at those points.

t	v	i
0	0	0
$\pi/4$	0.354	8.04×10^{-7}
$\pi/2$	0.5	2.25×10^{-4}
$5\pi/4$	-0.354	-10^{-12}
$3\pi/2$	-0.5	-10^{-12}

The variations of $v(t)$ and $i(t)$ are sketched in Figure 1.8.

An important distinction between the v-i curves of Figures 1.6 and 1.7 is that the curve of Figure 1.6 is symmetric about the origin, while that of

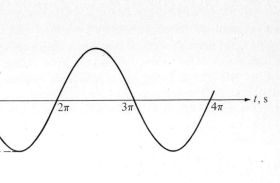

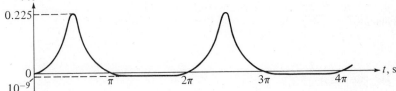

Figure 1.8 $v(t)$ and $i(t)$ of Example 1.

Figure 1.7 is not. This is because the direction of a voltage (or current) is inconsequential to an incandescent lamp, but this is not the case with a diode. A device whose electric characteristic is the same in either direction is said to be *bilateral*. (All LTI and LTV devices are bilateral.) A device whose electric characteristic is different in the two directions (as evidenced by the nonsymmetry of its *v-i* curve) is said to be *nonbilateral*.

Another property of the *v-i* curves of Figures 1.6 and 1.7 is their *monotonicity*. This means that their slopes (or first derivatives) are always positive. Some nonlinear devices have nonmonotonic *v-i* curves. For these devices to be physically defined, they must be single-valued with respect to one of the two variables (v or i).

Figure 1.9(a) gives a *v-i* curve that has a single-valued voltage for any

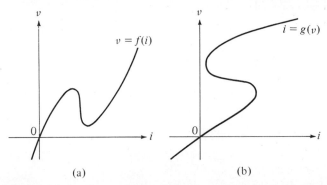

Figure 1.9 (a) The *v-i* curve characteristic of a current-controlled NL resistor. (b) The *v-i* curve characteristic of a voltage-controlled NL resistor.

given current. A device with such a curve is said to be *current-controlled*. Figure 1.9(b) gives a *v-i* curve that has a single-valued current for any given voltage. A device with this curve is said to be *voltage-controlled*. A nonlinear element with a monotonic *v-i* curve is both voltage- *and* current-controlled.

Nonlinear time-varying elements certainly exist and are conceivable. However, since very little research has been done on this type of element, we shall not discuss them here.

An important property of all types of resistors is that the voltage across one at any instant depends only on the current at that instant, or vice versa. What happened to the device before a particular instant does not affect it at that instant. A device or system that has this property is said to be *memoryless*.

1.4 The capacitor

A *capacitor* is an electrostatic energy-storage device whose stored energy is in an electric field and can be directly related to the electric charge (in coulombs) stored in the device. The external electrical behavior of a capacitor can be completely characterized by the charge-versus-voltage (*q-v*) curve. The simplest capacitor is the *linear time-invariant* (LTI) capacitor, which has a linear *q-v* curve, as shown in Figure 1.10. Analytically such a capacitor is characterized by either of the following two equations:

$$q(t) = Cv(t) \tag{1.9}$$

$$v(t) = Sq(t) \tag{1.10}$$

in which C is a constant known as the *capacitance* and S is another constant known as the *elastance*. When q is in coulombs and v is in volts, C has a unit of *farads* (represented by the letter F). Clearly,

$$CS = 1 \tag{1.11}$$

The simplest example of an LTI capacitor is the parallel-plate capacitor illustrated in Figure 1.11. Its capacitance is

$$C = \epsilon \frac{A}{d} \tag{1.12}$$

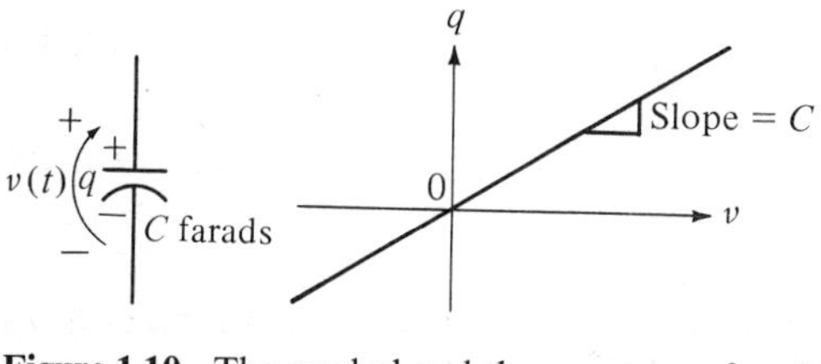

Figure 1.10 The symbol and the *q-v* curve of an LTI capacitor.

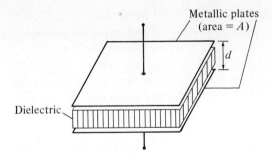

Figure 1.11 A simple parallel-plate capacitor.

where ϵ is the permittivity of the dielectric material that occupies the space between the plates, A is the area of each plate, and d is the distance between the plates.

Capacitors can be made of metal foil and paper, special plastics, or ceramics. In a modern completely integrated circuit, a capacitor may simply be the characteristic of a certain part of a complicated structure and never appear in isolated form.

In most of our problems, we wish to find the voltage–current relationship of an element and (1.9) and (1.10) are not suitable for those purposes. Since the current is also the time rate of change of the stored charge, we have

$$i(t) = \frac{dq}{dt} \tag{1.13}$$

or

$$q(t) = \int_{t_0}^{t} i(\tau)\, d\tau + q(t_0) \tag{1.14}$$

Hence the voltage–current relationship of a capacitor for $t > t_0$ is given by

$$v(t) = \frac{q(t_0)}{C} + \frac{1}{C}\int_{t_0}^{t} i(\tau)\, d\tau = v(t_0) + \frac{1}{C}\int_{t_0}^{t} i(\tau)\, d\tau \tag{1.15}$$

where $v(t_0)$ is the initial voltage and $q(t_0)$ is the initial charge of the capacitor. Alternatively we have

$$i(t) = C\frac{dv}{dt} \tag{1.16}$$

For example, in Figure 1.12(a), the current $i(t)$ is known, and given by Figure 1.12(b). If the capacitor has an initial voltage $v(t_0)$ of 2 volts, then the voltage for $t > 0$ is that given in Figure 1.12(c).

A *linear time-varying* (LTV) *capacitor* is one in which the q-v relation is linear at any particular time, but the slope of the q-v line varies as time

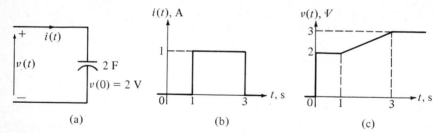

(a) (b) (c)

Figure 1.12

goes on. Such a capacitor may be characterized by the relationship

$$q(t) = C(t)v(t) \tag{1.17}$$

Differentiating both sides of (1.17) yields the current–voltage relationship

$$i(t) = \frac{d}{dt}q(t) = C(t)\frac{d}{dt}v(t) + v(t)\frac{d}{dt}C(t) \tag{1.18}$$

The right-hand side of (1.18) has one term more than (1.16). We may regard (1.16) as a special case of (1.18), in which $dC/dt = 0$.

An example of LTV capacitance is that of a tuning capacitor in a radio receiver when its shaft is being rotated. The capacitance becomes a function of time, but the q-v relationship of the capacitor is linear at any given instant.

A *nonlinear capacitor* is one whose q-v curve is not a straight line. An example is the varactor diode. A typical characteristic of such a device is shown in Figure 1.13, which gives the slope of its q-v curve versus the voltage.

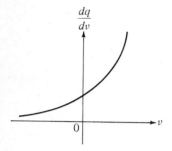

Figure 1.13 A typical characteristic of an NL capacitor.

1.5 The inductor

An *inductor* is an electromagnetic energy-storage device whose stored energy is in the form of a magnetic field which can be directly related to the magnetic flux ϕ (in webers). The electrical properties of an inductor can be characterized by the flux-versus-current (ϕ-i) curve. The simplest type is the linear time-invariant (LTI) inductor, which has a linear ϕ-i curve, as shown in Figure 1.14. Analytically such an inductor has the relationship

$$N\phi(t) = Li(t) \tag{1.19}$$

where N is the number of turns of the inductor and L is the *inductance* of the inductor. When ϕ is in webers and i is in amperes, the inductance is in *henrys* (represented by the letter H).

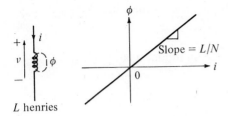

Figure 1.14 The symbol and the ϕ-i curve of an LTI inductor.

A simple inductor arrangement is a coil wound around a magnetic core, which can be any of the various magnetic materials or air, as shown in Figure 1.15. A current i in the coil is accompanied by a flux ϕ in the core.

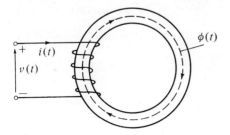

Figure 1.15 A typical inductor arrangement.

These two quantities are related by the equation

$$\phi = \frac{\mu N A}{l} i \tag{1.20}$$

where A is the cross-sectional area of the core, l is the average length of the magnetic path, N is the number of turns in the coil, and μ is the permeability of the core material. The flux linking the N-turn coil is

$$\Phi = N\phi \tag{1.21}$$

and is called the *flux linkage*. We have

$$\Phi = \frac{\mu N^2 A i}{l}$$

(1.22)

For such a coil, the inductance is

$$L = \frac{\mu N^2 A}{l}$$

(1.23)

In an equation similar to (1.13), we find that the voltage across an inductor and the flux through it are related by

$$v(t) = \frac{d\Phi}{dt}$$

(1.24)

Hence the voltage–current relationship in an inductor is

$$v(t) = L\frac{di}{dt}$$

(1.25)

or, for $t > t_0$,

$$i(t) = i(t_0) + \frac{1}{L}\int_{t_0}^{t} v(\tau)\, d\tau$$

(1.26)

For example, a 2-henry inductor has the current and voltage directions shown in Figure 1.16(a). If the current $i(t)$ is as shown in Figure 1.16(b), then the voltage $e(t)$ will be the curve in Figure 1.16(c).

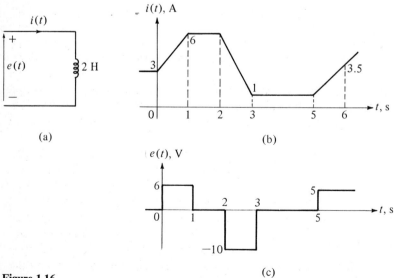

Figure 1.16

Like a capacitor, an inductor can also be linear time-varying and nonlinear time-invariant.

From (1.15) and (1.26), it is clear that the quantities in a capacitor or an inductor at time t depend on what went on before t. A system that contains these devices, or similar ones, is clearly not memoryless. It is a *memory system.*

1.6 Remarks on two-terminal elements

In the three previous sections we described three very basic and useful two-terminal circuit elements. At this point we need to stress the difference between a circuit element and a physical device. A physical device is an item that exists and is used in an actual circuit. A circuit element is a mathematical model of a physical device. It is to be hoped that the model we specify represents its physical counterpart with sufficient accuracy for all practical purposes. In actuality, however, it's not always possible to represent a device by a mathematical model accurately enough for all circumstances. Hence we should recognize and bear in mind the possibility of a discrepancy between the actual performance of a device and that predicted from its mathematical model.

For example, when we speak of a carbon resistor of a certain resistance, say 100 ohms, we have an idealized model that satisfies (1.1) exactly. The element would have an electrical characteristic given by (1.1) whether i was 1 microampere or 1 mega-ampere. But any practical carbon resistor would probably be burned out long before a few amperes were reached.

It is important to realize that a pure idealized element of any of the three types does not exist. A wire-wound resistor is bound to have some inductance associated with it. An inductance coil inevitably has some resistance. The leads of any device are bound to contribute some inductance, resistance, and capacitance—no matter how small—to its model. But two points are important. (1) In many situations a circuit element does represent a device adequately. (2) For engineering purposes, we have to make our models simple enough so that the analysis and design processes are manageable. The important thing is that we recognize the limitations of our models and stay within the conditions under which they are valid.

A somewhat similar attitude is necessary as we compare LTI and LTV or nonlinear (NL) elements. As you will see, the theory of LTI circuits is very manageable, elegant, and precise. But the capability of LTI circuits is rather limited, and there can be very large discrepancies between what LTI circuit theory tells us and what actually happens in the real-world domain. On the other hand, an LTV or NL network can do a great deal more than an LTI network. But the theory of these networks is much more complex and unruly. In the last few decades, a great deal of research has been done on LTV and NL networks, with many significant results.

However, LTI circuit theory remains the down-to-earth foundation of electrical engineering. That is why we shall first concentrate on the development and elucidation of basic LTI circuits, with only occasional reference to LTV and NL circuits. Nevertheless you should be aware of the fact that LTV and NL circuits not only do exist, but also offer numerous opportunities for further specialized study and fertile ground for research.

1.7 Independent sources

An *independent voltage source* is an idealized circuit element that constrains the potential difference between the two terminals to which it is connected. The symbol for an independent voltage source is shown in Figure 1.17(a), where the condition $e_{ba} = e(t)$ must always be satisfied. When the $e(t)$ of a source is constant (independent of both time and the current through it), it becomes a dc (direct-current) source and is sometimes referred to as a *battery*, with the symbol shown in Figure 1.17(b). Thus $e_{dc} = E$.

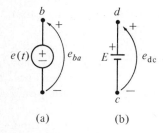

(a) (b)

Figure 1.17 (a) Symbol for an independent voltage source. (b) Alternative symbol for independent constant-voltage source—the battery.

A *signal generator* or an *alternator* has characteristics that approach those of an ideal independent voltage source whose voltage varies sinusoidally with respect to time. A battery has characteristics that are very close to those of a dc voltage source.

There is no restriction on the amount or direction of current that may flow through a voltage source. This is determined entirely by the circuit to which the source is connected.

A voltage source whose voltage is identically equal to zero is equivalent to a short circuit. Such a voltage source is said to be *idle* or *inactive*.

An *independent current source* is an idealized circuit element that constrains the current flowing through the branch in which it is inserted. The symbol for a current source is shown in Figure 1.18, where $i_{in} = i_{out} = i_s(t)$ must always be satisfied.

A current source whose current is identically equal to zero is equivalent to an open circuit. Such a current source is said to be *idle* or *inactive*. The

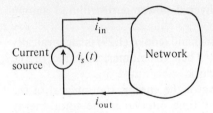

Figure 1.18 Symbol for a current source.

voltage across a current source can be of any value and is determined, not by the source, but by the external circuit to which it is connected. For example, constant-current independent sources are often used in integrated circuits for biasing.

1.8 Power and energy

The power being delivered to a two-terminal network (also known as a *one-port**) at any instant is equal to the product of the voltage across its two terminals and the current flowing into the terminal with the assumed higher potential (which is equal to the current flowing out of the terminal with the lower potential) at that instant. This sign convention is illustrated in Figure 1.19, and the instantaneous power is given by

$$p(t) = v(t)i(t) \tag{1.27}$$

When v is given in volts and i in amperes, the unit for the power is *watts* (represented by the letter W).

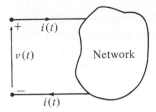

Figure 1.19 A network with two external terminals.

The power given by (1.27) is the power delivered to the network as a whole. It does not matter how complicated the network is, or what types (LTI, LTV, or NL) of elements are contained in the network. The equation

---

* A *port* is a terminal pair of a network that is accessible for external connection. For a terminal pair to form a port, the current entering one of the terminals must be equal to that leaving the other terminal.

does not, however, tell us how the delivered power is distributed among the elements in the network.

When one of the quantities on the right-hand side of (1.27) is algebraically negative, the power becomes negative. Then the numerical value of the power is the power supplied by the network.

Since the power is the time derivative of the energy, the integral of the power delivered to a network over any time interval is the total energy delivered to the network during that time interval. Thus, for the arrangement of Figure 1.19, the energy delivered to the network between t_1 and t_2 is

$$w(t_1, t_2) = \int_{t_1}^{t_2} p(\tau)\, d\tau = \int_{t_1}^{t_2} v(\tau) i(\tau)\, d\tau \tag{1.28}$$

Again (1.28) is applicable regardless of the type or complexity of the network. When power is given in watts and time in seconds, the unit for the energy is *joules* (represented by the letter J).

If the "network" is a simple LTI resistor, as in Figure 1.20, the power delivered to (or absorbed by) the resistor is

$$p(t) = i(t)v(t) = Ri^2(t) = \frac{v^2(t)}{R} \tag{1.29}$$

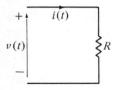

Figure 1.20

If the "network" is a time-invariant (LTI or NL) capacitor, the energy stored in the capacitor, assuming that the capcitor has zero energy when both q and v are zero (call that instant $t_1 = 0$), is

$$w(t) = w(0, t) = \int_0^t v(\tau) i(\tau)\, d\tau$$

Since $i(t) = dq(t)/dt$, we may write $i(\tau)\, d\tau$ as $dq(\tau)$. Thus

$$w(t) = \int_0^{q(t)} v(\tau)\, dq(\tau) \tag{1.30}$$

The last integral is equal to the shaded area to the left of the q-v curve of the capacitor in Figure 1.21. The quantity $q(t)$ is the final value of the charge.

This conclusion is valid whether the q-v curve is linear or not. When the

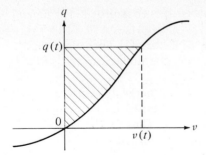

Figure 1.21 The q-v curve of an NL capacitor. Shaded area indicates the energy stored in the capacitor.

q-v curve is linear, then $v(t) = q(t)/C$ and (1.30) becomes

$$w(t) = \frac{1}{C}\int_0^{q(t)} q\,dq = \frac{1}{2C}q^2(t) = \tfrac{1}{2}Cv^2(t) = \tfrac{1}{2}q(t)v(t) \tag{1.31}$$

EXAMPLE 2   The q-v curve of an NL capacitor is given by

$$v = \frac{10^4 q}{10^4 - q^2}$$

where v is in volts and q is in coulombs. (a) If the initial charge is zero, what is the energy required to introduce 20 coulombs of charge into the capacitor? (b) What if the final charge is changed to -20 coulombs?

SOLUTION   (a) From (1.30), we have

$$w = \int_0^{20} \frac{10^4 q}{10^4 - q^2}\,dq = -\left.\frac{10^4}{2}\ln(10^4 - q^2)\right|_0^{20}$$

$$= \frac{10^4}{2}\ln\frac{10,000}{9600} = 204.11 \text{ J}$$

(b) $$w = \int_0^{-20} \frac{10^4 q}{10^4 - q^2}\,dq = \int_0^{20} \frac{10^4 q}{10^4 - q^2}\,dq = 204.11 \text{ J}$$

EXAMPLE 3   For a capacitor with the current and initial voltage given in Figure 1.12, find the power delivered to and the energy stored in the capacitor for all $t > 0$.

SOLUTION   The current, voltage, and charge in the capacitor as functions of time are reproduced in Figure 1.22. Since $p(t) = v(t)i(t)$, the power delivered to the capacitor as a function of time is readily obtained by multiplying v and i at any and all t.

The energy stored in the capacitor as a function of time may be obtained

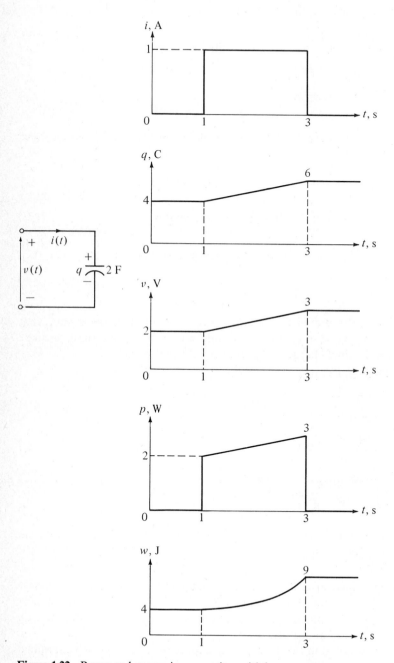

Figure 1.22 Power and energy in a capacitor with known current.

by several methods. From (1.31), we have

$$w(t) = \tfrac{1}{4}q^2(t) = v^2(t) = \tfrac{1}{2}q(t)v(t)$$

Any of these three expressions will give $w(t)$ readily. The other method would be to use the general relationship (1.28). Since $p(t) = 2 + \tfrac{1}{2}(t-1) = (t+3)/2$ for $1 < t < 3$, $w(t)$ for that time interval is given by

$$w(t) = w(0) + \int_1^t p(\tau)\, d\tau$$

$$= 4 + \int_1^t \frac{\tau+3}{2}\, d\tau = 4 + \left(\frac{\tau^2}{4} + \frac{3\tau}{2} \right)\Bigg|_1^t$$

$$= \tfrac{1}{4}(t^2 + 6t + 9)$$

For t outside this range, $w(t)$ is constant, since $p(t) = 0$. The variation of $w(t)$ is shown in Figure 1.22.

If the "network" is a time-invariant (LTI or NL) inductor, and if we assume that the inductor has no energy stored in it when both Φ and i are zero (call that instant $t_1 = 0$), the energy stored in it is

$$w(t) = \int_0^t v(\tau) i(\tau)\, d\tau = \int_0^{\Phi(t)} i(\tau)\, d\Phi(\tau) \tag{1.32}$$

since $v(\tau)\, d\tau = d\Phi(\tau)$. The last integral is equal to the shaded area to the left of the Φ-i curve of the inductor in Figure 1.23.

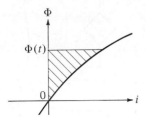

Figure 1.23 The Φ-i curve of an NL inductor. Shaded area indicates the energy stored in the inductor.

If the inductor is linear, then $\Phi(t) = Li(t)$. Equation (1.32) reduces to

$$w(t) = \frac{1}{L} \int_0^{\Phi(t)} \Phi(t)\, d\Phi = \frac{1}{2L}\Phi^2(t) = \tfrac{1}{2}Li^2(t) = \tfrac{1}{2}\Phi(t)i(t) \tag{1.33}$$

The energy delivered to an LTI or NL resistor is dissipated as thermal energy and cannot be recovered electrically. The energy delivered to an LTI or NL capacitor or inductor is stored in that device. All the energy is recoverable electrically. These last two devices are *lossless*.

1.9 Controlled sources

A *controlled* (or *dependent*) *source* is a voltage or current source whose strength is a function of another electrical quantity. The symbols for controlled sources are diamond-shaped boxes, as shown in Figure 1.24. In many textbooks, no distinction is made between the symbol for a controlled source and that for an independent source. Philosophically speaking, such a distinction is not necessary, since a controlled source is indistinguishable from an independent one except that the strength of the controlled source is related to some other electric quantity, while that of the independent one is not. However, for practical purposes, a special symbol—such as those diamond-shaped boxes—helps to call our attention to the fact that the source is not independent.

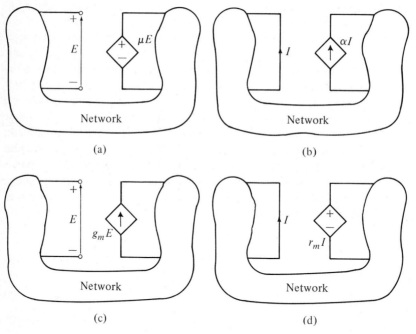

Figure 1.24   (a) Symbol for a voltage-controlled voltage source.   (b) Symbol for a current-controlled current source.   (c) Symbol for a· voltage-controlled current source. (d) Symbol for a current-controlled voltage source.

There are four possible types of controlled sources.

1   *Voltage-controlled voltage source* [Figure 1.24(a)] The ratio between the controlled voltage and the controlling voltage, μ, is known as the voltage-amplification factor, the voltage gain, or simply the voltage ratio. This controlled source may also be identified with the *ideal voltage amplifier*.

2 *Current-controlled current source* [Figure 1.24(b)] The ratio between the controlled current and the controlling current, α, is known as the current-amplification factor, the current gain, or simply the current ratio. This controlled source may also be identified with the *ideal current amplifier*.

3 *Voltage-controlled current source* [Figure 1.24(c)] The ratio between the controlled current and the controlling voltage, g_m, has the dimension of the conductance and is known as the transconductance or the mutual conductance. This controlled souce is also known as a *voltage-to-current transducer*.

4 *Current-controlled voltage source* [Figure 1.24(d)] The ratio between the controlled voltage and the controlling current, r_m, has the dimension of a resistance and is known as the mutual resistance. This controlled source is also known as the *current-to-voltage transducer*.

In these descriptions all the proportionality constants—μ, α, g_m, and r_m—are tacitly assumed to be real constants (either positive or negative). For the majority of our circuit applications, this assumption is both necessary and convenient. These controlled sources would be LTI and memoryless. However, there are occasions in which these quantities may be either nonlinear or time-varying. Also, in other situations, some of these devices may become memory devices. (For example, a controlled quantity may be proportional to the derivative of the controlling quantity.)

Controlled sources are frequently used in conjunction with other elements to form circuit models of many electronic devices. For example, as will be discussed in Chapter 8, the field-effect transistor, whose symbol is shown in Figure 1.25(a), has an equivalent circuit for small signals, shown in Figure 1.25(b). Many practical amplifiers can be represented by controlled sources together with other LTI elements.

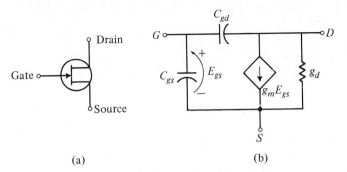

(a)   (b)

Figure 1.25 Symbol and small-signal equivalent circuit of a field-effect transistor.

Another important device is the bipolar transistor, which will be treated in Chapter 9. Its symbol and one of its equivalent circuits are shown in Figure 1.26(a) and (b), respectively.

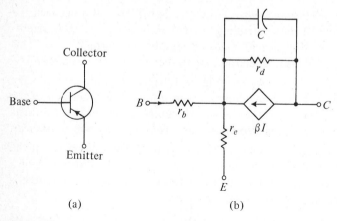

Figure 1.26 Symbol and small-signal equivalent circuit of a bipolar transistor.

1.10 Concluding remarks

In this chapter, we have described some of the most basic and useful circuit elements, in terms of both their terminal characteristics and their salient features. Of the various types, we will be dealing mostly with the LTI and the NL types in this volume.

After the introducing of these elements, our next step ought to be to connect them together to accomplish various engineering tasks. But before we can do that, we must first examine what happens to a circuit when we connect a number of elements in certain ways. We want to learn what governs the behavior of a network under various excitations. In the next chapter, we shall describe several basic, general rules and techniques for analyzing networks made up of circuit elements.

Problems

1.1 The arrangement in Figure P1.1 simulates an LTV resistor. The switch is closed to terminal 1 at $t = 0$, remains so for 1 second, and then is moved to terminal 2. It continues to alternate between 1 and 2 every second. Sketch $e(t)$ for the $i(t)$ given.

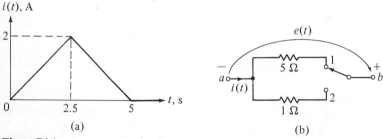

Figure P1.1

1.2 A nonlinear resistor has the *v-i* curve given by $v = i^2$
(a) Sketch the *v-i* curve.
(b) Given that $i(t) = \cos 5t + \sin 8t$, write the corresponding $v(t)$ in the form of linear trigonometric terms (sine and cosine only, no square or product thereof). This problem illustrates that an NL element is capable of producing frequencies that are not contained in the quantity applied to the element.

1.3 Sketch the current $i(t)$ through the LTI capacitor in Figure P1.3.

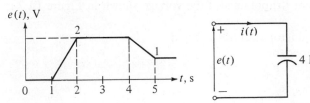

Figure P1.3

1.4 Assuming $e(0) = 0$, sketch the voltage $e(t)$ across the LTI capacitor in Figure P1.4.

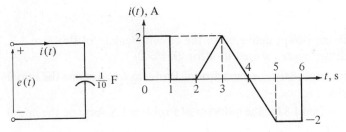

Figure P1.4

1.5 Assuming $i(0) = 0$, sketch the current $i(t)$ through the LTI inductor in Figure P1.5.

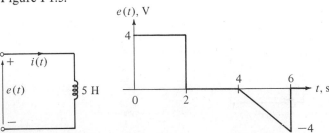

Figure P1.5

1.6 Sketch the voltage $e(t)$ across the LTI inductor in Figure P1.6.

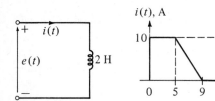

Figure P1.6

1.7 Sketch the current $i(t)$ obtained if the voltage shown in Figure P1.7 is applied to
    (a) a 2-henry inductor with $i(0) = 0$ and
    (b) a 2-farad capacitor.

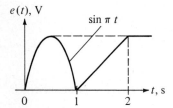

Figure P1.7

1.8 (a) Sketch the power delivered to the circuit element of Problem 1.3.
    (b) Sketch the energy stored in it for all $t > 0$.

1.9 Repeat Problem 1.8 for the capacitor of Problem 1.4. Assume the initial charge to be zero.

1.10 Repeat Problem 1.8 for the inductor of Problem 1.5. Assume the initial current to be zero.

1.11 Repeat Problem 1.8 for the inductor of Problem 1.6.

1.12 Based on the definitions of circuit elements you have been given so far, do you find any inconsistency in either of the circuits of Figure P1.12? If so, describe the inconsistency of that circuit.

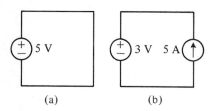

Figure P1.12

1.13 Is the resistor of Problem 1.2 current-controlled or voltage-controlled?

1.14 An NL capacitor has the q-v characteristic $q = v^2$. Given that the voltage across this capacitor is

$$v(t) = 1 + 0.1 \sin t$$

what is its current, $i(t)$? Express your answer in terms of linear trigonometric terms only.

1.15 The inductance of an LTV inductor is given by

$$L(t) = t + \tanh t$$

Find its voltage if the current through it is equal to $10 \sin 10t$.

1.16 The q-v curve of an NL capacitor is given by

$$q = v + \tanh v$$

Find the energy required to charge the capacitor
  (a) from 0 volt to 1 volt and
  (b) from 1 volt to 3 volts.

1.17 Show that the energy delivered to an LTV capacitor from $t = t_1$ to $t = t_2$ is

$$w(t_1, t_2) = \int_{t=t_1}^{t=t_2} v(t)\, dq(t)$$

2 | NETWORK EQUILIBRIUM EQUATIONS AND ANALYSIS OF LTI NETWORKS

Before we take up the various aspects of basic circuit laws, we should define a few terms.

A *node* is a terminal to which more than one element is connected. A *branch* is any subnetwork that is connected to the rest of the network only at two terminals. Usually a branch consists of only a single element. Sometimes, however, a series or a parallel combination of elements as a whole

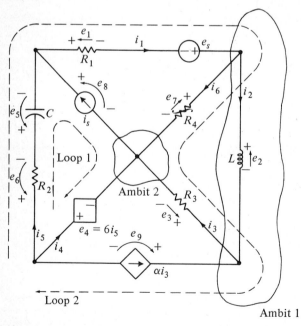

Figure 2.1 A network designed to illustrate the various terms used in this chapter.

may be considered a branch (for example, the $C\text{-}R_2$ series combination of Figure 2.1). In general, the internal complexity of a branch is arbitrary.

A *loop* is a closed path traced along a sequence of branches. For example, in Figure 2.1, loop 1 traces resistor R_2, capacitor C, independent source i_s, and controlled voltage source, $6i_5$. Loop 2 traces R_2, C, R_1, e_s, NL resistor R_4, R_3, and controlled current source αi_3.

A *mesh* is a loop whose interior is empty. As an example, loop 1 of Figure 2.1 is also a mesh. Whether a loop is also a mesh or not will sometimes depend on how a network is drawn.

An *ambit* is a closed imaginary curve (in a two-dimensional drawing of a circuit) or surface (in a three-dimensional construction of a circuit) that intersects a number of branches of a network. (It is understood that each branch can be intersected only once by an ambit.) The branches that are intersected by an ambit form a *cutset*.* For example, in Figure 2.1, the branches in which i_1, i_6, i_3, and αi_3 flow form a cutset. Ambit 1 intersects this cutset. The simplest ambit is one that can be drawn to enclose only a node; for example, ambit 2 of Figure 2.1.

2.1 Kirchhoff's laws

Two basic laws must be satisfied by the voltages and currents of a network composed of elements defined in the previous chapter. These are *Kirchhoff's laws*, which can be stated as follows:

Kirchhoff's current law (KCL)   The sum of all currents entering any ambit at any instant must be zero.

Kirchhoff's voltage law (KVL)   The sum of all voltage rises around any loop at any instant must be zero.

These two laws, KCL and KVL, must be satisfied at all times whether the network is LTI, LTV, or NL. Examples of networks that do not satisfy these laws are transmission lines, along which charges may accumulate, and antennas, which may radiate energy.

For example, in the network of Figure 2.1:

Around loop 1: $\qquad\qquad -e_6 - e_5 - e_8 + 6i_5 = 0$

Around loop 2: $\quad -e_6 - e_5 - e_1 + e_s - e_7 + e_3 - e_9 = 0$

For ambit 1: $\qquad\qquad\quad \alpha i_3 - i_3 - i_6 + i_1 = 0$

For ambit 2: $\qquad\qquad\quad -i_s + i_4 + i_3 + i_6 = 0$

---

* A more formal definition of a cutset is "a set of minimum number of branches whose removal will separate the network into *two* unconnected parts." However, for our purposes, this fine distinction between a formal cutset and the set of branches intersected by an ambit need not be emphasized.

Kirchhoff's two laws are a direct consequence of the theories of conservation of charge flow and conservation of energy in a system. They are sometimes stated in an alternative way:

KCL   The algebraic sum of all currents entering an ambit must be equal to the algebraic sum of all currents leaving the ambit. (Each current entering or leaving may be either positive or negative.)

KVL   The algebraic sum of all voltage rises from one node to another is independent of the path traced. (Each voltage rise may be either positive or negative.)

There is no difference in the technical merit of these two versions, or of any other version of the KCL and the KVL. As you analyze more circuits, you may gradually develop a personal preference for the way certain steps are implemented. The only thing that matters is that these steps are performed correctly.

Numerous other KVL and KCL equations might be written for this network of Figure 2.1. In general, any and all of these equations must be satisfied.

EXAMPLE 1   The source currents i_1, i_2, i_3, and i_4 in Figure 2.2 are known. Express the resistor currents i_5, i_6, i_7, and i_8 in terms of these source currents and evaluate them.

SOLUTION   For each current to be evaluated, we choose an ambit that intersects only the corresponding branch and branches in which the currents are already known. Thus we get

$$i_5 = i_1 - i_2 = 5 - 3 = 2 \text{ A}$$

$$i_6 = i_3 - i_4 = 6 - 2 = 4 \text{ A}$$

$$i_7 = i_1 - i_3 + i_4 = 5 - 6 + 2 = -1 \text{ A}$$

$$i_8 = i_1 - i_2 - i_3 = 5 - 3 - 6 = -4 \text{ A}$$

EXAMPLE 2   The source voltages e_1, e_2, e_3, and e_4 in Figure 2.3 are known. Express the capacitor voltages e_5, e_6, e_7, and e_8 in terms of these source voltages and evaluate them.

SOLUTION   For each capacitor voltage to be evaluated, we choose a loop that traces only that capacitor and a number of voltage sources. Thus we have

$$e_5 = e_1 - e_2 - e_3 = -2 - 5 - 6 = -13 \text{ V}$$

$$e_6 = e_1 - e_2 = -2 - 5 = -7 \text{ V}$$

$$e_7 = e_4 + e_3 + e_2 = 3 + 6 + 5 = 14 \text{ V}$$

$$e_8 = e_4 + e_3 = 3 + 6 = 9 \text{ V}$$

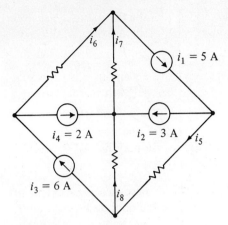

Figure 2.2

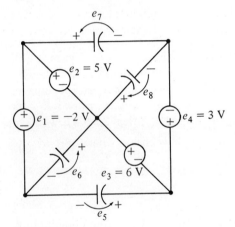

Figure 2.3

2.2 Series and parallel connection of like elements

Two elements are said to be connected *in series* if an identical current flows through both of them. They are said to be connected *in parallel* if they are connected to the same pair of nodes. When elements of the same type are connected in series or in parallel, certain simple relationships may be derived. These relationships are frequently useful in simplifying a network-analysis problem.

1 *Resistors in series*   Figure 2.4(a) depicts two resistors connected in series. By KCL, we know that the same current i must flow through both R_1 and R_2. By KVL, we know that $e = e_1 + e_2$. From these observations, it is quite

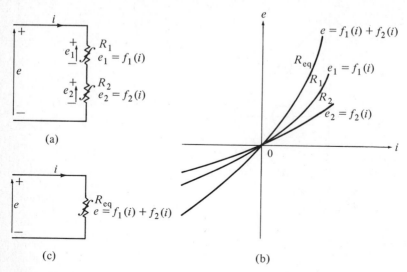

Figure 2.4 Two resistors connected in series.

clear that, if the v-i curves of R_1 and R_2 are those given in Figure 2.4(b), then the relationship between e and i of the combination must be given by the curve whose ordinate is the sum of the ordinates of the R_1 and R_2 curves. Hence the series combination may be replaced by another resistor R_{eq}, as shown in Figure 2.4(c). If both R_1 and R_2 are linear, then by KVL we have

$$e = i(R_1 + R_2) \tag{2.1}$$

Hence

$$R_{eq} = R_1 + R_2 \tag{2.2}$$

Thus, when two linear resistors are connected in series, the combination is equivalent to another linear resistor whose resistance is the sum of the two individual resistances. The same statement can be made for several resistors connected in series.

2 *Resistors in parallel*   Figure 2.5(a) depicts two resistors connected in parallel. By KCL, we have $i = i_1 + i_2$. By KVL, we know that e is also the voltage that appears across each resistor. If the v-i curves of G_1 and G_2 are as shown in Figure 2.5(b), then the parallel combination will have a v-i curve whose abscissa (current) for any ordinate (voltage) is the sum of the abscissas of the individual curves of G_1 and G_2. The parallel combination may then be replaced by an equivalent resistor [Figure 2.5(c)], whose v-i characteristic is given by curve G_{eq} of Figure 2.5(b).

   If both resistors are linear, then

$$i = e(G_1 + G_2) \tag{2.3}$$

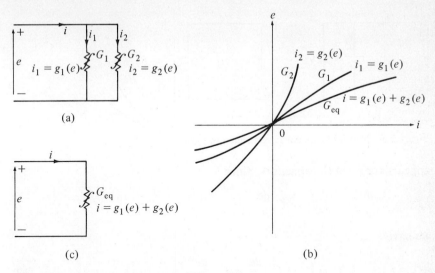

(a)

(c)

(b)

Figure 2.5 Two resistors connected in parallel.

Hence

$$G_{eq} = G_1 + G_2 \tag{2.4}$$

Or, the conductance of the parallel combination is equal to the sum of the individual conductances. Similarly, if several conductors are connected in parallel, the conductance of the combination is simply the sum of the individual conductances.

Equation (2.4) is frequently expressed in terms of resistances:

$$R_{eq} = \frac{1}{G_{eq}} = \frac{R_1 R_2}{R_1 + R_2} \tag{2.5}$$

in which $R_{eq} = 1/G_{eq}$, $R_1 = 1/G_1$, and $R_2 = 1/G_2$. Expressed verbally, the equation states that the resistance of the parallel combination of two resistors is equal to the product divided by the sum of the resistances of the individual resistors.

When several resistors are connected in parallel, the following relationship is more convenient:

$$\frac{1}{R_{eq}} = \frac{1}{R_1} + \frac{1}{R_2} + \frac{1}{R_3} + \cdots \tag{2.6}$$

especially when a calculator is used.

3 *Parallel connection of linear capacitors* When two LTI capacitors are connected in parallel, as shown in Figure 2.6(a), we have $i = i_1 + i_2$ and e

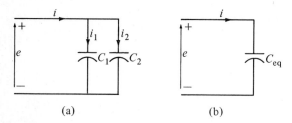

Figure 2.6 Two LTI capacitors connected in parallel.

appears across both capacitors. Since

$$i_1(t) = C_1 \frac{de}{dt}, \qquad i_2(t) = C_2 \frac{de}{dt}$$

we have

$$i(t) = i_1(t) + i_2(t) = (C_1 + C_2)\frac{de}{dt} = C_{eq}\frac{de}{dt} \qquad (2.7)$$

Equation (2.7) describes the relationship between $e(t)$ and $i(t)$ of the parallel combination, which is identical to the relationship of a simple capacitor shown in Figure 2.6(b), if its capacitance is made to be

$$C_{eq} = C_1 + C_2 \qquad (2.8)$$

Hence, when two linear capacitors are connected in parallel, the combination is equivalent to another linear capacitor whose capacitance is the sum of the capacitances of the individual capacitors. The same is true for several capacitors connected in parallel.

4 *Series connection of two linear capacitors.* When two LTI capacitors are connected in series, as shown in Figure 2.7(a), we have $e = e_1 + e_2$ and $i(t)$ flows through both capacitors. Since

$$e_1(t) = e_1(0) + S_1 \int_0^t i(\tau)\, d\tau, \qquad e_2(t) = e_2(0) + S_2 \int_0^t i(\tau)\, d\tau \qquad (2.9)$$

we have

$$e(t) = e_1(0) + e_2(0) + (S_1 + S_2)\int_0^t i(\tau)\, d\tau$$

$$= e(0) + S_{eq}\int_0^t i(\tau)\, d\tau \qquad (2.10)$$

Equation (2.10) is the v-i relationship of another equivalent capacitor whose elastance S_{eq} is given by

$$S_{eq} = S_1 + S_2 \qquad (2.11)$$

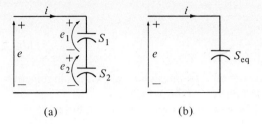

(a)   (b)

Figure 2.7 Two LTI capacitors connected in series.

In words, (2.11) states that the elastance of the series combination of two capacitors is equivalent to the sum of the elastances of the individual capacitors. A similar statement can be made for several capacitors connected in parallel. However, the following relationships would be more convenient:

$$C_{eq} = \frac{C_1 C_2}{C_1 + C_2}, \qquad \frac{1}{C_{eq}} = \frac{1}{C_1} + \frac{1}{C_2} + \frac{1}{C_3} + \cdots \tag{2.12}$$

since elastances are rarely used except in derivations of formulas and theoretical developments.

5 *Series and parallel combinations of linear inductors*   It is easy to prove in an analogous fashion the following statements.

The equivalent inductance of several inductors connected in series is the sum of the individual inductances.

The equivalent inductance of several inductors connected in parallel is equal to the reciprocal of the sum of the reciprocals of the individual inductances. For two inductors connected in parallel, $L_{eq} = L_1 L_2/(L_1 + L_2)$.

6 *Voltage-division rule*   Any time we find two linear resistors in series in any part of a network, as in Figure 2.8, we have

$$i = \frac{e}{R_1 + R_2}, \qquad e_1 = iR_1, \qquad e_2 = iR_2 \tag{2.13}$$

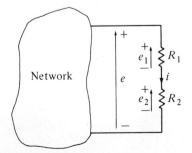

Figure 2.8   Notations used in the voltage-division rule.

Equations (2.13) give

$$e_1 = \frac{R_1}{R_1 + R_2} e, \qquad e_2 = \frac{R_2}{R_1 + R_2} e \qquad (2.14)$$

These relationships are known as the *voltage-division rule*. This arrangement is sometimes known as the *potentiometer* or *voltage divider*.

Similarly, for two capacitors in series, as in Figure 2.7(a), we have

$$e_1 = \frac{S_1}{S_1 + S_2} e = \frac{C_2}{C_1 + C_2} e$$

$$e_2 = \frac{S_2}{S_1 + S_2} e = \frac{C_1}{C_1 + C_2} e \qquad (2.15)$$

and, for two inductors in series,

$$e_1 = \frac{L_1}{L_1 + L_2} e, \qquad e_2 = \frac{L_2}{L_1 + L_2} e \qquad (2.16)$$

Equations (2.14), (2.15), and (2.16) are true whether the e's are constant or functions of time.

7 Current-division rule   When two LTI resistors are connected in parallel, as in Figure 2.9, we have

$$e = \frac{i}{G_1 + G_2}, \qquad i_1 = G_1 e, \qquad i_2 = G_2 e \qquad (2.17)$$

Equations (2.17) give

$$i_1 = \frac{G_1}{G_1 + G_2} i = \frac{R_2}{R_1 + R_2} i$$

$$i_2 = \frac{G_2}{G_1 + G_2} i = \frac{R_1}{R_1 + R_2} i \qquad (2.18)$$

These relationships are known as the *current-division rule*.

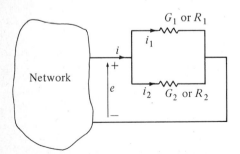

Figure 2.9   Notations used in the current-division rule.

Similarly, for two capacitors in parallel, as shown in Figure 2.6(a), we have

$$i_1 = \frac{C_1}{C_1 + C_2} i, \qquad i_2 = \frac{C_2}{C_1 + C_2} i \qquad (2.19)$$

Likewise, for two inductors in parallel, we have

$$i_1 = \frac{L_2}{L_1 + L_2} i, \qquad i_2 = \frac{L_1}{L_1 + L_2} i \qquad (2.20)$$

Again (2.18), (2.19), and (2.20) are valid regardless of the time variation of the currents.

EXAMPLE 3   Find the currents in the circuit of Figure 2.10(a).

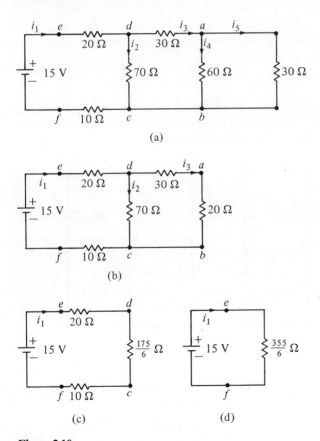

Figure 2.10

SOLUTION   By applying the series and parallel combinations of the resistances, we obtain the equivalent resistance connected to the battery in several steps in parts (b) through (d) of Figure 2.10. Hence, from Figure 2.10(d), we have

$$i_1 = \frac{15}{355/6} = \frac{18}{71} \text{ A}$$

In Figure 2.10(b), we can easily see that

$$i_2 = \frac{50}{50+70} i_1 = \frac{50}{120} \times \frac{18}{71} = \frac{15}{142} \text{ A}$$

$$i_3 = \frac{70}{50+70} i_1 = \frac{70}{120} \times \frac{18}{71} = \frac{21}{142} \text{ A}$$

In Figure 2.10(a), we see that

$$i_4 = \frac{30}{60+30} i_3 = \frac{30}{90} \times \frac{21}{142} = \frac{7}{142} \text{ A}$$

$$i_5 = \frac{60}{30+60} i_3 = \frac{60}{90} \times \frac{21}{142} = \frac{7}{71} \text{ A}$$

EXAMPLE 4   Five capacitors are connected to a battery, as shown in Figure 2.11(a). Find the charge contained in each of the capacitors. Also calculate the total energy stored in the capacitors.

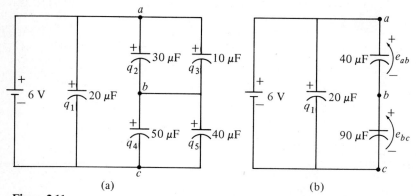

(a)   (b)

Figure 2.11

SOLUTION   The two pairs of capacitances in parallel can be combined directly, as in Figure 2.11(b). By (2.15), we have

$$e_{ab} = \tfrac{90}{130} \times 6 = \tfrac{54}{13} = 4.154 \text{ V}, \qquad e_{bc} = \tfrac{40}{130} \times 6 = \tfrac{24}{13} = 1.846 \text{ V}$$

Thus we have the following:

$$q_1 = 6 \times 20 \times 10^{-6} = 120 \ \mu\text{C}$$

$$q_2 = \tfrac{54}{13} \times 30 \times 10^{-6} = 124.6 \ \mu\text{C}$$

$$q_3 = \tfrac{54}{13} \times 10 \times 10^{-6} = 41.54 \ \mu\text{C}$$

$q_4 = \frac{24}{13} \times 50 \times 10^{-6} = 92.31 \ \mu C$

$q_5 = \frac{24}{13} \times 40 \times 10^{-6} = 73.85 \ \mu C$

The equivalent capacitance connected to the battery is

$C_{eq} = 20 + \dfrac{40 \times 90}{130} = 47.69 \ \mu F$

The charge in a capacitor with this capacitance when its voltage is 6 volts would be

$q = 6 \times 47.69 = 286.14 \ \mu C$

The energy stored in this capacitor would be

$w = \frac{1}{2} \times 286.14 \times 6 = 858.4 \ \mu J$

This should also be the sum of all energies stored in the five capacitors in Figure 2.11(a), or

$w = \frac{1}{2}(6 \times 120 + 4.154 \times 124.6 + 4.154 \times 41.54$

$+ 1.846 \times 92.31 + 1.846 \times 73.85)$

$= 858.4 \ \mu J$

EXAMPLE 5   In the circuit of Figure 2.12, we know that $i(t) = 18 \cos 1000t$. Find $e(t)$ and $i_1(t)$.

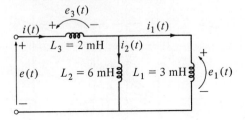

Figure 2.12

SOLUTION   From (2.20), we obtain

$i_1(t) = \frac{6}{9}i(t) = 12 \cos 1000t$ A

$e_1(t) = L_1 \dfrac{di_1}{dt} = -3 \times 10^{-3} \times 12 \times 1000 \times \sin 1000t$

$= -36 \sin 1000t$ V

$e_3(t) = L_3 \dfrac{di}{dt} = -2 \times 10^{-3} \times 18 \times 1000 \times \sin 1000t$

$= -36 \sin 1000t$ V

$e(t) = e_1(t) + e_3(t) = -72 \sin 1000t$ V

EXAMPLE 6   The NL resistor R_1 of Figure 2.13(a) has the v-i characteristic shown in Figure 2.13(b). Resistor R_2 is LTI with a resistance of 1 ohm. Resistor R_3 is a diode whose v-i characteristic is linear in each direction — the resistance is 0.2 ohm when i_3 is positive and 10 ohms when i_3 is negative. Find the v-i characteristic of the combination R_t.

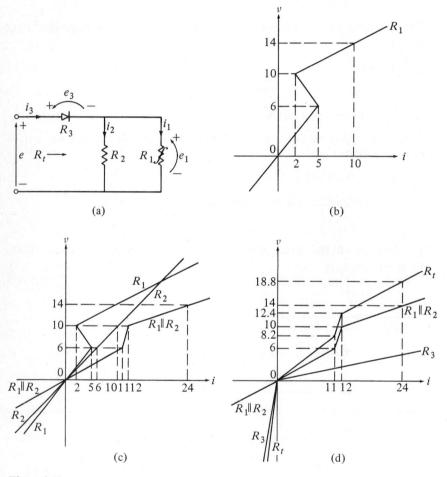

Figure 2.13

SOLUTION   The v-i characteristics of R_1 and R_2 are shown simultaneously in Figure 2.13(c). Now, for any value of v, i_1 and i_2 are additive, or

$$i_3 = i_1 + i_2$$

Hence the abscissa of the v-i characteristic of the parallel combination of R_1 and R_2 is the sum of the abscissas of the characteristics of R_1 and R_2.

Thus we obtain the v-i characteristic of $R_1 \| R_2$ (the parallel combination of R_1 and R_2); this is shown in both Figure 2.13(c) and Figure 2.13(d).

Figure 2.13(d) shows the v-i characteristics of $R_1 \| R_2$ and R_3 simultaneously. Since these two parts are connected in series, e_1 and e_3 are additive for any i_3, or

$$e = e_1 + e_3$$

Hence the ordinate of the e-versus-i_3 characteristic is the sum of the ordinates of $R_1 \| R_2$ and R_3 for any value of i_3. Figure 2.13(d) shows the e-versus-i_3 characteristic, which is labeled R_t.

2.3 Numbers of independent voltage and current variables

The purpose of a circuits-analysis problem is to find all the voltages $e_j(t)$ and currents $i_j(t)$ in a given network. Generally the voltages and currents in a circuit are not all independent. The voltage and the current in an element or branch are usually directly related to each other. Some of the currents (or voltages) in a circuit may be related in some very simple manner. Hence it is not always necessary to find all the voltages and currents in a network at once. We shall examine in some detail how to determine the appropriate variables to use in solving a circuit problem.

For example, in the circuit of Figure 2.14, there are ten branches and seven nodes. Hence there are ten voltages and ten currents. Of the ten

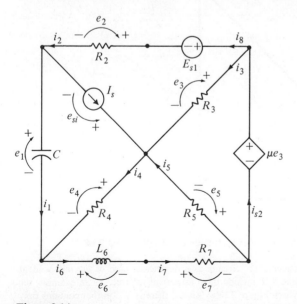

Figure 2.14

voltages, E_{s1} is independent and μe_3 is dependent, so that these two voltages are either known or related to another voltage in the network. Hence there are really only eight voltage variables. However, many of these voltages (e_1, e_2, e_3, e_4, e_5, e_6, e_7, and e_{si}) are interrelated. For example, $e_4 + e_5 + e_6 + e_7 = 0$. Likewise, out of the ten currents, I_s is independent, $i_2 = i_8$, $i_6 = i_7$, $i_2 = i_1 + I_s$, and so on.

In addition, we have relationships such as

$$i_2 R_2 = e_2 \quad \text{and} \quad e_1 = \frac{1}{C} \int_{-\infty}^{t} i_1(\tau)\, d\tau$$

and so forth. Hence there is no need to consider all the voltages and currents in a circuit as the variables in our analysis. We would like to use as few variables as possible, but, at the same time, we must be sure that we have picked a sufficient number. We can conveniently handle this consideration by means of *network topology*, which is a highly developed branch of network theory. Here we would like to introduce some of the basic concepts and simple rules of this area, so that we can solve a network-analysis problem in a reasonably organized fashion.

A *network tree* is that part of a network that includes all voltage sources* (both controlled and independent) and just enough nonsource branches

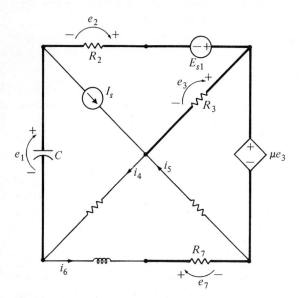

Figure 2.15 Example of a tree (heavy lines) for the circuit of Figure 2.14.

* It is frequently helpful to consider short circuits as a degenerate case of the independent voltage source with zero voltage and to include them as part of the tree. As an example, see the bottom short circuit of the tree in Figure 2.16(a). Also, if there is a loop that contains only voltage sources, the tree may embody all these sources without any complication.

(this excludes all current sources) to connect all nodes without forming any closed paths. Obviously we can construct many network trees for a given network. For example, the branches shown in heavy lines in Figure 2.15 form one possible tree of the network of Figure 2.14.

The following are some of the properties of a network tree.

1   A tree contains no closed loop.

2   The voltage difference between any two nodes in a network is completely defined by the voltages in a tree.

3   If no voltage outside a tree is known and if one or more of the voltages in a tree is not known, then some of the relative node voltages will be undefined.

4   All other branch voltages in the network are determinable if the voltages in a tree are known because of item 2 above.

5   No voltage in a tree is expressible in terms of other voltages in that same tree, since no closed path exists in a tree.

Hence the unknown voltages in a tree, when used as a set of unknown variables for analysis, are independent of other nontree voltages (therefore are necessary) and completely define all voltages in the network (therefore are sufficient).

Since the voltages of independent voltage sources are known quantities and since those of controlled voltage sources can be expressed in terms of other quantities in the network, the presence of these voltage sources does not contribute any additional unknowns.

A *network cotree* is that part of a network that complements a tree. A cotree contains all current sources* (both controlled and independent) and a number of nonsource elements. Branches of a cotree are called *chords* or *links*. The network cotree of the network tree of Figure 2.15 is shown in light lines.

A cotree associated with a tree has the following properties.

1   The currents in the links are independent. We can see this by starting with a tree and adding one link at a time. Each addition of such a link completes a loop in the network. Thus any link current has a complete path to flow along without using any other link.

2   All tree-branch currents are expressible in terms of link currents, and link currents alone. We can see this from the fact that a closed ambit can always be drawn that intersects one tree branch, no other tree branch, and some links.

3   If one or more of the link currents are not known, then some of the tree branch currents will be undefined.

* A cotree may contain cutsets that are made up of current sources only.

4 No closed ambit can be drawn that intersects only links. Hence link currents are not expressible in terms of one another.

Thus, if we use the unknown currents in a cotree as unknown variables of a circuit-analysis problem, we find that they are not only independent (therefore necessary), but also that they enable us to determine all currents in the tree branches (therefore are sufficient).

Since the currents in independent current sources are known quantities and since those of controlled current sources may be expressed in terms of other quantities in the network, the presence of these current sources does not contribute any additional unknowns.

Again using the network of Figure 2.14 as an example, we should be able to express all the currents and voltages in the network in terms of either a set of tree voltages or a set of link currents. Specifically, if we choose the tree of Figure 2.15, we can express all the electric quantities in the network in terms of the tree voltages—e_1, e_2, e_3, e_7, μe_3, and E_{s1}. By KVL, we have

$$e_4 = e_1 + e_2 + E_{s1} - e_3, \qquad e_5 = e_3 - \mu e_3$$

$$e_6 = -e_7 + \mu e_3 - E_{s1} - e_2 - e_1, \qquad e_{si} = e_2 + E_{s1} - e_3$$

From the v-i relationships of the elements in the links, we obtain

$$i_4 = \frac{e_4}{R_4} = \frac{e_1 + e_2 + E_{s1} - e_3}{R_4}, \qquad i_5 = \frac{e_5}{R_5} = \frac{e_3 - \mu e_3}{R_5}$$

$$i_6 = \frac{1}{L_6} \int_{-\infty}^{t} e_6(\tau)\, d\tau$$

$$= \frac{1}{L_6} \int_{-\infty}^{t} [-e_7(\tau) + \mu e_3(\tau) - E_{s1} - e_2(\tau) - e_1(\tau)]\, d\tau$$

By KCL, we have

$$i_1 = i_6 - i_4, \qquad i_2 = i_1 + I_s$$

$$i_3 = i_4 - i_5 - I_s, \qquad i_{s2} = -i_5 + i_6$$

From these relationships, we see that it is straightforward to express i_1, i_2, i_3, i_7, i_8, and i_{s2} in terms of voltages along the tree.

Also, in an analogous fashion, we can express all electric quantities in terms of the link currents i_4, i_5, i_6, and I_s. By KCL, we have

$$i_1 = i_6 - i_4, \qquad i_2 = I_s - i_4 + i_6, \qquad i_3 = i_4 - I_s - i_5$$

and, of course,

$$i_7 = i_6, \qquad i_8 = i_2 = I_s - i_4 + i_6$$

By the *v-i* relationship in each branch, we have

$$e_1 = \frac{1}{C}\int_{-\infty}^{t} i_1(\tau)\,d\tau = \frac{1}{C}\int_{-\infty}^{t} [i_6(\tau)-i_4(\tau)]\,d\tau$$

$$e_2 = i_2 R_2 = R_2(I_s - i_4 + i_6), \qquad e_3 = R_3 i_3 = R_3(i_4 - I_s - i_5)$$

$$e_4 = R_4 i_4, \qquad e_5 = R_5 i_5, \qquad e_6 = L_6\frac{di_6}{dt}, \qquad e_7 = R_7 i_7 = R_7 i_6$$

2.4   Network equilibrium equations

After determining the number and location of the key unknowns to be used in the analysis of a network, we next need to write out the equations that these unknowns must satisfy, and then solve them by various means. These equations must be written in such a manner that (1) they are independent and (2) there are as many independent equations as there are unknowns.

Numerous systems have been developed to write out a set of network equilibrium equations that satisfy these requirements. These different schemes constitute a segment of the general area of *circuit theory*. Usually, each method has its unique applications. For example, some are especially useful for computer-aided analysis of a network. Another method may be most suitable for the analysis of nonlinear networks.

The following sections outline four of the most fundamental methods, which make use of the development presented in the previous section.

2.5   Cutset analysis

In this scheme the unknown variables are tree-branch voltages. The procedure may be outlined as follows.

1   Choose a network tree.

2   Assign an unknown voltage variable to each nonsource tree branch. (If a tree branch consists of a voltage source, either independent or controlled, then this tree-branch voltage is either known or dependent.)

3   Apply KVL to express all link voltages in terms of tree-branch voltages.

4   Express all branch currents (including those of the controlled current sources) in terms of the tree-branch voltage variables.

5   Choose an appropriate set of ambits and write a KCL equation for each of them.

6   Solve the set of equations for all the unknown variables.

One key step in cutset analysis is to pick ambits in step 5 such that their KCL equations are independent. One of the following two rules will always accomplish this (although these are not the only possible choices): (a) Choose each ambit so that it intersects only one nonsource tree branch (and some links). Choose one ambit for each nonsource tree branch. (b) Starting with one ambit that intersects only one nonsource tree branch, form successive ambits such that each new ambit intersects only one new nonsource tree branch. Hence each new ambit intersects only one new tree branch, some links, and a number of tree branches that have already been intersected by previous ambits.

EXAMPLE 7   In Figure 2.16(a), the branches shown in heavy lines are to be the tree for this analysis. We arbitrarily assign a direction for each of the three unknown voltages along the tree, e_1, e_2, and e_3. Now the voltages

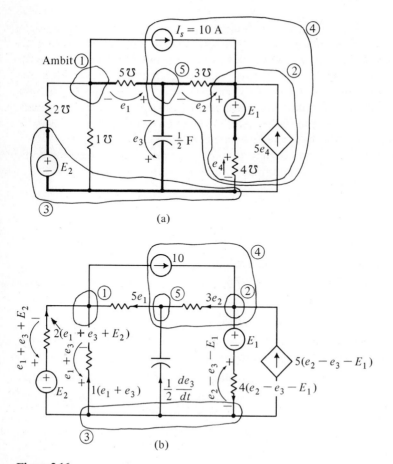

(a)

(b)

Figure 2.16

across the other three resistors can be expressed in terms of these tree voltages and the voltages of the independent voltage sources. This is done in Figure 2.16(b). Next, all the currents in the network are expressed in terms of these voltages, as also shown in Figure 2.16(b).

To obtain a set of three independent equations, we may follow either scheme (a) or scheme (b). Following scheme (a), we write the KCL equations for ambits 1, 2, and 3 in Figure 2.16(a). The equivalanets of these three ambits are also indicated in Figure 2.16(b). The KCL equations for these ambits are:

Ambit 1: $5e_1 + (e_1 + e_3) + 2(e_1 + e_3 + E_2) = 10$

Ambit 2: $3e_2 + 4(e_2 - e_3 - E_1) = 5(e_2 - e_3 - E_1) + 10$

Ambit 3: $2(e_1 + e_3 + E_2) + (e_1 + e_3) + \dfrac{1}{2}\dfrac{de_3}{dt} + 5(e_2 - e_3 - E_1)$

$$= 4(e_2 - e_3 - E_1)$$

Following scheme (b), we start with an ambit that intersects only one tree branch, say ambit 1. The second ambit must intersect one new tree branch, say e_3, but it may also intersect tree branch e_1 (though it does not have to). Let's choose ambit 4, as shown in Figure 2.16(a). The equivalent of this ambit is shown in Figure 2.16(b). The third ambit must intersect another new tree branch, e_2. But it may also intersect e_1 or e_3, or both. Ambit 5 might thus be chosen. Hence the following ambit equations are independent:

Ambit 1: $5e_1 + (e_1 + e_3) + 2(e_1 + e_3 + E_2) = 10$

Ambit 4: $5e_1 + 4(e_2 - e_3 - E_1) = \dfrac{1}{2}\dfrac{de_3}{dt} + 10 + 5(e_2 - e_3 - E_1)$

Ambit 5: $3e_2 + \dfrac{1}{2}\dfrac{de_3}{dt} = 5e_1$

This completes the cutset analysis through step 5. Since these are differential equations, solving them is not an easy matter. We shall not complete step 6 for this particular circuit at this point.

EXAMPLE 8   Find all currents in Figure 2.17(a) by cutset analysis.

SOLUTION   With the choice of tree shown in Figure 2.17(b), the unknown variables are denoted by E_1, E_2, and E_3. By KVL, we have

$$E_4 = E_2 + E_3, \qquad E_5 = E_1 + E_2 + E_3, \qquad E_6 = E_1 + E_2 - 5$$

Using method (a), we pick the ambits indicated in Figure 2.17(b). The ambit equations are

$$I_1 + I_5 + I_6 = 3 + 1 = 4, \qquad I_2 + I_4 + I_5 + I_6 = 3 + 1 = 4,$$

$$I_3 + I_4 + I_5 = 1$$

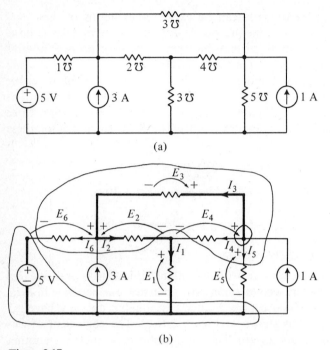

Figure 2.17

Substituting $I_1 = 3E_1$, $I_2 = 2E_2$, $I_3 = 3E_3$, $I_4 = 4E_4$, $I_5 = 5E_5$, and $I_6 = E_6$, we have

$$9E_1 + 6E_2 + 5E_3 = 9, \qquad 6E_1 + 12E_2 + 9E_3 = 9,$$

$$5E_1 + 9E_2 + 12E_3 = 1$$

By Cramer's rule, we have

$$\Delta = \begin{vmatrix} 9 & 6 & 5 \\ 6 & 12 & 9 \\ 5 & 9 & 12 \end{vmatrix} = 375, \qquad E_1 = \frac{1}{\Delta}\begin{vmatrix} 9 & 6 & 5 \\ 9 & 12 & 9 \\ 1 & 9 & 12 \end{vmatrix} = \frac{106}{125}$$

$$E_2 = \frac{1}{\Delta}\begin{vmatrix} 9 & 9 & 5 \\ 6 & 9 & 9 \\ 5 & 1 & 12 \end{vmatrix} = \frac{151}{125}, \qquad E_3 = \frac{1}{\Delta}\begin{vmatrix} 9 & 6 & 9 \\ 6 & 12 & 9 \\ 5 & 9 & 1 \end{vmatrix} = -\frac{147}{125}$$

Hence

$$I_1 = 3E_1 = \frac{318}{125} \text{ A}, \qquad I_2 = 2E_2 = \frac{302}{125} \text{ A}$$

$$I_3 = 3E_3 = -\frac{441}{125} \text{ A}, \qquad I_4 = 4(E_2 + E_3) = \frac{16}{125} \text{ A}$$

$$I_5 = 5(E_1 + E_2 + E_3) = \frac{550}{125} = \frac{22}{5} \text{ A}, \qquad I_6 = E_1 + E_2 - 5 = -\frac{368}{125} \text{ A}$$

The validity and development of cutset analysis are easy to follow from the theory of network trees. As a practical matter, this analysis is difficult and often awkward to implement. For most circuits, a modified version of cutset analysis—node analysis—is usually preferred. The steps of node analysis are outlined in Section 2.7.

2.6 Loop analysis

In loop analysis, the unknown variables are link currents. From Section 2.3 it is quite clear that, if we start with a tree, the introduction of each link creates a closed loop through some tree branches. A convenient notion of this approach is to imagine that each link current "flows" through only those tree branches with which a link forms a closed loop. Currents in such a flow pattern are known as *loop currents*. It should be clear that each tree-branch current is simply the sum of all the loop currents that flow through that branch, and that the KCL is automatically satisfied for all ambits, since a loop current that enters an ambit must also leave the ambit.

The loop analysis procedure may then be outlined as follows.

1 Choose a tree and thus its corresponding cotree.

2 Assign a current variable to each nonsource link. (If a link consists of a current source, either independent or controlled, then the link current is either known or dependent.)

3 Express all tree-branch currents in terms of the link currents by summing up all loop currents that flow through each branch. This step is equivalent to drawing one ambit for each tree branch such that it intersects only that tree branch (and some links) and then applying KCL to that ambit.

4 Express all branch voltages (including those of the controlled voltage sources) in terms of link current variables.

5 Choose an appropriate set of loops and write a KVL equation for each loop.

6 Solve these equations for the unknown variables.

Again it is important that the loops chosen in step 5 give as many independent equations as there are unknown key variables. One of the following schemes will enable us to achieve this: (a) Choose loops such that each loop includes only one link and a number of tree branches. (b) Start with one loop that has only one link along it. Then the ensuing loops will be such that each new loop traces only one new link, a number of tree branches, and/or links that have already been traced.

EXAMPLE 9   For the network of Figure 2.14 and the tree choice of Figure 2.15, the loop currents will be as indicated in Figure 2.18.

The currents in all branches of the network are indicated in Figure 2.19. Note that this process is equivalent to expressing all tree-branch currents in terms of the link currents in such a way that KCL is satisfied for the five ambits shown, each of which intersects only one tree branch.

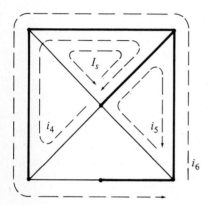

Figure 2.18

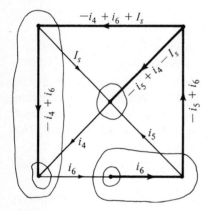

Figure 2.19

After all the currents in the network have been expressed in terms of the three independent unknowns i_4, i_5, and i_6, and the known source current, we can express all branch voltages in terms of these currents. These voltages are shown in Figure 2.20.

Following scheme (a) in choosing the loops to write out the KVL equations, we have

Link 4: $\quad R_4 i_4 + R_3(i_4 - i_5 - I_s) - E_{s1} - R_2(i_6 + I_s - i_4)$

$$-\frac{1}{C}\int_{-\infty}^{t} [i_6(\tau) - i_4(\tau)] \, d\tau = 0$$

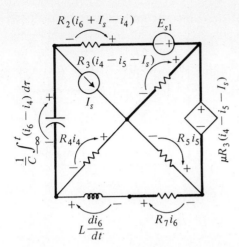

Figure 2.20

Link 5: $\quad R_5 i_5 + \mu R_3(i_4 - i_5 - I_s) - R_3(i_4 - i_5 - I_s) = 0$

Link 6: $\quad L\dfrac{di_6}{dt} + \dfrac{1}{C}\displaystyle\int_{-\infty}^{t} [i_6(\tau) - i_4(\tau)]\, d\tau + R_2(i_6 + I_s - i_4)$

$$+ E_{s1} - \mu R_3(i_4 - i_5 - I_s) + R_7 i_6 = 0$$

We can then solve these three equations for i_4, i_5, and i_6.

You may have noticed that we did not use the link containing the current source. Because the voltage across a current source is not constrained by the source itself, this voltage is not relevant to the analysis problem. There are only three independent unknown currents, i_4, i_5, and i_6, and only three KVL equations are needed. The voltage across the current source can be found through the tree voltages once the three current variables have been found.

EXAMPLE 10 By loop analysis, find the current distribution in the bridge circuit of Figure 2.21(a) and the voltage across the current source.

SOLUTION First we denote the five branch currents by I_1, I_2, I_3, I_4, and I_5, as shown in Figure 2.21(a). With the choice of the tree in Figure 2.21(b), I_1 and I_2 are the link currents and will be used as the unknown variables. By summing up the loop currents in each branch of Figure 2.21(b), we have

$$I_3 = I_1 + 10, \qquad I_4 = I_1 - I_2 + 10, \qquad I_5 = I_2 - 10$$

Around loop 1 and loop 2, we have

$$4I_1 + 2I_3 + 6I_4 = 0, \qquad 5I_2 + 3I_5 - 6I_4 = 0$$

Substitution yields

$$12I_1 - 6I_2 = -80, \qquad -6I_1 + 14I_2 = 90$$

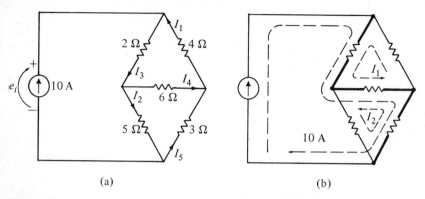

(a)   (b)

Figure 2.21

Solution of these equations gives

$$I_1 = -\frac{145}{33} \text{ A}, \qquad I_2 = \frac{50}{11} \text{ A}$$

Thus

$$I_3 = \frac{185}{33} \text{ A}, \qquad I_4 = \frac{35}{33} \text{ A}, \qquad I_5 = -\frac{180}{33} \text{ A}$$

The voltage across the current source is

$$e_i = 2I_3 + 5I_2 = -4I_1 - 3I_5$$

$$= 2I_3 + 6I_4 - 3I_5 = -4I_1 - 6I_4 + 5I_2 = \frac{1120}{33} \text{ V}$$

The equivalent resistance seen by the current source is thus

$$R_{eq} = \frac{e_i}{10} = \frac{112}{33} \, \Omega$$

2.7   Node analysis

When it is possible to choose a tree for a network such that all the tree branches are connected to a common node, the direct application of cutset analysis (outlined in Section 2.5) results in an especially simple set of rules for writing the equations necessary to solve the independent unknowns. Figure 2.22 is an example of such a network tree.

With this choice of tree, we see that each ambit chosen according to rule (a) of Section 2.5 encircles the node that is not the common node of the tree. A further simplification is effected if, instead of using the tree-branch voltages as the unknown variables, we *ground* the node common to all the branches and use the *node voltages with reference to ground* as the unknown variables. This greatly reduces the complexity of the diagram used in the analysis.

If such a choice of tree is not possible, we may still follow the procedure if we introduce a dummy tree branch between each node that is not connected to the common node. These dummy branches serve only to define the voltages

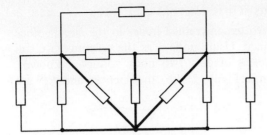

Figure 2.22 A network tree whose branches are all connected to a common node.

of these nodes with respect to the common node. They draw no currents. A tree that includes one or more such dummy tree branches is called a *pseudo-tree*. Figure 2.23(b) shows such a pseudo-tree for the network of Figure 2.23(a) when node a is chosen as the common node. Thus all branch voltages are still expressible in terms of these pseudo-tree voltages, as shown in Figure 2.23(c).

The following set of rules can be followed in carrying out the node analysis of a circuit.

1 Choose a reference node. Call it the ground or the datum node.

2 Assign a voltage unknown variable to each unconstrained node or each group of constrained nodes. (Two or more nodes connected by voltage sources, either independent or controlled, are constrained to one another as far as their voltages are concerned. Hence only one unknown variable is needed for each group of these nodes.)

3 Express all node voltages in terms of these voltage variables.

4 Express all branch currents (including those of the controlled current sources) in terms of these node voltages.

5 Write a KCL equation for each unconstrained node or each ambit encircling a group of constrained nodes (except the reference node).

6 Solve these equations simultaneously for the node voltages.

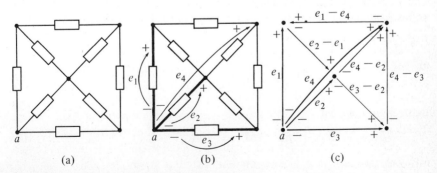

Figure 2.23 The pseudo-tree of a network graph.

EXAMPLE 11   Find all currents in the circuit of Figure 2.24(a).

SOLUTION   There are only two unconstrained nodes in the circuit, since nodes 2, 3, and 4 are constrained. Using node 5 as the reference, we can define the node voltages in terms of only two node voltage unknowns. One such designation is shown in Figure 2.24(b), in which E_1 and E_2* are

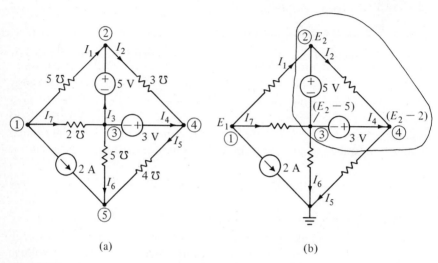

(a)   (b)

Figure 2.24

the unknown variables. All nonsource branch currents can be expressed in terms of these two voltages, namely,

$$I_1 = 5(E_1 - E_2), \qquad I_2 = 3[E_2 - (E_2 - 2)] = 6$$
$$I_5 = 4(E_2 - 2), \qquad I_6 = 5(E_2 - 5), \qquad I_7 = 2[E_1 - (E_2 - 5)]$$

For node 1, KCL gives

$$-I_1 - I_7 - 2 = 0 \qquad \text{or} \qquad 5(E_1 - E_2) + 2(E_1 - E_2 + 5) + 2 = 0$$

The other KCL equation should be written for the ambit that encircles nodes 2, 3, and 4, as indicated in Figure 2.24(b). KCL for this ambit gives

$$I_1 + I_7 - I_6 - I_5 = 0$$

or

$$5(E_1 - E_2) + 2(E_1 - E_2 + 5) - 5(E_2 - 5) - 4(E_2 - 2) = 0$$

Rearranging, we get

$$7E_1 - 7E_2 = -12, \qquad 7E_1 - 16E_2 = -43$$

* We could also use E_3 or E_4 in place of E_2 here.

Solving, we obtain

$$E_1 = \frac{109}{63} \text{ V}, \qquad E_2 = \frac{31}{9} \text{ V}$$

whence

$$I_1 = -\frac{60}{7} \text{ A}, \qquad I_5 = \frac{50}{9} \text{ A}, \qquad I_6 = -\frac{70}{9} \text{ A}, \qquad I_7 = \frac{46}{7} \text{ A}$$

We can, if we wish, readily find the two voltage source currents, they are

$$I_3 = I_2 - I_1 = \frac{102}{7} \text{ A}, \qquad I_4 = I_5 - I_2 = -\frac{2}{9} \text{ A}$$

EXAMPLE 12   For small-signal ac applications, we may consider the capacitors of the transistor amplifier circuit of Figure 2.25(a) as short circuits. The 24-volt power supply is also a short circuit to ground for ac. The transistor may be replaced by the equivalent circuit marked off by the dashed box in Figure 2.25(b). Given that $I_s = 1 \ \mu\text{A}$, find the load current I_L.

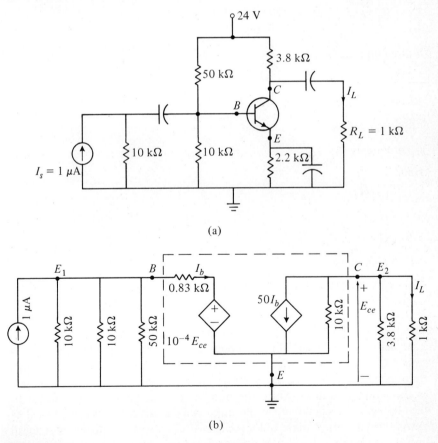

(a)

(b)

Figure 2.25

SOLUTION   The circuit of Figure 2.25(b) has three unconstrained nodes. Choose terminal E as the reference and use the voltages at B and C as the unknown variables. The node equations are

$$\frac{E_1}{10\,\text{k}} + \frac{E_1}{10\,\text{k}} + \frac{E_1}{50\,\text{k}} + I_b = 10^{-6}, \qquad \frac{E_2}{10\,\text{k}} + \frac{E_2}{3.8\,\text{k}} + \frac{E_2}{1\,\text{k}} + 50I_b = 0$$

where

$$I_b = \frac{E_1 - 10^{-4} \times E_2}{0.83\,\text{k}}$$

and each k represents the multiplier 10^3. Substituting I_b into the node equations and multiplying through by the factor k, we have

$$\frac{E_1}{10} + \frac{E_1}{10} + \frac{E_1}{50} + \frac{E_1}{0.83} - \frac{10^{-4} \times E_2}{0.83} = 10^{-3}$$

$$\frac{E_2}{10} + \frac{E_2}{3.8} + E_2 + \frac{50E_1}{0.83} - \frac{50 \times 10^{-4}E_2}{0.83} = 0$$

Simplifying, we obtain

$$1.425E_1 - 1.205 \times 10^{-4}E_2 = 10^{-3}$$

$$60.24E_1 + 1.357E_2 = 0$$

Eliminating E_1 gives

$$E_2 = -31.04\,\text{mV}$$

Hence

$$I_L = -31.04\,\mu\text{A}$$

2.8   Mesh analysis

The mesh-analysis method may be compared to loop analysis much as node analysis is compared to cutset analysis. A major limitation of mesh analysis is that it is applicable only to a *planar* network, that is, one that can be drawn on a plane without any of its branches crossing any other.

As defined at the start of the chapter, a mesh* is a loop whose interior is empty. Given a network with a chosen tree, the addition of each link increases the number of meshes by exactly one. Hence the number of meshes is identical to the number of links. Since the number of nonsource links is equal to the number of independent current unknowns, mesh currents can be used as current unknowns in place of loop currents in an analysis problem. A mesh current is simply a loop current that flows in a loop that is also a mesh.

* By "mesh," we tacitly mean "interior mesh."

Unlike the loop currents in loop analysis, a mesh current need not always be identifiable with an actual branch current in the circuit.

When a link has a current source (independent or controlled) in it, it places a constraint on the two adjacent mesh currents much as a voltage source constrains the voltages of two nodes. These two mesh currents are no longer independent of each other. Hence the number of independent mesh currents is equal to the number of nonsource links in a network.

The rules for mesh analysis are as follows.

1 Assign a mesh-current variable to each mesh.

2 For each current source, equate its source current to the total mesh current flowing through it.

3 Use the voltage–current relationship of each nonsource element and express each branch voltage in terms of the mesh currents.

4 Write a KVL equation for each mesh that has no current source and for each loop that would become a mesh if current sources were removed.

5 Solve for the mesh currents obtained from steps 2 and 4.

6 In most problems, it is possible to express one mesh current in terms of the other when they are constrained. When this is done, step 2 is automatically satisfied and only the KVL equations obtained in step 4 need be solved.

EXAMPLE 13 Find the currents in the circuit of Figure 2.24(a).

SOLUTION This network has four meshes. The mesh currents are designated i_1, i_2, i_3, and i_4, as shown in Figure 2.26. One of these meshes, $i_3 = -2$, is constrained. Writing out the loop equations around meshes 1, 2, and 4, we get

$$-\tfrac{1}{5}i_1 - 5 - \tfrac{1}{2}(i_1 + 2) = 0, \qquad -\tfrac{1}{5}(2 + i_2) + 3 - \tfrac{1}{4}i_2 = 0,$$
$$-5 + 3 + \tfrac{1}{3}i_4 = 0$$

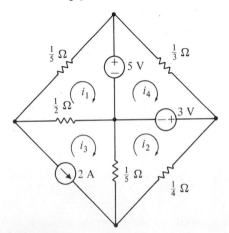

Figure 2.26

We readily solve these three equations to get

$$i_1 = -\tfrac{60}{7} \text{ A}, \qquad i_2 = \tfrac{52}{9} \text{ A}, \qquad i_4 = 6 \text{ A}$$

We can now obtain all the currents in the circuit by combining the appropriate mesh currents. These results can be compared with those in Example 11.

EXAMPLE 14   The circuit of Figure 2.27 contains a controlled source. The procedure for handling a controlled source is no different from that for

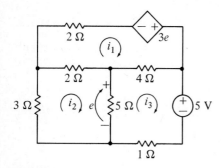

Figure 2.27

handling an independent source. With the mesh designation shown, we have

$$-2(i_1 - i_2) - 2i_1 + 3e - 4(i_1 - i_3) = 0$$
$$-3i_2 - 2(i_2 - i_1) - 5(i_2 - i_3) = 0$$
$$-5(i_3 - i_2) - 4(i_3 - i_1) - 5 - i_3 = 0$$

Now we recognize that $e = 5(i_2 - i_3)$. Substituting this relationship into the mesh equations and rearranging give

$$8i_1 - 17i_2 + 11i_3 = 0, \qquad -2i_1 + 10i_2 - 5i_3 = 0,$$
$$-4i_1 - 5i_2 + 10i_3 = -5$$

Using Cramer's rule, we have

$$\Delta = \begin{vmatrix} 8 & -17 & 11 \\ -2 & 10 & -5 \\ -4 & -5 & 10 \end{vmatrix} = 470, \qquad i_1 = \frac{1}{\Delta} \begin{vmatrix} 0 & -17 & 11 \\ 0 & 10 & -5 \\ -5 & -5 & 10 \end{vmatrix} = \frac{255}{94}$$

$$i_2 = \frac{1}{\Delta} \begin{vmatrix} 8 & 0 & 11 \\ -2 & 0 & -5 \\ -4 & -5 & 10 \end{vmatrix} = -\frac{9}{47}, \qquad i_3 = \frac{1}{\Delta} \begin{vmatrix} 8 & -17 & 0 \\ -2 & 10 & 0 \\ -4 & -5 & -5 \end{vmatrix} = -\frac{23}{47}$$

We can now readily find the various quantities throughout the network.

EXAMPLE 15   Analyze the transistor amplifier circuit of Figure 2.25 by mesh analysis.

SOLUTION   The equivalent circuit of Figure 2.25(b) has three unconstrained nodes. Therefore only two voltage unknowns are necessary if either cutset or node analysis is used. Since there are seven nonsource branches, a direct application of either loop or mesh analysis would require five unknowns. We observe that there are two groups of three resistances that are directly connected in parallel. If these resistances were combined, the circuit would be greatly simplified. Some computation will give

$$10 \text{ k}\Omega \| 10 \text{ k}\Omega \| 50 \text{ k}\Omega = 4.545 \text{ k}\Omega, \qquad 10 \text{ k}\Omega \| 3.8 \text{ k}\Omega \| 1 \text{ k}\Omega = 0.7336 \text{ k}\Omega$$

Thus we may replace the circuit of Figure 2.25(b) by that shown in Figure 2.28, which has only one unconstrained mesh. Writing the KVL equation

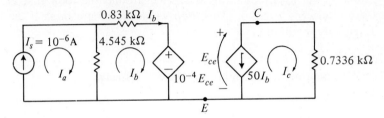

Figure 2.28

around mesh b, we get

$$4.545 \text{ k}(I_b - I_a) + 0.83 \text{ k}I_b + 10^{-4}E_{ce} = 0$$

Since

$$I_a = 10^{-6}, \qquad I_c = -50I_b, \qquad E_{ce} = 0.7336 \times 10^3 \times I_c = -36.68I_b$$

we have

$$4.545 \text{ k}I_b - 4.545 \times 10^{-3} + 0.83 \text{ k}I_b - 3.668I_b = 0$$

$$(4.545 \text{ k} + 0.83 \text{ k} - 3.668)I_b = 4.545 \times 10^{-3}$$

$$I_b = 0.8462 \times 10^{-6}$$

Hence

$$I_c = -42.3 \times 10^{-6}$$

This is the current flowing into the parallel combination of $10 \text{ k}\Omega \| 3.8 \text{ k}\Omega \| 1 \text{ k}\Omega$. We can now apply the current-division rule to find I_L.

$$I_L = \frac{1/1 \text{ k}}{1/10 \text{ k} + 1/3.8 \text{ k} + 1/1 \text{ k}} I_c = \frac{1}{1.3632} I_c = -31.04 \text{ } \mu\text{A}$$

This result can be compared with that of Example 12.

EXAMPLE 16 Find the mesh currents in the circuit of Figure 2.29.

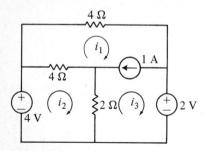

$4\,\Omega$

Figure 2.29

SOLUTION   Meshes 1 and 3 are constrained by the 1-A current source: $i_1 - i_3 = 1$. One of the KVL equations is written around the loop that is the composite of meshes 1 and 3. (This loop would become a mesh if the current source were removed.)

$$4i_1 + 4(i_1 - i_2) + 2(i_3 - i_2) = -2$$

The other KVL equation is written around mesh 2, namely,

$$4(i_2 - i_1) + 2(i_2 - i_3) = 4$$

Eliminating i_3, we get

$$10i_1 - 6i_2 = 0, \qquad -6i_1 + 6i_2 = 2$$

Solving these equations, we get

$$i_1 = \tfrac{1}{2}\,\text{A}, \qquad i_2 = \tfrac{5}{6}\,\text{A}, \qquad i_3 = -\tfrac{1}{2}\,\text{A}$$

All branch currents can now be found readily.

As mentioned earlier, the procedure for mesh analysis outlined here is valid only for planar networks. Figure 2.30 shows the configuration of an

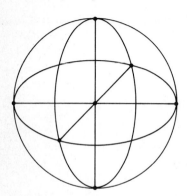

Figure 2.30   Example of a nonplanar network graph.

example of a nonplanar network. This network has seven nodes, so that its tree has six branches, and there are nine links. But it is not clear how many meshes it has. Hence the application of mesh analysis is limited to planar networks. All the other analysis methods outlined in this chapter are applicable to both planar and nonplanar networks.

2.9 Concluding remarks

Any network, linear or nonlinear, must satisfy Kirchhoff's two laws and the four systematic methods developed in this chapter for writing the necessary and sufficient equilibrium equations for analysis. It is heuristically obvious that the solution of these equations is easier when the network is made up of only linear elements. We might further expect that, among linear networks, those with only LTI elements would be easiest to solve. In fact, we did not even give an example with LTV elements in the network. Since LTI network analysis is very basic and important for electrical engineers, it is advantageous for us to concentrate on this class of network first.

When an LTI network contains energy-storing elements, the network equations are integro-differential equations. The solution of these equations is more complicated, especially when source quantities are time functions. When an LTI network contains resistors only, the solution of the network equilibrium equations is purely algebraic and simple. This was illustrated by examples in Sections 2.7 and 2.8.

A natural question one might raise at this point is "When do we use what method to analyze a given circuit?" The only valid answer to this question is "It depends." It depends on the circuit. It depends on the habits one develops through the years. And don't forget, there are other schemes of analysis not dealt with in this chapter.

Usually, for a given network, it is advisable to first construct a tree—any tree—and count the number of independent unknown voltages and independent unknown currents. The number of independent voltage unknowns is equal to the number of nonsource tree branches. The number of independent current unknowns is equal to the number of nonsource links. This immediately determines the number of simultaneous equations that we have to set up and solve. If we have far fewer voltage unknowns than current unknowns, cutset or node analysis will be preferable to loop or mesh analysis. If the opposite is true, then the choice is obviously the opposite. If the numbers are close, either the choice is not clear-cut or other considerations will have to be taken into account.

For most practical problems, it is generally true that node- and mesh-analysis methods are easier to carry out than cutset- and loop-analysis methods. However, cutset- and loop-analysis methods are useful as an intermediate step in the logical development of a systematic formulation of mesh- and node-analysis techniques.

In this chapter, most of the network examples that we solved completely were memoryless and had constant source strengths. This was intentional, because solving this class of network problems is usually easiest. We did not want the essence of the techniques to be obscured by the difficulty of mathematics. These techniques are equally valid when the network is not memoryless and the sources are dynamic. However, in those cases, solving the network equations, once you have obtained them, may not be a simple task. We shall address the solving of more general network equations later as more mathematical tools are developed or become available to us.

Problems

2.1 In the circuit shown in Figure P2.1, it is known that $V_a - V_e = 10$ V, $V_b - V_e = 35$ V, $V_b - V_d = 22$ V, $V_c - V_d = -11$ V, $I_1 = 3$ A, and $I_2 = -1$ A. Determine $V_a - V_b$, $V_b - V_c$, $V_d - V_e$, $V_e - V_b$, $V_e - V_c$, $V_d - V_a$, and I_3.

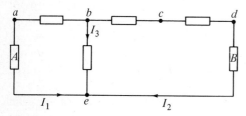

Figure P2.1

2.2 In figure P2.2, the following voltages are known: $V_{10} = 1$ V, $V_{20} = 2$ V, $V_{30} = 3$ V, $V_{40} = -4$ V, and $V_{50} = 5$ V. Find V_{12}, V_{23}, V_{34}, V_{45}, V_{51}, V_{13}, and V_{35}.

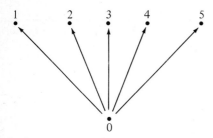

Figure P2.2

2.3 In Figure P2.3, the following currents are known: $I_1 = 1$ A, $I_2 = 2$ A, $I_3 = 3$ A, $I_4 = -4$ A, and $I_5 = 5$ A. Find I_6, I_7, I_8, I_9, I_{10}, I_{11}, and I_{12}.

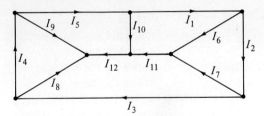

Figure P2.3

2.4 What is the value of *I* in Figure P2.4?

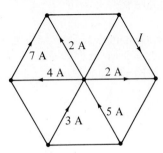

Figure P2.4

2.5 For the circuit of Figure P2.5(a), sketch $v(t)$ corresponding to the current given in Figure P2.5(b).

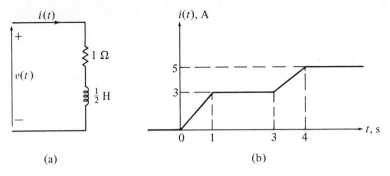

Figure P2.5

2.6 Suppose that $e(t)$ is given in Figure P2.6(a) and $i(t)$ is given in Figure P2.6(b). Sketch $i_1(t)$ of Figure P2.6(c).

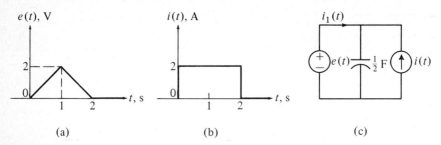

(a)   (b)   (c)

Figure P2.6

2.7 Determine all six voltages in the circuit of Figure P2.7.

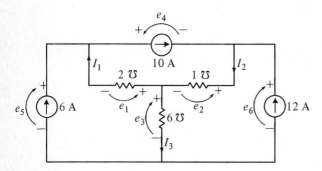

Figure P2.7

2.8 In the circuit shown in Figure P2.8, it is known that $V_{be} = -2$ V, $V_{cd} = 4$ V, $V_{de} = -9$ V, $V_{ef} = 6$ V, and $V_{af} = 10$ V. Determine V_{ab}, V_{bc}, V_{ca}, I_1, I_2, and I_3.

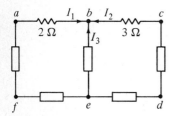

Figure P2.8

2.9 In the circuit shown in Figure P2.9, it is known that $I_1 = 5$ A, $I_2 = -3$ A, $I_3 = -6$ A, $I_4 = 2$ A, $I_5 = 3$ A, and $I_6 = 7$ A. Determine V_1, V_2, and V_3.

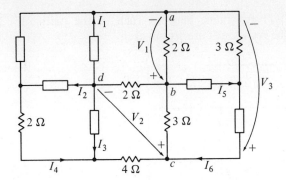

Figure P2.9

2.10 In the circuit of Figure P2.10, what are the values of I_1 and I_3? [*Hint*: This problem looks very complicated, but it really isn't. A little thought will save a lot of work.]

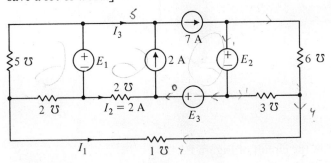

Figure P2.10

2.11 In the circuit of Figure P2.11, it is known that $V_2 = 10$ V. Determine I_1 and V_1.

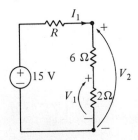

Figure P2.11

2.12 Find the equivalent LTI resistance between each of the pairs of terminals of Figure P2.12. The resistances are 1 ohm each.

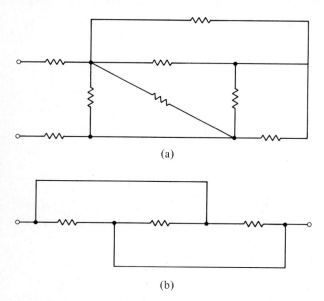

(a)

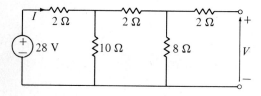

(b)

Figure P2.12

2.13 Find I and V in the circuit of Figure P2.13.

$$I \quad 2\,\Omega \quad \quad 2\,\Omega \quad \quad 2\,\Omega$$

28 V $\quad$ 10 Ω $\quad$ 8 Ω $\quad$ V

Figure P2.13

2.14 In the circuit of Figure P2.14, it is known that $I_1 = 3$ A, $I_2 = -2$ A, $I_3 = 4$ A, $I_4 = 6$ A, $I_5 = -7$ A, and $I_6 = 5$ A. Determine the voltage rises from a to b and from c to d.

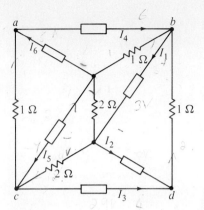

Figure P2.14

$\partial 8$ $\partial 9$

2.15 Determine V in Figure P2.15.

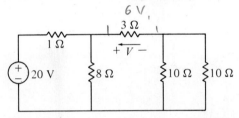

Figure P2.15

2.16 Determine an expression for I_1 in terms of the other constants of the circuit of Figure P2.16. G_1, G_2, and G_3 are the conductances of the elements shown.

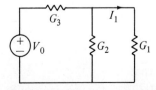

Figure P2.16

2.17 Determine the voltages V_1, V_2, and V_3 in the circuit of Figure P2.17.

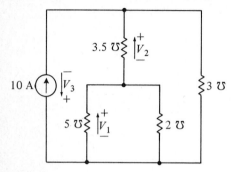

Figure P2.17

2.18 Determine V_1 and I_1 in the circuit of Figure P2.18.

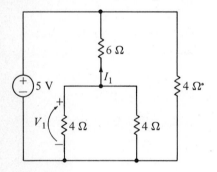

Figure P2.18

2.19 When two LTI capacitors are connected in parallel, as shown in Figure 2.6, show that

$$i_j = \frac{C_j}{C_1+C_2}\, i, \quad j = 1 \text{ or } 2$$

2.20 When two LTI capacitors are connected in series, as shown in Figure 2.7, and if $e_1(0) = e_2(0) = 0$, show that

$$e_j = \frac{S_j}{S_1+S_2}\, e, \quad j = 1 \text{ or } 2$$

2.21 The q-v curves of two capacitors, C_1 and C_2, are given in Figure P2.21(a). What is the q-v curve of the series combination of Figure P2.21(b)? What is it when they are in parallel, as shown in Figure P2.21(c)?

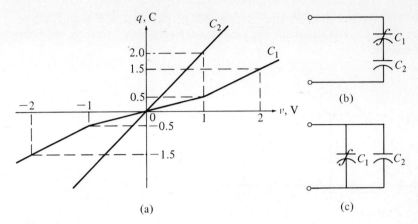

Figure P2.21

2.22 Extend the voltage-division rule to three resistors in series.

2.23 Extend the current-division rule to three resistors in parallel. Express the formulas in terms of both the conductances and the resistances.

2.24 In the circuit of Figure 2.1, use the branches containing R_1, R_2, R_3, R_4, and the voltage sources as tree branches. Express all quantities in the network in terms of the link currents i_s, i_2, and i_5 and of e_s. Assume $e_7 = f(i_6)$.

2.25 The *graph* of a network is a simplified network diagram from which network elements are omitted. Figure P2.25(a) is the voltage graph and Figure P2.25(b) is the current graph of a given network. For these graphs, express each link voltage (in light lines) in terms of the tree-branch voltages (in heavy lines) and each tree-branch current in terms of the link currents.

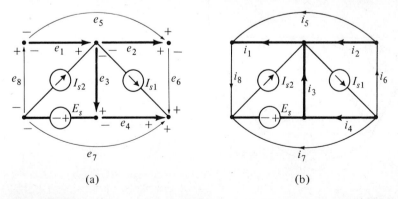

Figure P2.25

2.26 Use the tree and the tree-branch voltage variables of Figure P2.26 to write the KCL equations for the ambits, each of which intersects only one tree branch.

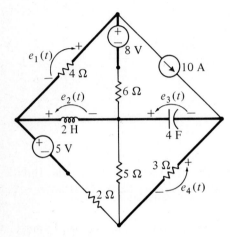

Figure P2.26

2.27 The tree-branch voltages e_1, e_2, e_3, and e_4 are designated as shown in Figure P2.27. Choose ambits so that each intersects only one tree branch. Write the ambit equations for solving the network.

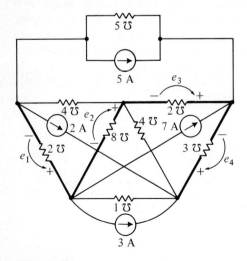

Figure P2.27

2.28 Use cutset analysis to find the current I of Figure P2.28.

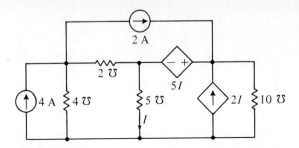

Figure P2.28

2.29 For the circuit of Figure P2.29, with the tree as shown, write three independent loop equations in terms of the link currents. Then solve for these currents.

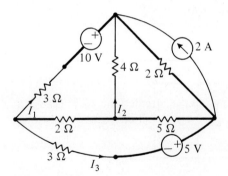

Figure P2.29

2.30 Use the three link currents shown in Figure P2.30 to write the three KVL equations around the loops, each of which traces only one link.

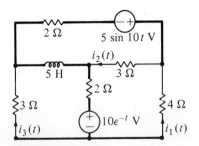

Figure P2.30

2.31 For the chosen tree in the circuit of Figure P2.31, find I_1 and I_2 by loop analysis.

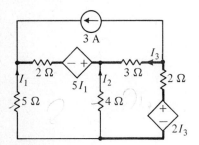

Figure P2.31

2.32 (a) Write the node equations for the three ungrounded nodes shown in Figure P2.32.
  (b) Solve for the three node voltages.

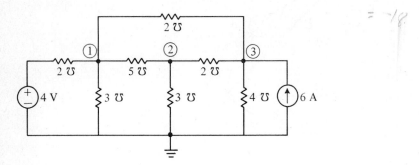

Figure P2.32

2.33 Use node analysis to determine e_0 in Figure P2.33.

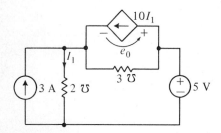

Figure P2.33

2.34 Find i and e of Figure P2.34 by node analysis.

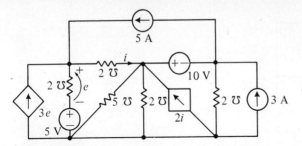

Figure P2.34

2.35 Write the five node equations for the node analysis of the circuit of Figure P2.35. Collect like terms and place constants on the right-hand side of each equation.

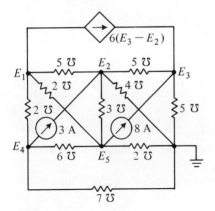

Figure P2.35

2.36 Use mesh analysis to determine I_1 in Figure P2.36.

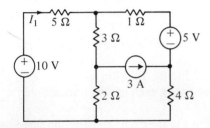

Figure P2.36

2.37 Write the three mesh equations for the network of Figure P2.37.

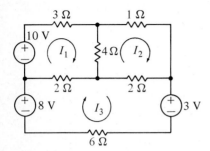

Figure P2.37

2.38 Find i_1 of Figure P2.38 by mesh analysis. What is the equivalent resistance seen by the source?

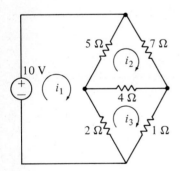

Figure P2.38

2.39 (a) Using the heavy-lined branches of Figure P2.39(b) as the tree, write the three KCL equations for the three ambits each of which intersects only one tree branch.

(b) Using node 0 as the reference node, write the three node equations [Figure P2.39(a)].

(c) Using the three link currents of Figure P2.39(b) as unknowns, write the KVL equations for the three loops, each of which traces only one link.

(d) Using the three meshes defined in Figure P2.39(a), write the three mesh equations.

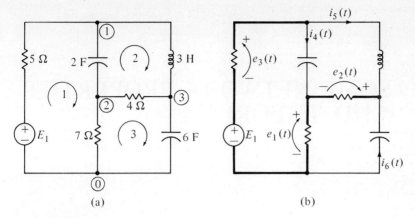

Figure P2.39

2.40 Find I of Figure P2.40.

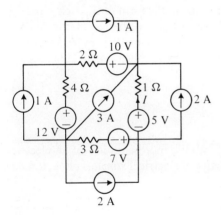

Figure P2.40

3 | SOME NETWORK PROPERTIES AND THEOREMS

In this chapter, we shall describe several properties of certain classes of networks. A few of these properties are stated in the form of theorems, partly for convenience and partly for historical reasons. We find some properties helpful in simplifying the solution of particular network problems. Others are used to derive additional theorems or to explain phenomena in networks.

3.1 Linear networks

The block diagram of Figure 3.1 is a symbolic representation of an electric network. The input function $x(t)$ represents an electrical *stimulus or excitation*

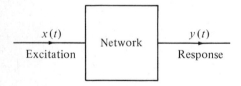

$$x(t)$$
Excitation — Network — $$y(t)$$
Response

Figure 3.1 Block diagram of a network.

that causes the network to respond in a certain way. This function could represent either a source or the output of another network, and it could be either a voltage or a current. As a result of the application of $x(t)$, there occurs a certain current or voltage in the network—the *response*. This response is also known as the *output* and is represented by the function $y(t)$.

A network is *additive* if its response to several excitations is always the sum of its responses when these excitations are applied individually. In other words, if a network is additive and if its response due to $x_1(t)$ is $y_1(t)$ and that due to $x_2(t)$ is $y_2(t)$, then its response due to $x_1(t)+x_2(t)$ is $y_1(t)+y_2(t)$.

A network is *homogeneous* if, when its excitation is multiplied by a constant, its response is also multiplied by the same constant. In other words, if $y(t)$ is the response of a homogeneous network when its excitation is $x(t)$, then the response of this network is $ky(t)$ when its excitation is $kx(t)$.

A network is *linear* if it's both additive and homogeneous. If $y_1(t)$ and $y_2(t)$ are the responses of a linear network when excited by $x_1(t)$ and $x_2(t)$ respectively, then its response due to $k_1 x_1(t)+k_2 x_2(t)$ is $k_1 y_1(t)+k_2 y_2(t)$.

Theorem A network containing only *LTI elements* that contain no initial energy is a *linear network*.

Such networks include those with LTI resistors, LTI capacitors, LTI inductors, and LTI controlled sources. They may also contain a host of other LTI multiterminal elements such as gyrators, transformers, the mutual inductance, impedance converters, and circulators, some of which will be defined or described later. In addition, any energy-storing elements must not have any initial energy stored before $x(t)$ is applied.

Independent sources must be excluded from a linear network. Since independent sources are generally used to excite a linear network, the entire arrangement—the linear network plus its external sources—is sometimes described as "linear." One should realize, however, that in this usage the adjective "linear" describes only the part of the arrangement that is seen by the sources, not the entire arrangement.

Since a network with initially idle LTI elements is linear, it has all the properties of a linear network. In addition to additivity and homogeneity, such a network has the following two properties.

The *differentiability* property of a linear network implies that, if the input $x(t)$ is replaced by its derivative $x'(t)$, then the response $y(t)$ is replaced by $y'(t)$.

The *integrability* property of a linear network implies that, if the input $x(t)$ is replaced by its integral,

$$x^{(-1)}(t) = \int_{-\infty}^{t} x(\tau)\, d\tau$$

then the response $g(t)$ is replaced by $g^{(-1)}(t)$.

3.2 Superposition theorem

If a network is linear, then the current in any branch (or the voltage between any two points) of the network is the sum of all the currents in that branch (or of all the voltages between those two points), each of which is calculated with only one independent source active at a time. While one independent source is active, all other independent sources are idled: Voltage sources are reduced to short circuits and current sources are reduced to open circuits.

Figure 3.2 illustrates the application of this theorem. In Figure 3.2(a), there are three independent sources connected to N. In each of the parts (b) to (d) of Figure 3.2, the network is excited by only one of the three sources. Two points, 1 and 2, and one branch are singled out to demonstrate the application of the superposition theorem at those localities.

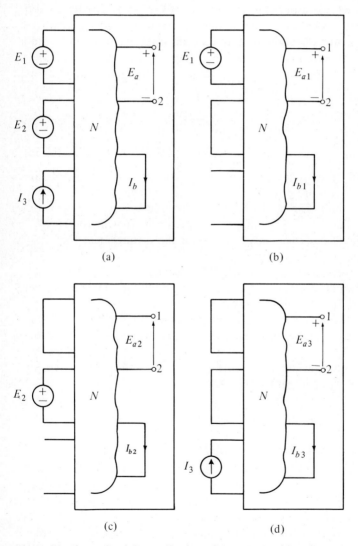

Figure 3.2 Example of the application of the superposition theorem.

The following equations are based on the superposition theorem:

$$E_a = E_{a1} + E_{a2} + E_{a3} \tag{3.1}$$
$$I_b = I_{b1} + I_{b2} + I_{b3} \tag{3.2}$$

Network N in all four parts of Figure 3.2 is the same network internally. This includes all controlled sources, if any.

The theorem states that, in order for the theorem to be valid, all elements in the network must be initially idle. This implies that all the capacitors have no initial charge and all the inductors have no intial current. Later on we shall see how an inductor with an initial current may be replaced by an inductor that is initially idle (has zero current) properly connected with an independent source. Also an initially charged capacitor may be replaced by an initially empty capacitor (with zero charge or voltage) in conjunction with an independent source. With these equivalences, the superposition theorem also becomes applicable to networks that are not initially idle.

The distinction between the superposition and the additivity properties of a linear network lies in the fact that additivity pertains only to the sum of the values of a single source, while superposition pertains to the total effect of several sources. In a way, the additivity property might be regarded as a special case of the superposition property.

For example, according to the superposition theorem, the circuit of Figure 3.3(a) could be replaced by the two separate circuits shown in Figure 3.3(b) and (c). The currents and voltages in (a) would be the sums of the corresponding currents and voltages in parts (b) and (c). If we then set up the mesh equations for (b) and (c), they would read

$$5I_{1a} - 3I_{2a} = 10, \qquad -3I_{1a} + 8I_{2a} = 0 \tag{3.3}$$

and

$$5I_{1b} - 3I_{2b} = 0, \qquad -3I_{1b} + 8I_{2b} = -5 \tag{3.4}$$

If we wrote the mesh equations for Figure 3.3(a) directly, they would read

$$5I_1 - 3I_2 = 10, \qquad -3I_1 + 8I_2 = -5 \tag{3.5}$$

A simple manipulation shows that, if I_{1a}, I_{1b}, I_{2a}, and I_{2b} satisfy (3.3) and (3.4), then the addition of (3.3) and (3.4) will result in (3.5), if

$$I_1 = I_{1a} + I_{1b}, \qquad I_2 = I_{2a} + I_{2b} \tag{3.6}$$

A generalization of this procedure would constitute a proof of the superposition theorem. A formal proof of this theorem is given in Appendix A.

For example, the circuit of Figure 3.4(a) contains three independent sources and can be analyzed as the three separate circuits shown in Figure 3.4(b), (c), and (d). Each of these circuits can be analyzed by using a series or parallel combination of resistances and voltage- or current-division rules.

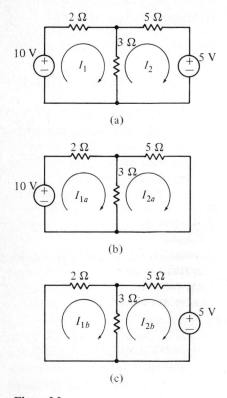

(a)

(b)

(c)

Figure 3.3

The currents in each branch of the original network are obtained by summing up the currents in each component network. The result is summarized in Figure 3.4(e).

EXAMPLE 1   Find the output voltage E_o of the transistor equivalent circuit of Figure 3.5(a).

SOLUTION   Since this circuit contains only LTI elements and is excited by two independent sources, it can be analyzed by the superposition of two separate circuits. For the circuit of Figure 3.5(b), in which only the voltage source is active, we have

$$I_{b1} = \frac{10^{-3}}{1\ k} = 1\ \mu A$$

$$E_{o1} = -50 \times i_b \times \frac{40\ k \times 10\ k}{50\ k}$$

$$= -50 \times 10^{-6} \times 8\ k = -0.4\ V$$

For the circuit of Figure 3.5(c), in which only the current source is active,

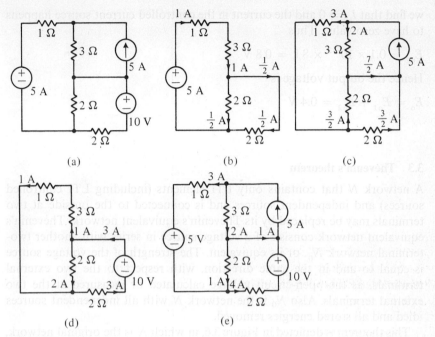

Figure 3.4

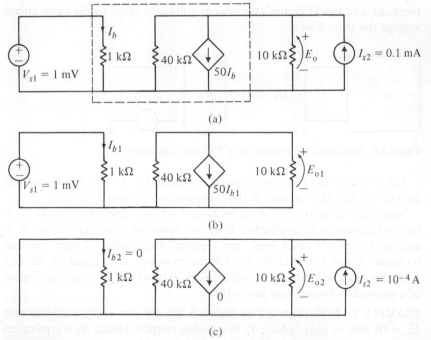

Figure 3.5

we find that $I_{b2} = 0$ and the current in the controlled current source happens to have zero value. Thus

$$E_{o2} = 0.1 \times 10^{-3} \times 8\,k = 0.8\ V$$

Hence the output voltage is

$$E_o = E_{o1} + E_{o2} = 0.4\ V$$

3.3 Thévenin's theorem

A network N that contains only LTI elements (including LTI controlled sources) and independent sources and is connected to the outside at two terminals may be replaced by its Thévenin's equivalent network. Thévenin's equivalent network consists of a voltage source in series with another two-terminal network N_0, or its equivalent. The strength of the voltage source is equal to and in the same direction, with respect to the two external terminals, as the open-circuit voltage calculated or measured at the two external terminals. Also N_0 is the network N with all independent sources idled and all stored energies removed.

This theorem is depicted in Figure 3.6, in which N is the original network, N_0 is the same network with all independent sources idled and stored energies removed, and the Thévenin's equivalent voltage is equal to the open-circuit voltage rise from b to a.

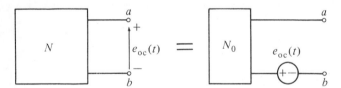

Figure 3.6 Schematic representation of Thévenin's theorem.

The proof of this theorem is given in Appendix A. The proof depends only on the fact that, within N, the superposition property prevails.

Note that no restriction need be placed on the network external to N for the theorem to be applicable. Both two-terminal networks—network N and its Thévenin's equivalent—are identical electrically, as seen between terminals a and b. Generally the internal network of N loses its identity when it is replaced by its equivalent network. Hence the Thévenin's equivalent of a network is for *external* use only.

EXAMPLE 2   In the network of Figure 3.7(a), we can easily calculate that $E_{oc} = 10$, and we may reduce N_0 to a 9-ohm resistor. Hence N_0 is equivalent to the network of Figure 3.7(b) at terminals a and b.

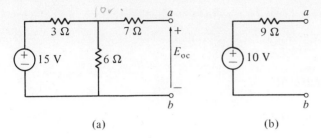

Figure 3.7

EXAMPLE 3   Find the voltage E_2 of the circuit of Figure 3.8(a).

SOLUTION   We first obtain the Thévenin's equivalent of that part of the network to the left of terminals a and b. We can easily see that

$$i = \frac{2 \times 10^{-3}}{100} = 0.02 \text{ mA}$$

$$E_{oc} = 1000 \times 10 \times 0.02 \times 10^{-3} = 0.2 \text{ V}$$

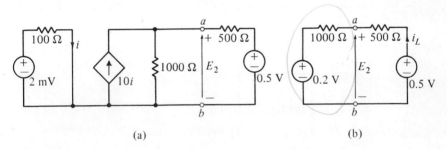

(a)   (b)

Figure 3.8

The network N_0 is reducible to a 1000-ohm resistor. Hence, as far as the part of the network to the right of terminals a and b is concerned, the circuit is equivalent to that shown in Figure 3.8(b). For the circuit of Figure 3.8(b),

$$i_L = \frac{0.5 - 0.2}{1000 + 500} = \frac{0.3}{1.5} \times 10^{-3} = 0.2 \text{ mA}$$

$$E_2 = 0.5 - 500 \times 0.2 \times 10^{-3} = 0.4 \text{ V}$$

This is the same E_2 as that in Figure 3.8(a).

EXAMPLE 4   The circuit of Figure 3.9(a) represents the equivalent circuit of a transistor amplifier. Find its Thévenin's equivalent circuit at terminals a and b.

SOLUTION   Under open-circuit conditions the voltage e_{ab} is quite easy to calculate. We have

$$i = \frac{e_s}{500}$$

$$e_{ab} = e_{oc} = 460i + 0.9i \times 10^6$$

$$= \frac{900,460}{500} e_s = 1.801 \sin t \text{ V}$$

The Thévenin's equivalent circuit is shown in Figure 3.9(b).

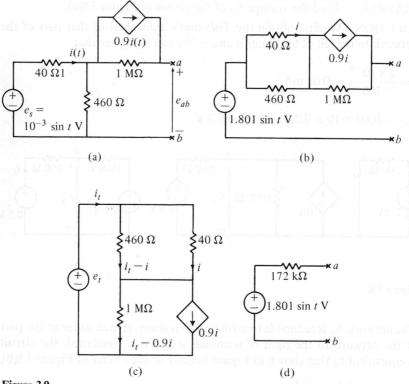

(a)   (b)

(c)   (d)

Figure 3.9

Here, because of the presence of a controlled source in N_0, we cannot immediately reduce N_0 to a single equivalent resistance. To find the equivalent Thévenin's resistance, we could apply a test voltage e_t across N_0, as shown in Figure 3.9(c), and then calculate the current i_t drawn by N_0. From Figure 3.9(c), we have

$$40i = 460(i_t - i)$$

$$(i_t - 0.9i) \times 10^6 + 40i = e_t$$

Elimination of i gives

$$172 \times 10^3 i_t = e_t$$

Hence the equivalent resistance of N_0 is

$$R_{eq} = \frac{e_t}{i_t} = 172 \text{ k}\Omega$$

and the Thévenin's equivalent circuit of Figure 3.9(b) may be further simplified to that shown in Figure 3.9(d).

3.4 Norton's theorem

A network N, which contains only LTI elements (including LTI controlled sources) and independent sources and is connected to the outside at two terminals, can be replaced by its Norton's equivalent network. Norton's equivalent network consists of a current source in parallel with N_0 or its equivalent. The strength of the current source is the short-circuit current at the two external terminals. The direction of the current source is such that the same current will flow in the short circuit if the two external terminals are short-circuited. The network N_0 is network N with all independent sources idled and all stored energies removed.

This theorem is depicted in Figure 3.10, in which N is the original network, N_0 is the same network with all independent sources idled and stored energies removed, and Norton's equivalent current is equal to the short-circuit current of N. (Note the direction of i_{sc} in both circuits.)

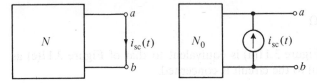

Figure 3.10 Schematic representation of Norton's theorem.

The proof of Norton's theorem is given in Appendix A. Again this theorem depends only on the fact that the superposition property prevails within N. Other remarks made in connection with Thévenin's theorem are also applicable to Norton's theorem.

EXAMPLE 5   Find the Norton's equivalent circuit for the network of Figure 3.11(a) at terminals a and b.

SOLUTION   To find I_{sc}, we use the superposition property. Activating only one source at a time, we get the two separate circuits shown in Figure

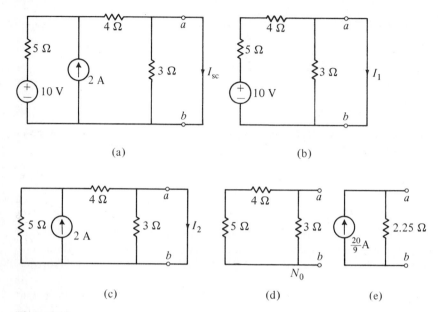

Figure 3.11

3.11(b) and (c). In these circuits, we have

$$I_1 = \tfrac{10}{9} \text{ A}, \qquad I_2 = 2 \times \tfrac{5}{9} = \tfrac{10}{9} \text{ A}$$

Hence

$$I_{sc} = \tfrac{20}{9} \text{ A}$$

Network N_0 is shown in Figure 3.11(d). The resistance between its terminals is

$$R_{eq} = \frac{9 \times 3}{12} = 2.25 \ \Omega$$

Thus the circuit of Figure 3.11(a) is equivalent to that of Figure 3.11(e) as far as what is external to the circuit is concerned.

Since the Thévenin's equivalent circuit and the Norton's equivalent circuit of a network must also be equivalent to each other, they can be obtained from each other. If N_0 contains only LTI resistors and LTI controlled sources, it can be reduced to a simple equivalent LTI resistor. Calling the resistance of this resistor R_{eq}, we get the two equivalent circuits shown in Figure 3.12. From these two circuits, it is clear that

$$R_{eq} = \frac{v_{oc}}{i_{sc}} \tag{3.7}$$

This relationship is sometimes easier to use than getting R_{eq} directly from N_0.

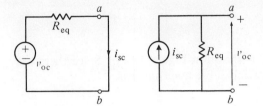

Figure 3.12 Relationship between quantities in the Norton's and the Thévenin's equivalent circuits.

EXAMPLE 6 Find the Norton's and Thévenin's equivalent circuits of the network of Figure 3.13(a) at terminals a and b.

SOLUTION To find V_{oc}, we shall use mesh analysis, which will have two mesh equations. In Figure 3.13(a),

$$10 - 5I_1 = 10I_1 + 5(I_1 - I_2), \qquad 5I_1 = 5(I_2 - I_1) + 8I_2$$

Rearranging gives

$$20I_1 - 5I_2 = 10, \qquad -10I_1 + 13I_2 = 0$$

Solving gives

$$I_2 = \tfrac{10}{21} \text{ A}$$

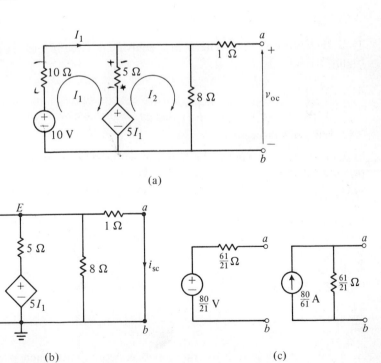

(a)

(b)

(c)

Figure 3.13

Thus

$$v_{oc} = 8I_2 = \tfrac{80}{21} \text{ V}$$

The circuit used to obtain i_{sc} is shown in Figure 3.13(b). Since there are only two unconstrained nodes, we shall use node analysis:

$$\frac{E-10}{10} + \frac{E-5I_1}{5} + \frac{E}{8} + \frac{E}{1} = 0$$

with

$$I_1 = \frac{10-E}{10}$$

Solving yields

$$E = \tfrac{80}{61}$$

Hence

$$i_{sc} = \tfrac{80}{61} \text{ A}$$

From (3.7)

$$R_{eq} = \frac{80/21}{80/61} = \frac{61}{21} \ \Omega$$

Thus the Norton's and Thévenin's equivalent circuits are as shown in Figure 3.13(c).

3.5 Tellegen's theorem

Suppose we have two networks N and N' with the same number of branches (n) and identical interconnections. We denote the voltages in N by e_j $(j = 1, 2, ..., n)$ and the currents in the corresponding branches of N' by i'_j $(j = 1, 2, ..., n)$. The element or elements contained in a branch of N need not have any similarity to those in the corresponding branch of N'. We further require that the direction of each voltage in N relative to its corresponding current in N' be made uniform throughout the two networks. That is to say, e_j and i'_j must be either all pointed in the same direction or all opposite to each other. *Tellegen's theorem* states that

$$\sum_{j=1}^{n} e_j i'_j = 0 \tag{3.8}$$

As an example, Figure 3.14 shows two networks with each pair of corresponding voltages and currents pointed in the opposite direction. The

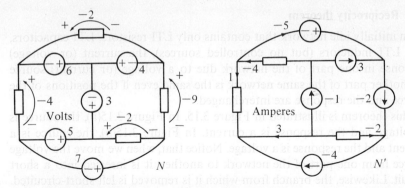

Figure 3.14 Circuits used to illustrate Tellegen's theorem.

only similarity between the two networks is that they have the same topological configuration. Tellegen's theorem states that

$$(-2)(-5) + 6(-4) + 4 \times 3 + (-4) \times 1 + 3(-1) + (-9)(-2) + 5$$
$$\times 3 + (-2)(-2) + 7(-4) = 0$$

which is indeed the case.

In the general proof of Tellegen's theorem given in Appendix A, the only requirement that is imposed on the voltages of N is that they satisfy KVL and the only requirement on the currents of N' is that they satisfy KCL. The elements can be linear or nonlinear.

An important application of Tellegen's theorem occurs when N and N' are actually the same network but represent the voltage and current distributions respectively at two different instants. Tellegen's theorem assures us that

$$\sum_{j=1}^{n} e_j(t_1) i_j(t_2) = 0 \qquad (3.9)$$

for any t_1 and t_2.

If $t_1 = t_2$, Tellegen's theorem reduces to

$$\sum_{j=1}^{n} e_j(t_1) i_j(t_1) = 0 \qquad (3.10)$$

which is commonly known as the *law of conservation of power*. Equation (3.10) states that the algebraic sum of all power supplied (or consumed) by all the branches in a network at any instant must be zero. This is a conclusion that one might infer by sheer common sense. If a network is a self-contained one (with no radiation or absorption of energy from external sources), whatever power is dissipated in a number of elements of the network must come from the remainder of the network.

3.6 Reciprocity theorem

In an initially idle network that contains only LTI resistors, LTI capacitors, and LTI inductors (but no controlled sources), the current (or voltage) response in one part of the network due to a voltage (or current) source in another part of the same network is the same even if the positions of the source and the response are interchanged.

This theorem is illustrated in Figure 3.15. In Figure 3.15(a), the source is a voltage and the response is a current. In Figure 3.15(b), the source is a current and the response is a voltage. Notice that, when we move the voltage source from one part of the network to another, it is inserted into a short circuit. Likewise, the branch from which it is removed is left short-circuited. Similarly, when a current source is moved from one place to another, its original branch is left open and it is attached to the two nodes between which the original voltage response was measured.

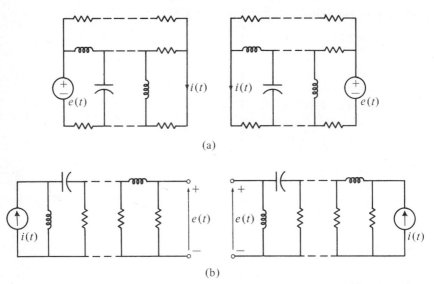

(a)

(b)

Figure 3.15 Circuits used to illustrate the reciprocity theorem.

EXAMPLE 7 To find the current distribution in the circuit of Figure 3.16(a), we may use the superposition theorem. The circuit of Figure 3.16(a) can be analyzed in two steps, as shown in Figure 3.16(b) and (c), in which only one source is active in each circuit. Both of these circuits are very easy to analyze, since they involve only series-parallel connections. We can then readily obtain the currents in each circuit, which are shown in the figure.

By superposition, we obtain

$$I_1 = \tfrac{42}{5} - \tfrac{2}{5} = 8 \text{ A} \qquad I_2 = \tfrac{24}{5} - \tfrac{4}{5} = 4 \text{ A}$$

$I_3 = \frac{28}{5} - \frac{18}{5} = 2 \text{ A} \qquad I_4 = \frac{6}{5} + \frac{24}{5} = 6 \text{ A}$

$I_5 = \frac{16}{5} + \frac{14}{5} = 6 \text{ A} \qquad I_6 = \frac{18}{5} - \frac{8}{5} = 2 \text{ A}$

The reciprocity theorem is illustrated by the fact that the ratios of the currents in the branches with idled sources to the source strengths are equal in Figures 3.16(b) and (c), namely,

$$\frac{2/5}{10} = \frac{4/5}{20}$$

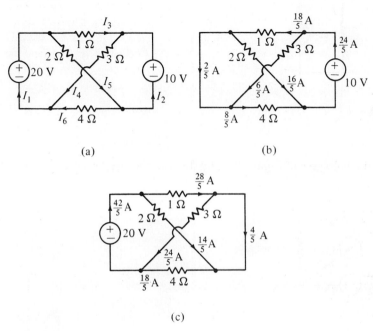

(a)   (b)

(c)

Figure 3.16

3.7 Concluding remarks

In illustrating the various theorems in this chapter, we have used mostly memoryless networks with dc sources. This was done primarily because these networks can be easily handled, and so the main thrust of each problem is not obscured by the complexity of the mathematics involved. You should not be misled by these examples into thinking that all of these theorems are limited to this class of network with this class of excitations. The circumstances in which each theorem applies are spelled out in the theorem. You would do well to scrutinize these conditions. We'll illustrate the applicability of the theorems as the occasion arises.

Problems

3.1 Find the current I of Figure P3.1 by applying the superposition theorem.

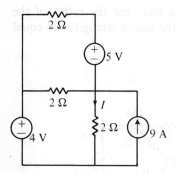

Figure P3.1

3.2 Find the voltage e of Figure P3.2 by the superposition theorem.

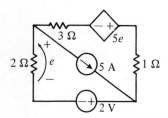

Figure P3.2

3.3 Find the current I of Figure P3.3 by using the suposition theorem.

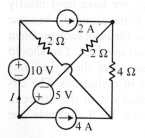

Figure P3.3

3.4 Find I of Figure P3.4 by the superposition method.

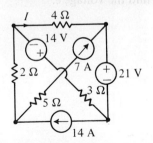

Figure P3.4

3.5 Find the Thévenin's equivalent circuit of the network in Figure P3.5 at terminals A and B.

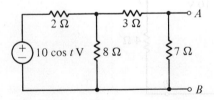

Figure P3.5

3.6 Find the Thévenin's equivalent circuit of the network of Figure P3.6 at terminals a and b.

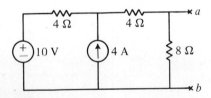

Figure P3.6

3.7 Replace that portion of the network within the dashed lines in Figure P3.7 by its Thévenin's equivalent circuit, and then find the voltage *e*.

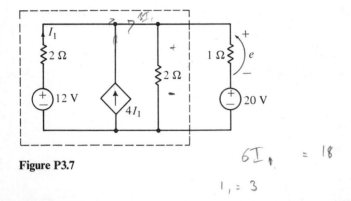

Figure P3.7

$6I_1 = 18$

$I_1 = 3$

3.8 Find the current *I* of Figure P3.8 by first finding the Thévenin's equivalent circuit at terminals *A* and *B*.

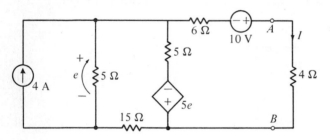

Figure P3.8

3.9 Replace that portion of the network within the dashed lines in Figure P3.9 by its Norton's equivalent circuit, and then find *I*.

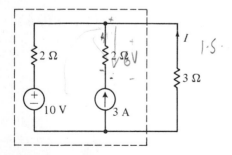

Figure P3.9

3.10 For the circuit of Figure P3.10, find current I by first finding the Norton's equivalent circuit at terminals A and B.

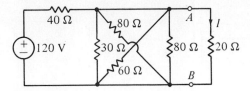

Figure P3.10

3.11 Find the current I of Figure P3.11 using Norton's theorem in the process.

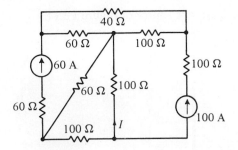

Figure P3.11

3.12 Find I of Figure P3.12.

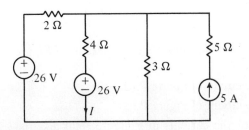

Figure P3.12

3.13 Find e_o of Figure P3.13.

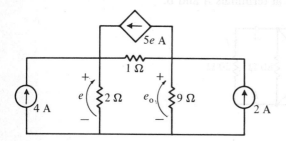

Figure P3.13

3.14 Find the current I_x in the 20-volt voltage source of Figure P3.14.

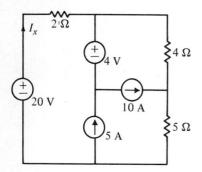

Figure P3.14

3.15 Find the currents and voltages in all elements in the circuit of Figure P3.1. Then verify Tellegen's theorem.

3.16 Repeat Problem 3.15 for the circuit of Figure P3.2.

3.17 Repeat Problem 3.15 for the circuit of Figure P3.3.

3.18 Verify Tellegen's theorem for the currents in Figure 3.16(a) and the voltages in Figure 3.16(b), and vice versa.

3.19 Find the current I_x in Figure P3.19 by using the answer in Problem 3.10 and the reciprocity theorem.

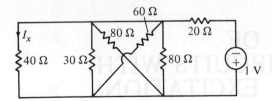

Figure P3.19

3.20 For the circuit of Figure P3.20, find the equivalent resistance R_{eq} seen by the independent source e_s.

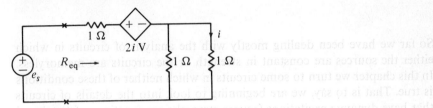

Figure P3.20

4 | ANALYSIS OF SIMPLE CIRCUITS WITH DYNAMIC EXCITATIONS

So far we have been dealing mostly with the analysis of circuits in which either the sources are constant in strength or the circuits are memoryless. In this chapter we turn to some circuits in which neither of these conditions is true. That is to say, we are beginning to look into the details of circuits that have dynamic excitations (source strengths are functions of time) and memory elements (inductors and capacitors). We shall include relatively simple circuits only.

4.1 Singularity functions

First let us define a series of functions that are known as the singularity functions. These are extremely helpful in both the formulation of many circuit problems and the neat, compact description of many circuit phenomena.

The first singularity function is the *unit step function*, depicted in Figure 4.1(a):

$$u_{-1}(t) = 0, \quad t < 0$$

$$= 1, \quad t \geq 0 \tag{4.1}$$

Thus a discontinuous jump of A units that takes place at $t = T$, as shown in Figure 4.1(b), is denoted by $Au_{-1}(t - T)$.

The unit step function can be used to specify the point at which a function commences. For example, if we have $f(t) = \sin t$, we have a sinusoid that lasts from $t = -\infty$ to $t = \infty$. But $(\sin t)u_{-1}(t)$ will be zero before $t = 0$ and assumes the sinusoidal variation after $t = 0$.

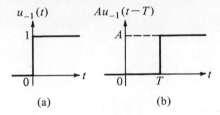

Figure 4.1 The step functions.

The integral of $u_{-1}(t)$ is denoted by

$$u_{-2}(t) = \int_{-\infty}^{t} u_{-1}(\tau)\, d\tau \tag{4.2}$$

Hence

$$u_{-2}(t) = 0, \quad t < 0$$
$$= t, \quad t > 0 \tag{4.3}$$

This is known as the *unit ramp function* and is depicted in Figure 4.2.

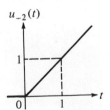

Figure 4.2 The unit ramp function.

Integrating $u_{-2}(t)$, we get the *unit parabola function*, or

$$u_{-3}(t) = \int_{-\infty}^{t} u_{-2}(\tau)\, d\tau \tag{4.4}$$

and explicitly

$$u_{-3}(t) = 0, \quad t < 0$$
$$= \tfrac{1}{2}t^2, \quad t > 0 \tag{4.5}$$

This function is depicted in Figure 4.3.

As we keep integrating these functions, we obtain a series of higher-order singularity functions. However, functions with subscripts beyond -3 are rarely useful for our purposes.

Following the pattern of the previous development, if we differentiate $u_{-1}(t)$, we obtain a function that is zero everywhere except at $t = 0$. This is

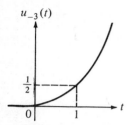

Figure 4.3 The unit parabola function.

known as an *impulse function* and is denoted by

$$u_0(t) = \frac{d}{dt} u_{-1}(t) \tag{4.6}$$

or

$$u_{-1}(t) = \int_{-\infty}^{t} u_0(t)\, dt \tag{4.7}$$

Equation (4.7) states that the area under the impulse is equal to the height of the step function—unity. Hence $u_0(t)$ is known as the *unit impulse function*. It is symbolically represented in Figure 4.4.

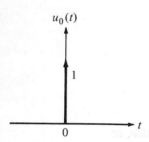

Figure 4.4 The unit impulse function.

In order to gain some insight into the significance of an impulse function, let's look at the arrangement of Figure 4.5(a). An ideal voltage source is connected directly across a capacitance of C farads. It is obvious that $e_C(t) = e(t)$. Suppose the source voltage $e(t)$ varies with time, as shown in Figure 4.5(b). Since

$$i(t) = C \frac{de_C}{dt} \tag{4.8}$$

the variation of $i(t)$ is as shown in Figure 4.5(c). We see that the current is a constant pulse. The area under the pulse is CE coulombs and this remains unchanged even if T is changed.

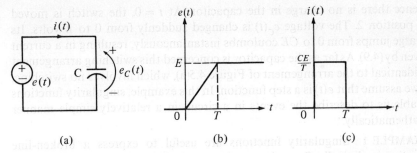

(a)

Figure 4.5 (a) Charging of a capacitor directly by a voltage source. (b) A finite-ramp voltage function. (c) The current in the circuit of (a) when $e(t)$ is given in (b).

A moment's reflection will reveal to you that the voltage source is changing the voltage across the capacitor at a constant rate until it reaches E volts. Since the voltage is proportional to the charge in a capacitor, the source is also charging the capacitor at a constant rate (coulombs per second) until the final charge reaches CE coulombs. A constant charging rate means a constant current. After the charge has reached CE coulombs, it stays constant and the current is zero.

So T is the duration of charging. If T is decreased, the rate of charging (CE/T) will increase proportionally. But the total charge transferred is CE coulombs, no matter what T is.

Now suppose we let T approach zero. This means that $e(t)$ is suddenly changed from 0 to E volts at $t = 0$. The voltage $e(t)$ of Figure 4.5(b) approaches an E-volt step. The current $i(t)$ now behaves rather dramatically in that it approaches a pulse that is infinitely high but lasts for an infinitesimally short instant. The area of this pulse remains CE coulombs. In the limit, we have a current that is a CE-coulomb impulse occurring at $t = 0$. Physically this simply means that a lump of charge is being transferred from the source to the capacitor instantaneously. We describe this charge transfer by saying that the current is an impulse function, that is,

$$i(t) = CEu_0(t) \tag{4.9}$$

The switching arrangement of Figure 4.6 produces this very same current. The capacitor is short-circuited before $t = 0$. There is no voltage across it.

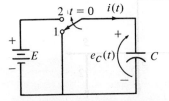

Figure 4.6 The sudden charging of a capacitor by a battery.

Hence there is no charge in the capacitor. At $t = 0$, the switch is moved to position 2. The voltage $e_c(t)$ is changed suddenly from 0 to E volts. Its charge jumps from 0 to CE coulombs instantaneously, resulting in a current given by (4.9). As far as the capacitor is concerned this switching arrangement is identical to the arrangement of Figure 4.5(a), which involves no switching, if we assume that $e(t)$ is a step function. In this example, singularity functions enable us to describe the events in a circuit in a relatively simple manner mathematically.

EXAMPLE 1   Singularity functions are useful to express a broken-line function analytically. Several examples are given in Figure 4.7. The function

$$f_1(t) = 5u_{-2}(t-1) - 5u_{-2}(t-2)$$

is known as a *finite ramp*. The rectangular pulse function

$$f_2(t) = u_{-1}(t-t_1) - u_{-1}(t-t_2)$$

is also known as the *window function* or the *gating function*. Function $f_3(t)$ is an arbitrary example and can be expressed as

$$f_3(t) = 2u_{-1}(t-1) + u_{-2}(t-1) - u_{-2}(t-3) - 2u_{-1}(t-3) - 2u_{-1}(t-5)$$

Another arbitrary example is

$$f_4(t) = 2u_0(t-1) + u_{-1}(t-1) - u_{-1}(t-3) - 2u_0(t-3) - 2u_0(t-5)$$

which is the derivative of $f_3(t)$.

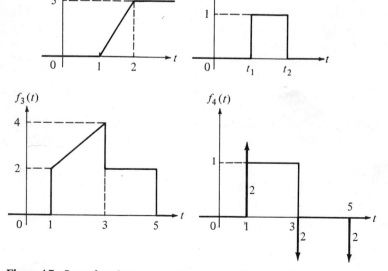

Figure 4.7   Some functions expressible in terms of singularity functions.

4.2 Step and impulse responses of first-order circuits

Chapter 2 gave a systematic method of writing out a set of equations from which a number of key unknown circuit quantities can be solved. When a network consists of only LTI resistors and LTI controlled sources, the set of equations obtained are not only algebraic but also linear. The solution of these simultaneous equations is fairly easy, even if the independent source strengths are functions of time.

When capacitors and inductors are present, these network equations are not as easy to solve. They are, as a matter of fact, simultaneous integro-differential equations. Special techniques are generally required to solve for the unknowns in these equations; we shall discuss these techniques in Chapter 15. Before we study some of these special techniques, it would be beneficial to examine some circuits whose behavior can be determined by more elementary methods.

Figure 4.8 shows a series R-C combination excited by a voltage source.

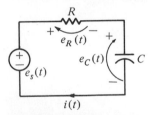

Figure 4.8 Charging of a capacitor through a resistor.

Assume that

$$e_s(t) = u_{-1}(t) \tag{4.10}$$

or

$$\begin{aligned} e_s(t) &= 0, \quad t < 0 \\ &= 1, \quad t > 0 \end{aligned} \tag{4.11}$$

The situation is equivalent to connecting a 1-volt battery across the series combination at $t = 0$ that was previously short-circuited, in a manner similar to that shown in Figure 4.6.

Since $e_s(t) = 0$ for $t < 0$, we might expect $i(t)$ to be zero before $t = 0$. For $t > 0$, by applying KVL around the loop, we have

$$Ri(t) + \frac{1}{C} \int_0^t i(\tau)\, d\tau = 1 \tag{4.12}$$

Differentiating yields

$$R\frac{di}{dt} + \frac{i}{C} = 0 \tag{4.13}$$

By rearranging we get

$$\frac{di}{i} = -\frac{1}{RC} dt$$

After integration, we have

$$\ln i = -(1/RC)t + K$$

or

$$i(t) = \epsilon^K \epsilon^{-(1/RC)t} = K_1 \epsilon^{-(1/RC)t} \qquad (4.14)$$

As far as (4.13) is concerned, K_1 of (4.14) may be any constant. To suit the situation at hand, however, only one value for K_1 is allowable. Since the capacitor is initially uncharged, its charge must remain zero at $t = 0^+$. [For the capacitor to acquire a finite charge instantaneously, an impulse current must be present. Since this current also flows through R, an impulse voltage would be required in $e(t)$.] Hence, at $t = 0^+$, the voltage across the capacitor is zero, or

$$e_R(0^+) = 1$$

or

$$i(0^+) = \frac{1}{R} \qquad (4.15)$$

Forcing this to be satisfied by (4.14), we have $K_1 = 1/R$ and

$$i(t) = \frac{1}{R} \epsilon^{-(1/RC)t}, \qquad t > 0 \qquad (4.16)$$

To summarize the behavior of the circuit for all time, we can write

$$i(t) = \frac{1}{R} \epsilon^{-(1/RC)t} u_{-1}(t), \qquad \text{for all } t \qquad (4.17)$$

Here the unit step function serves to indicate that $i(t) = 0$, for $t < 0$.

A plot of the expression in (4.17) is shown in Figure 4.9(a). This phenomenon is known as "the charging of a capacitor through a resistor." Figure 4.9(a) indicates the rate of charging at any time. The way the charge accumulates in the capacitor is given by

$$q(t) = \int_0^t i(\tau) \, d\tau = C(1 - \epsilon^{-(1/RC)t}) u_{-1}(t) \qquad (4.18)$$

and is shown in Figure 4.9(b).

Both curves in Figure 4.9 have the same shape—they are both exponential—although one is "decaying" while the other is "building up." Other than the initial and final values, the shape of these curves depends only on

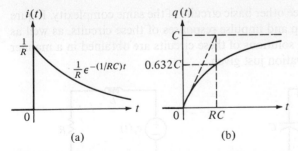

Figure 4.9 Current and charge variations of the capacitor-charging process.

the quantity RC, commonly known as the *time constant*. The following are two interpretations frequently given for the time constant of an exponential curve.

1 Using (4.17) and (4.18), we can write

$$\frac{dq}{dt}\bigg|_{t=0} = i(0) = \frac{1}{R}$$

This is the slope of the $q(t)$ curve of Figure 4.9(b) at the origin. If we draw a straight line tangent to the curve at the origin and extend it until it intersects $q = C$, the distance of this intersect from the vertical axis is RC as shown. Hence the time constant is defined as "the time required to charge a capacitor up to its final value had its rate of charge continued at the initial value."

2 At $t = RC$, $q = C(1-1/\epsilon) = 0.632C$. Hence RC is also the time required for the capacitor to be charged up to 63.2% of its final value.

The response of a circuit to a unit-step excitation is known as the *step response* of the circuit, denoted here by $g(t)$. In this particular example, $g(t)$ happens to be a current. In other problems, it may be either a voltage or a current.

The response of a circuit to a unit-impulse excitation $u_0(t)$ is known as the *impulse response* of the network. It is usually denoted by $h(t)$. Since

$$u_0(t) = \frac{d}{dt}u_{-1}(t)$$

the impulse response of the circuit in Figure 4.8 is the derivative of the $i(t)$ of (4.17), or

$$h(t) = \frac{d}{dt}g(t) = \frac{1}{R}\epsilon^{-t/RC}u_0(t) - \frac{1}{R^2C}\epsilon^{-t/RC}u_{-1}(t)$$

Since $u_0(t)$ is zero everywhere except at $t = 0$, we have

$$h(t) = \frac{1}{R}u_0(t) - \frac{1}{R^2C}\epsilon^{-t/RC}u_{-1}(t) \tag{4.19}$$

We can formulate three other basic circuits of the same complexity. Figure 4.10 summarizes the step and impulse responses of these circuits, as well as the one just solved. The solutions of these circuits are obtained in a manner very similar to the derivation just given.

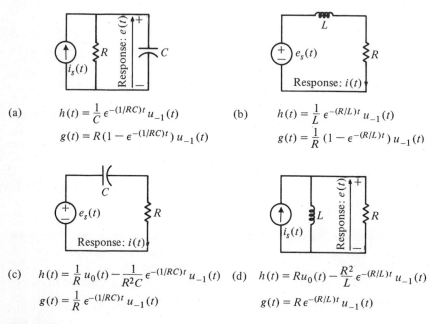

(a) $\quad h(t) = \dfrac{1}{C} e^{-(1/RC)t} u_{-1}(t)$

$\quad\quad g(t) = R(1 - e^{-(1/RC)t}) u_{-1}(t)$

(b) $\quad h(t) = \dfrac{1}{L} e^{-(R/L)t} u_{-1}(t)$

$\quad\quad g(t) = \dfrac{1}{R}(1 - e^{-(R/L)t}) u_{-1}(t)$

(c) $\quad h(t) = \dfrac{1}{R} u_0(t) - \dfrac{1}{R^2 C} e^{-(1/RC)t} u_{-1}(t)$

$\quad\quad g(t) = \dfrac{1}{R} e^{-(1/RC)t} u_{-1}(t)$

(d) $\quad h(t) = R u_0(t) - \dfrac{R^2}{L} e^{-(R/L)t} u_{-1}(t)$

$\quad\quad g(t) = R e^{-(R/L)t} u_{-1}(t)$

Figure 4.10 Summary of responses of first-order circuits: $h(t)$ is the response when the excitation is a unit impulse; $g(t)$ is the response when the excitation is a unit step.

4.3 Application of basic techniques to solve more complex circuit problems

Armed with the solutions given in Figure 4.10, we can solve a number of more complicated circuit problems by various techniques. The following few examples will serve to illustrate some of the possibilities. Recognition of these possibilities depends largely on the ingenuity and experience of the solver. It is difficult to lay down a definite set of rules that are generally applicable.

EXAMPLE 2   Given the circuit of Figure 4.11(a) with

$$e_s(t) = u_{-1}(t)$$

we can apply Thévenin's theorem to the part of the network that is connected to the capacitor (at terminals a and b). It is easy to verify that

$$e_{eq}(t) = \frac{R_1}{R_1 + R_2} u_{-1}(t) \tag{4.20}$$

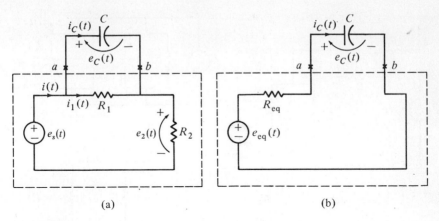

(a)   (b)

Figure 4.11

$$R_{eq} = \frac{R_1 R_2}{R_1 + R_2} \tag{4.21}$$

As far as capacitor C is concerned, the circuit is equivalent to that shown in Figure 4.11(b). Now, from Figure 4.10(c), we can write

$$i_C(t) = \frac{1}{R_2} \epsilon^{-t/R_{eq}C} u_{-1}(t) \tag{4.22}$$

From (4.22) we can get

$$e_C(t) = \frac{1}{C} \int_{-\infty}^{t} i_C(\tau)\, d\tau = \frac{R_1}{R_1 + R_2} (1 - \epsilon^{-(1/R_{eq}C)t}) u_{-1}(t) \tag{4.23}$$

Recall our cautionary label that Thévenin's theorem is for external use only. We must go back to Figure 4.11(a) to obtain other quantities in the original circuit. For example,

$$i_1(t) = \frac{e_C(t)}{R_1} = \frac{1}{R_1 + R_2} (1 - \epsilon^{-(1/R_{eq}C)t}) u_{-1}(t) \tag{4.24}$$

If we wish to obtain the source current $i(t)$, we can use the relationship

$$i(t) = i_1(t) + i_C(t)$$

and substitute (4.22) and (4.24) into the expression. Note that this source current is different from that of Figure 4.11(b).

EXAMPLE 3   For the circuit of Figure 4.12(a) we can apply Norton's theorem to that part of the circuit to the left of terminals a and b. If

$$e_s(t) = u_{-1}(t)$$

then the short-circuit current is the sum of the currents through C_1 and R_1

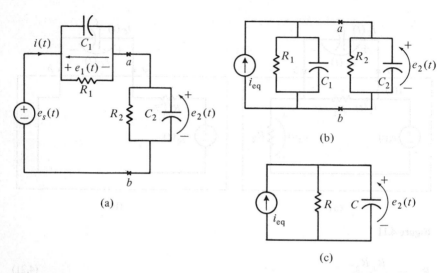

Figure 4.12

with $e_s(t)$ applied across them directly. Or

$$i_{eq}(t) = \frac{1}{R_1}u_{-1}(t) + C_1 u_0(t) \tag{4.25}$$

Hence, as far as R_2 and C_2 are concerned, parts (a) and (b) of Figure 4.12 are equivalent. But the circuit of Figure 4.12(b) can be further reduced to that of Figure 4.12(c), in which

$$R = \frac{R_1 R_2}{R_1 + R_2}, \qquad C = C_1 + C_2$$

We may make use of the superposition theorem, since i_{eq} is made up of a step function and an impulse function. The response to each of these is obtained from Figure 4.10(a). Specifically

$$e_2(t) = \frac{R}{R_1}[1 - \epsilon^{-(1/RC)t}]u_{-1}(t) + \frac{C_1}{C}\epsilon^{-(1/RC)t}u_{-1}(t) \tag{4.26}$$

Voltage $e_2(t)$ of (4.26) is the same voltage that appears across C_2 in both Figure 4.12(a) and Figure 4.12(b). Again you are cautioned not to use Figure 4.12(b) to obtain the expressions for quantities in that part of the circuit to the left of terminals a and b in Figure 4.12(a).

EXAMPLE 4   Suppose we want to find $i(t)$ of Figure 4.13(a) for the source voltage of Figure 4.13(b). Since

$$e_s(t) = u_{-1}(t) + u_{-1}(t-1) - 2u_{-2}(t-2) + 2u_{-2}(t-3) \tag{4.27}$$

we may invoke the superposition theorem and regard $e_s(t)$ as being made up of four singularity functions. The response of the circuit of Figure 4.13(a) to a step function can be found from Figure 4.10(c). We also need the response of the circuit to a unit ramp. Since

$$u_{-2}(t) = \int_0^t u_{-1}(\tau)\, d\tau$$

the response $i(t)$ of this circuit to a unit ramp voltage function is

$$g^{(-1)}(t) = \frac{1}{R}\int_0^t \epsilon^{-(1/RC)\tau}\, d\tau = C(1-\epsilon^{-(1/RC)t})u_{-1}(t) \qquad (4.28)$$

Hence the $i(t)$ corresponding to the $e_s(t)$ of Figure 4.13(b) is

$$i(t) = \frac{1}{R}\epsilon^{-(1/RC)t}u_{-1}(t) + \frac{1}{R}\epsilon^{-(1/RC)(t-1)}u_{-1}(t-1)$$

$$- 2C[1-\epsilon^{-(1/RC)(t-2)}]\,u_{-1}(t-2) + 2C[1-\epsilon^{-(1/RC)(t-3)}]\,u_{-1}(t-3) \qquad (4.29)$$

A typical variation of (4.29) is shown in Figure 4.13(c).

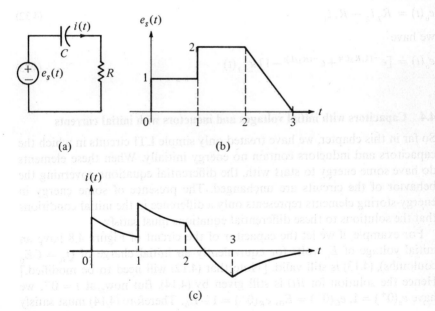

Figure 4.13

EXAMPLE 5   Suppose we desire to find $e_o(t)$ of Figure 4.14. This problem may appear to be quite complicated at first. But since the voltage source is connected across the two series branches directly, we can find $i_1(t)$ and

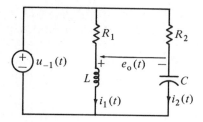

Figure 4.14

$i_2(t)$ independently of each other. From Figure 4.10(b) and (c), we have

$$i_1(t) = \frac{1}{R_1}[1 - \epsilon^{-(R_1/L)t}] u_{-1}(t) \tag{4.30}$$

and

$$i_2(t) = \frac{1}{R_2} \epsilon^{-(1/R_2C)t} u_{-1}(t) \tag{4.31}$$

respectively. Since

$$e_o(t) = R_2 i_2 - R_1 i_1 \tag{4.32}$$

we have

$$e_o(t) = [\epsilon^{-(1/R_2C)t} + \epsilon^{-(R_1/L)t} - 1] u_{-1}(t) \tag{4.33}$$

4.4 Capacitors with initial voltages and inductors with initial currents

So far in this chapter, we have treated only simple LTI circuits in which the capacitors and inductors contain no energy initially. When these elements do have some energy to start with, the differential equations governing the behavior of the circuits are unchanged. The presence of some energy in energy-storing elements represents only a difference in the initial conditions that the solutions to these differential equations must satisfy.

For example, if we let the capacitor of the circuit of Figure 4.8 have an initial voltage of E_0 volts (or equivalently an initial charge of $Q_0 = CE_0$ coulombs), (4.13) is still valid. [Note that (4.12) will need to be modified.] Hence the solution for $i(t)$ is still given by (4.14). But now, at $t = 0^+$, we have $e_s(0^+) = 1$, $e_C(0^+) = E_0$, $e_R(0^+) = 1 - E_0$. Therefore (4.14) must satisfy

$$i(0^+) = \frac{1 - E_0}{R} \tag{4.34}$$

instead of (4.15). Imposing this initial condition on (4.14) yields

$$i(t) = \frac{1 - E_0}{R} \epsilon^{-(1/RC)t} u_{-1}(t) \tag{4.35}$$

An alternative way of accounting for initially stored energy in a capacitor or an inductor is to replace the element with its Thévenin's or Norton's equivalent. For convenience, we shall assume that we wish to observe the behavior of the element only for $t > 0$. What happens before $t = 0$ is of no concern to us. If the actual starting time is other than $t = 0$, we merely advance or delay the reference in time.

1 For a capacitor C with a voltage E_0 at $t = 0$:

(a) The voltage in its Thévenin's equivalent circuit is a constant E_0 volts, since this capacitor will retain all its charge (hence the voltage) when it is open-circuited.

(b) The current in its Norton's equivalent circuit is an impulse function of CE_0 coulombs, since when this capacitor is short-circuited this amount of charge will flow through the short circuit instantaneously.

The Thévenin's or Norton's equivalent circuit of such a capacitor is the appropriate combination of the equivalent source and a capacitor with the same capacitance and no initial energy. This equivalence is shown in Figure 4.15(a).

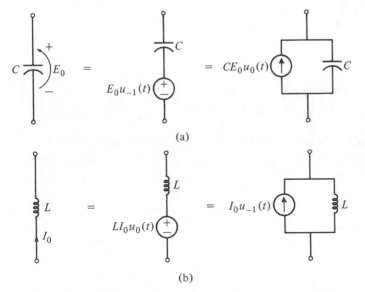

(a)

(b)

Figure 4.15 Thévenin's and Norton's equivalent circuits of elements with initial energies.

2 For an L-henry inductor with a current I_0 at $t = 0$:

(a) The voltage in its Thévenin's equivalent circuit is an impulse function of LI_0 webers,* since the opening of a current I_0 abruptly changes the current from I_0 to zero.

---

* A weber is equivalent to a volt-second or ampere-henry.

(b) The current in its Norton's equivalent circuit is a constant I_0 amperes, since a short circuit allows the current in the inductor to flow indefinitely.

The Thévenin's or Norton's equivalent circuit of such an inductor is the appropriate combination of the equivalent source and an inductor of the same inductance with no initial energy. This equivalence is shown in Figure 4.15(b).

EXAMPLE 6 Let us consider the circuit of Figure 4.16(a). The capacitor with a voltage E_0 is connected to the 1-volt battery through a resistance R at $t = 0$. For $t > 0$, this circuit is equivalent to that in Figure 4.16(b), in which it is understood that C is uncharged at $t = 0$. We can see that the current in this equivalent circuit is given by (4.35) as well.

Again a word of caution. The equivalence between the charged C of Figure 4.16(a) and its Thévenin's equivalent relates only to their behavior at the terminals. For example, we do not expect the voltage across the capacitor $e_c(t)$ in Figure 4.16(a) to be the same as the voltage across the capacitor in Figure 4.16(b). However, if the voltages are taken over the entire branch between a and b, they must, of course, be identical.

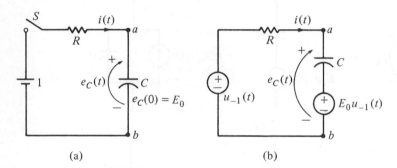

(a)   (b)

Figure 4.16

EXAMPLE 7 In the circuit of Figure 4.17(a), switch S has been open for a long time, so that an equilibrium has been reached in the rest of the circuit. At $t = 0$, S is closed. Find $i(t)$ and $e_c(t)$ for $t > 0$.

SOLUTION The status of the circuit prior to $t = 0$ is shown in Figure 4.17(b). The capacitor has an initial voltage of 8 volts. From the equivalence shown in Figure 4.15(a), we know that the circuit for $t > 0$ is equivalent to that shown in Figure 4.17(c). The branch containing the capacitor is short-circuited by the switch and is therefore unaffected by the current source or the 2-ohm resistor. From the model circuit of Figure 4.10(c), we can write

$$i(t) = 8\epsilon^{-2t} \tag{4.36}$$

To obtain $e_c(t)$ in the original circuit, we now take the voltage across the

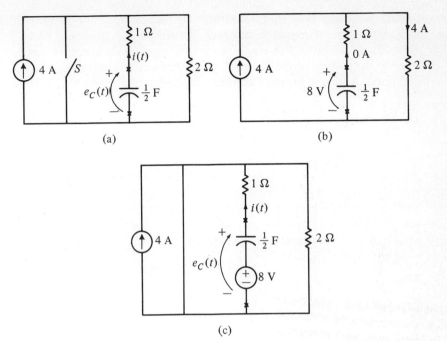

(a) (b)

(c)

Figure 4.17

entire series combination of the initially empty capacitor and the equivalent voltage source, or

$$e_C(t) = 8 - 2 \int_0^t i(\tau)\, d\tau = 8 - 8(1 - \epsilon^{-2t}) = 8\epsilon^{-2t} \tag{4.37}$$

4.5 Classical approach to the solution of a complex circuit problem

When the circuit to be analyzed is more complex than the simple ones treated in the previous two sections, a set of simultaneous equations including the integrals and derivatives of several variables is involved. (For an example, see Section 2.6.) By the superposition theorem, we can always analyze the circuit with only one independent source at a time. In each of these component circuits, we focus our attention on one of the variables as *the* response of that circuit. We then try to eliminate all other variables. The problem is thus reduced to the solution of a single differential equation involving only one unknown—the quantity to be considered as the response. (This can always be done.) Once "the response" is known, we can usually calculate the other quantities easily if we should need to find them.

At this time we do not wish to go into the procedure of reducing a set of simultaneous integro-differential equations down to a single differential equation involving only one unknown. The simple example below will illustrate the general approach, however.

The circuit of Figure 4.18 contains three energy-storing elements. Let us designate the voltage across R_2, $e_2(t)$, as the response. Using mesh-analysis techniques, with mesh currents as indicated, we have

$$R_1 i_1 + \left(\frac{1}{C_1} + \frac{1}{C_2}\right) \int_{-\infty}^{t} i_1(\tau)\,d\tau - \frac{1}{C_2} \int_{-\infty}^{t} i_2(\tau)\,d\tau = e_s(t) \tag{4.38}$$

$$-\frac{1}{C_2} \int_{-\infty}^{t} i_1(\tau)\,d\tau + \frac{1}{C_2} \int_{-\infty}^{t} i_2(\tau)\,d\tau + L\frac{di_2}{dt} + i_2 R_2 = 0 \tag{4.39}$$

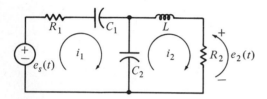

Figure 4.18

Since $e_2 = R_2 i_2$, it would be just as well to find $i_2(t)$. Differentiating (4.38) and (4.39), we get

$$R_1 \frac{di_1}{dt} + \left(\frac{1}{C_1} + \frac{1}{C_2}\right) i_1 - \frac{1}{C_2} i_2 = \frac{d}{dt} e_s(t) \tag{4.40}$$

$$i_1 = LC_2 \frac{d^2 i_2}{dt^2} + R_2 C_2 \frac{di_2}{dt} + i_2 \tag{4.41}$$

Differentiating (4.41), we get

$$\frac{di_1}{dt} = LC_2 \frac{d^3 i_2}{dt^3} + R_2 C_2 \frac{d^2 i_2}{dt^2} + \frac{di_2}{dt} \tag{4.42}$$

Substituting (4.41) and (4.42) into (4.40) gives

$$R_1 LC_2 \frac{d^3 i_2}{dt^3} + \left(R_1 R_2 C_2 + \frac{LC_2}{C_1} + L\right) \frac{d^2 i_2}{dt^2} + \left(R_1 + R_2 + \frac{R_2 C_2}{C_1}\right) \frac{di_2}{dt}$$

$$+ \frac{1}{C_1} i_2 = \frac{d}{dt} e_s(t) \tag{4.43}$$

The next step in this procedure is the solution of (4.43) with de_s/dt known. Once we know i_2, we can compute e_2 and i_1 with relative ease.

This example may not be typical in the complexity of its mathematics, but it is typical in making a direct attack on the solution of a fairly complicated circuit problem.

Since some of you may not yet have had a course in differential equations, we shall mention a few pertinent points about the solution of the special types of differential equations that we will encounter in networks with LTI elements and the nature of the techniques for solving them.

The differential equation that the response of an LTI network must satisfy is a linear one with constant coefficients. Here the word "linear" refers to the fact that there are no powered terms of the derivatives [such as $(di/dt)^2$]. The general form of this differential equation is

$$\frac{d^n i}{dt^n} + a_{n-1}\frac{d^{n-1} i}{dt^{n-1}} + \cdots + a_1\frac{di}{dt} + a_0 i = e(t) \tag{4.44}$$

where $e(t)$, in general, is a combination of various derivatives of the excitation. The solution of such an equation always consists of two parts, or

$$i(t) = i_p(t) + i_c(t) \tag{4.45}$$

Here $i_p(t)$ denotes a function that, when substituted in place of $i(t)$ in the left-hand side of (4.44), gives the right-hand side function $e(t)$. This part is known as the *particular integral*. You can see that the task of finding such a function is not always an easy one. In fact, there is not always a straight-forward procedure except for special functions that appear in $e(t)$. Fortunately for us, some of the more easily solvable functions are also the more useful ones in electrical systems. Also, since we are dealing with existing electric quantities rather than abstract functions, there are ways to find out what some of these particular integrals are for certain $e(t)$. The forms of some of the better-known particular integrals corresponding to certain excitations are listed in Table 4.1.

Table **4.1** Particular integrals for some excitations

Excitation	Form of particular integral*
Constant	Constant
$\epsilon^{\alpha t}$	$A\epsilon^{\alpha t}$
t^n	$At^n + Bt^{n-1} + Ct^{n-2} + \cdots$
$\cos \omega t$ or $\sin \omega t$	$A \cos \omega t + B \sin \omega t$
$\epsilon^{\alpha t} \cos \omega t$ or $\epsilon^{\alpha t} \sin \omega t$	$\epsilon^{\alpha t}(A \cos \omega t + B \sin \omega t)$

* These forms will not be applicable if the "frequency" of the excitation coincides with the "frequency" of the transient response.

Once we have found an $i_p(t)$ for a differential equation of the type of (4.44), then we have a function that satisfies

$$\frac{d^n i_p}{dt^n} + a^{n-1}\frac{d^{n-1} i_p}{dt^{n-1}} + \cdots + a_1\frac{di_p}{dt} + a_0 i_p = e(t) \tag{4.46}$$

We have not finished even though it is true that, if we let $i(t) = i_p(t)$, then this $i(t)$ satisfies (4.44). This solution is not complete because any $i_c(t)$ that satisfies

$$\frac{d^n i_c}{dt^n} + a^{n-1} \frac{d^{n-1} i_c}{dt^{n-1}} + \cdots + a_1 \frac{di_c}{dt} + a_0 i_c = 0 \qquad (4.47)$$

can obviously be included in $i(t)$ and this new $i(t)$ will still satisfy (4.44). Any $i_c(t)$ that satisfies (4.47) is said to satisfy the *homogeneous part* of (4.44). An $i_c(t)$ that includes all possible functions that satisfy (4.47) is called the *complementary function* of (4.44). The *complete solution* of (4.44) should include both the particular integral and the complementary function.

The standard method for finding the complementary function of a linear differential equation with constant coefficients is to let

$$i_c(t) = \epsilon^{pt}$$

and substitute it into (4.47). This results in an equation in p that reads

$$p^n + a_{n-1} p^{n-1} + \cdots + a_1 p + a_0 = 0 \qquad (4.48)$$

There are n roots from this equation. Let these roots be denoted by $p_1, p_2, \ldots, p_n$. Assuming that the roots are all distinct, then we have

$$i_c(t) = K_1 \epsilon^{p_1 t} + K_2 \epsilon^{p_2 t} + \cdots + K_n \epsilon^{p_n t} \qquad (4.49)$$

in which $K_1, K_2, \ldots, K_n$ are constants and may assume any values as far as satisfying (4.47) is concerned. These are known as arbitrary constants.

If one of the roots, say p_1, of (4.48) is of multiplicity m, then the contribution of that root to $i_c(t)$ is

$$(K_1 + K_2 t + \cdots + K_m t^{m-1}) \epsilon^{p_1 t}$$

We observe that the two parts of the complete solution of a linear differential equation with constant coefficients stem from two distinct origins. The particular integral $i_p(t)$ is the circuit's response to the excitation. It is totally excitation-dependent. If $e(t)$ is doubled, the corresponding $i_p(t)$ is doubled. From Table 4.1, we see that, if $e(t)$ is an exponential function, $i_p(t)$ will be another exponential function with the same exponent. If $e(t)$ is a sinusoid, $i_p(t)$ is another sinusoid with the same frequency. In the context of a circuit-analysis problem, the particular integral part of a response is known as the *steady-state response*.

On the other hand, the form of the complementary function $i_c(t)$ does not depend on the excitation function at all. Actually, it is determined completely by the nature of the circuit. The fact that the right-hand side of (4.47) is zero suggests that the circuit response would be $i_c(t)$ if the circuit were left alone. Of course, some energy must be present in the circuit when $e(t)$ is set to zero. But the form of $i_c(t)$ must be that of (4.49). The arbitrary constants change if different energies are present when we set $e(t)$ to zero.

In the context of a circuit-analysis problem, the complementary function is known as the *transient response*. When we change from one excitation to another, the steady-state response of the circuit will eventually change from the original one (including the possibility of zero) to another. The presence of the transient response allows the circuit to change gradually from one steady state to another. This is accomplished mathematically by adjusting the arbitrary constants in the complementary function. In short, the steady-state response does not contain arbitrary constants and the form of the transient response does not depend on the excitation.

The remarks made here are not meant to be rigorous or mathematically sound. You should view them as additional material to your differential equations course. For those of you who have had that course, these remarks should serve as a review of this particular aspect of the course. For those who have not yet taken it, we hope that you will gain enough background to deal with the material that follows immediately, and later with that part of the differential equations course. The lucky few who may be dealing with this material at the very same time in your mathematics course should find the two courses mutually helpful. In any case, you should cross-refer between this course and your differential equations course, either now or later, and not replace one with the other.

4.6 Responses of a second-order circuit—*RLC* series circuit

Step response

Let the source voltage of Figure 4.19 be a unit step or

$$e_s(t) = u_{-1}(t)$$

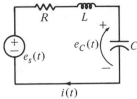

$$i(t)$$

Figure 4.19 An *RLC* series circuit.

and let the circuit be initially idle. The KVL equation reads

$$L\frac{di}{dt} + Ri + \frac{1}{C}\int_0^t i(\tau)\,d\tau = 1, \qquad t > 0 \tag{4.50}$$

Differentiation gives

$$L\frac{d^2i}{dt^2} + R\frac{di}{dt} + \frac{1}{C}i = 0 \tag{4.51}$$

The steady-state response in this case is zero, since a dc current cannot flow through a capacitor. Hence the complete solution is made up entirely of the transient response. We let

$$i_c(t) = \epsilon^{pt}$$

Here p must satisfy the equation

$$Lp^2 + Rp + \frac{1}{C} = 0 \tag{4.52}$$

which has two roots

$$p_1, p_2 = -\frac{R}{2L} \pm \sqrt{\frac{R^2}{4L^2} - \frac{1}{LC}} \tag{4.53}$$

Depending on the values of the elements, the radical in (4.53) may be real, imaginary, or zero. Assuming that $1/LC > R^2/4L^2$,* then we may write

$$p_1, p_2 = -\alpha \pm j\beta \tag{4.54}$$

where $\alpha = R/2L$ and $\beta = \sqrt{1/LC - R^2/4L^2}$. The complementary function is

$$i(t) = K_1 \epsilon^{(-\alpha + j\beta)t} + K_2 \epsilon^{(-\alpha - j\beta)t} \tag{4.55}$$

This is also the complete solution for this example.

We see that, as long as $R > 0$, $i(t) \to 0$ as $t \to \infty$. Now we must find K_1 and K_2 to satisfy the initial conditions. Since $q(0) = 0$ and $i(0) = 0$, we deduce that

$$i(0^+) = 0, \quad e_C(0^+) = 0, \quad L\frac{di}{dt}\bigg|_{t=0^+} = 1$$

Setting $i(0^+)$ of (4.55) to zero gives

$$K_1 + K_2 = 0$$

Setting $di/dt|_{t=0^+}$ of (4.55) equal to $1/L$ gives

$$K_1 = \frac{1}{2j\beta L}$$

Hence

$$i(t) = \frac{1}{2j\beta L}\epsilon^{(-\alpha + j\beta)t} - \frac{1}{2j\beta L}\epsilon^{(-\alpha - j\beta)t}$$

$$= \frac{1}{\beta L}\epsilon^{-\alpha t}\left(\frac{\epsilon^{j\beta t} - \epsilon^{-j\beta t}}{2j}\right)$$

$$= \frac{1}{\beta L}\epsilon^{-\alpha t}\sin\beta t, \quad t \geq 0 \tag{4.56}$$

---

* The other two cases are left as exercises (Problems 4.17 and 4.20).

Thus, for the circuit of Figure 4.19, we get

$$g(t) = \frac{1}{\beta L} \epsilon^{-\alpha t} \sin \beta t \, u_{-1}(t)$$

A typical variation of $i(t)$ of (4.56) is shown in Figure 4.20.

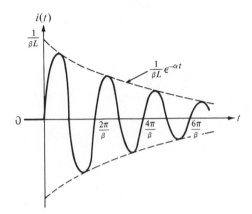

Figure 4.20   A response that has a damped oscillation.

Impulse response

If $e_s(t) = u_0(t)$, the corresponding $i(t)$ may be obtained by differentiating the $i(t)$ of (4.56). Thus, for the circuit of Figure 4.19, we have the impulse response

$$h(t) = \frac{d}{dt} g(t) = \frac{1}{L} \epsilon^{-\alpha t} \left(\cos \beta t - \frac{\alpha}{\beta} \sin \beta t \right) u_{-1}(t) \qquad (4.57)$$

Response to other excitations

Suppose we want to find the complete response of the *RLC* of Figure 4.19 with $R = 10$, $L = 5$, and $C = \frac{1}{160}$ to $e_s(t) = \cos 8t \, u_{-1}(t)$. Here we have

$$\alpha = \frac{R}{2L} = 1, \qquad \beta = \sqrt{\frac{1}{LC} - \frac{R^2}{4L^2}} = \sqrt{31}$$

The differential equation for $t > 0$ is

$$L \frac{d^2 i}{dt^2} + R \frac{di}{dt} + \frac{1}{C} i = -8 \sin 8t \qquad (4.58)$$

From Table 4.1, we can assume the steady-state current to be

$$i_p(t) = A \cos 8t + B \sin 8t \qquad (4.59)$$

Substitution of this $i_p(t)$ for $i(t)$ in (4.58) gives

$$-320A \cos 8t - 320B \sin 8t - 80A \sin 8t + 80B \cos 8t + 160A \cos 8t$$

$$+ 160B \sin 8t = -8 \sin 8t \tag{4.60}$$

Since this equation must be satisfied for any value of t, the coefficients of the cosine term and the sine term on one side of (4.60) must be equal to the like terms on the other side of the equation. Hence we have

$$-160A + 80B = 0, \qquad -80A - 160B = -8$$

Solution of these two simultaneous equations gives

$$A = \tfrac{1}{50}, \qquad B = \tfrac{1}{25}$$

or

$$i_p(t) = \tfrac{1}{50} \cos 8t + \tfrac{1}{25} \sin 8t$$

The complementary function is the same as the one given by (4.55). The complete solution of the problem at hand is

$$i(t) = K_1 \epsilon^{(-1+j\sqrt{31})t} + K_2 \epsilon^{(-1-j\sqrt{31})t} + \tfrac{1}{50} \cos 8t + \tfrac{1}{25} \sin 8t \tag{4.61}$$

The two arbitrary constants K_1 and K_2 can now be adjusted to satisfy the initial conditions, which are identical to those of the step-response case, since $e_s(0^+) = 1$. Hence

$$K_1 + K_2 + \tfrac{1}{50} = i(0) = 0$$

$$K_1(-1+j\sqrt{31}) + K_2(-1-j\sqrt{31}) + \tfrac{8}{25} = \frac{di}{dt}\bigg|_{t=0^+} = \tfrac{1}{5}$$

Solution of these two simultaneous equations yields

$$K_1 = -\frac{1}{100} + j\frac{7}{100\sqrt{31}}, \qquad K_2 = -\frac{1}{100} - j\frac{7}{100\sqrt{31}}$$

Thus the complete solution is

$$i(t) = \left(-\frac{1}{100} + j\frac{7}{100\sqrt{31}}\right)\epsilon^{(-1+j\sqrt{31})t} + \left(-\frac{1}{100} - j\frac{7}{100\sqrt{31}}\right)\epsilon^{(-1-j\sqrt{31})t}$$

$$+ \frac{1}{50} \cos 8t + \frac{1}{25} \sin 8t$$

$$= -\frac{1}{50}\epsilon^{-t} \cos \sqrt{31}t - \frac{7}{50\sqrt{31}}\epsilon^{-t} \sin \sqrt{31}t + \frac{1}{50} \cos 8t + \frac{1}{25} \sin 8t$$

$$= -0.0321\epsilon^{-t} \cos (\sqrt{31}t - 51.5°) + 0.0447 \cos (8t - 63.4°) \tag{4.62}$$

4.7 Concluding remarks

The few circuit problems treated in this chapter are not only important in their own right but also serve to introduce some basic concepts that will be used frequently in more complex circuits.

The simple RC and RL circuits are both easy to analyze and are used in many actual electric or electronic circuits. (Or else, many circuits have component parts that can be identified as such circuits.) The notion of the time constant is universal to circuits with only one energy-storing element. The RLC circuit, which is also used in many applications, receives further treatment in Chapter 12.

The summary of all first-order circuits in Figure 4.10 is a good illustration of the principle of *duality*. If, for example, you observe the similarity between the expressions for $h(t)$ and $g(t)$ in Figure 4.10(a) and (b), you will discover that they are exactly alike if every L is replaced by C, every R is replaced by $G = 1/R$, every voltage is replaced by a current, and every series connection is replaced by a parallel connection; and the reverse is equally true. This, of course, is no coincidence. It is the consequence of the fact that the equations governing the electrical behavior of these two circuits are identical in form and therefore must have similar solutions, if the appropriate replacement of corresponding quantities takes place. In other words, we should be able to obtain the results in Figure 4.10(b) from those in (a) merely by observing the similarity of the mathematical relationships. These two circuits are said to be *dual* to each other. Likewise the circuits in Figure 4.10(c) and (d) are dual to each other.

Extending this principle of duality to the circuit of Figure 4.19, we can say that, if $i_s(t)$ of Figure 4.21 is a unit step, then $e(t)$ will be

$$e(t) = \frac{1}{\beta C}\epsilon^{-\alpha t}\sin\beta t \tag{4.63}$$

where $\alpha = G/2C$ and $\beta = \sqrt{1/LC - G^2/4C^2}$. Equation (4.63) is the dual of (4.56).

For a more complex circuit in which the elements are not all connected either in series or in parallel, the dual is not as easily obtained. But a systematic method of obtaining the dual of any circuit, if it exists, is available.

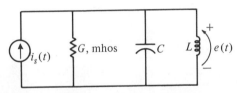

Figure 4.21 A GCL parallel circuit.

This method is a branch of network theory, called network topology, and its details are beyond the scope of this volume.

The complete solutions of some of the simple circuits in this chapter also serve to point out the two distinct types of response in a memory circuit under dynamic excitations—the transient and the steady-state responses. As you can see, the complete solution of a complicated circuit is usually very laborious with the classical method. Until we have studied some special techniques designed to handle complex circuits, we shall leave them and turn our attention in the next chapter to a more important and more practical class of circuit problems, in which the excitation is either exponential or sinusoidal and for which only the steady-state response is of interest.

Problems

4.1 Sketch the following functions:

(a) $f_1(t) = 2u_{-2}(t) - 2u_{-2}(t-1) - 2u_{-2}(t-2) + 2u_{-2}(t-3)$

(b) $f_2(t) = [2 - u_{-1}(t)][1 - u_{-1}(t-2)]$

(c) $f_3(t) = u_{-2}(t) - 2u_{-2}(t-1) + u_{-2}(t-2).$

4.2 Write the functions depicted in Figure P4.2 in terms of the singularity functions.

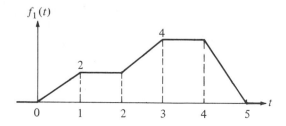

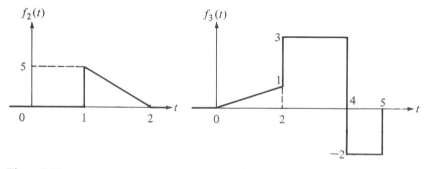

Figure P4.2

4.3 Write $e(t)$ of Figure P4.3(a) in terms of the singularity functions. Suppose that this $e(t)$ is applied to the circuit of Figure P4.3(b). Sketch $i_1(t)$, $i_2(t)$, and $i_3(t)$.

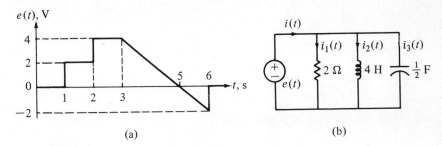

(a)   (b)

Figure P4.3

4.4 The response of a linear network to a unit step excitation is $g(t) = \epsilon^{-t}u_{-1}(t)$. What would be its response if the excitation were (a) $f_1(t)$ of Problem 4.2? (b) $f_2(t)$ of Problem 4.2? (c) $f_3(t)$ of Problem 4.2? (d) $(d/dt)f_2(t)$ of Problem 4.2?

4.5 In Figure P4.5, $e(t) = 3u_{-1}(t)$ volts. Find $i(t)$.

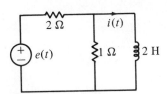

Figure P4.5

4.6 For the circuit of Figure P4.6, determine $e(t)$ and $i(t)$ for (a) $i_s(t) = u_0(t)$, (b) $i_s(t) = u_{-1}(t)$.

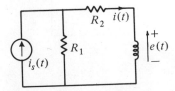

Figure P4.6

4.7 If $e_s(t) = u_{-2}(t)$ for the circuit of Figure P4.7, what is $i(t)$?

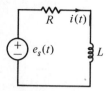

Figure P4.7

4.8 Find $i(t)$ and $e_2(t)$ of Figure 4.11(a).

4.9 Find $i(t)$ and $e_1(t)$ of Figure 4.12(a).

4.10 In the circuit of Figure P4.10, $e_s(t) = 9u_{-1}(t)$ volts. Find the voltage $e(t)$.

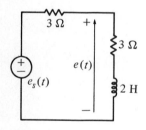

Figure P4.10

4.11 By the principle of superposition find $i(t)$ of Figure P4.11(c) for $e(t)$ given by (a) Figure P4.11(a), (b) Figure P4.11(b).

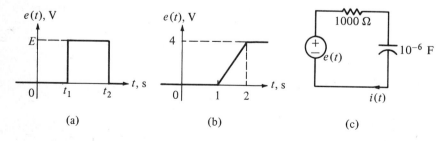

(a)   (b)   (c)

Figure P4.11

4.12 The voltage source $e_s(t)$ of the circuit in Figure P4.12(a) is given by the diagram in Figure P4.12(b). Find $i(t)$. Give your result in a sketch with a proper equation for each part of the curve.

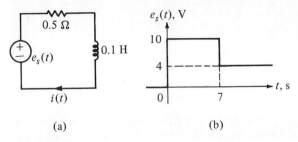

(a)   (b)

Figure P4.12

4.13 The source voltage $e_s(t)$ of the circuit in Figure P4.13(a) is given in Figure P4.13(b). Find the equation for the voltage across the capacitor, $e_C(t)$.

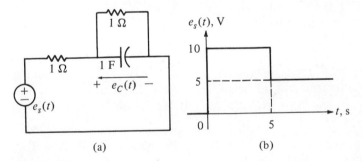

(a)   (b)

Figure P4.13

4.14 In Figure P4.14, the switch has been open for a long time and then is closed at $t = 1$. Determine the expression for i valid for $t > 1$.

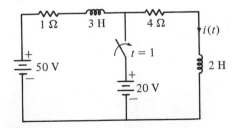

Figure P4.14

4.15 In Figure P4.15, the switch has been open for a long time and then is closed at $t = 0$. Determine the expression for $i(t)$ valid for $t > 0$.

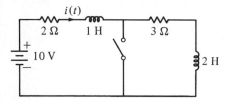

Figure P4.15

4.16 In the circuit of Figure P4.16, the switch is closed for a long time and then opened at $t = 0$. Find the expression for the voltage $e(t)$ after the switch is opened.

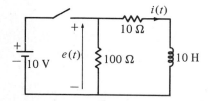

Figure P4.16

4.17 For the *RLC* series of Figure 4.19 with $e_s(t) = u_{-1}(t)$, write the expression $i(t)$ for the case in which $R^2/4L^2 > 1/LC$. Let $\alpha = R/2L$ and $\lambda = \sqrt{R^2/4L^2 - 1/LC}$. In particular, sketch $i(t)$ for $R = 4$, $L = 1$, and $C = \frac{1}{2}$.

4.18 Repeat Problem 4.17 for $e_s(t) = u_0(t)$.

4.19 Find $i(t)$ for the circuit of Figure 4.19, with $R = 1\ \Omega$, $C = 10$ F, $L = 10$ H, and $e_s(t) = \sin t\, u_{-1}(t)$.

4.20 For the circuit of Figure 4.19, find its step response given that $R^2/4L^2 = 1/LC$.
[*Hint:* Apply L'Hôpital's rule to (4.56) as $\beta \to 0$.]

4.21 In the circuit of Figure P4.21, the capacitor is charged to 1 V before $t = 0$ with the polarity shown. At $t = 0$, the switch is closed. Find $i(t)$ after $t = 0$.

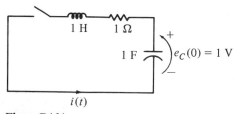

Figure P4.21

4.22 The switch of Figure P4.22 has been closed for a long time before $t = 0$. At $t = 0$, it is opened. Find $i(t)$ for $t > 0$.

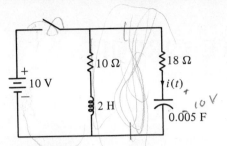

Figure P4.22

5 | STEADY-STATE CIRCUIT ANALYSIS

In this chapter we shall focus our attention on the solution of *steady-state responses* of LTI networks. In many circuit problems, the steady-state response is the only quantity that is of interest. Often, in practical situations, the transient part of a response lasts for such a short time that it is of no great consequence. For example, consider the distribution of power in a power system. Under normal operating conditions, the distribution of power does not change rapidly from minute to minute. In an audio system, each note usually lasts long enough to be considered a sustained oscillation. Furthermore, as you will see later, any transient analysis can be related to the steady-state analysis through the Fourier or Laplace transform. Hence a familiarity with steady-state analysis is an important basis for the understanding of many phenomena in electric circuits.

5.1 Complex arithmetic and Euler's formula

Before we undertake a more detailed study of steady-state circuit analysis, let us summarize the rational operations of complex numbers and point out the important implications of Euler's formula. Again, refer to any good mathematics text for more details if you feel the need for them.

A complex number in rectangular form has two parts: the real and the imaginary. The two parts are distinguished by the quantity $\sqrt{-1} = j$, which multiplies the imaginary part. Let

$$C = a + jb \tag{5.1}$$

where C is the complex number, a is the real part, and b is the imaginary part. A complex number may be treated as the sum of two numbers, as the plus sign of (5.1) implies. Thus

$$(a+jb) + (c+jd) = (a+c) + j(b+d) \tag{5.2}$$

$$(a+jb) - (c+jd) = (a-c) + j(b-d) \tag{5.3}$$

$$(a+jb)(c+jd) = (ac-bd) + j(ad+bc) \tag{5.4}$$

$$\frac{(a+jb)}{(c+jd)} = \frac{(a+jb)(c-jd)}{(c+jd)(c-jd)} = \frac{ac+bd}{c^2+d^2} + j\frac{bc-ad}{c^2+d^2} \tag{5.5}$$

The last operation, (5.5), is the division and can always be simplified by the rationalization procedure indicated there.

A very useful relationship in the manipulation of complex numbers and functions is Euler's formula, which reads

$$e^{jy} = \cos y + j \sin y \tag{5.6}$$

A simple way to show the validity of this relationship is to look at the infinite series expansions of the three quantities in (5.6) and thereby verify the formula.

It is customary to display a complex number graphically by the co-ordinate system shown in Figure 5.1, in which the real part is assigned to the horizontal axis and the imaginary part to the vertical axis. Much like a vector, a complex number can be expressed in either rectangular or polar form. From Figure 5.1 and with (5.6), we can write

$$C = a + jb = \sqrt{a^2+b^2}\, e^{j[\tan^{-1}(b/a)]} = |C|\, e^{j\phi} \tag{5.7}$$

This relationship implies the following:

$$|C| = \sqrt{a^2+b^2}$$

$$\phi = \tan^{-1}(b/a)$$

$$a = |C| \cos \phi \tag{5.8}$$

$$b = |C| \sin \phi$$

$$a + jb = |C|(\cos \phi + j \sin \phi)$$

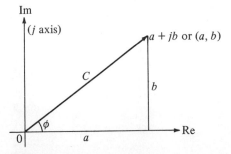

Figure 5.1 Relationship of the four quantities in a complex number.

The exponential form of a complex number is usually preferable to the rectangular form for multiplication and division, since

$$|C_1| \, \epsilon^{j\phi_1} \times |C_2| \, \epsilon^{j\phi_2} = |C_1||C_2| \, \epsilon^{j(\phi_1 + \phi_2)} \tag{5.9}$$

$$\frac{|C_1| \, \epsilon^{j\phi_1}}{|C_2| \, \epsilon^{j\phi_2}} = \frac{|C_1|}{|C_2|} \, \epsilon^{j(\phi_1 - \phi_2)} \tag{5.10}$$

A complex number in exponential form is frequently written as

$$|C| \, \epsilon^{j\phi} = |C| \, \underline{/\phi} \tag{5.11}$$

This is the *polar* form of the complex number. We can simply regard the polar form of a complex number as an alternative way of writing the number in exponential form. In other words, $\underline{/\phi}$ is the shorthand representation of $\epsilon^{j\phi}$. $|C|$ is known as the *magnitude* or *absolute value* of C, and ϕ is known as the *angle* or *argument* of C.

The notation "Re" is used to denote "the real part of [the complex number that follows]." Thus

$$\mathrm{Re}[a+jb] = a \tag{5.12}$$

$$\mathrm{Re}[|C| \, \epsilon^{j\phi}] = |C| \cos \phi \tag{5.13}$$

$$\mathrm{Re}[A+B] = \mathrm{Re}[A] + \mathrm{Re}[B] \tag{5.14}$$

The notation "Im" is used to denote "the imaginary part of [the complex number that follows]." Thus

$$\mathrm{Im}[a+jb] = b \tag{5.15}$$

$$\mathrm{Im}[|C| \, \epsilon^{j\phi}] = |C| \sin \phi \tag{5.16}$$

$$\mathrm{Im}[A+B] = \mathrm{Im}[A] + \mathrm{Im}[B] \tag{5.17}$$

Note that the imaginary part of a complex number is itself a real number.

A complex number with its imaginary part changed in sign is known as the *conjugate* of that number. It is denoted by an asterisk.

$$(a+jb)^* = a - jb \tag{5.18}$$

The following relationships are easily shown to be correct:

$$(|C| \, \epsilon^{j\phi})^* = |C| \, \epsilon^{-j\phi} \tag{5.19}$$

$$(C^*)^* = C \tag{5.20}$$

$$CC^* = |C|^2 \tag{5.21}$$

$$\frac{A}{B} = \frac{AB^*}{|B|^2} \tag{5.22}$$

$$C + C^* = 2 \, \mathrm{Re}[C] \tag{5.23}$$

$$C - C^* = 2 \, \mathrm{Im}[C] \tag{5.24}$$

We can readily obtain the logarithm of a complex number if the number is expressed in exponential form:

$$\ln(|C|e^{j\phi}) = \ln|C| + j\phi \tag{5.25}$$

A complex number is multivalued when it is expressed in exponential or polar form. That is,

$$|C|e^{j\phi} = |C|e^{j(\phi + 2k\pi)} \tag{5.26}$$

where k is any integer, since $\cos(\phi + 2k\pi) = \cos\phi$ and $\sin(\phi + 2k\pi) = \sin\phi$. Several special cases of (5.26) are as follows.

$$e^{j2k\pi} = 1$$

$$e^{j(2k+1)\pi} = -1$$

$$e^{j(\pi/2)} = j$$

$$e^{-j(\pi/2)} = -j$$

The nth root of a complex number has n values:

$$(|C|e^{j\phi})^{1/n} = |C|^{1/n}e^{j[(\phi + 2k\pi)/n]}, \qquad k = 0, 1, 2, \ldots, (n-1) \tag{5.27}$$

EXAMPLES   The following are a few examples of operations involving complex numbers:

$$2 + j3 = \sqrt{13}\,e^{j56.3°} = 3.606\,\underline{/56.3°}$$

$$6\,\underline{/-110°} = -2.052 - j5.638$$

$$\frac{3+j5}{2-j1} = \frac{(3+j5)(2+j1)}{(2-j1)(2+j1)} = \frac{6-5+j10+j3}{5} = \frac{1+j13}{5}$$

$$= 0.2 + j2.6$$

$$\frac{3+j5}{2-j1} = \frac{\sqrt{34}\,\underline{/59.03°}}{\sqrt{5}\,\underline{/-26.57°}} = \sqrt{6.8}\,\underline{/85.6°}$$

$$= 2.60768(\cos 85.6° + j\sin 85.6°)$$

$$= 0.2 + j2.6$$

$$\text{Re}[15\,\underline{/-120°}] = 15\cos 120° = -15\cos 60° = -7.5$$

$$\text{Im}[15\,\underline{/-120°}] = -15\sin 120° = -15\sin 60° = -12.99$$

$$\ln[3+j4] = \ln[5\,\underline{/53.1°}] = \ln 5 + j53.1° = 1.609 + j0.927$$

$$(1)^{1/2} = (e^{j2n\pi})^{1/2} = e^{jn\pi} = 1e^{j0} \quad \text{or} \quad 1e^{j\pi} = \pm 1$$

$$(1)^{1/3} = (e^{j2n\pi})^{1/3} = e^{j(2n/3)\pi} = 1e^{j0} \quad \text{or} \quad 1e^{j120°} \quad \text{or} \quad 1e^{-j120°}$$

$$= 1 + j0 \quad \text{or} \quad (-0.5 + j0.866) \quad \text{or} \quad (-0.5 - j0.866)$$

$(j3)^{1/3} = [3\epsilon^{j(\pi/2 + 2n\pi)}]^{1/3}$

$\qquad = 1.442 \,\underline{/30°} \qquad$ or $\qquad 1.442 \,\underline{/150°} \qquad$ or $\qquad 1.442 \,\underline{/-90°}$

$\qquad = 1.249 + j0.721 \qquad$ or $\qquad -1.249 + j0.721 \qquad$ or $\qquad 0 - j1.442$

$3 \,\underline{/j2} = 3\epsilon^{j(j2)} = 3\epsilon^{-2} = 0.406$

$5 \cos x + 3 \sin x = 5 \cos x + 3 \cos(x - 90°)$

$\qquad = \mathrm{Re}[5\epsilon^{jx}] + \mathrm{Re}[3\epsilon^{j(x-90°)}]$

$\qquad = \mathrm{Re}[5\epsilon^{jx} + 3\epsilon^{j(x-90°)}]$

$\qquad = \mathrm{Re}[5\epsilon^{jx} + 3\epsilon^{-j90°}\epsilon^{jx}]$

$\qquad = \mathrm{Re}[(5+3\,\underline{/-90°})\epsilon^{jx}]$

$\qquad = \mathrm{Re}[(5-j3)\epsilon^{jx}]$

$\qquad = \mathrm{Re}[\sqrt{34}\,\epsilon^{-j30.96°}\epsilon^{jx}]$

$\qquad = \mathrm{Re}[5.831\epsilon^{j(x-30.96°)}]$

$\qquad = 5.831 \cos(x - 30.96°)$

5.2 Steady-state response of a network to the excitation ϵ^{st}

A special class of excitations (voltage or current) that are extremely important in the study of many electrical and electronic systems are those that have the form $A\epsilon^{st}$, where A and s are both complex in general. Later on we shall see why these excitations are so important, but we first look at a series of examples that show how easy it is to get the steady-state part of the responses to such excitations.

In Figure 5.2, the differential equation is

$$L\frac{di}{dt} = E\epsilon^{st} \tag{5.28}$$

Integrating, we get

$$Li = \frac{E}{s}\epsilon^{st}$$

or

$$i(t) = \frac{E}{sL}\epsilon^{st} = I\epsilon^{st} \tag{5.29}$$

which is the steady-state part of $i(t)$ in Figure 5.2. Note that

$$I = \frac{E}{sL} \tag{5.30}$$

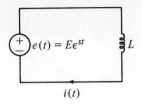

Figure 5.2 An inductance excited by an exponential voltage.

As another example, in Figure 5.3, we have

$$Ri + L\frac{di}{dt} = E\epsilon^{st} \tag{5.31}$$

Since the steady-state response has the form

$$i(t) = I\epsilon^{st}$$

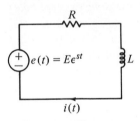

Figure 5.3 An RL series combination excited by an exponential voltage.

we may substitute this into (5.31) to obtain

$$RI\epsilon^{st} + sLI\epsilon^{st} = E\epsilon^{st} \tag{5.32}$$

Hence

$$I = \frac{E}{R+sL} \tag{5.33}$$

In Figure 5.4, we have

$$Ri + L\frac{di}{dt} + \frac{1}{C}\int i \, dt = E\epsilon^{st} \tag{5.34}$$

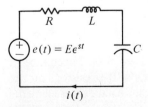

Figure 5.4 An RLC series combination excited by an exponential voltage.

Again we may assume that

$$i(t) = I\epsilon^{st}$$

So we have

$$RI\epsilon^{st} + sLI\epsilon^{st} + \frac{1}{sC}I\epsilon^{st} = E\epsilon^{st}$$

Hence

$$I = \frac{E}{R + sL + (1/sC)} \tag{5.35}$$

From these examples we see that, in the steady-state analysis of RLC networks containing excitations of the type $A\epsilon^{st}$, the quantities that really matter are those appearing in front of the exponential term of each quantity, such as I and E. These coefficients are known as the *complex amplitudes* of the respective quantities.

Furthermore, we can easily show by analysis similar to the preceding examples that the complex amplitudes of the voltage and current in an R, L, or C can be related by simple multiplication or division in much the way voltages and currents are related by Ohm's law in an LTI resistor. Figure 5.5 summarizes these relationships.

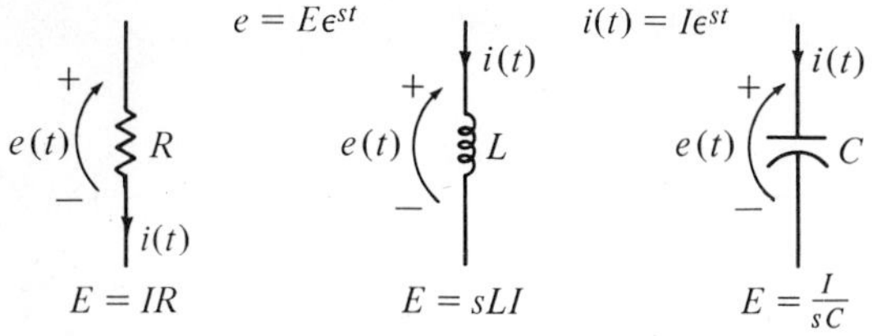

Figure 5.5 Relationships between voltage and current complex amplitudes in linear elements.

The proportionality constants between the complex amplitudes of the voltage and the current in an inductor or capacitor play a similar role to that of the resistance in a resistor. These quantities are called the *impedances* (of which the resistance is a subclass). The reciprocal of an impedance is an *admittance* (of which the conductance is a subclass).

In Figure 5.2, we have only one element, whose impedance is equal to sL. Hence the voltage–current relationship is that given by (5.30). In Figure 5.3, we have two elements in series. It can be said that the total impedance of the series combination is the sum of the impedances of the resistor and the inductor. Thus we have (5.33). Likewise, in Figure 5.4, we have three elements in series. Hence the overall impedance is the sum of the impedances of the three individual elements. Thus we have (5.35).

We can indeed generalize this observation to apply to more complicated networks. When we focus our attention on the complex amplitudes of the electric quantities in a network, when its excitations are all of the $A\epsilon^{st}$ type, and when we are only interested in the steady-state response of the network, we may deal with a substitute network in which only complex numbers need appear. Each source strength $A\epsilon^{st}$ is replaced by another source of strength A. Each inductor of L henrys is replaced by an impedance of sL ohms. Each capacitor of C farads is replaced by an impedance of $1/sC$ ohms. All resistors and controlled sources (with real coefficients) remain unchanged. Each unknown quantity in the original network gives rise to an unknown complex amplitude in the substitute network.

In the substitute network, each element must satisfy one of the voltage–current relationships given in Figure 5.5, depending on the type of element. In addition, since KCL (or KVL) must be satisfied by all instantaneous currents (or voltages) in every ambit (or loop), the appropriate equation must also be satisfied by the complex amplitudes of all currents (or voltages). All the theorems and properties of Chapter 3 must also be satisfied by the complex amplitudes. Hence we can reduce every such problem to one that involves only algebraic equations. In fact, all such problems can be analyzed just like networks that include only resistors, controlled sources, and batteries. The only difference is that we are now dealing with complex rather than real quantities.

EXAMPLE 1   Suppose we are interested in finding the steady-state part of the current in the middle branch of the network in Figure 5.6, with

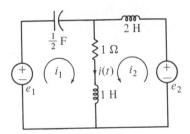

Figure 5.6

$e_1(t) = E_1\epsilon^{st} = (3+j4)\epsilon^{st}$ and $e_2(t) = E_2\epsilon^{st} = 3\epsilon^{st}$. We might use mesh analysis, with i_1 and i_2 as mesh currents. Using the impedance concept just described and the assumption that $i_1 = I_1\epsilon^{st}$ and $i_2 = I_2\epsilon^{st}$, we write

$$\left(1 + s + \frac{2}{s}\right)I_1 + (1+s)I_2 = E_1 = 3 + j4$$

$$(1+s)I_1 + (1+3s)I_2 = E_2 = 3 + j0$$

whence we get

$$I_1 = \frac{1}{\Delta} \begin{vmatrix} E_1 & 1+s \\ E_2 & 1+3s \end{vmatrix} = \frac{(1+3s)E_1 - (1+s)E_2}{\Delta}$$

$$I_2 = \frac{1}{\Delta} \begin{vmatrix} 1+s+\dfrac{2}{s} & E_1 \\ 1+s & E_2 \end{vmatrix} = \frac{[1+s+(2/s)]E_2 - (1+s)E_1}{\Delta}$$

where

$$\Delta = \begin{vmatrix} 1+s+\dfrac{2}{s} & 1+s \\ 1+s & 1+3s \end{vmatrix} = 2s^2 + 2s + 6 + \frac{2}{s}$$

$$I_1 + I_2 = \frac{2sE_1 + (2/s)E_2}{2s^2 + 2s + 6 + (2/s)} \tag{5.36}$$

Substituting the complex amplitudes at hand, we get

$$I = I_1 + I_2 = \frac{j8s + 6s + (6/s)}{2s^2 + 2s + 6 + (2/s)} \tag{5.37}$$

It is tacitly implied that

$$i(t) = I\epsilon^{st} \tag{5.38}$$

In this problem, the quantity s is deliberately left in literal form so that any complex number may be substituted in its place. For example, suppose $s = j$ or

$$e_1 = (3+j4)\epsilon^{jt}, \qquad e_2 = 3\epsilon^{jt}$$

then

$$i(t) = \frac{j8(j) + j6 + (6/j)}{2j^2 + 2j + 6 + (2/j)}\epsilon^{jt} = -2\epsilon^{jt} \tag{5.39}$$

Note that, for us to take advantage of the substitution, all sources must have the same value for s. If they do not, then we can use the superposition theorem and group sources of the same s in each subnetwork. After all the subnetworks have been analyzed using only complex numbers, we can interpret each answer with the appropriate value of s. Finally we simply add up all answers in the time-function form.

EXAMPLE 2   Suppose in Figure 5.6 we have

$$e_1(t) = (3+j4)\epsilon^{jt}, \qquad e_2(t) = 3\epsilon^{-t}$$

We need to solve two separate problems, each with a different value of s. We can, however, make use of the results obtained in Example 1. Our two subproblems are as follows.

(a) For $s = j$, $E_1 = 3 + j4$, and $E_2 = 0$, from (5.19) we obtain

$$I_a = -2 + j1.5, \qquad i_a(t) = (-2 + j1.5)\epsilon^{jt}$$

(b) For $s = -1$, $E_1 = 0$, and $E_2 = 3$, we obtain

$$I_b = -1.5, \qquad i_b(t) = -1.5\epsilon^{-t}$$

The complete answer is

$$i(t) = i_a(t) + i_b(t) = (-2 + j1.5)\epsilon^{jt} - 1.5\epsilon^{-t}$$

EXAMPLE 3   In the common-emitter amplifier circuit of Figure 5.7(a), $i_s = I_s\epsilon^{st}$. For small-signal, high-frequency operation, we can replace the transistor by its equivalent circuit, shown in Figure 5.7(b). The dc supply terminal $-V_{CC}$ is grounded for ac. Capacitors C, C_1, and C_2 are large enough to be regarded as short circuits (their impedances approach zero). The circuit element values are

$$R_s = 1\,\text{k}\Omega \qquad R_1 = R_2 = 2\,\text{k}\Omega$$

$$R_L = 1\,\text{k}\Omega \qquad R_c = 1\,\text{k}\Omega$$

The transistor parameters are

$$r_b = 100\,\Omega \qquad r_e = 250\,\Omega \qquad C_c = 5\,\text{pF}$$

$$C_e = 75\,\text{pF} \qquad g_m = 0.2\,\mho$$

Find the steady-state part of $i_L(t)$ as a function of s and t.

SOLUTION   By combining all resistors that are directly in parallel we get the circuit of Figure 5.7(c), in which only complex amplitudes of all quantities are involved and in which

$$R_t = R_s \| R_1 \| R_2 = 500, \qquad R_L' = R_c \| R_L = 500$$

Using node analysis, we have

$$\frac{E_b}{500} + \frac{E_b - E_e}{100} = I_s$$

$$\frac{E_e - E_b}{100} + \frac{E_e}{250} + E_e s \times 75 \times 10^{-12} + (E_e - E_c)s \times 5 \times 10^{-12} = 0$$

$$(E_c - E_e)s \times 5 \times 10^{-12} + 0.2E_e + \frac{E_c}{500} = 0$$

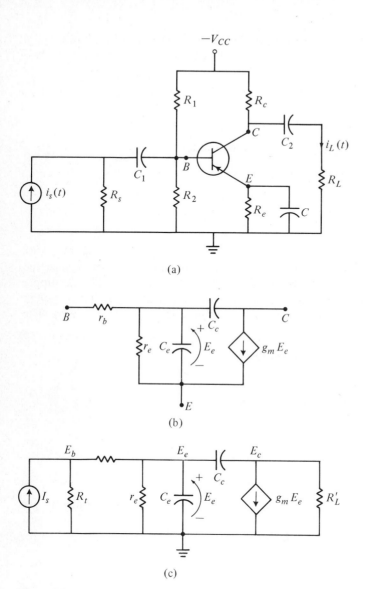

(a)

(b)

(c)

Figure 5.7

Simplifying yields

$$1.2E_b - E_e = 100I_s$$

$$-E_b + (1.4 + 8 \times 10^{-9}s)E_e - 5 \times 10^{-10}sE_c = 0$$

$$(20 - 5 \times 10^{-10}s)E_e + (0.2 + 5 \times 10^{-10}s)E_c = 0$$

Hence we arrive at the following.

$$E_c = \frac{\begin{vmatrix} 1.2 & -1 & 100I_s \\ -1 & 1.4+8\times 10^{-9}s & 0 \\ 0 & 20-5\times 10^{-10}s & 0 \end{vmatrix}}{\begin{vmatrix} 1.2 & -1 & 0 \\ -1 & 1.4+8\times 10^{-9}s & -5\times 10^{-10}s \\ 0 & 20-5\times 10^{-10}s & 0.2+5\times 10^{-10}s \end{vmatrix}}$$

$$= \frac{-100(20-5\times 10^{-10}s)I_s}{1.2(1.4+8\times 10^{-9}s)(0.2+5\times 10^{-10}s)-}{(0.2+5\times 10^{-10}s)+6\times 10^{-10}s(20-5\times 10^{-10}s)}$$

$$= \frac{5\times 10^{-8}(s-4\times 10^{10})I_s}{4.5\times 10^{-18}(s^2+31.69\times 10^8 s+3.022\times 10^{16})} \tag{5.40}$$

This voltage E_c is also the complex amplitude of the voltage at terminal C in Figure 5.7(a). Hence the complex amplitude of $i_L(t)$ is

$$I_L = \frac{E_c}{R_L} = \frac{1.111\times 10^7(s-4\times 10^{10})I_s}{s^2+31.69\times 10^8 s+3.022\times 10^{16}}$$

$$i_L(t) = \frac{1.111\times 10^7(s-4\times 10^{10})I_s}{s^2+31.69\times 10^8 s+3.022\times 10^{16}}\,\epsilon^{st} \tag{5.41}$$

Now if, for instance,

$$i_s(t) = 10^{-3}\epsilon^{j10^8 t}$$

then $s = j10^8$, $I_s = 10^{-3}$, and

$$I_L = \frac{1.11\times 10^7(j10^8-4\times 10^{10})\times 10^{-3}}{(2.022+j31.69)\times 10^{16}}$$

$$= -1.39\epsilon^{-j86.4°}\ \text{mA}$$

$$i_L(t) = 1.39\epsilon^{j93.6°}\epsilon^{j10^8 t} = 1.39\epsilon^{j(10^8 t+93.6°)}\ \text{mA} \tag{5.42}$$

5.3 Classes of circuit problems implied by an exponential excitation

We did not give any physical interpretation to the electric quantities that appeared in the previous section. We do not get disturbed when we hear of a "5-ampere current." But what does a "$j5$-ampere current" mean?

The important thing in the previous section was not the interpretation of a voltage or current that is a complex quantity or function. Rather, it was the solution that we should obtain when we analyze a circuit according to all the rules and theorems that govern the behavior of LTI networks. For example, we were only concerned there with finding out what is the current through an LTI 10-ohm resistor if we apply a $(20+j30)$-volt potential difference across it. The answer is $(2+j3)$ amperes, period. Specifically, we analyzed some circuits and found out what the responses would be if the excitations were of the type $A\epsilon^{st}$.

However, these theoretical developments will only be valuable if they somehow correspond to certain real-world situations or else if we can fit an actual problem into a fictitious one. We shall now try to link some real electrical problems to the mathematically posed problems and make use of the technique developed in Section 5.2 for solving them.

There are at least three classes of practical circuit problems with excitations that can be fitted into this type of analysis. The steady-state solution of these problems is obtained by following exactly the pattern that was used in the previous section.

1 $K\epsilon^{\sigma t}$, where K and σ are both real. This waveshape is shown in Figure 5.8. The method described in Section 5.2 is directly applicable in such a situation. All we need to do is limit the complex amplitude C to be purely real and the variable s to be purely real, or $s = \sigma + j0$.

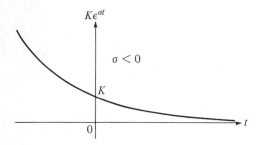

Figure 5.8 The function $K\epsilon^{\sigma t}$.

EXAMPLE 4   Suppose we desire to find the steady-state part of the current $i(t)$ of Figure 5.9(a). We have $K = 1$, $s = -2$, and the complex amplitude

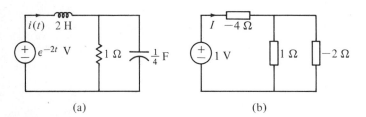

(a)   (b)

Figure 5.9

network is shown in Figure 5.9(b). By applying the series-parallel combination relationship, we can easily find that

$$I = \frac{1}{-4+[1(-2)/(1-2)]}$$

Hence the answer is

$$i(t) = -\tfrac{1}{2}\epsilon^{-2t} \text{ A} \tag{5.43}$$

2 $K \cos(\omega t + \phi)$, where K, ω, and ϕ are all real. From (5.7) we have

$$Ke^{j\phi}e^{j\omega t} = K \cos(\omega t + \phi) + jK \sin(\omega t + \phi) \tag{5.44}$$

Hence we may write

$$K \cos(\omega t + \phi) = \text{Re}[Ke^{j\phi}e^{j\omega t}] \tag{5.45}$$

When we encounter an excitation quantity of the form $A \cos(\omega t + \phi)$, we can instead find the answer to another excitation Ae^{st}, but let $A = Ke^{j\phi}$ and $s = 0 + j\omega$. After finding the solution to this substitute excitation, we simply keep only its real part. This real part should be the answer when the excitation is $K \cos(\omega t + \phi)$.

EXAMPLE 5 Suppose we want to find $i(t)$ in the circuit of Figure 5.10(a), with

$$e_1(t) = 10 \cos(2t - 30°), \qquad e_2(t) = 5 \cos(2t + 45°) \tag{5.46}$$

We may solve, instead, a problem in which

$$e_1(t) = 10\epsilon^{-j30°}\epsilon^{j2t}, \qquad e_2(t) = 5\epsilon^{j45°}\epsilon^{j2t} \tag{5.47}$$

We may solve the circuit of Figure 5.10(a) with these excitations in terms of the complex amplitudes, if we are interested only in the steady-state parts. We obtain such a network by replacing every element by its impedance (or

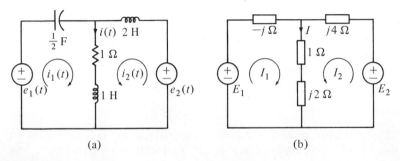

(a) (b)

Figure 5.10

admittance) for $s = j2$ as shown in Figure 5.10(b), in which

$$E_1 = 10 \underline{/-30°} = 8.66 - j5$$

$$E_2 = 5 \underline{/45°} = 3.535 + j3.535$$

Using mesh analysis, we have

$$(1+j)I_1 + (1+j2)I_2 = E_1 = 10 \underline{/-30°}$$

$$(1+j2)I_1 + (1+j6)I_2 = E_2 = 5 \underline{/45°}$$

Thus

$$\Delta = (1+j)(1+j6) - (1+j2)^2 = -2 + j3$$

$$I_1 = \frac{1}{\Delta} \begin{vmatrix} 10 \underline{/-30°} & 1+j2 \\ 5 \underline{/45°} & 1+j6 \end{vmatrix} = \frac{1}{\Delta}[(1+j6)10 \underline{/-30°} - (1+j2)5 \underline{/45°}]$$

$$I_2 = \frac{1}{\Delta} \begin{vmatrix} 1+j & 10 \underline{/-30°} \\ 1+j2 & 5 \underline{/45°} \end{vmatrix} = \frac{1}{\Delta}[(1+j)5 \underline{/45°} - (1+j2)10 \underline{/-30°}]$$

$$I = I_1 + I_2 = \frac{1}{\Delta}[j4 \times 10 \underline{/-30°} - j5 \underline{/45°}] = \frac{40 \underline{/60°} + 5 \underline{/-45°}}{-2+j3}$$

$$= \frac{20 + j34.642 + 3.535 - j3.535}{-2+j3}$$

$$= \frac{(23.535 + j31.107)(-2-j3)}{(-2+j3)(-2-j3)}$$

$$= \frac{46.25 - j132.82}{13} = 3.558 - j10.22$$

$$= 10.82 \underline{/-70.8°}$$

Thus the $i(t)$ for the excitations of (5.47) is

$$i(t) = 10.82\epsilon^{-j70.8°}\epsilon^{j2t} \tag{5.48}$$

and that for the excitations of (5.46) is

$$i(t) = 10.82 \cos(2t - 70.8°) \tag{5.49}$$

Actually, when we replaced the e's of (5.46) by those of (5.47), we also solved another problem in which

$$e_1(t) = 10 \sin(2t - 30°), \qquad e_2(t) = 5 \sin(2t + 45°) \tag{5.50}$$

since these are the "imaginary parts" of the $e(t)$'s of (5.47). If we want to find the $i(t)$ when e_1 and e_2 are given by (5.50), we merely take the "imaginary part of the $i(t)$ of (5.48)." This is one of the happier things in life in that we are, in effect, solving a larger problem with less effort. This is possible because the exponential function is actually easier to manage than the trigonometric functions.

An alternative way of handling the voltage excitations of (5.50) would be to rewrite each sine function as a cosine function and then to work with the real parts of a similar function. That is, write

$$e_1(t) = 10 \sin(2t - 30°) = 10 \cos(2t - 120°)$$

$$= \text{Re}[10 \underline{/-120°} \, \epsilon^{j2t}]$$

$$e_2(t) = 5 \sin(2t + 45°) = 5 \cos(2t - 45°)$$

$$= \text{Re}[5 \underline{/-45°} \, \epsilon^{j2t}]$$

Then let $s = j2$, $E_1 = 10 \underline{/-120°}$, and $E_2 = 5 \underline{/-45°}$ and proceed as before.

This class of functions, the sinusoids, is encountered in many electrical engineering problems. The solution of the steady-state part of a circuit under sinusoidal excitation is known as *alternating-current circuit analysis*. Many books have been written about it. But, if you understand the material in this section, you will have mastered the fundamental principles of ac circuit analysis. More about this class of problem appears in the remainder of the chapter.

3 $K\epsilon^{\sigma t} \cos(\omega t + \phi)$, where K, σ, ω, and ϕ are real constants. If $\sigma < 0$, this waveshape is an exponentially decaying sinusoid, as shown in Figure 5.11. The relationship between this function and the exponential function used in Section 5.2 is

$$K\epsilon^{\sigma t} \cos(\omega t + \phi) = \text{Re}[K\epsilon^{j\phi}\epsilon^{\sigma t}\epsilon^{j\omega t}] \qquad (5.51)$$

or

$$A = K\epsilon^{j\phi} \qquad (5.52)$$

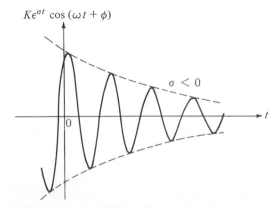

Figure 5.11 The function $K\epsilon^{\sigma t} \cos(\omega t + \phi)$.

$$s = \sigma + j\omega \qquad (5.53)$$

When only the steady-state solution is desired in a circuit with such excitations, the problem can be handled in exactly the same manner as for the steady (undecayed) sinusoids.

5.4 Alternating-current circuit analysis

In the previous section, we mentioned the fact that, when the excitations of a network are sinusoidal, the network is generally referred to as an *alternating-current* (ac) *network*. You can carry out the steady-state analysis of an ac network using the complex amplitudes only. Since this type of problem is a very important one, we shall devote space to some special aspects of it and introduce some commonly used jargon.

The complex amplitude of a sinusoid

$$e(t) = E_m \cos(\omega t + \phi) \qquad (5.54)$$

is $E_m \underline{/\phi}$. This quantity is also known as a *phasor* or sometimes, erroneously, as a *vector*. It is convenient to think of complex amplitudes as vectors because the rules for addition and subtraction of complex numbers are the same as those for vectors. For example, we can add

$$E_{m1} \underline{/\phi_1} + E_{m2} \underline{/\phi_2} = E_{mt} \underline{/\phi_t} \qquad (5.55)$$

by the usual parallelogram method, as illustrated in Figure 5.12. But that is where the similarity between vectors and complex amplitudes ends. We can multiply complex numbers as in (5.4) and (5.9), but the multiplication of vectors is usually defined very differently. For this reason, engineers have coined the term "phasor" as an alternative to "complex amplitude."

The quantity in (5.54) is a periodic function of time t. It repeats itself every T seconds where

$$\omega T = 2\pi \qquad (5.56)$$

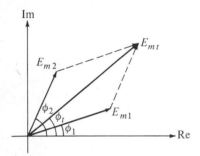

Figure 5.12 Addition of complex numbers like vectors.

The time interval T, in which the variation of the function completes a cycle, is known as the *period*. The reciprocal of T is the *frequency* (f), which indicates the number of cycles the function completes every second. The number of cycles per second is termed hertz (Hz). The coefficient

$$\omega = \frac{2\pi}{T} = 2\pi f \qquad (5.57)$$

is the *angular frequency* and has a unit of *radians per second*. The quantity ϕ is known as the *phase angle*.

The more generalized usage of the term "impedance," denoted by Z (or "admittance," denoted by Y), signifies the ratio of the complex amplitude of a voltage (current) to that of a current (voltage). The real part of an impedance (admittance) is known as the resistance, denoted by R (conductance, denoted by G), and the imaginary part is known as the reactance, denoted by X (susceptance, denoted by B).

If an impedance (admittance) is the ratio of a voltage (current) to a current (voltage) at the same two terminals of a network, it is called a *driving-point* impedance (admittance). Otherwise it is called a *transfer* impedance (admittance).

The transfer or driving-point impedance or admittance of a network containing memory elements is a function of the frequency (or ω). For example, the impedance of an L-henry inductance is

$$j\omega L \ \Omega$$

which varies from 0 to $j\infty$ as ω varies from 0 to $+\infty$. For a more complex network, the impedance or admittance function will also be more complicated. This aspect of circuit analysis will be studied in Chapter 11. For the present we shall limit our scope to the analysis of circuits in which the frequency is known and fixed at that particular value.

When two complex amplitudes, expressed in polar form, have the same phase angle, they are said to be *in phase*. When their angles are 90° apart, they are said to be in *quadrature phase*. If they are 180° apart, they are the negatives of each other, or *opposite in polarity*.

A sinusoidal electric quantity, say

$$i(t) = I_m \cos(\omega t + \phi) \qquad (5.58)$$

has a maximum value of I_m. Such a quantity is usually referred to not by this maximum value, but by its *effective value*. The effective value of any periodic quantity (whether sinudoidal or not) is the equivalent dc quantity, which, applied to an LTI resistor, renders the same *average power*. In the case of the current of (5.58), the average power dissipated in a resistance of R ohms is

$$P = \frac{1}{T}\int_0^T i^2 R \, dt = \frac{R}{T}\int_0^T I_m^2 \cos^2(\omega t + \phi)\, dt = \frac{I_m^2 R}{2} \qquad (5.59)$$

The effective value I_e should be such that

$$I_e^2 R = \frac{I_m^2 R}{2} \qquad (5.60)$$

Thus

$$I_e = \frac{I_m}{\sqrt{2}} \qquad (5.61)$$

for sinusoids. In general, the effective value of a periodic quantity $f(t)$ is given by

$$I_e = \sqrt{\frac{1}{T} \int_0^T f^2(t)\, dt} \qquad (5.62)$$

We see that the effective value of a quantity is also equal to the square root of the mean of the quantity squared. This relationship is valid for nonsinusoidal quantities as well. It is commonly known as the root-mean-square (rms) value of the quantity.

Thus, if we have a sinusoidal voltage

$$e(t) = E_m \cos(\omega t + \phi) \qquad (5.63)$$

it has an effective value of $E_e = E_m/\sqrt{2}$. When we speak of household voltage being 110 volts, we mean that its effective value is 110 volts. Its maximum voltage with respect to ground is 155.56 volts.

Sinusoidal quantities are usually specified by their rms values. This is especially convenient when calculations of powers are involved. If we require the time-domain expression of a quantity corresponding to a complex amplitude, then the factor $\sqrt{2}$ should be restored. In other words, a complex amplitude of $E_e \, \underline{/\phi}$ V implies a time function of

$$\sqrt{2}\, E_e \cos(\omega t + \phi) \text{ V}$$

Henceforth, when we talk about a complex amplitude or phasor of a sinusoid, it shall be understood that we are talking about its effective value.

To review the formulation of an ac circuit problem, let us summarize the steps taken.

1 The original problem is the analysis of the steady-state part of a circuit under sinusoidal excitation. An example is shown in Figure 5.13(a), in which $e_a(t)$ is known and the steady-state part of $i_a(t)$ is sought.

2 We replace the circuit of Figure 5.13(a) by that of Figure 5.13(b), in which all quantities are exponential functions. The quantities in circuit (a) are the real parts of the corresponding quantities in (b). Namely, $e_a(t) = \text{Re}[e_b(t)]$ and $i_a(t) = \text{Re}[i_b(t)]$.

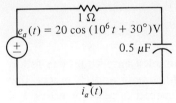

(a) Circuit with sinusoidal excitation

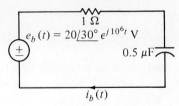

(b) Circuit with complex exponential excitation. [Real parts of voltages and currents are identical to those in (a).]

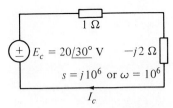

(c) Complex amplitude equivalent circuit [maximum values]

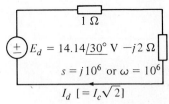

(d) Complex amplitude equivalent circuit [effective values]

Figure 5.13 Examples illustrating the evolution of a steady-state analysis problem into a complex amplitude circuit problem.

3 To find the quantities in circuit (b), each voltage or current is replaced by its complex amplitude (or phasor or "vector") and, at the same time, each circuit element is replaced by its impedance or admittance. The analysis of this circuit is identical to that of a network with LTI resistors, only now all quantities are generally complex numbers. Such a circuit for the circuit of Figure 5.13(b) is shown in Figure 5.13(c).

4 In practical ac circuits, we use the effective values, instead of the maximum values, of all voltages and currents. This does not affect the impedance and admittance values. The analysis of this circuit is identical to that of the circuit using maximum values.

For the circuits of Figure 5.13, we have

$$I_d = \frac{14.14 \, \underline{/30°}}{1 - j2} = \frac{14.14 \, \underline{/30°}}{2.236 \, \underline{/-63.4°}} = 6.324 \, \underline{/93.4°} \text{ A}$$

which implies that

$$I_c = \sqrt{2} I_d = 8.94 \, \underline{/93.4°} \text{ A}$$

which, in turn, implies that

$$i_b(t) = I_c \, e^{j10^6 t} = 8.94 e^{j(10^6 t + 93.4°)} \text{ A}$$

which gives

$$i_a(t) = \text{Re}[i_b(t)] = 8.94 \cos(10^6 t + 93.4°) \text{ A}$$

The analysis of an ac circuit in terms of complex amplitudes can follow all the rules and methods developed in Chapters 2 and 3, except that now we are dealing with complex numbers instead of real quantities. For example, impedances and admittances connected in series or in parallel may be combined in exactly the same way as resistances and conductances.

EXAMPLE 6   Find the equivalent impedance between terminals a and b in the circuit of Figure 5.14 for $\omega = 100$.

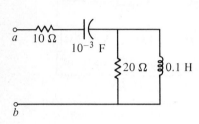

Figure 5.14

SOLUTION

$$Z_{ab} = 10 - j\frac{1}{100 \times 10^{-3}} + \frac{20(j0.1 \times 100)}{20 + j10}$$

$$= 10 - j10 + \frac{j200(20 - j10)}{(20 + j10)(20 - j10)}$$

$$= 10 - j10 + \frac{2000 + j4000}{500}$$

$$= 10 - j10 + 4 + j8$$

$$= 14 - j2 \ \Omega$$

Similarly, the voltage- and current-division rules also apply to the complex amplitudes of voltages and currents in a circuit.

To help us visualize the various ac quantities in an ac circuit, it is sometimes expedient to construct a "phasor diagram," similar to a vector diagram, by treating each phasor like a vector. Figure 5.1 shows a phasor diagram. Such diagrams are especially helpful in giving us an idea of the relative magnitudes and phase angles among the various quantities in an ac circuit, as well as how these combine to satisfy the KVL and the KCL in the circuit. This is best illustrated by an example.

EXAMPLE 7   For the ac circuit of Figure 5.15, $E_s = 100$ V. Find all currents and construct appropriate phasor diagrams for all quantities in the circuit.

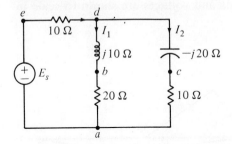

Figure 5.15

SOLUTION   Arbitrarily choose E_s as the reference, or let

$$E_s = 100 \underline{/0°}$$

We can easily find the equivalent impedance seen by the source by series-parallel combinations.

$$Z_{eq} = 10 + \frac{(20+j10)(10-j20)}{30-j10} = 10 + \frac{22.36 \underline{/26.6°} \times 22.36 \underline{/-63.4°}}{31.62 \underline{/-18.4°}}$$

$$= 10 + 15.81 \underline{/-18.4°} = 10 + 15 - j5 = 25 - j5 \ \Omega$$

$$I = \frac{100}{25-j5} = \frac{100(25+j5)}{650} = 3.846 + j0.769 = 3.922 \underline{/11.3°} \ A$$

Applying the current-division rule, we get

$$I_1 = \frac{10-j20}{30-j10} I = \frac{(1-j2)(3+j)}{10} I = (0.5-j0.5)I$$

$$= 2.308 - j1.538 = 2.774 \underline{/-33.7°} \ A$$

Hence

$$I_2 = \frac{20+j10}{30-j10} I = \frac{(2+j)(3+j)}{10} I = (0.5+j0.5)I$$

$$= 1.538 + j2.308 = 2.774 \underline{/56.3°} \ A$$

$$E_{ba} = 20I_1 = 46.16 - j30.76 = 55.48 \underline{/-33.7°} \ V$$

$$E_{db} = j10I_1 = 15.38 + j23.08 = 27.74 \underline{/56.3°} \ V$$

$$E_{ca} = 10I_2 = 15.48 + j23.08 = 27.74 \underline{/56.3°} \ V$$

$$E_{dc} = -j20I_2 = 46.16 - j30.76 = 55.48 \underline{/-33.7°} \ V$$

$$E_{da} = E_{db} + E_{ba} = E_{dc} + E_{ca} = 61.54 - j7.68 = 62.02 \underline{/-7.1°} \text{ V}$$

$$E_{ed} = 10I = 38.46 + j7.69 = 39.22 \underline{/11.3°} \text{ V}$$

The phasor diagrams for the currents and voltages are shown to scale in Figure 5.16.

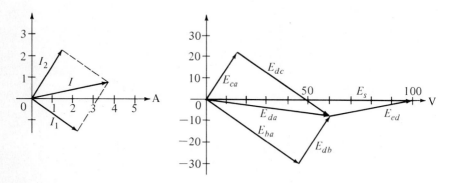

Figure 5.16   Phasor diagrams of currents and voltages in the circuit of Figure 5.15.

EXAMPLE 8   In the circuit of Figure 5.17(a), $e_s = 1.414 \cos(10^6 t)$ V. The impedance values of the capacitors are given for $\omega = 10^6$. Find the steady-state current $i(t)$ in the middle branch.

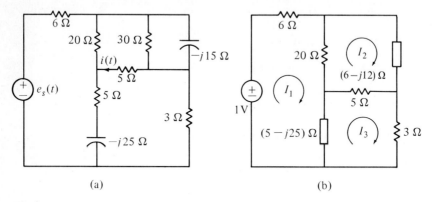

Figure 5.17

SOLUTION   Since we are dealing with an ac circuit, we may replace $e_s(t)$ by its complex amplitude (in effective value)

$$E_s = 1 \underline{/0°}$$

As we are not interested in the details of the parallel combination of the 30-ohm resistor and the 15-ohm capacitor, we can combine them into a single impedance whose value is

$$(30)\|(-j15) = \frac{(-j15)\times 30}{30-j15} = \frac{-j30}{2-j1} = \frac{-j30(2+j)}{5} = 6 - j12 \ \Omega$$

The ac circuit is shown in Figure 5.17(b). Here we choose to use mesh analysis. We have

$$(31 - j25) I_1 \qquad - 20 I_2 \quad -(5-j25) I_3 = 1$$

$$-20 I_1 + (31 - j12) I_2 \qquad - 5 I_3 = 0$$

$$-(5-j25) I_1 \qquad - 5 I_2 + (13 - j25) I_3 = 0$$

Solving, we get

$$\Delta = \begin{vmatrix} 31 - j25 & -20 & -5 + j25 \\ -20 & 31 - j12 & -5 \\ -5 + j25 & -5 & 13 - j25 \end{vmatrix}$$

$$= (31 - j25)(31 - j12)(13 - j25) + 100(-5 + j25) + 100(-5 + j25)$$

$$\quad -(-5 + j25)^2(31 - j12) - 400(13 - j25) - 25(31 - j25)$$

$$= -20{,}082 - j31{,}436 - 500 + j2500 - 500 + j2500 + 21{,}600 + j550$$

$$\quad - 5200 + j10{,}000 - 775 + j625$$

$$= -5457 - j15{,}261 = 16{,}207 \underline{/-109.68°}$$

$$I_2 = \frac{-1}{\Delta} \begin{vmatrix} -20 & -5 \\ -5 + j25 & 13 - j25 \end{vmatrix} = \frac{1}{\Delta}[20(13 - j25) + 5(5 - j25)]$$

$$= \frac{1}{\Delta}(285 - j625)$$

$$I_3 = \frac{1}{\Delta} \begin{vmatrix} -20 & 31 - j12 \\ -5 + j25 & -5 \end{vmatrix} = \frac{1}{\Delta}[100 + (31 - j12)(5 - j25)]$$

$$= \frac{1}{\Delta}(-45 - j835)$$

$$I = I_2 - I_3 = \frac{1}{\Delta}(330 + j210) = \frac{391.13 \underline{/32.5°}}{16{,}207 \underline{/-109.68°}} = 0.0241 \underline{/142.18°}$$

Since I is the complex amplitude of $i(t)$, we can write

$$i(t) = \text{Re}[\sqrt{2} I e^{j\omega t}] = 0.0341 \cos(10^6 t + 142.18°) \text{ A}$$

5.5   Power in an ac circuit

Suppose we have a network whose terminal voltage and current are

$$i(t) = \sqrt{2}\,|I|\cos(\omega t + \phi) \tag{5.64}$$

$$e(t) = \sqrt{2}\,|E|\cos(\omega t + \psi) \tag{5.65}$$

Figure 5.18 represents this situation schematically. The two rectangular boxes represent two meters. The ammeter reading indicates the rms value of $i(t)$, or $|I|$. The voltmeter reading indicates the rms value of $e(t)$, or $|E|$.

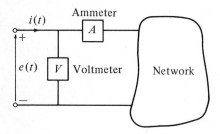

Figure 5.18   Notations used in explaining the powers delivered to a network.

The power delivered to that network at any instant is

$$p(t) = 2\,|I|\,|E|\cos(\omega t + \phi)\cos(\omega t + \psi) \tag{5.66}$$

The average of this power over a complete period is given by

$$P = \frac{1}{T}\int_0^T p(t)\,dt \tag{5.67}$$

Let $\theta = \omega t$. Then $\omega T = 2\pi$ and (5.67) becomes

$$P = \frac{1}{2\pi}\int_0^{2\pi} 2\,|E|\,|I|\cos(\theta + \phi)\cos(\theta + \psi)\,d\theta$$

$$= \frac{|E|\,|I|}{2\pi}\int_0^{2\pi}[\cos(2\theta + \phi + \psi) + \cos(\phi - \psi)]\,d\theta$$

$$= |E|\,|I|\cos(\phi - \psi) \tag{5.68}$$

Since the complex amplitudes of $i(t)$ and $e(t)$ are $|I|\underline{/\phi}$ and $|E|\underline{/\psi}$, respectively, we see that the average power delivered to a two-terminal network is equal to the product of the magnitudes of their voltage and current times the cosine of the angle between their complex amplitudes. (Note the proper relative polarities between the two complex amplitudes.) This average power is known as the *active*, or *real*, power, or *wattage*. This is also the reading of a wattmeter properly connected to measure the power delivered to the network on an average basis.

The quantity

$$P_a = |I|\,|E| \tag{5.69}$$

has the dimension of the power, but it does not always tell us the actual power delivered to the network. This product is called the *apparent power* and is usually expressed in *volt-amperes* (VA). It is simply the product of the ammeter reading and the voltmeter reading, as indicated in Figure 5.18.

If the network is such that $\phi = \psi$, then the voltage and the current are in phase, and the network draws only real power. This network is equivalent to a resistance. The power is given by

$$P = |I|\,|E| = |I|^2 R = \frac{|E|^2}{R} \tag{5.70}$$

where R is the equivalent resistance seen at the terminals.

If the network is such that $|\phi - \psi| = 90°$, then the voltage and current are in quadrature phase and the network draws no real power. Such a network is said to be purely reactive and is equivalent to a pure reactance. The network draws a *reactive power* of

$$Q = |I|\,|E| = |I|^2 |X| = \frac{|E|^2}{|X|} \tag{5.71}$$

A reactive power is expressed in *volt-amperes reactive* (VAR). There are two situations in which a network is purely reactive. If $\phi = \psi + 90°$, then the network is purely capacitive (the currrent leads the voltage by 90°). If $\psi = \phi + 90°$, then the network is purely inductive (the voltage leads the current by 90°). Usually, when we give the information about a reactive power, we also need to specify which of these two types of reactive power we are talking about.

If $|\phi - \psi| = 180°$, then P is a negative number, which means that the network is actually supplying an amount of power to whatever is connected to it. When

$$|\phi - \psi| \neq 0°, \quad \text{or} \quad 90°, \quad \text{or} \quad 180° \tag{5.72}$$

we have a situation that is intermediate between purely resistive and purely reactive. In this case, P and P_a are given by (5.68) and (5.69), respectively. But

$$Q = |I|\,|E| \sin |\psi - \phi| \tag{5.73}$$

This Q is capacitive if*

$$0 < \phi - \psi < 180° \qquad (I \text{ leads } E) \tag{5.74}$$

---

* In some texts an algebraic sign is associated with one type of reactive power, while the opposite sign is associated with the other type. There is some advantage, along with some confusion, to this convention.

and inductive if

$$0 < \psi - \phi < 180° \qquad (E \text{ leads } I) \tag{5.75}$$

The three powers in an ac network given by (5.68), (5.69), and (5.73) clearly satisfy

$$P_a^2 = P^2 + Q^2 \tag{5.76}$$

and these three quantities form the three sides of a right triangle, as shown in Figure 5.19. Knowledge of any two of these quantities will enable us to

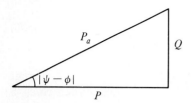

Figure 5.19 Relationship of real power, reactive power, and apparent power.

find the third one. Sometimes the ratio P/P_a, the *power factor*, is a more meaningful and informative quantity, especially in the power industry. Clearly, if the power factor and one of the three quantities of (5.76) are known, the other two quantities can also be found.

We shall now use the results obtained for the circuit of Figure 5.15 to illustrate the various powers in an ac circuit. The voltage and current values are reproduced in Figure 5.20*

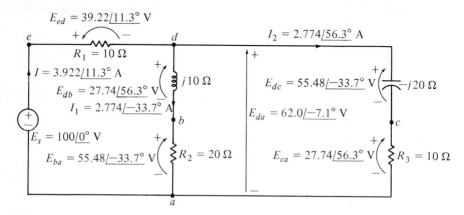

Figure 5.20

* The notation $\underline{/_B^A}$ is used to denote the "phase angle difference between complex numbers *A* and *B*." For our present purposes, the angle will always be taken as positive.

The real power delivered to $R_1 = |I||E_{ed}| = |I|^2 R_1$

$\qquad = 3.922 \times 39.22 = (3.922)^2 \times 10 = 153.8$ W

The real power delivered to $R_2 = |I_1||E_{ba}| = |I_1|^2 R_2$

$\qquad = 2.774 \times 55.48 = (2.774)^2 \times 20 = 153.8$ W

The real power delivered to $R_3 = |I_2||E_{ca}| = |I_2|^2 R_3$

$\qquad = 2.774 \times 27.74 = (2.774)^2 \times 10 = 76.9$ W

Total power delivered by the source $= |E_s||I| \cos \underline{/^I_{E_s}}$

$\qquad = 100 \times 3.922 \times \cos 11.3° = 384.7$ W

$\qquad =$ sum of real powers delivered to R_1, R_2, and R_3

Reactive power delivered to the inductance

$\qquad = |I_1||E_{db}| = |I_1|^2 |X_L| = 2.774 \times 27.74$

$\qquad = (2.774)^2 \times 10 = 76.9$ VAR $\qquad$ (inductive)

Reactive power delivered to the capacitor

$\qquad = |I_2||E_{dc}| = |I_2|^2 |X_C|$

$\qquad = 2.774 \times 55.48 = |2.774|^2 \times 20$

$\qquad = 153.8$ VAR $\qquad$ (capacitive)

Total reactive power delivered by the source

$\qquad = |E_s||I| \sin \underline{/^I_{E_s}} = 100 \times 3.922 \times \sin 11.3°$

$\qquad = 76.9$ VAR $\qquad$ (capacitive, since I leads E_s)

The powers in each of the series branches can also be found for the whole branch.

Real power delivered to branch abd

$\qquad = |I_1||E_{da}| \cos \underline{/^{I_1}_{E_{da}}} = 2.774 \times 62 \times \cos 26.6°$

$\qquad = 153.8$ W

Reactive power delivered to branch abd

$\qquad = |I_1||E_{da}| \sin \underline{/^{I_1}_{E_{da}}} = 2.774 \times 62 \times \sin 26.6°$

$\qquad = 76.9$ VAR $\qquad$ (inductive, since I_1 lags E_{da})

Apparent power delivered to branch $abd = |I_1||E_{da}|$

$\qquad = 2.774 \times 62 = 172$ VAR

Power factor of branch $abd = 153.9/172 = \cos 26.6° = 0.895$

Power delivered to branch *acd*

$$= |I_2||E_{da}|\cos\underline{/\tfrac{I_2}{E_{da}}} = 2.774 \times 62 \times \cos 63.4° = 76.9\text{ W}$$

Reactive power delivered to branch *acd*

$$= |I_2||E_{da}|\sin\underline{/\tfrac{I_2}{E_{da}}} = 2.774 \times 62 \times \sin 63.4°$$
$$= 153.8\text{ VAR} \qquad (\text{capacitive, since } I_2 \text{ leads } E_{da})$$

Apparent power delivered to branch *acd*

$$= |I_2||E_{da}| = 2.774 \times 62 = 172\text{ VAR}$$

Power factor of branch *acd* $= 76.9/172 = \cos 63.4° = 0.448$

Power delivered to the parallel combination between *a* and *d*

$$= |I||E_{da}|\cos\underline{/\tfrac{I}{E_{da}}} = 3.922 \times 62 \times \cos 18.4° = 230.7\text{ W}$$

Reactive power delivered to the parallel combination

$$= |I||E_{da}|\sin\underline{/\tfrac{I}{E_{da}}} = 3.922 \times 62 \times \sin 18.4°$$
$$= 76.9\text{ VAR} \qquad (\text{capacitive, since } I \text{ leads } E_{da})$$

Apparent power delivered to the parallel combination

$$= |I||E_{da}| = 3.922 \times 62 = 243.1\text{ VAR}$$

Power factor of the parallel combination

$$= 230.7/243.1 = \cos 18.4° = 0.949$$

The preceding calculations indicate that there are several ways to calculate powers in a circuit. In particular, in a series or parallel combination of branches, the powers of the combination may be found either by summing up the powers in the components or by calculating the power delivered to the combination as a whole. We shall return to this example shortly and use it to illustrate this principle of conservation of power.

The power industry frequently uses expressions of the type, "A load is consuming 100 kW at 0.8 power factor leading." The word "leading" indicates that the current is leading the voltage. (In a power system the voltage is usually taken as the reference.) So the statement indicates a load in which

$$P_a = 125\text{ kVA}, \qquad P = 100\text{ kW}, \qquad Q = 75\text{ kVAR} \qquad (\text{capacitive})$$

Thus, for Figure 5.20, we could verbally describe the power delivered to the parallel combination between *a* and *d* as either "230.7 watts at a power factor of 0.949 leading," or (rarely) "76.9 capacitive VAR at 0.949 power factor."

When we know the complex amplitudes of $i(t)$ and $e(t)$ of Figure 5.18, we have a very simple way to find all three powers going into the network with one operation. Let

$$I = |I| \underline{/\phi}, \qquad E = |E| \underline{/\psi} \tag{5.77}$$

represent the complex amplitudes. Then, if we take the complex conjugate of one complex amplitude and multiply it into the other, we have

$$\mathcal{R} = I^*E \qquad \text{or} \qquad E^*I \tag{5.78}$$

Then

$$P_a = |\mathcal{R}|, \qquad P = \text{Re}[\mathcal{R}], \qquad Q = \text{Im}[\mathcal{R}] \tag{5.79}$$

The quantity $\mathcal{R}$ is known as the *complex power*. For example, if we have

$$I = 2 \underline{/50°} \text{ A}, \qquad E = 100 \underline{/20°} \text{ V}$$

then

$$\mathcal{R} = I^*E = 200 \underline{/-30°} = 173.2 - j100 \text{ VA} \tag{5.80}$$

The average power is 173.2 watts and the reactive power is 100 VAR (capacitive). We can infer that the reactive power is capacitive from the fact that I leads E. This fact manifests itself in the form of a minus sign in the imaginary part of $\mathcal{R}$. If this sign were positive, it would indicate an inductive reactive power.

On the other hand, if we had chosen to take the conjugate of E instead of I or, equivalently, if we had chosen the alternative definition of $\mathcal{R}$ given in (5.78) or

$$\mathcal{R} = E^*I \tag{5.81}$$

then the interpretation of the sign of the imaginary part of $\mathcal{R}$ would be exactly reversed.

Again returning to the network of Figure 5.20, we find the following quantities.

The complex power delivered *to* branch *abd*

$$= I_1^*E_{da} = (2.308 + j1.538)(61.54 - j7.68) = 153.8 + j76.9 \text{ VA}$$

The complex power delivered *to* branch *acd*

$$= I_2^*E_{da} = (1.538 - j2.308)(61.54 - j7.68) = 76.9 - j153.8 \text{ VA}$$

The complex power delivered to R_1

$$= I^*E_{ed} = (3.846 - j0.769)(38.46 + j7.69) = 153.8 + j0 \text{ VA}$$

The complex power delivered *by* the source

$$= I^*E_s = (3.846 - j0.769)(100 + j0) = 384.6 - j76.9 \text{ VA}$$

$$= I_1^*E_{da} + I_2^*E_{da} + I^*E_{ed}$$

In an ac network, the voltages across the various branches E_k, with $k = 1, 2, ..., n$, obviously satisfy KVL. Likewise the currents through the various branches I_k, with $k = 1, 2, ..., n$, satisfy KCL. If we take the complex conjugates of all these currents, we get I_k^* ($k = 1, 2, ..., n$). Obviously, this set of I_k^* also satisfies KCL. If, in addition, the directions of the current and voltage in each branch have been chosen so that they oppose each other, as shown in Figure 5.21, Tellegen's theorem asserts that

$$\sum_{k=1}^{n} I_k^* E_k = \sum_{k=1}^{n} \mathscr{R}_k = 0 \tag{5.82}$$

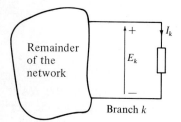

Branch k

Figure 5.21   Voltage and current directions in one branch of a network.

where $\mathscr{R}_k$ is the complex power delivered to branch k. Equation (5.82) implies that the algebraic sum of the complex powers delivered *to* all branches of an ac network must vanish. This conclusion may be called the "law of conservation of complex power" of an ac network. Furthermore, from (5.79) we may write

$$\mathscr{R}_k = P_k + jQ_k \tag{5.83}$$

Equation (5.82) implies that

$$\sum_{k=1}^{n} P_k = 0 \tag{5.84}$$

and

$$\sum_{k=1}^{n} Q_k = 0 \tag{5.85}$$

Equation (5.84) may be termed the "law of conservation of (real) power" in an ac network. Likewise, equation (5.85) may be termed the "law of conservation of reactive power." These "laws" simply mean that each of the powers (complex, real, and reactive) delivered *to* one part of an ac network must be equal to the power of the same type supplied by the remainder of the network. The conservation of powers is illustrated by the various computations for the circuit of Figure 5.20 earlier in this section.

A few words of caution. Since powers are products of voltages and currents, they do not satisfy the superposition theorem. Also the law of conservation of power does not generally apply to the apparent power.

EXAMPLE 9   Three transmission lines are sending power from a power plant to three substations. At the plant, instruments indicate that line 1 is transmitting 5 MW at a power factor of 0.95 lagging, line 2 is transmitting 2 MVA at a power factor of 0.9 leading, and line 3 is transmitting 100 kVAR (capacitive) and 1 MW. What is the power factor at the plant?

SOLUTION

$$\text{Reactive power of line 1} = 5 \times \tan[\cos^{-1}(0.95)]$$

$$= 5 \times \tan 18.2° = 5 \times 0.3288$$

$$= 1.644 \text{ MVAR} \qquad \text{(inductive)}$$

$$\text{Real power of line 2} = 2 \times 0.9 = 1.8 \text{ MW}$$

$$\text{Reactive power of line 2} = 2 \times \sin[\cos^{-1}(0.9)] = 2 \times \sin 25.8°$$
$$= 2 \times \sqrt{1-(0.9)^2} = 0.872 \text{ MVAR} \qquad \text{(capacitive)}$$

$$\text{Total real power at the plant} = 5 + 1.8 + 1 = 7.8 \text{ MW}$$

$$\text{Total reactive power at the plant} = 1.644 - 0.872 - 0.1$$

$$= 0.672 \text{ MVAR (inductive)}$$

$$\text{Apparent power at the plant} = \sqrt{(7.8)^2+(0.672)^2} = 7.829 \text{ MVA}$$

$$\text{Power factor at the plant} = 7.8/7.829 = 0.996 \qquad \text{(lagging or inductive)}$$

EXAMPLE 10   At the input of a submarine cable, which can be approximated by an RC series combination, the voltmeter reading is 2300 volts, the ammeter reading is 4.75 amperes, the wattmeter reading is 494 watts, and the frequency is 60 Hz. Find R and C.

SOLUTION   The equivalent circuit of the cable is shown in Figure 5.22.

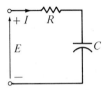

Figure 5.22   Equivalent circuit of a cable at one frequency.

We have

$$|I|^2 R = 494 \text{ W}$$

Hence

$$R = \frac{494}{(4.75)^2} = 21.89 \ \Omega$$

The apparent power $= 2300 \times 4.75 = 10,925$ VA

The reactive power $= \sqrt{(10,925)^2 - (494)^2} = 10,914$ VAR

$$X_C = \frac{10,914}{(4.75)^2} = 483.7 \ \Omega$$

$$C = \frac{1}{2\pi \times 60 \times 483.7} = 5.484 \times 10^{-6} \ \text{F}$$

EXAMPLE 11   A transmission line has a resistance of 15 ohms and an inductive reactance of 20 ohms. The voltage at the power plant is 13,200 volts. At the receiving end of the transmission line an induction motor is consuming 700 kW and draws a current of 65 amperes. Find the voltage at the motor and the power factor at the plant.

SOLUTION   Use the notation shown in Figure 5.23. Since the motor is of the induction type, it always has a lagging power factor. We can replace it with an RL series impedance.

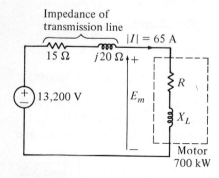

Figure 5.23

$$R = \frac{700,000}{(65)^2} = 165.7 \ \Omega$$

The impedance seen by the source has a magnitude equal to

$$|Z| = \frac{13,200}{65} = 203.1 \ \Omega$$

and we have

$$(15 + 165.7)^2 + (20 + X_L)^2 = (203.1)^2$$

Solving for X_L, we get

$X_L = 72.7$

Using the voltage as the reference, we have

$$I = \frac{13,200 \,\underline{/0^\circ}}{180.7 + j92.7} = 65 \,\underline{/-27.2^\circ} \text{ A}$$

Power factor at the plant $= \cos 27.2^\circ = 0.89$.

And

$$E_M = \frac{165.7 + j72.7}{180.7 + j92.7} \times 13,200 = \frac{180.9 \,\underline{/23.7^\circ}}{203.1 \,\underline{/27.2^\circ}} \times 13,200$$

$$= 11,757 \,\underline{/-3.5^\circ} \text{ V}$$

5.6 Maximum power transfer

In many electronic applications the objective is to obtain as much power as possible from the circuit. We might ask: What is the maximum power obtainable from a network consisting of LTI elements and independent sources? Figure 5.24 shows that this question is equivalent to asking how to vary the load impedance so that maximum power is delivered from network N to that impedance. An example of such a situation is the case

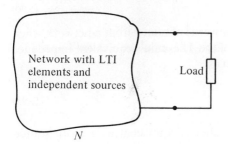

Network with LTI elements and independent sources

Load

N

Figure 5.24 A network with a load.

in which N represents an audio amplifier and the load is the impedance of a loudspeaker. Another example is the case in which N represents a radio transmitter and the load is an antenna.

To facilitate the solution of such a problem, we may first replace network N by its Thévenin's equivalent circuit and the load by its equivalent impedance. The circuit is reduced to that of Figure 5.25, in which E_s, R_s, and X_s are fixed and R_L and X_L are allowed to vary. Now we have

$$I = \frac{E_s}{R_s + R_L + j(X_s + X_L)} \tag{5.86}$$

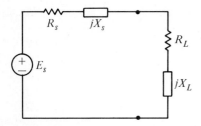

Figure 5.25 Equivalent circuit to that in Figure 5.24.

The power delivered to the load is

$$P_L = |I|^2 R_L = \frac{|E_s|^2 R_L}{(R_s + R_L)^2 + (X_s + X_L)^2} \tag{5.87}$$

To maximize P_L with respect to R_L and X_L, we set

$$\frac{\partial P_L}{\partial R_L} = 0 \tag{5.88}$$

$$\frac{\partial P_L}{\partial X_L} = 0 \tag{5.89}$$

Simultaneous solution of (5.88) and (5.89) yields

$$R_L = R_s, \qquad X_L = -X_s \tag{5.90}$$

Equation (5.90) says that maximum power is obtained from a network when the load impedance is the conjugate of the Thévenin's equivalent impedance of the network. This maximum power is

$$P_{L\,max} = \frac{|E_s|^2}{4R_s} \tag{5.91}$$

EXAMPLE 12   The output of an amplifier is equivalent to a 2-volt source connected in series with a $(2+j5)$-ohm impedance. What is the maximum power available from this amplifier?

SOLUTION   The arrangement is equivalent to that shown in Figure 5.25. The maximum power is delivered to the load when

$$Z_L = R_L + jX_L = 2 - j5 \ \Omega$$

Then

$$|I_L| = \tfrac{2}{4} = 0.5 \ \text{A}$$

and the power delivered to Z_L is

$$P_L = |I_L|^2 R_L = (0.5)^2 \times 2 = 0.5 \ \text{W}$$

We see in the preceding example that, when the maximum power is delivered to the load, the same amount of power is dissipated in the equivalent series resistance (R_s) of the amplifier. From the 2-volt source (E_s) point of view, the efficiency is exactly 50%. Hence, when maximum power is desired, we are usually not too interested in power efficiency. Rather, we are given a source with a fixed internal impedance and our objective is to design a load such that as much power as possible is extracted from the source. If efficiency is of primary concern, as in electric power systems, then the design objective is to make the source resistance as low as possible.

5.7 Concluding remarks

In this chapter we have concentrated on the steady-state response of LTI networks under dynamic excitations. You should not be misled by this emphasis to infer that the transient responses in circuits are not important. In many circuits, the transient response is the only one of interest because we utilize this response to perform certain functions. In those circuits, the transient response is all-important.

Nevertheless, steady-state solutions, particularly those under sinusoidal excitations, remain the bread-and-butter part of most electrical and electronic engineering problems. Alternating-current analysis is an indispensable skill that you must acquire in order to handle most engineering problems. We cannot overemphasize the need for an adequate amount of practice and familiarity with the terminology and details of this class of problems.

Although in the last few chapters we have used some simple practical circuits as examples, our primary goal has been to introduce you to the basic ideas and techniques of analysis. We believe that we have now reached a plateau. You should have acquired sufficient knowledge to begin to tackle some more real-world-oriented aspects of electrical circuits. We shall therefore turn in the next chapter to some simple electronic devices, their models, and how they are used in circuits.

Problems

5.1 Evaluate:

(a) $(8+j7)(5 \underline{/30°})(\epsilon^{-j39°})(0.3-j0.1)$

(b) $\dfrac{(8.5+j34)(20\epsilon^{-j25°})60(\cos 10° + j \sin 10°)}{(25 \underline{/20°})(37 \underline{/23°})}$

(c) $\dfrac{25/30° \times 10\epsilon^{j27°} \times (14-j13)}{1-j2}$

(d) $13 \underline{/15°} + j1.5 \times 6\epsilon^{(1-j30°)}$

5.2 Find:
(a) $\mathrm{Re}[(3+j5)\times 4 \underline{/50°} \times 7\epsilon^{-j20°}]$
(b) $\mathrm{Re}[10 \underline{/50°} \times \epsilon^{j20°}]$
(c) $\mathrm{Re}[10 \underline{/50°} \times \epsilon^{j\omega t}]$
(d) $\mathrm{Im}[E\epsilon^{j\omega t}]$, where $E = |E|\epsilon^{j\theta}$

5.3 By vector addition, simplify the following expressions into one trigonometric term:
(a) $12\cos\omega t + 20\sin\omega t$
(b) $5\sin(\omega t+30°) + 8\cos(\omega t-50°)$
(c) $4\sin(\omega t+120°) + 5\cos(\omega t+180°) + 16\cos(\omega t-20°)$

5.4 The complex current in a steady-state ac circuit is given by the formula $I = V/Z$, where V = complex voltage and Z = complex impedance. Fill in the missing values in the following table:

V	I	Z
110		$10+j20$
$110\underline{/45°}$		$10+j20$
$16\underline{/13.2°}$	$1.00-j0.748$	
	$13\underline{/76°}$	$19.1+j0.909$
	$4\underline{/85°}$	$-11+j18.2$
$110\underline{/90°}$	$2.38\underline{/6°}$	
$76+j54$	$7.19-j4.89$	

5.5 In the circuit of Figure P5.5, $e_s(t) = 20\cos 500t$ volts. Find the steady-state part of $i(t)$, with $R = 40$ ohms and $L = 0.06$ henry. Also find the steady-state part of the voltage across the inductance, $e_L(t)$.

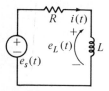

Figure P5.5

5.6 In the circuit shown in Figure P5.6, $i = 15 \cos(\omega t + 0°)$ and $i_1 = 10 \cos(\omega t - 30°)$. Find $e(t)$.

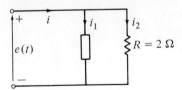

Figure P5.6

5.7 In the circuit of Figure P5.7, $E = 100 \underline{/0°}$ and $\omega = 10$. Find I, I_1, and I_2.

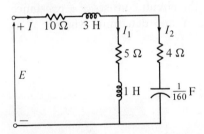

Figure P5.7

5.8 In the circuit of Figure P5.8, $I_s = 1 \underline{/0°}$ and $\omega = 1$. Find I_1, I, E, and E_C, and plot a phasor diagram showing all five complex amplitudes.

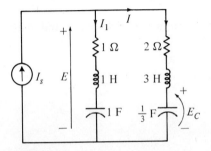

Figure P5.8

5.9 In the circuit of Figure P5.9, $E_s = 15 \big/ 30°$ volts and $\omega = 1$. Find E and I.

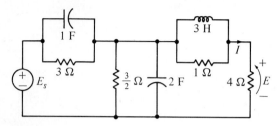

Figure P5.9

5.10 The current in a circuit is $i = 2\cos(\omega t - 30°)$ A, when the applied voltage is $e = 50\cos \omega t$ V. (a) Suppose that the circuit consists of a resistance and a reactance in series. Find R and X and determine whether X is inductive or capacitive. (b) Suppose that the circuit consists of a resistance and a reactance in parallel. Find R and X and determine whether X is inductive or capacitive.

5.11 In the circuit of Figure P5.11, find I_C and I_L.

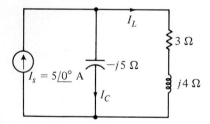

Figure P5.11

5.12 Find the impedance Z and the admittance Y between a and b in Figure P5.12.

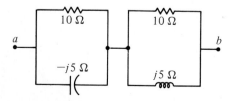

Figure P5.12

5.13 Find the complex amplitude of the current in the 10-ohm resistor in Figure P5.13.

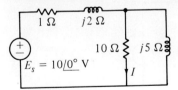

Figure P5.13

5.14 In Figure P5.14, $E_R = 1 \underline{/0°}$ volt. Find E_s and I.

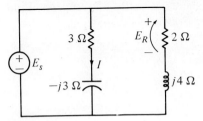

Figure P5.14

5.15 Find currents I_1, I_2, and I_3 in the circuit of Figure P5.15.

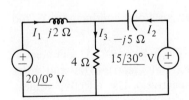

Figure P5.15

5.16 Find the following quantities in the circuit shown in Figure P5.16: I, E, I_e, E_i.

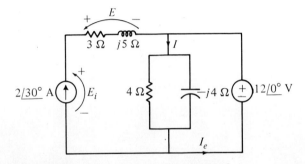

Figure P5.16

5.17 Find the voltages across both current sources E_1 and E_2 in Figure P5.17.

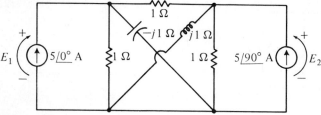

Figure P5.17

5.18 In Figure P5.18, $E = 100 + j150$ volts and $I = 10 / 35°$ amperes. Find the average power and the reactive power drawn by the load.

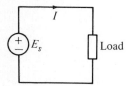

Figure P5.18

5.19 Given that the load of Problem 5.18 consists of a resistance R and a reactance X in series, find R and X.

5.20 Given that the load of Problem 5.18 consists of a conductance G and a susceptance B in parallel, find G and B.

5.21 In the circuit of Figure P5.21, $e_s(t) = 100 \cos(10t - 30°)$. Under steady-state conditions: (a) Find the phasors of $e_s(t)$, $i(t)$, $e_R(t)$, $e_L(t)$, and $e_C(t)$. (Denote them by E_s, I, E_R, E_L, and E_C respectively. Use effective values.) (b) Find $i(t)$, $e_R(t)$, $e_L(t)$, and $e_C(t)$. (c) Compute the average power in the resistor. (d) Compute the reactive powers in the capacitor and the inductor. (e) Compute the apparent power, the average power, and the reactive power supplied by the voltage source, using only phasors E and I.

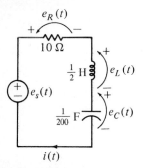

Figure P5.21

5.22 (a) Find the complex amplitudes of all currents in the network shown in Figure P5.22. Indicate the direction of each of your currents on your diagram. (b) Calculate the real and reactive powers supplied by each source. (c) Calculate the real and reactive powers in each branch. (d) Verify that the sum of the results obtained in part (c) is the same as the sum of those obtained in part (b).

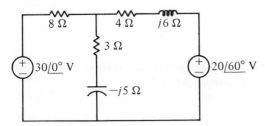

Figure P5.22

5.23 An impedance load consisting of a 12-ohm resistance and a 16-ohm inductive reactance in series is connected across a 60-hertz, 100-volt source. Find the capacitance of a capacitor that may be paralleled with this load to bring the power factor to 1.

5.24 One branch of a parallel circuit takes 1000 volt-amperes at 0.6 power factor lagging and the other branch takes 800 volt-amperes at 0.8 power factor leading. Find the total power, the total volt-amperes, and the power factor of the circuit.

5.25 A voltage with an rms value of 110 volts is applied to a series *RL* branch. The power delivered to the resistance is 50 watts. The voltage measured across the pure inductance is 75 volts rms. Find the value of the resistance and the reactance.

5.26 The average power delivered by the current source of Figure P5.26 is 320 watts. Find the value of the inductive reactance.

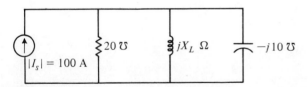

Figure P5.26

5.27 In the circuit shown in Figure P5.27, $|E| = 50$ volts. The power delivered by the source is 312.5 watts. Find the value of X_C.

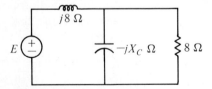

Figure P5.27

5.28 In Figure P5.28, find the maximum power deliverable to the load impedance Z when it is allowed to assume any value.

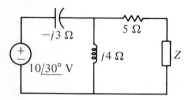

Figure P5.28

5.29 In the circuit shown in Figure P5.29, R_L is variable and can assume any positive value. Derive an expression for the value of R_L in terms of R_s and X_s for the maximum power consumed in R_L.

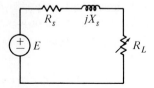

Figure P5.29

5.30 In the circuit of Figure P5.30, E, R_s, X_s, and R_L are known. What is the value of X_L that will make the power delivered to R_L a maximum?

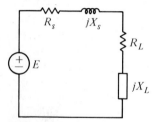

Figure P5.30

6 | TWO-TERMINAL ELECTRONIC DEVICES AND THEIR CIRCUIT MODELS

Having covered certain basic rules that govern the performance of electric networks and some techniques for analyzing them, we now turn to the physics and models of a few simple electronic devices, the analysis of circuits including these devices, and some of their applications. We hope in this volume to provide you with a familiarity with these subjects. A thorough treatment of any one area in depth would be a major undertaking in itself and is not the intent of this volume.

The simplest useful electronic device is the *diode*. A diode is a two-terminal nonlinear circuit element whose characteristic is either nonbilateral (having low resistance in one direction and high resistance in the other) or highly nonlinear. We shall give a brief qualitative description of several of the more common diodes, some analysis methods, and examples of circuits involving these devices.

6.1 Intrinsic and extrinsic semiconductors

Germanium and silicon are the two most common semiconductor materials employed in electronic devices. The atoms of these materials are tetravalent—each has four electrons in its outermost shell. A pure crystal of these materials is a lattice made up of repeated units, each of which occupies a cubic space. Within each cubic unit, one atom is located at the center and four atoms are located at four of its vertices, as shown in Figure 6.1. Each double line between a pair of neighboring atoms indicates a covalent bond: The two electrons are shared by these two atoms. These electrons are known as the valence electrons. The result is a rigid single-crystal structure, which is an insulator at 0°K.

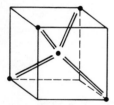

Figure 6.1   Crystal structure of intrinsic semiconductors.

At room temperature, some of the valence electrons may acquire sufficient energy through thermal agitation to leave the valence sites. When this occurs, they become *free electrons* and are able to cause conduction much like the free electrons in metals that make the latter such good conductors. At the same time, the absence of a valence electron leaves a vacancy in the structure, called a *hole*, which may be filled by another electron from a nearby covalent bond or by another free electron. When a succession of such events occurs, each event being caused by the motion of an electron going from one covalent bond to another, it appears that the hole is moving in the opposite direction. Hence holes also contribute to conduction. Figure 6.2 is a two-dimensional illustration of such events.

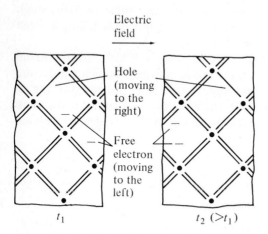

Figure 6.2   Two-dimensional model of atoms and carriers in an intrinsic semiconductor.

Pure semiconductors producing conduction this way are called *intrinsic semiconductors*. The conductivity of an intrinsic semiconductor depends on the type of material and the temperature. These factors determine the density of carriers (electrons and holes). Another factor that affects the conductivity of a material is the mobility of the carriers. As might be expected, as the temperature is increased, more carriers become available and the conductivity is increased.

Intrinsic semiconductors have two distinct drawbacks as materials for electronic devices. One is that their conductivities are generally too low and too temperature-dependent. The other is that it is difficult to produce multi-electrode devices from them. Hence intrinsic semiconductors are limited to special-purpose devices such as the thermistor—a resistor whose resistance is temperature-dependent.

If certain impurity atoms are introduced into the crystal lattice, a different type of semiconductor, the *extrinsic*, is produced. There are two types of extrinsic semiconductors.

If the impurity atoms are pentavalent, such as phosphorus (P^{15}), arsenic (As^{33}), or antimony (Sb^{51}), each atom will have an extra electron that will very readily become a free electron (requiring very little energy). (The probability of each of these fifth electrons becoming a free electron is essentially unity at room temperature.) Such an atom is called a *donor*, and this semiconductor is said to be of the *n* type. Figure 6.3 represents this situation.

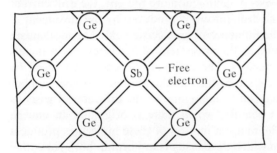

Figure 6.3 Two-dimensional model of a donor atom in a crystal lattice.

If the impurity atoms are trivalent, for example, boron (B^5), aluminum (Al^{13}), gallium (Ga^{31}), or indium (In^{49}), then there will be an empty covalent bond, or a hole, associated with each impurity atom. Such an atom is called an *acceptor*, and the semiconductor is said to be of the *p* type. This situation is symbolically represented in Figure 6.4.

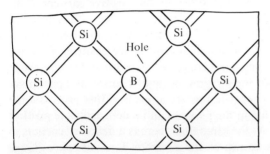

Figure 6.4 Two-dimensional model of an acceptor atom in a crystal lattice.

The introduction of impurity into the crystal structure is known as *doping*. This can be done while the material is in a molten or gaseous state. It can also be done by the diffusion process.

Frequently, in an extrinsic semiconductor, both types of impurity are present. For example, a lightly doped *n*-type crystal could subsequently be heavily doped with *p*-type impurities. The result is a *p*-type semiconductor. Also intrinsic carriers are always present, although their number is usually much less than the number of impurity carriers.

6.2 The *p-n* junction and the semiconductor diode

The *p-n* junction is the boundary separating a *p* region on one side and an *n* region on the other. It is the basic building block of many semiconductor devices. This section contains a qualitative description of the physics that underlies the behavior of the *p-n* junction.

In a semiconductor, two types of conduction are present: the drift current and the diffusion current. The drift current is produced by the movement of electrons and holes under the influence of an electric field. The mechanism of this current flow is the same as the movement of free electrons in metals that makes them good conductors. The diffusion current is produced by the net migration of carriers caused by the random motion of a large number of carriers. This latter mechanism is analogous to the diffusion of gaseous molecules in two parts of a chamber when there is originally an uneven distribution of molecules. The random motion of these molecules produces an eventual redistribution, in which the density is uniform in both parts, due to a net flow of molecules from one part of the chamber to the other.

In a semiconductor, we may imagine that in the *p* region there is a net distribution of holes that are carriers and of negative ions that are the ionized acceptor atoms and are not free to move by ordinary applied electric force. In the *n* region there is a net distribution of free electrons that are carriers and of positive ions that are ionized donor atoms and are not free to move by ordinary applied electric force.

When a *p* region is placed next to an *n* region, the positive carriers in the *p* region and the negative carriers in the *n* region tend to diffuse into the opposite region. This process will not go on indefinitely, however. When a hole diffuses into the *n* region it recombines with a free electron, resulting in the appearance of a net positive charge, or a positive ion. Likewise, when an electron diffuses into the *p* region, it gives rise to the appearance of a net negative charge, or a negative ion. As a result of this process a net surplus of negative ions appears in the *p* region and a net surplus of positive ions appears in the *n* region. At the same time there is a deficit of carriers in the transition region. This is known as the *depletion layer* or *space-charge region*.

A schematic diagram of this state of affairs is shown in Figure 6.5. Figure 6.5(a) indicates the distribution of majority carriers (which are electrons in the *n* region or holes in the *p* region). Figure 6.5(b) indicates the distribution of net charges. The presence of such a charge distribution represents an electrostatic potential build-up across the layer. This potential tends to make it more difficult for the holes to diffuse from the *p* to the *n* region and for the electrons to diffuse in the opposite direction. An equilibrium is soon reached.

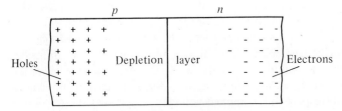

(a) Distribution of majority carriers

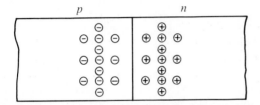

(b) Distribution of net charges (ions)

Figure 6.5 Ion and carrier distributions near a *p-n* junction.

Although the diffusion process continues at room temperature, the diffusion of every carrier across the junction is accompanied by the diffusion of another carrier of the same type in the opposite direction. Hence, at equilibrium, no net current flows across the junction.

When a potential difference is applied across a *p-n* junction in such a direction that the *p* region is set at a lower potential than the *n* region, the junction is said to be *reverse-biased*. This arrangement is illustrated in Figure 6.6(a). The effect of this external bias is to widen the depletion layer and

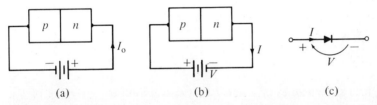

Figure 6.6 (a) A reverse-biased *p-n* junction diode. (b) A forward-biased *p-n* junction diode. (c) Symbol of a junction diode.

increase the potential barrier at the junction. The distance between the effective regions with the p-type and n-type carriers is widened. As a result, the diffusion of majority carriers into the other region becomes more difficult. If the reverse voltage is sufficiently high, the current is entirely due to the drift of minority carriers (electrons in the p region and holes in the n region). This current I_0 is known as the *reverse saturation current*. It is a function of the material, of geometry, and of temperature.

When the external potential is reversed in polarity, as shown in Figure 6.6(b), the junction is *forward-biased* and the potential barrier across the depletion layer is lowered. Also the distances separating the boundaries of the majority carrier regions are narrowed. This tends to encourage the diffusion of majority carriers. In fact, in this bias polarity, the diffusion current dominates the junction currents, while the drift current becomes negligible. In an idealized p-n junction, the diffusion current increases exponentially with respect to the applied voltage.

Quantitatively, the V-I characteristic of an ideal p-n junction with the direction convention of Figure 6.6(c) is given by

$$I = I_0(e^{V/\eta V_T} - 1) \qquad (6.1)$$

in which η is unity, V is in volts, and

$$V_T = \frac{kT}{q} \qquad (6.1a)$$

where q is the electronic charge, k is Boltzmann's constant, and T is the absolute temperature in degrees Kelvin. At room temperature (25°C)

$$V_T = 25.69 \text{ mV}$$

Table **6.1**

V	I
-0.2	$-0.9996 I_0$
-0.1	$-0.9796 I_0$
0	0
0.1	$48.04 I_0$
0.2	$2.40 \times 10^3 I_0$
0.3	$1.18 \times 10^5 I_0$
0.4	$5.78 \times 10^6 I_0$
0.5	$2.84 \times 10^8 I_0$

Table 6.1 lists a few values of V and I that correspond to this value of V_T. We see that, when $V = -0.2$ V, the reverse current is practically saturated. Figure 6.7 plots the current-versus-voltage curve for positive values of V. The

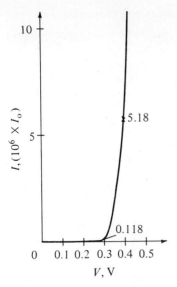

Figure 6.7   Typical silicon and germanium diode characteristics in the forward-biased region.

current remains practically zero until approximately 0.25 V and then abruptly increases at a very rapid rate. This gives an apparent threshold phenomenon. Actually it is the result of an exponential function being plotted on a linear scale. Nevertheless this thresholdlike characteristic is significant, especially when a diode is used in connection with other circuit elements. The voltage at which this thresholdlike phenomenon takes place is known as the *cut-in* voltage or the *threshold* voltage.

   In reality, the cut-in voltage for a germanium diode is in the range between 0.2 and 0.3 V. However, for a silicon diode, it is between 0.5 and 0.7 V. There are two reasons for this higher value. (1) A silicon diode typically has a much lower I_0 than a germanium one, usually by several orders of magnitude. (2) The coefficient η in (6.1) should be 2 in a silicon p-n junction for low currents because in the depletion region recombinations of carriers become more significant.

EXAMPLE 1   The diode D of Figure 6.8(a) has a reverse saturation current of 10 μA. Find the current I in the circuit at 25°C.

SOLUTION   There are three apparently different methods of finding the current.

Analytical method   From (6.1) we have the following (I denotes the value of i and V_D denotes the value of v_D when they are constant):

$$I = 10^{-5}(e^{V_D/0.02569} - 1) \tag{6.2}$$

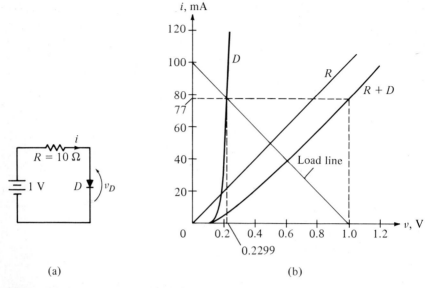

(a) (b)

Figure 6.8 (a) A resistor-diode circuit. (b) Graphical and load-line methods of analyzing the circuit in (a).

Solving for V_D, we get

$$V_D = 0.02569 \ln(I \times 10^5 + 1)$$

KVL requires that

$$0.02569 \ln(I \times 10^5 + 1) + 10I = 1 \qquad (6.3)$$

This is a nonlinear equation, and generally must be solved by some numerical techniques. However, since (6.3) is reasonably simple, a trial-and-error method will readily yield the solution, which is

$$I = 0.077 \text{ A} \qquad \text{and} \qquad V_D = 0.23 \text{ V}$$

Table **6.2**

v (V)	i (mA)
0.1	0.48
0.15	3.43
0.2	24.04
0.21	35.48
0.22	52.37
0.23	77.29
0.24	114.1

Graphical method   We can first obtain the v-i characteristic of the diode through (6.1). Several key values of v and i are given in Table 6.2 and the characteristic is plotted as curve D in Figure 6.8(b). As we explained in Section 2.2, the v-i characteristic of the series combination of R and D can be obtained by adding up their voltages for each current. This is shown as curve $R+D$ in Figure 6.8(b). From this combined characteristic, we easily see that, for $v = 1$ V, $i = 77$ mA.

Load-line method   A variation of the preceding two methods is to regard the diode characteristic and the circuit relationship external to the diode as two requirements that must be satisfied simultaneously. The circuit relationship external to the diode clearly must satisfy

$$1 - 10I = V_D \tag{6.4}$$

This is the equation of a straight line, known as the *load line*, that passes through the points $(1,0)$ and $(0,0.1)$ in the i-v plane, as shown in Figure 6.8(b). The point at which the load line intersects the diode characteristic gives the set of values for I and V_D that satisfies both the diode characteristic and the load line. From Figure 6.8(b), we see that $I = 0.077$ A.

6.3   Small-signal analysis—The dynamic resistance of a diode

Take the circuit of Figure 6.9(a), in which an LTI resistor is connected in series with a diode. The source voltage is the superposition of a constant

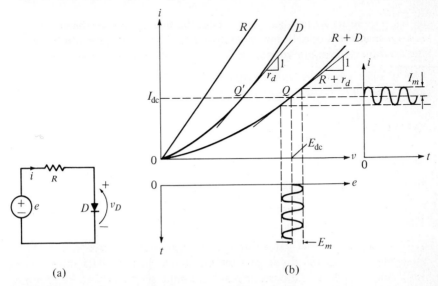

(a)   (b)

Figure 6.9 Response of a diode circuit to a small ac signal.

(dc) component and an ac component, or

$$e(t) = E_{dc} + E_m \sin \omega t \tag{6.5}$$

If E_m is sufficiently small that the covered part of the i-v characteristic can be considered linear, then the response $i(t)$ will be

$$i(t) = I_{dc} + I_m \sin \omega t \tag{6.6}$$

To find I_{dc}, we may set E_m to zero and analyze the circuit in the same way as we did the circuit of Figure 6.8(a). This determines the *operating (or quiescent) point* Q (I_{dc}, E_{dc}). The ratio between E_m and I_m is equal to the reciprocal of the slope of the combined characteristic of the diode and the resistor in the vicinity of the operating point, as shown in Figure 6.9(b). In other words, the equivalent resistance seen by the ac component is

$$\frac{E_m}{I_m} = \frac{dv}{di}\bigg|_{at\,Q} = r_{ac} \tag{6.7}$$

This resistance is made up of two components, the LTI resistance R and the reciprocal of the slope of the diode characteristic at its operating point Q'. In other words,

$$r_{ac} = R + r_d \tag{6.8}$$

where

$$r_d = \frac{dv_D}{di}\bigg|_{at\,Q'} \tag{6.9}$$

This last quantity is known as the *dynamic*, the *small-signal*, or the *incremental resistance* of the diode. In many small-signal applications, the diode may be replaced by its dynamic resistance.

EXAMPLE 2 The dynamic resistance of the diode whose characteristic is given by (6.2) is

$$r_d = \frac{dv_D}{di} = \frac{0.02569 \times 10^5}{I \times 10^5 + 1}$$

At the operating point $I = 0.077$ A, we have

$$r_d = \tfrac{2569}{7701} = 0.334 \; \Omega$$

EXAMPLE 3 In the circuit of Figure 6.10(a). $e(t) = 1.5 + 0.02 \sin 10^4 t$. The diode characteristic is given in Figure 6.10(b). Find $e_o(t)$.

SOLUTION Since the capacitor is open circuit to dc, we can find the quiescent point of the diode by drawing a load line with its intersects at 1.5 V and 15 mA. The quiescent point is found graphically to be (7.5 mA, 0.75 V). At this point, we estimate r_d to be 40 Ω. The circuit for the ac

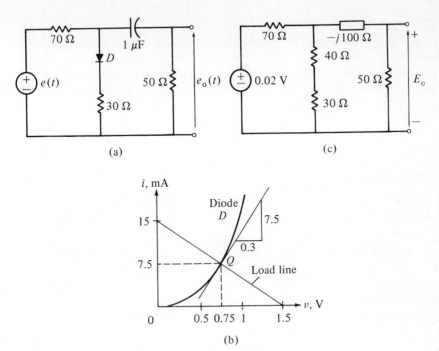

Figure 6.10

components is given in Figure 6.10(c). From this circuit we find that*

$E_o = 0.0038 \underline{/49.6°}$

Since $e_o(t)$ has no dc component, we have

$e_o(t) = 0.0038 \sin(10^4 t + 49.6°)$ V

6.4 Other diodes

There are many other two-terminal electronic devices that bear the name of diode. An account of any one of them would take up more space than we have available here. However, we shall briefly mention several of the more important devices, their characteristics, and some of their applications.

Vacuum diode   The vacuum diode is an electronic device with two electrodes encased in an evacuated enclosure. The cathode is an electron source usually made of thoriated tungsten or oxide-coated Konal metal. The latter type is found in most vacuum tubes and can be heated indirectly by an ac filament.

---

* Here the maximum values have been used for both the source-voltage and E_o complex amplitudes.

The anode (or plate) is simply a rugged plate, usually made of nickel or iron. Figure 6.11 shows the symbol for a vacuum diode. When the anode assumes a potential positive with respect to the cathode, electrons migrate from the cathode to the anode, resulting in a positive plate current i_P in the direction shown in Figure 6.11. Since the anode is not an emitter, normally a negative i_P is not possible.

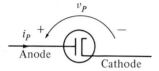

Figure 6.11 Symbol for a vacuum diode.

Assuming that the cathode is heated to a sufficiently high temperature to supply an adequate amount of electrons, i_P will increase as v_P is increased. The manner in which i_P increases with v_P is determined by what is known as the space-charge-limited condition. The term "space charge" refers to the electrons that are in transit from the cathode to the anode. These negative charges, to some degree, form a partial shield to prevent the plate from attracting more electrons away from the cathode. The only way the plate current can increase is for the plate to attract the electrons from the cathode at a faster rate and thereby reduce the electron density near the cathode. When a diode is space-charge-limited, its v-i relationship is governed by

$$i_P = G v_P^{3/2} \tag{6.10}$$

Equation (6.10) is known as the *Child-Langmuir law* or *three-halves-power law*. In an actual device, the power of the v_P term may deviate slightly from $\frac{3}{2}$. The proportionality constant G (the perveance) depends on the geometry of the device and is usually obtained experimentally. A typical space-charge-limited v-i curve is labeled T_4 in Figure 6.12.

On the other hand, if the cathode is a relatively poor emitter or its temperature is too low, the current will follow the three-halves-power law only up to the point at which all the emitted electrons are attracted by the plate. Beyond this point, any further increase in plate voltage cannot substantially increase the plate current. The diode is then said to be operating under temperature-limited conditions. This situation is illustrated by the curves labeled T_1 and T_2 in Figure 6.12. The curve labeled T_3 corresponds to a condition that is neither completely temperature-limited nor completely space-charge-limited.

The principles of circuit analysis involving vacuum diodes are exactly the same as the analysis of semiconductor diodes. The dynamic resistance of a vacuum diode is known as the *plate resistance*. For a diode whose v-i

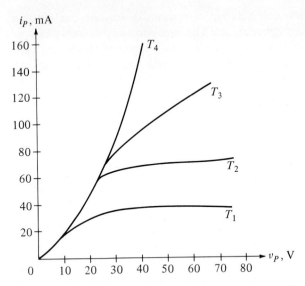

Figure 6.12 Typical vacuum diode characteristics at various cathode temperatures.

characteristic is given by (6.10), the plate resistance is given by

$$r_p = \frac{dv_P}{di_P} = \frac{2}{3}\frac{v_P}{i_P} \qquad (6.11)$$

Avalanche and Zener diodes When the reverse bias voltage across a *p-n* junction reaches a certain magnitude, a process somewhat similar to the breakdown of gases (spark) occurs. Electrons and holes travel with sufficient velocity to further ionize other atoms. Such a process can become self-sustaining and the voltage across the junction becomes virtually independent of the current. This phenomenon is known as the *avalanche breakdown* and the junction becomes an avalanche diode. The symbol for an avalanche diode and a sample characteristic are given in Figure 6.13.

When the concentration of doping is increased beyond the level at which avalanche breakdown may take place, a similar *v-i* characteristic due to an

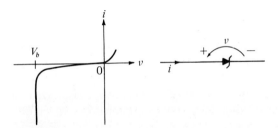

Figure 6.13 Symbol for an avalanche or Zener diode and a typical characteristic.

entirely different process—the field-emission breakdown—occurs. Such a junction is known as the Zener diode. The breakdown voltage V_b can be controlled by the amount of doping. These two types of diode are very similar in characteristics and applications. For practical purposes, they are seldom differentiated.

One of the main applications of the Zener diode is in a voltage-regulator circuit. A simple regulator circuit is shown in Figure 6.14. As long as e_s is

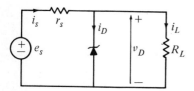

Figure 6.14 A voltage-regulator circuit using a Zener diode.

sufficiently higher than the breakdown voltage of the diode V_b, the voltage across the diode and the load resistor will remain essentially constant and equal to $|V_b|$. Since $|e_s|$ can fluctuate over a wide range, the difference between e_s and $|V_b|$ will be sustained by the $i_s r_s$ drop. As a result, v_D remains essentially constant. As the value of R_L varies, i_L will also vary. The variation in R_L will affect only i_D, not v_D.

Tunnel (Esaki) diode   When a narrow p-n junction exists between two highly doped p and n regions and when the junction is forward-biased, quantum tunneling takes place at low voltages. This process gives a large peak near the origin in the v-i characteristic of the diode. Figure 6.15 shows the symbol for a tunnel diode and a typical characteristic. The region with a negative

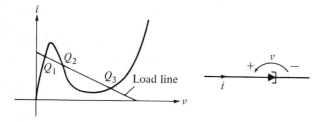

Figure 6.15 Symbol and typical characteristic of a tunnel diode.

slope indicates a negative dynamic resistance. A negative resistance is a power-supplying device and is used to provide amplification in certain amplifiers.

A tunnel diode is a voltage-controlled device. When a resistance of appropriate value is connected in series with it, the load line will intersect its characteristic at three points. This is shown in Figure 6.15, with the three intersects labeled Q_1, Q_2, and Q_3. Point Q_2 is not stable. Hence its operating point can be either Q_1 or Q_3. The fact that this device, so arranged, can have two stable operating points enables us to use the tunnel diode as a memory device. A tunnel diode switch has extremely high switching speeds compared with other devices.

6.5 The ideal diode and the piecewise linear model of a diode

The v-i characteristic of an ideal diode is made up of the negative half of the voltage axis and the positive half of the current axis, as shown in Figure 6.16. This characteristic simply means that, when v is negative, $i = 0$

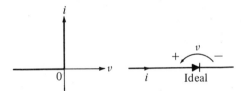

Figure 6.16 The ideal diode.

and, when i is positive, then $v = 0$. Hence such a device is a short circuit for any forward current and an open circuit when the voltage across it is negative.

The concept of an ideal diode is convenient either as the first-order approximation of an actual diode to aid us in visualizing the functions of various diodes in a circuit, or as an idealized device for constructing approximate piecewise linear models of nonlinear two-terminal elements.

Figure 6.17 illustrates how a number of idealized elements and their characteristics may be combined to give a *piecewise linear v-i* characteristic. The only rules used in the sequence of steps are the series and parallel combinations of NL elements outlined in Section 2.2. By processes similar to this, a variety of broken-line curves can be constructed to approximate the actual device characteristics. This is usually done to facilitate the analysis of circuits involving these devices. Also new nonlinear characteristics can be artificially created to perform certain circuit functions. This latter facet of circuit theory is known as *synthesis of nonlinear elements*.

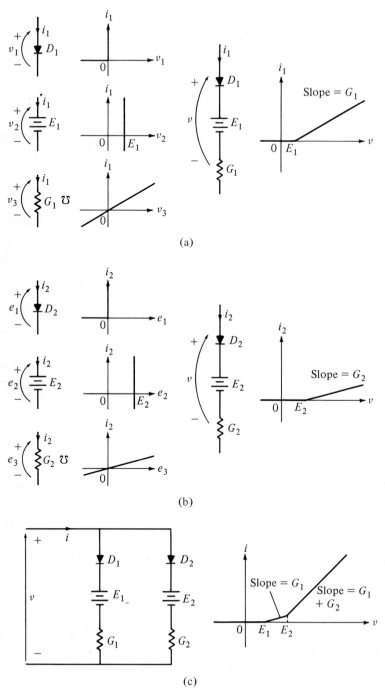

(a)

(b)

(c)

Figure 6.17 Combining basic elements to form a piecewise linear characteristic.

6.6 Practical diode circuits

In this section we shall describe a few commonly seen diode circuits. For simplicity, we assume that all diodes are ideal.

A half-wave rectifier In Figure 6.18, a sinusoidal voltage source is connected across a load resistor through a diode. When the source voltage is negative, no current·can flow through the diode. When the source voltage is positive, the diode will be conducting and the source is effectively connected directly across the resistor. Hence the output voltage $e_o(t)$ is as shown in Figure 6.18.

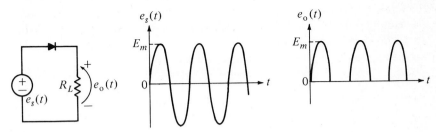

Figure 6.18 A half-wave rectifier circuit.

If $e_o(t)$ were actually applied directly across R_L as shown, then the effective value of the voltage across R_L would be $E_m/2$. However, in most rectifier applications, $e_o(t)$ is applied to a load resistor after passing through a filter that eliminates most of the ac content of $e_o(t)$. In that case, what appears across the load resistor is very nearly a dc voltage with a value that is equal to the average value of $e_o(t)$, which is

$$E_{dc} = \frac{1}{2\pi} \int_0^\pi E_m \sin t \, dt = \frac{E_m}{\pi} \tag{6.12}$$

A full-wave rectifier A bridge arrangement utilizing four diodes is shown in Figure 6.19. Whenever $e_s(t)$ in nonzero, the value of $e_s(t)$ appears across R_L. When $e_s(t)$ is negative, D_2 and D_3 conduct while the other two diodes are

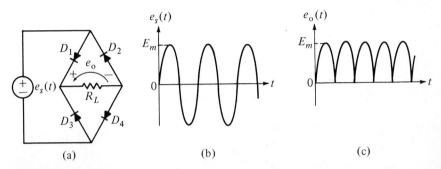

(a)   (b)   (c)

Figure 6.19 A full-wave rectifier circuit.

off. When $e_s(t)$ is positive, D_1 and D_4 conduct while the other two diodes are off. Hence the output voltage $e_o(t)$ is the same as $e_s(t)$ with its negative half reversed sign, as shown in Figure 6.19(c). In other words, $e_o(t) = |e_s(t)|$. If $e_o(t)$ appears directly across R_L, then the effective value of $e_o(t)$ is $E_m/\sqrt{2}$. If $e_o(t)$ is applied across R_L after filtering, then the dc voltage across R_L is

$$E_{dc} = \frac{1}{2\pi} \int_0^{2\pi} E_m |\sin t| \, dt = \frac{2E_m}{\pi} \tag{6.13}$$

A clipper In the circuit of Figure 6.20, we see that, whenever $e_s(t) > E$, the diode conducts, causing a voltage drop across the resitance R. During this conduction period, the output is equal to the battery voltage E. When $e_s(t) < E$, the diode is open and $e_o(t) = e_s(t)$. The result is a clipping effect on the applied $e_s(t)$. This is illustrated in Figure 6.20(b).

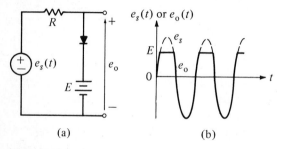

(a)   (b)

Figure 6.20 A clipper circuit.

When the diode of the clipper circuit of Figure 6.20(a) is reversed, the circuit will reverse-clip the applied voltage, as shown in Figure 6.21.

When two clippers, one of the type in Figure 6.20 and the other of the type in Figure 6.21, are connected in parallel, the circuit slices the portion of the applied voltage that lies between the two battery voltages. This circuit, depicted in Figure 6.22, is also known as a *slicer*.

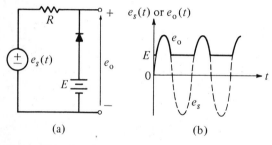

(a)   (b)

Figure 6.21 Another clipper circuit.

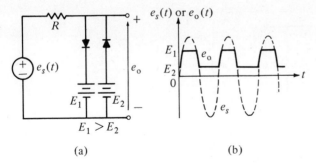

Figure 6.22 A slicer circuit.

A peak rectifier When a sinusoidal voltage is applied across a capacitor through a diode, as shown in Figure 6.23(a), the diode will conduct during the first positive portion of $e_s(t)$. If the resistance value of R is very small, the capacitor will follow the source voltage until it reaches its first peak. Thereafter the capacitor voltage remains constant because the voltage across the diode is never such as to cause it to conduct again. This is shown in Figure 6.23(b).

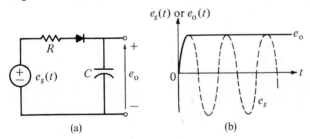

Figure 6.23 A peak-rectifier circuit.

A peak detector If a load resistor R_L is connected across a capacitor, as shown in Figure 6.24(a), the circuit works just like the peak rectifier during the first half of the first positive lobe of $e_s(t)$. After that peak, the diode is off. But now the capacitor will discharge through R_L as soon as the diode is off. The rate of discharge depends on the time constant $R_L C$. The capacitor will again be charged up to the peak value of $e_s(t)$ the next time $e_s(t) > e_o(t)$ occurs. The output $e_o(t)$ is shown in Figure 6.24(b).

   An important difference between a peak rectifier and a peak detector is that the $e_o(t)$ of a peak rectifier always retains the highest voltage reached previously. Ideally there is no way for the capacitor to lose its charge or voltage. On the other hand, the output voltage of a peak detector can rise as well as drop, if the peak of $e_s(t)$ should fluctuate. This property is used to obtain the envelope of an amplitude-modulated signal. The process is illustrated in Figure 6.24(c).

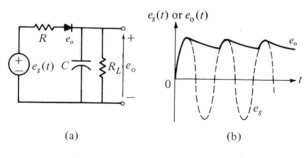

(a)   (b)

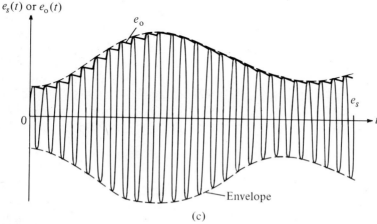

(c)

Figure 6.24 (a) A peak-detector circuit. (b) Input and output of (a) when the former is sinusoidal. (c) Input and output of (a) when the former is an amplitude-modulated sinusoid.

The half-wave rectifier, the full-wave rectifier, the peak rectifier, and the peak detector can all be used to derive a dc power supply from an ac source. The application of these circuits depends on the equivalent value of R_L. In a peak rectifier R_L is assumed to be infinity. Hence this circuit is used when no dc current is called for and the dc voltage is equal to the peak value of the ac supply. In a peak detector, R_L is large but finite. This circuit gives a dc voltage that is very nearly the peak value of the ac supply. To maintain this dc voltage level, the time constant $R_L C$ must be large compared with the period of the ac source. The half-wave and full-wave rectifiers are used chiefly in situations where the dc current or power, rather than the dc voltage, is the primary consideration. In these situations, the equivalent R_L is relatively low. Examples of these applications are audio equipment, storage battery chargers, and the power supply to electrolysis plants.

A clamper Figure 6.25(a) shows a diode clamper circuit. This is actually the same circuit as the peak rectifier of Figure 6.23(a) except that the output

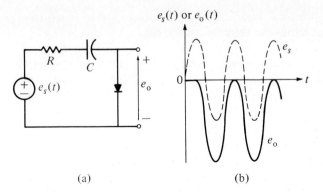

Figure 6.25 A clamper circuit.

voltage is taken across the diode instead of the capacitor. The output voltage can never be positive. In fact, it will have the same waveshape as the input, although their peaks differ by the capacitor voltage, which is equal to the maximum of $e_s(t)$. The input and output waveforms of a clamper are shown in Figure 6.25(b). Clamper circuits are used in television receivers and ac electronic voltmeters.

The OR circuit In binary logic circuits we are concerned only with whether a voltage is high or low. For instance, a voltage in the range between 0 and 0.5 V may be regarded as low, while one in the range between 4.0 and 5.0 V may be regarded as high.

An OR circuit, commonly known as an OR gate, has one output and two or more inputs. The output voltage is low if all input voltages are low. The output voltage is high if any one or several input voltages are high.

Figure 6.26 shows a diode OR circuit with three inputs. If we assume that the input voltages are unequal and at least one of them is positive, then all diodes will be off except the one that is connected to the most positive input voltage. With that diode on, all other diodes will be reverse-biased. Hence, in general, e_o will be equal to the input voltage that is positive and has the highest value. The circuit performs the function of an OR gate.

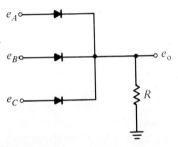

Figure 6.26 An OR circuit.

In a circuit using practical diodes, the output voltage will be equal to the highest input voltage minus the drop across the diode.

The AND circuit Another basic binary circuit is the AND gate. An AND gate has one output and two or more input voltages. The output voltage will be at a high level only if all input voltages are at a high level.

In Figure 6.27, $e_o = 0$ if any of the three input voltages is zero, since the output terminal will be grounded through the diode and the input terminal with the zero voltage. If all three input voltages are positive, then the diode connected to the lowest of the three voltages will be on and e_o will assume this lowest voltage. In other words, e_o is equal to the lowest of three positive input voltages. Hence, if *all* three input voltages are above a certain "high" level, then e_o will be high.

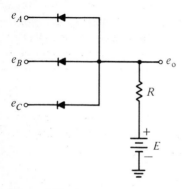

Figure 6.27 An AND circuit.

In an AND gate using junction diodes, E is higher than the high level of the two-level system. Hence, when all input voltages are high, e_o is equal to the high voltage plus the drop across the diode. Other logic circuits using diodes as well as other devices are discussed in Chapter 17.

6.7 Concluding remarks

This chapter covered four major topics: (1) A qualitative description of several diode devices. (2) Methods for the analysis of simple circuits involving diodes. These methods are useful in many engineering problems. However, we should point out that they are applicable only to simple circuits, such as series-parallel combinations. For more complex circuits, special analytical techniques are required, which are beyond the scope of this volume. (3) The superposition of an ac signal on top of a dc signal. Similar situations will arise frequently in Chapters 8, 9, and 10. (4) Several practical diode circuits.

These circuits were described with the assumption that the diodes were ideal. This helped us see how each device and circuit functions. Most actual circuits differ from the idealized ones only by the voltage drops across the diodes. In a semiconductor diode, this drop is usually a fraction of a volt.

We now turn to multiterminal devices and the analysis of circuits involving these devices. Many ideas and techniques developed in this chapter for circuits with two-terminal devices will be very helpful when dealing with multiterminal devices.

Problems

6.1 Calculate and plot the v-i characteristic of an ideal silicon p-n junction diode ($\eta = 1$) at room temperature (25°C). The reverse saturation current is 1 pA. Cover the voltage range from -0.2 to $+0.65$ V.

6.2 The reverse saturation current of a junction diode is temperature-dependent. It has been found that it roughly doubles for every increment of 10°C. In other words, if $I_0(T)$ at T_1 is I_{01}, then at any other temperature $I_0(T)$ is approximately given by

$$I_0(T) = 2^{0.1(T-T_1)} \times I_{01}$$

Calculate the factor by which the current will be multiplied when the temperature is increased from 25°C to 150°C. The voltage across the junction is 0.4 V.

6.3 The diode of Problem 6.1 is connected in series with a resistor of 20 Ω. Find the current, given that the series combination is connected to a 2-volt battery in such a way that the diode is forward-biased.

6.4 The v-i characteristic of the diode in Figure P6.4(a) is given in Figure P6.4(b). Find the current through the diode.

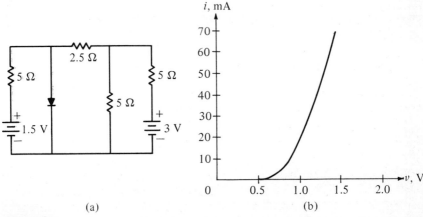

(a)

(b)

Figure P6.4

6.5 Each diode in the circuit of Figure P6.5 may be described by a cut-in voltage and the slope of a straight-line approximation in the forward-conducting region. For D_1, $V_y = 0.2$ V and the slope is 20 V/A. For D_2, $V_y = 0.6$ V and the slope is 15 V/A. Find the diode currents, given (a) $R = 10$ kΩ, (b) $R = 1$ kΩ.

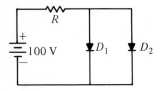

Figure P6.5

6.6 The i-v characteristic of each of the diodes in the circuit of Figure P6.6(a) is given in Figure 6.6(b). Sketch the I-V characteristic of the circuit.

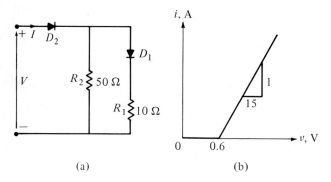

(a)   (b)

Figure P6.6

6.7 The diode of Figure P6.7 has a reverse saturation current of 1 μA and $\eta = 1.4$ at 25°C.
 (a) Find the quiescent current of the diode.
 (b) Find the ac component of the output voltage e_o.

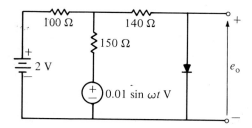

Figure P6.7

6.8 Repeat Problem 6.7 for the circuit of Figure P6.8.

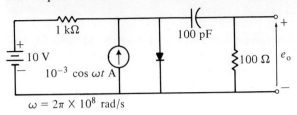

$\omega = 2\pi \times 10^8$ rad/s

Figure P6.8

6.9 The vacuum diode in the circuit of Figure P6.9 has a temperature-limited current of 0.1 mA and in the space-charge-limited region satisfies the three-halves-power law with $G = 0.02$ mA/$V^{3/2}$. Plot e_o versus e_i.

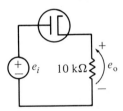

Figure P6.9

6.10 The i-v characteristic of the vacuum tube of Figure P6.10(a) is given in Figure 6.10(b). Find the i-e characteristic of the series combination.

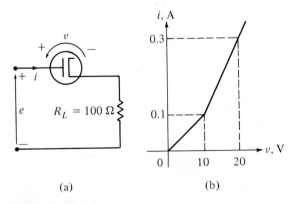

(a)   (b)

Figure P6.10

6.11 Find i in Problem 6.10 for $e = 25$ volts by constructing the load line.

6.12 In a certain space-charge-limited diode that follows the three-halves-power law, a current of 5 mA results from the application of 100 V. What is the maximum plate voltage that can be applied before the plate dissipation exceeds 16 watts?

6.13 The characteristic of the vacuum diode in Figure P6.13 (a) is given in Figure P6.13(b). Find the current in the diode.

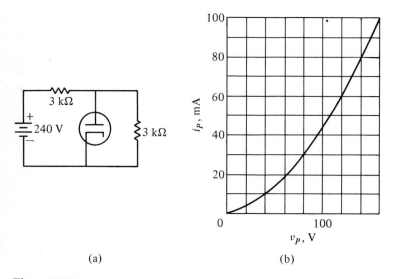

(a)   (b)

Figure P6.13

6.14 The Zener diode of Figure P6.14 has a breakdown voltage of 18 V. This voltage is constant as long as i_D falls between 200 mA and 2 A. Find the value of r_s such that the voltage across R_L is maintained for $22 < V_s < 27$.

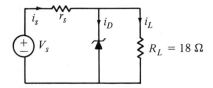

Figure P6.14

6.15 Sketch the *e-i* characteristic of the parallel combination of Figure P6.15.

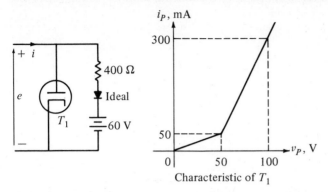

Characteristic of T_1

Figure P6.15

6.16 Sketch the voltage across the diode as a function of time in the circuit of Figure P6.16. What are the exact values of e_o at $t = \pi/4$ and $t = \pi/2$?

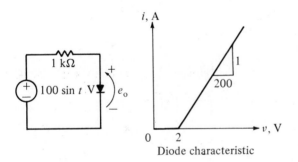

Diode characteristic

Figure P6.16

6.17 Sketch the *i-v* characteristic of the circuit of Figure P6.17.

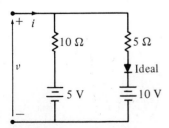

Figure P6.17

6.18 Design a circuit using resistors, batteries, and ideal diodes such that, when e_s of Figure P6.18 is applied to this circuit, another voltage e_o of the same figure will be produced.

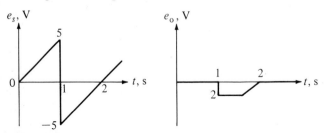

Figure P6.18

6.19 Sketch the waveform of the output voltage e_o in Figure P6.19.

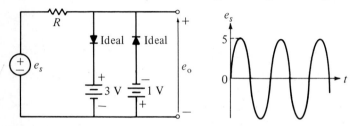

Figure P6.19

6.20 Sketch the three output voltage waveforms in the circuits of Figure P6.20.

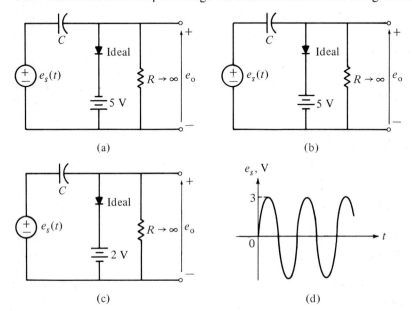

Figure P6.20

7 | TWO-PORT AND THREE-TERMINAL LINEAR NETWORKS

So far we have limited ourselves to networks that involve only two-terminal elements. Although controlled sources are four-terminal devices, they are actually special arrangements that include two-terminal sources whose strengths depend on other two-terminal quantities. As we shall soon see, certain other widely used electric devices are basically multiterminal devices. Whenever possible, we would prefer to use for these devices circuit models that contain two-terminal elements only. In some cases, this is not possible. Hence it is necessary for us to develop some techniques to deal with elements or component networks that have more than two terminals. We shall place most of our emphasis on two-port networks and three-terminal elements. The treatment of networks with more ports or terminals is similar to that of these limited cases.

Matrix notations are used frequently in this chapter, as well as in some subsequent chapters. It is assumed that you are somewhat familiar with these notations and terminology. If this is not the case, you will find a brief summary of matrix algebra in Appendix B. This appendix is organized so that it can also be used as a regular chapter for instruction.

7.1 Definitions of two-port parameters

A network or device that is seen to have two terminal pairs as points of access is known as a *two-terminal pair network*, or a *two-port*. The convention for a two-port is shown in Figure 7.1. There are four port quantities associated with each two-port, E_1, E_2, I_1, and I_2. These quantities are either dc values or time functions, when the two-port contains only memoryless elements, or complex amplitudes when the network is analyzed for its steady-state response with a complex frequency s, of which ac is a special case when $s = j\omega$.

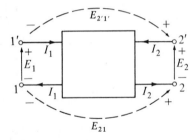

Figure 7.1 Notations in a two-port.

In order to formulate a general convention for describing the relationship among the four port quantities of a two-port, we may let any two of the four quantities be the independent variables. If we let, say, E_1 and I_2 be the independent variables, then we have the situation of Figure 7.2, in which

$$I_{1a} \propto E_1, \qquad I_{1b} \propto I_2$$
$$E_{2a} \propto E_1, \qquad E_{2b} \propto I_2 \tag{7.1}$$

or

$$I_{1a} = g_{11} E_1, \qquad I_{1b} = g_{12} I_2,$$
$$E_{2a} = g_{21} E_1, \qquad E_{2b} = g_{22} I_2 \tag{7.2}$$

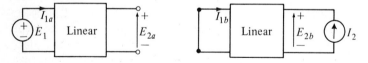

Figure 7.2 Arrangements used to find the g parameters of a two-port.

where the g's will depend on the network and its parameters. By the superposition theorem, we have the following relationship.

$$I_1 = g_{11} E_1 + g_{12} I_2, \qquad E_2 = g_{21} E_1 + g_{22} I_2 \tag{7.3}$$

Equation (7.3) is frequently written in matrix form, that is,

$$\begin{bmatrix} I_1 \\ E_2 \end{bmatrix} = \begin{bmatrix} g_{11} & g_{12} \\ g_{21} & g_{22} \end{bmatrix} \begin{bmatrix} E_1 \\ I_2 \end{bmatrix} \tag{7.4}$$

By choosing various pairs of port quantities as the independent variables, we can formulate five other pairs of equations similar to (7.3) or (7.4). These equations and their parameters are summarized in Table 7.1.

We get an interpretation of any one of the 24 parameters in Table 7.1 by investigating the defining equation associated with the matrix in which the parameter appears. For example, parameter z_{12} appears in the equation

$$E_1 = z_{11} I_1 + z_{12} I_2$$

Table **7.1** Two-port matrices

1 Impedance matrix $[z]$	**2** Admittance matrix $[y]$
$$\begin{bmatrix} E_1 \\ E_2 \end{bmatrix} = \begin{bmatrix} z_{11} & z_{12} \\ z_{21} & z_{22} \end{bmatrix} \begin{bmatrix} I_1 \\ I_2 \end{bmatrix}$$	$$\begin{bmatrix} I_1 \\ I_2 \end{bmatrix} = \begin{bmatrix} y_{11} & y_{12} \\ y_{21} & y_{22} \end{bmatrix} \begin{bmatrix} E_1 \\ E_2 \end{bmatrix}$$
3 Hybrid matrix $[h]$	**4** Hybrid matrix $[g]$
$$\begin{bmatrix} E_1 \\ I_2 \end{bmatrix} = \begin{bmatrix} h_{11} & h_{12} \\ h_{21} & h_{22} \end{bmatrix} \begin{bmatrix} I_1 \\ E_2 \end{bmatrix}$$	$$\begin{bmatrix} I_1 \\ E_2 \end{bmatrix} = \begin{bmatrix} g_{11} & g_{12} \\ g_{21} & g_{22} \end{bmatrix} \begin{bmatrix} E_1 \\ I_2 \end{bmatrix}$$
5 Transmission matrix $[F]$ (chain matrix)	**6** Reverse transmission matrix $[\mathscr{F}]$
$$\begin{bmatrix} E_1 \\ I_1 \end{bmatrix} = \begin{bmatrix} A & B \\ C & D \end{bmatrix} \begin{bmatrix} E_2 \\ -I_2 \end{bmatrix}$$	$$\begin{bmatrix} E_2 \\ I_2 \end{bmatrix} = \begin{bmatrix} \mathscr{A} & \mathscr{B} \\ \mathscr{C} & \mathscr{D} \end{bmatrix} \begin{bmatrix} E_1 \\ -I_1 \end{bmatrix}$$

If we set $I_1 = 0$, then z_{12} is the ratio of E_1 to I_2 or

$$z_{12} = \frac{E_1}{I_2}\bigg|_{I_1 = 0} \tag{7.5}$$

Hence, to obtain the z_{12} of a two-port, we open-circuit port 1 and excite port 2 with a source (voltage or current) and then compute the ratio of E_1 to I_2. One such arrangement is shown in Figure 7.3. Alternatively we could excite port 2 with a voltage source. However, this would require the computation of both E_1 and I_2 before z_{12} could be calculated. On the other hand, we cannot excite port 1 with either a voltage or a current source because we would then violate the assumption that I_1 is zero.

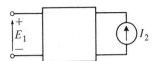

Figure 7.3 Arrangement used to find z_{12} of a two-port.

Similarly, if we want to obtain parameter D, the defining equation is

$$I_1 = CE_2 - DI_2$$

Then we have

$$D = -\frac{I_1}{I_2}\bigg|_{E_2 = 0} \tag{7.6}$$

This calls for the calculation of the short-circuit current at port 2 with port 1 excited, preferably by a current source, as shown in Figure 7.4. Again we

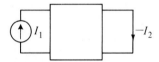

Figure 7.4 Arrangement used to find D of a two-port.

cannot excite port 2, because then we would have no assurance that $E_2 = 0$.

When a network is designated as a two-port, its port quantities are some-times not indicated on the diagram and they are automatically assumed to have the directions shown in Figure 7.1. In other words, unless otherwise marked, the left port is port 1 and the right port is port 2; the port voltages are from the lower terminal to the upper terminal; and the positive port currents enter the upper terminal.

EXAMPLE 1   Suppose we desire to obtain the two-port parameter B of the network in Figure 7.5. From matrix 5 of Table 7.1, we have

$$B = -\frac{E_1}{I_2}\bigg|_{E_2=0}$$

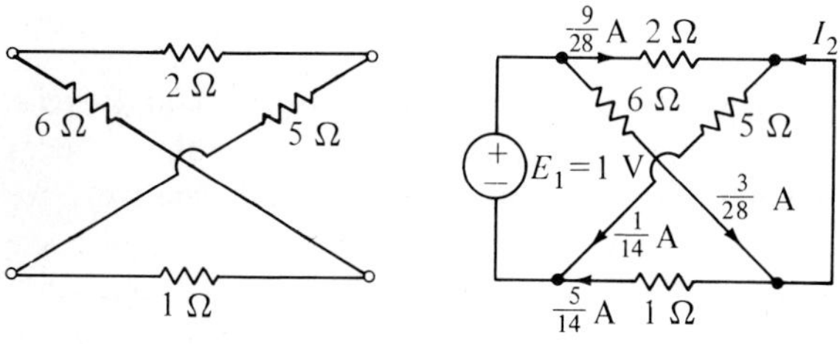

(a)

(b)

Figure 7.5

We can now excite the two-port with a voltage source at port 1 and calculate I_2 with port 2 shorted, as shown in Figure 7.5(b). We may further let $E_1 = 1$. Analysis of Figure 7.5(b) yields

$$I_2 = -\tfrac{1}{4}$$

Thus

$$B = -\frac{1}{I_2}\bigg|_{E_1=1,\,E_2=0} = 4\,\Omega$$

EXAMPLE 2   Suppose we wish to find the $[z]$ matrix of the two-port of Figure 7.6(a), which is the equivalent circuit of a voltage amplifier.* Parameter A_0 is the open-circuit voltage gain, R_i is the input resistance, and R_o the

---

* This amplifier circuit is quite frequently represented by the symbol of Figure 7.6(b). The input resistance R_i and the output resistance R_o are implied.

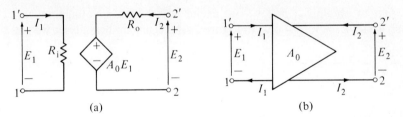

Figure 7.6 Equivalent circuit of and symbol for a differential-input, differential-output amplifier.

output resistance. Clearly

$$E_1 = R_i I_1 \tag{7.7}$$

$$E_2 - A_0 E_1 = I_2 R_o \tag{7.8}$$

Substituting (7.7) into (7.8) gives

$$E_2 = A_0 R_i I_1 + R_o I_2 \tag{7.9}$$

Equations (7.7) and (7.9) can be combined into the matrix equation

$$\begin{bmatrix} E_1 \\ E_2 \end{bmatrix} = \begin{bmatrix} R_i & 0 \\ A_0 R_i & R_o \end{bmatrix} \begin{bmatrix} I_1 \\ I_2 \end{bmatrix} \tag{7.10}$$

Comparison of (7.10) with the definition of the $[z]$ matrix in Table 7.1 gives

$$[z] = \begin{bmatrix} R_i & 0 \\ A_0 R_i & R_o \end{bmatrix} \tag{7.11}$$

The elements of the $[z]$ matrix of (7.11) can also be obtained individually, of course.

EXAMPLE 3 Figure 7.7(a) shows a low-frequency, small-signal circuit model of a junction transistor. It is desired to find the $[y]$ matrix of the circuit when it is used as a two-port.

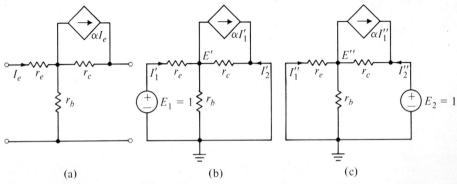

Figure 7.7 (a) The equivalent circuit of a transistor for small-signal ac analysis. (b) Arrangement used to evaluate y_{11} and y_{21} of (a). (c) Arrangement used to evaluate y_{12} and y_{22} of (a).

In order to obtain y_{11} and y_{21} we excite port 1 with a voltage source. Further, we let $E_1 = 1$, as shown in Figure 7.7(b). Using node analysis, we get

$$\frac{E'-1}{r_e} + \frac{E'}{r_b} + \frac{E'}{r_c} + \frac{\alpha(1-E')}{r_e} = 0$$

$$E' = \frac{(1-\alpha)/r_e}{(1/r_b)+(1/r_c)+[(1-\alpha)/r_e]} = \frac{(1-\alpha)r_b r_c}{r_e(r_b+r_c)+(1-\alpha)r_b r_c} = \frac{(1-\alpha)r_b r_c}{\Delta}$$

$$y_{11} = I_1' = \frac{1-E'}{r_e} = \frac{r_b+r_c}{\Delta} \qquad (7.12)$$

$$y_{21} = I_2' = -\frac{E'}{r_c} - \alpha I_1' = \frac{-r_b-\alpha r_c}{\Delta} \qquad (7.13)$$

To obtain y_{22} and y_{12}, we use the setup of Figure 7.7(c), with $E_2 = 1$. Again using node analysis, we have

$$\frac{E''}{r_e} + \frac{E''}{r_b} + \frac{E''-1}{r_c} - \frac{\alpha E''}{r_e} = 0$$

which gives

$$E'' = \frac{r_b r_e}{\Delta}$$

$$y_{12} = I_1'' = -\frac{E''}{r_e} = -\frac{r_b}{\Delta} \qquad (7.14)$$

$$y_{22} = I_2'' = \frac{1-E''}{r_c} - \alpha I_1'' = \frac{r_b+r_e}{\Delta} \qquad (7.15)$$

To summarize, the admittance matrix of the network of Figure 7.7(a) is

$$[y] = \frac{1}{\Delta} \begin{bmatrix} r_b+r_c & -r_b \\ -r_b-\alpha r_c & r_b+r_e \end{bmatrix} \qquad (7.16)$$

where $\Delta = r_e(r_b+r_c)+(1-\alpha)r_b r_c$.

EXAMPLE 4 Find the h parameters of the two-port of Figure 7.8 at 1 MHz.

SOLUTION Referring to Table 7.1 to find h_{11}, we leave port 2 short-circuited and evaluate the impedance seen at port 1.

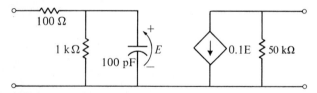

Figure 7.8

$$h_{11} = \frac{E_1}{I_1}\bigg|_{E_2=0} = 100 + \frac{1}{10^{-3}+j2\pi \times 10^6 \times 10^{-10}}$$

$$= 100 + \frac{10^3}{1+j0.6283} = 817.0 - j450.5\ \Omega$$

To find h_{12}, we leave port 1 open and find the voltage ratio between port 1 and port 2. We readily see that

$$h_{12} = \frac{E_1}{E_2}\bigg|_{I_1=0} = 0$$

To find h_{21}, we short-circuit port 2 and find the current ratio between port 2 and port 1, or

$$h_{21} = \frac{I_2}{I_1}\bigg|_{E_2=0} = \frac{0.1}{10^{-3}+j2\pi \times 10^6 \times 10^{-10}}$$

$$= \frac{100}{1+j0.6283} = 71.7 - j45.05$$

To find h_{22}, we short-circuit port 1 and evaluate the admittance seen at port 2. Since $E_1 = 0$, $I_1 = 0$, and $E = 0$, we have

$$h_{22} = \frac{I_2}{E_2}\bigg|_{I_1=0} = \frac{1}{50\ \text{k}} = 2 \times 10^{-5}\ \mho$$

7.2   Three-terminal and four-terminal two-ports

In Figure 7.1, no special requirement is imposed on the four terminals of the network other than that they are grouped into two pairs. One of the implications of this requirement is that the current flowing into terminal 1' (or 2') must be the same as the current flowing out of terminal 1 (or 2). But there are two other voltages present—$E_{2'1'}$ and E_{21}. Our two-port formulation says nothing about these two voltages. When we speak of a network as being a two-port, either we have no control over these voltages or they are of no interest to the problem at hand. Hence we should make no assumption regarding them based on our knowledge of the two-port alone. (Of course, by KVL, $E_1 + E_{2'1'} - E_2 - E_{21} = 0$ must always be satisfied regardless of how the two-port is used.)

For a given four-terminal network, a number of two-ports can be formed, depending on how the terminals are grouped in pairs. For example, if we take the network of Figure 7.5(a) and rearrange its terminals as shown in Figure 7.9(a), which is equivalent to Figure 7.9(b), a completely new two-port is formed. Unless we know the internal structure of a network, there is

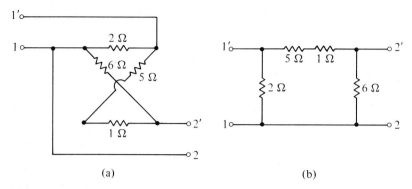

(a)   (b)

Figure 7.9 A different pairing of the terminals of the network of Figure 7.5, resulting in an entirely different two-port.

generally no simple relationship among the two-port parameters when their terminals are regrouped.

A special class of two-ports are those whose ports share a common terminal, for example, those of Figures 7.7 and 7.9. These are actually three-terminal networks adapted to the more general two-port formalism. In these examples, $E_{21} = 0$ and $E_{2'1'} = E_2 - E_1$. As soon as E_1 and E_2 are known, there can be no doubt as to what $E_{2'1'}$ is. In fact, as we shall see later, once we know the two-port parameters of a three-terminal two-port, the network is completely defined electrically. To emphasize the fact that a two-port is three-terminal, the representations of Figure 7.10 are frequently used.

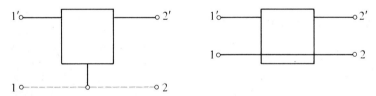

Figure 7.10 Three-terminal two-ports.

To study how a three-terminal two-port differs from a four-terminal one, first let us look again at the equivalent amplifier circuit of Figure 7.6(a). The two branches of the circuit are entirely separated from each other. In addition to E_1 and E_2, either E_{21} or $E_{2'1'}$ is completely arbitrary as far as the two-port is concerned. This is a *differential-input to differential-output* amplifier.

The amplifier equivalent circuits of Figure 7.11(a) and (b) have the same two-port parameters as the amplifier circuit of Figure 7.6. But these three networks are obviously different. The amplifier of Figure 7.11(a) is a *non-inverting amplifier* because the voltages at the two ports are in phase with

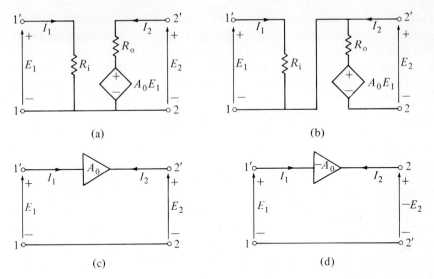

Figure 7.11 (a) Equivalent circuit of a noninverting amplifier. (b) Equivalent circuit of an inverting amplifier. (c) Symbol for a noninverting amplifier. (d) Symbol for an inverting amplifier.

respect to the common terminal. The amplifier of Figure 7.11(b) is an *inverting amplifier* because the polarities of the voltages at the two ports are opposite to each other with respect to the common terminal.*

7.3 Relationships among two-port parameters

When a network has only one port, its electric property is relatively easy to describe. There are only two electric quantities associated with the network—the voltage and the current. If we know either the admittance or the impedance of a one-port, then its external property is completely defined. Furthermore, once either of these two quantities is known, the other is readily obtained. Whether we choose to use the admittance or the impedance of a one-port will depend on the particular problem. For example, if we use node analysis, then we would prefer to use admittances.

The situation with two-ports is analogous. However, since there are four port quantities associated with a two-port, it takes four parameters, or a 2×2 matrix, to characterize it. And there are six possible descriptions for every two-port. The question naturally arises as to which of the six matrices should we use for a given two-port.

In theory, it does not matter which of the six matrices is used to describe a two-port, as long as the matrix exists. As we shall soon see, a one-to-one

---

* Noninverting and inverting amplifiers are frequently represented by the symbols of Figure 7.11(c) and (d), respectively. Unless otherwise indicated, $R_i = \infty$ and $R_o = 0$.

correspondence exists between any two matrices. For practical as well as historical reasons, certain matrices are more commonly used in certain areas. For example, the transmission or chain matrix $[F]$ is most often used for systems in which two-ports are cascaded, that is, the output of one two-port is connected directly to the input of the next two-port, such as repeater amplifiers, transmission lines, and so on. This also explains why the minus sign is associated with I_2 in part 5 of Table 7.1. This current $(-I_2)$ is actually the current leaving the top terminal of port 2 and is therefore equal to the current entering the top terminal of port 1 of the next two-port.

The $[y]$ and the $[z]$ matrices are the most basic two-port matrices. They are the direct extensions of the driving-point admittances and impedances of one-ports, and are used in most derivations of basic theorems and theoretical developments, particularly for networks containing resistances, capacitors, and inductances only. The $[h]$ matrix is used widely in transistor circuit analysis. This is primarily because these parameters are most easily measured for transistors. The $[g]$ and the $[\mathscr{F}]$ matrix are rarely used except in very unusual situations.

If any one of the six matrices for a two-port is given, any other matrix (if it exists) can be found simply by manipulating the variables until they appear in the form corresponding to the new matrix. Then the parameters of the new matrix are readily identified. For example, suppose we have

$$E_1 = z_{11}I_1 + z_{12}I_2, \qquad E_2 = z_{21}I_1 + z_{22}I_2 \tag{7.17}$$

and we want to obtain the hybrid matrix $[h]$ for this network. From the second equation of (7.17) we have

$$I_2 = -\frac{z_{21}}{z_{22}}I_1 + \frac{1}{z_{22}}E_2 \tag{7.18}$$

Substituting (7.18) into the first equation of (7.17) yields

$$E_1 = \left[z_{11} - \frac{z_{12}z_{21}}{z_{22}}\right]I_1 + \frac{z_{12}}{z_{22}}E_2$$

$$= \frac{|z|}{z_{22}}I_1 + \frac{z_{12}}{z_{22}}E_2 \tag{7.19}$$

where $|z| = z_{11}z_{22} - z_{12}z_{21}$ is the determinant of the $[z]$ matrix. Comparison of (7.18) and (7.19) with the defining equation of the $[h]$ matrix in Table 7.1 gives

$$\begin{bmatrix} h_{11} & h_{21} \\ h_{21} & h_{22} \end{bmatrix} = \begin{bmatrix} \dfrac{|z|}{z_{22}} & \dfrac{z_{12}}{z_{22}} \\ -\dfrac{z_{21}}{z_{22}} & \dfrac{1}{z_{22}} \end{bmatrix} \tag{7.20}$$

From (7.20) we easily see that, if $z_{22} = 0$ for a two-port, then the two-port does not have an $[h]$ matrix.

Table 7.2 Conversion of two-port parameters

	$[z]$		$[y]$		$[g]$		$[h]$		$[F]$		$[\mathcal{F}]$	
$[z]$	z_{11}	z_{12}	$\frac{y_{22}}{\lvert y\rvert}$	$-\frac{y_{12}}{\lvert y\rvert}$	$\frac{1}{g_{11}}$	$-\frac{g_{12}}{g_{11}}$	$\frac{\lvert h\rvert}{h_{22}}$	$\frac{h_{12}}{h_{22}}$	$\frac{A}{C}$	$\frac{\lvert F\rvert}{C}$	$\frac{\mathcal{D}}{\mathcal{C}}$	$\frac{1}{\mathcal{C}}$
	z_{21}	z_{22}	$-\frac{y_{21}}{\lvert y\rvert}$	$\frac{y_{11}}{\lvert y\rvert}$	$\frac{g_{21}}{g_{11}}$	$\frac{\lvert g\rvert}{g_{11}}$	$-\frac{h_{21}}{h_{22}}$	$\frac{1}{h_{22}}$	$\frac{1}{C}$	$\frac{D}{C}$	$\frac{\lvert\mathcal{F}\rvert}{\mathcal{C}}$	$\frac{\mathcal{A}}{\mathcal{C}}$
$[y]$	$\frac{z_{22}}{\lvert z\rvert}$	$-\frac{z_{12}}{\lvert z\rvert}$	y_{11}	y_{12}	$\frac{\lvert g\rvert}{g_{22}}$	$\frac{g_{12}}{g_{22}}$	$\frac{1}{h_{11}}$	$-\frac{h_{12}}{h_{11}}$	$\frac{D}{B}$	$-\frac{\lvert F\rvert}{B}$	$\frac{\mathcal{A}}{\mathcal{B}}$	$-\frac{1}{\mathcal{B}}$
	$-\frac{z_{21}}{\lvert z\rvert}$	$\frac{z_{11}}{\lvert z\rvert}$	y_{21}	y_{22}	$-\frac{g_{21}}{g_{22}}$	$\frac{1}{g_{22}}$	$\frac{h_{21}}{h_{11}}$	$\frac{\lvert h\rvert}{h_{11}}$	$-\frac{1}{B}$	$\frac{A}{B}$	$-\frac{\lvert\mathcal{F}\rvert}{\mathcal{B}}$	$\frac{\mathcal{D}}{\mathcal{B}}$
$[g]$	$\frac{1}{z_{11}}$	$-\frac{z_{12}}{z_{11}}$	$\frac{\lvert y\rvert}{y_{22}}$	$\frac{y_{12}}{y_{22}}$	g_{11}	g_{12}	$\frac{h_{22}}{\lvert h\rvert}$	$-\frac{h_{12}}{\lvert h\rvert}$	$\frac{C}{A}$	$-\frac{\lvert F\rvert}{A}$	$\frac{\mathcal{C}}{\mathcal{D}}$	$-\frac{1}{\mathcal{D}}$
	$\frac{z_{21}}{z_{11}}$	$\frac{\lvert z\rvert}{z_{11}}$	$-\frac{y_{21}}{y_{22}}$	$\frac{1}{y_{22}}$	g_{21}	g_{22}	$-\frac{h_{21}}{\lvert h\rvert}$	$\frac{h_{11}}{\lvert h\rvert}$	$\frac{1}{A}$	$\frac{B}{A}$	$\frac{\lvert\mathcal{F}\rvert}{\mathcal{D}}$	$\frac{\mathcal{B}}{\mathcal{D}}$
$[h]$	$\frac{\lvert z\rvert}{z_{22}}$	$\frac{z_{12}}{z_{22}}$	$\frac{1}{y_{11}}$	$-\frac{y_{12}}{y_{11}}$	$\frac{g_{22}}{\lvert g\rvert}$	$-\frac{g_{12}}{\lvert g\rvert}$	h_{11}	h_{12}	$\frac{B}{D}$	$\frac{\lvert F\rvert}{D}$	$\frac{\mathcal{B}}{\mathcal{A}}$	$\frac{1}{\mathcal{A}}$
	$-\frac{z_{21}}{z_{22}}$	$\frac{1}{z_{22}}$	$\frac{y_{21}}{y_{11}}$	$\frac{\lvert y\rvert}{y_{11}}$	$-\frac{g_{21}}{\lvert g\rvert}$	$\frac{g_{11}}{\lvert g\rvert}$	h_{21}	h_{22}	$-\frac{1}{D}$	$\frac{C}{D}$	$-\frac{\lvert\mathcal{F}\rvert}{\mathcal{A}}$	$\frac{\mathcal{C}}{\mathcal{A}}$
$[F]$	$\frac{z_{11}}{z_{21}}$	$\frac{\lvert z\rvert}{z_{21}}$	$-\frac{y_{22}}{y_{21}}$	$-\frac{1}{y_{21}}$	$\frac{1}{g_{21}}$	$\frac{g_{22}}{g_{21}}$	$-\frac{\lvert h\rvert}{h_{21}}$	$-\frac{h_{11}}{h_{21}}$	A	B	$\frac{\mathcal{D}}{\lvert\mathcal{F}\rvert}$	$\frac{\mathcal{B}}{\lvert\mathcal{F}\rvert}$
	$\frac{1}{z_{21}}$	$\frac{z_{22}}{z_{21}}$	$-\frac{\lvert y\rvert}{y_{21}}$	$-\frac{y_{11}}{y_{21}}$	$\frac{g_{11}}{g_{21}}$	$\frac{\lvert g\rvert}{g_{21}}$	$-\frac{h_{22}}{h_{21}}$	$-\frac{1}{h_{21}}$	C	D	$\frac{\mathcal{C}}{\lvert\mathcal{F}\rvert}$	$\frac{\mathcal{A}}{\lvert\mathcal{F}\rvert}$
$[\mathcal{F}]$	$\frac{z_{22}}{z_{12}}$	$\frac{\lvert z\rvert}{z_{12}}$	$-\frac{y_{11}}{y_{12}}$	$-\frac{1}{y_{12}}$	$-\frac{\lvert g\rvert}{g_{12}}$	$-\frac{g_{22}}{g_{12}}$	$\frac{1}{h_{12}}$	$\frac{h_{11}}{h_{12}}$	$\frac{D}{\lvert F\rvert}$	$\frac{B}{\lvert F\rvert}$	$\mathcal{A}$	$\mathcal{B}$
	$\frac{1}{z_{12}}$	$\frac{z_{11}}{z_{12}}$	$-\frac{\lvert y\rvert}{y_{12}}$	$-\frac{y_{22}}{y_{12}}$	$-\frac{g_{11}}{g_{12}}$	$-\frac{1}{g_{12}}$	$\frac{h_{22}}{h_{12}}$	$\frac{\lvert h\rvert}{h_{12}}$	$\frac{C}{\lvert F\rvert}$	$\frac{A}{\lvert F\rvert}$	$\mathcal{C}$	$\mathcal{D}$

Table 7.2 summarizes the relationships among the six matrices of a general two-port. You should learn to be able to derive any of these interrelationships. From Table 7.1 it should also be obvious that

$$\begin{bmatrix} z_{11} & z_{12} \\ z_{21} & z_{22} \end{bmatrix}\begin{bmatrix} y_{11} & y_{12} \\ y_{21} & y_{22} \end{bmatrix} = [U]$$

$$\begin{bmatrix} h_{11} & h_{12} \\ h_{21} & h_{22} \end{bmatrix}\begin{bmatrix} g_{11} & g_{12} \\ g_{21} & g_{22} \end{bmatrix} = [U] \tag{7.21}$$

$$\begin{bmatrix} A & \pm B \\ \pm C & D \end{bmatrix}\begin{bmatrix} \mathcal{A} & \mp\mathcal{B} \\ \mp\mathcal{C} & \mathcal{D} \end{bmatrix} = [U]$$

where $[U]$ is the identity or unit matrix. The two-port matrices that appear in the same equation in (7.21) are the inverse of each other. Hence we have

$$[z] = [y]^{-1}, \qquad [h] = [g]^{-1}$$

$$\begin{bmatrix} A & \pm B \\ \pm C & D \end{bmatrix} = \begin{bmatrix} \mathscr{A} & \mp \mathscr{B} \\ \mp \mathscr{C} & \mathscr{D} \end{bmatrix}^{-1}$$

(7.22)

7.4 Relationships in a loaded two-port

One of the most common applications of two-port parameters is the derivation of certain voltage-current relationships when the network is terminated in a load impedance at one of its ports. To be specific, let us consider the arrangement of Figure 7.12. One of the possible quantities of interest might be the input impedance

$$Z_i = \frac{E_1}{I_1}$$

Suppose we know the $[g]$ matrix of N; then we have

$$I_1 = g_{11} E_1 + g_{12} I_2, \qquad E_2 = g_{21} E_1 + g_{22} I_2$$

(7.23)

The load impedance places the constraint

$$E_2 = -I_2 Z_L$$

(7.24)

on E_2 and I_2. Substitution of (7.24) into the second equation of (7.23) gives

$$g_{21} E_1 + (g_{22} + Z_L) I_2 = 0$$

or

$$I_2 = -\frac{g_{21}}{g_{22} + Z_L} E_1$$

(7.25)

Substitution of (7.25) into the first equation of (7.23) gives

$$I_1 = g_{11} E_1 - \frac{g_{12} g_{21}}{g_{22} + Z_L} E_1$$

$$= \frac{g_{11} Z_L + |g|}{g_{22} + Z_L} E_1$$

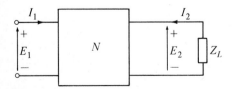

Figure 7.12 A loaded two-port.

Hence we have

$$Z_i = \frac{g_{22}+Z_L}{|g|+g_{11}Z_L} \tag{7.26}$$

When other two-port parameters of N are known, the procedure for finding Z_i is similar.

Table **7.3**

$$
\begin{array}{l}
Z_i = \dfrac{E_1}{I_1} = \dfrac{|z|+z_{11}Z_L}{z_{22}+Z_L} = \dfrac{y_{22}+Y_L}{|y|+y_{11}Y_L} = \dfrac{|h|+h_{11}Y_L}{h_{22}+Y_L} = \dfrac{g_{22}+Z_L}{|g|+g_{11}Z_L} = \dfrac{AZ_L+B}{CZ_L+D} = \dfrac{\mathcal{B}+\mathcal{D}Z_L}{\mathcal{A}+\mathcal{C}Z_L} \\[3mm]
A_v = \dfrac{E_2}{E_1} = \dfrac{z_{21}Z_L}{|z|+z_{11}Z_L} = \dfrac{-y_{21}}{y_{22}+Y_L} = \dfrac{-h_{21}}{|h|+h_{11}Y_L} = \dfrac{g_{21}Z_L}{g_{22}+Z_L} = \dfrac{Z_L}{B+AZ_L} = \dfrac{|\mathcal{F}|Z_L}{\mathcal{B}+\mathcal{D}Z_L} \\[3mm]
A_i = \dfrac{I_2}{I_1} = \dfrac{-z_{21}}{z_{22}+Z_L} = \dfrac{y_{21}Y_L}{|y|+y_{11}Y_L} = \dfrac{h_{21}Y_L}{h_{22}+Y_L} = \dfrac{-g_{21}}{|g|+g_{11}Z_L} = \dfrac{-1}{D+CZ_L} = \dfrac{-|\mathcal{F}|}{\mathcal{A}+\mathcal{C}Z_L} \\[3mm]
Z_{21} = \dfrac{E_2}{I_1} = \dfrac{z_{21}Z_L}{z_{22}+Z_L} = \dfrac{-y_{21}}{|y|+y_{11}Y_L} = \dfrac{-h_{21}}{h_{22}+Y_L} = \dfrac{g_{21}Z_L}{|g|+g_{11}Z_L} = \dfrac{Z_L}{D+CZ_L} = \dfrac{|\mathcal{F}|Z_L}{\mathcal{A}+\mathcal{C}Z_L} \\[3mm]
Y_{21} = \dfrac{I_2}{E_1} = \dfrac{-z_{21}}{|z|+z_{11}Z_L} = \dfrac{y_{21}Y_L}{y_{22}+Y_L} = \dfrac{h_{21}Y_L}{|h|+h_{11}Y_L} = \dfrac{-g_{21}}{g_{22}+Z_L} = \dfrac{-1}{B+AZ_L} = \dfrac{-|\mathcal{F}|}{\mathcal{B}+\mathcal{D}Z_L}
\end{array}
$$

Table 7.3 summarizes five different quantities that may be of interest in a loaded two-port. The quantity Z_i is the equivalent impedance seen at port 1. The quantity A_v is the ratio of the output voltage to the input voltage and is known as the *voltage ratio*, the *voltage-transfer function*, or the *voltage gain*. The quantity A_i is the ratio of the output current to the input current and is known as the *current ratio*, the *current-transfer function*, or the *current gain*. The quantity Z_{21}, which is the ratio of the output voltage to the input current, has the dimension of an impedance. Since the voltage and the current occur in two different parts of the network, Z_{21} is known as the *transfer impedance*. Similarly, the quantity Y_{21}, which is the ratio of the output current to the input voltage, is known as the *transfer admittance*. In Table 7.3, these five quantities are expressed in terms of all six sets of two-port parameters. You should be able to derive any one of these relationships.

7.5 Circuit models of two-ports with known parameters

Sometimes it is more convenient to replace a two-port whose parameter matrix is known by a circuit that includes controlled sources and one-ports (two-terminal elements) only. Once we have made this replacement, we can treat the branches in the equivalent two-port in the ordinary manner. Eight such equivalent circuits are shown in Figure 7.13.

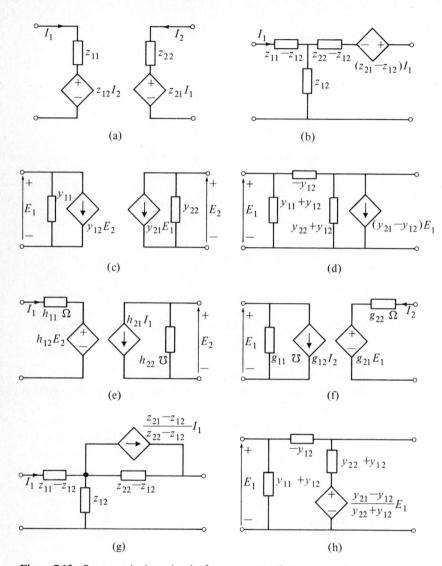

Figure 7.13 Some equivalent circuits for two-ports whose parameters are known.

7.6 The mutual inductance and the transformer

A two-terminal inductance is an element in which

$$Li = N\phi = \Phi \tag{7.27}$$

$$v = N\frac{d\phi}{dt} = \frac{d\Phi}{dt}\left(= L\frac{di}{dt}\right) \tag{7.28}$$

Here we assume that the element is self-contained and the three quantities i, v, and ϕ exist simultaneously. A current i is accompanied by a flux ϕ. Any change in i or ϕ is accompanied by a voltage, according to (7.28). Such an inductance is called a *self-inductance*.

Faraday's law (7.28) is not limited to a self-inductance. Any time the magnetic flux in a coil changes, a voltage accompanies it. When we put two coils near each other, each flux will produce a voltage in the other coil. This interaction is known as the *magnetic coupling*.

Figure 7.14 represents a pair of magnetically coupled coils. The magnetic flux that accompanies i_1 is*

$$\phi_1 = \phi_{11} + \phi_{21} \tag{7.29}$$

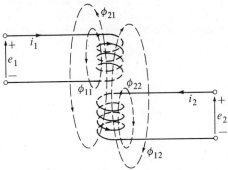

Figure 7.14   Schematic representation of the magnetic coupling between two coils.

in which ϕ_{11} links coil 1 only, while ϕ_{21} links both coils. Both ϕ_{11} and ϕ_{21} (hence ϕ_1) are proportional to i_1. The self-inductance of the first coil is

$$L_1 = \frac{N_1 \phi_1}{i_1} \tag{7.30}$$

Likewise the magnetic flux that accompanies i_2 is

$$\phi_2 = \phi_{22} + \phi_{12} \tag{7.31}$$

in which ϕ_{22} links coil 2 only, while ϕ_{12} links both coils. Both ϕ_{22} and ϕ_{12} are proportional to i_2. The self-induction of the second coil is

$$L_2 = \frac{N_2 \phi_2}{i_2} \tag{7.32}$$

Faraday's law says that

$$e_1 = N_1 \frac{d}{dt}(\phi_1 + \phi_{12}) \tag{7.33}$$

* Here, as in Section 1.5, each flux is assumed to link all turns of the coil(s).

But

$$\frac{d\phi_{12}}{dt} \propto \frac{di_2}{dt} \tag{7.34}$$

or

$$N_1 \frac{d\phi_{12}}{dt} = M_{12} \frac{di_2}{dt} \tag{7.35}$$

Substituting (7.30) and (7.35) into (7.33), we get

$$e_1 = L_1 \frac{di_1}{dt} + M_{12} \frac{di_2}{dt} \tag{7.36}$$

The proportionality constant M_{12} relates the voltage induced in coil 1 to the current in coil 2. This constant is known as the *mutual inductance*.

In a similar fashion, the voltage induced in coil 2 may be expressed in terms of the currents in the two coils as

$$e_2 = M_{21} \frac{di_1}{dt} + L_2 \frac{di_2}{dt} \tag{7.37}$$

In any linear medium, $M_{12} = M_{21} = M$. Such a pair of magnetically coupled coils is represented by the symbol of Figure 7.15. Thus the coils of Figure

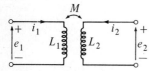

Figure 7.15 Symbol for two coupled inductances.

7.14 form a true two-port device that is unique. The relationships described in (7.36) and (7.37) form a two-port relationship that cannot be simulated by any combination of two-terminal inductances alone, except under special circumstances. One such circumstance occurs when the two-port of Figure 7.14 is made into a three-terminal one, as shown in Figure 7.16(a). Such a special coil is externally equivalent to the arrangement of two-terminal self-inductances shown in Figure 7.16(b).

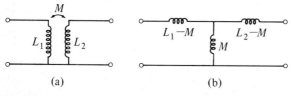

(a)　　　　　　　(b)

Figure 7.16 *T*-equivalent circuit of a pair of coupled coils with two terminals connected together.

In Figure 7.14, the directions of the fluxes produced by the two currents are the same, resulting in positive signs for the mutual terms. If one of the coils is physically turned end over end, the signs of the mutual terms must also be reversed. To identify this relative polarity, the dot convention is commonly used. This places a dot on one end of each of the coils, as shown in Figure 7.17. These dots must be so placed that, if the two currents (i_1 and

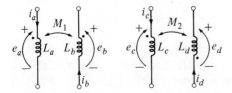

Figure 7.17 Dot convention for mutual inductances.

i_2) are either both entering or both leaving the dotted terminals of the coils, then the signs of the mutual terms are the same as the signs of the self-terms; if one current is entering and the other is leaving the dotted terminals, then the signs of the mutual terms are opposite to the signs of the self-terms. Thus, for the coils in Figure 7.17, we should have

$$e_a = L_a \frac{di_a}{dt} - M_1 \frac{di_b}{dt}, \qquad e_b = -L_b \frac{di_b}{dt} + M_1 \frac{di_a}{dt}$$

and

$$e_c = L_c \frac{di_c}{dt} + M_2 \frac{di_d}{dt}, \qquad e_d = -L_d \frac{di_d}{dt} - M_2 \frac{di_c}{dt}$$

EXAMPLE 5 Suppose we want to find the equivalent input inductance of the set of three magnetically coupled coils of Figure 7.18, whose mutual inductances are indicated there. The following KVL equations must hold:

$$e = 6 \frac{di}{dt} + 1 \frac{di_1}{dt} - 3 \frac{di_2}{dt} + 5 \frac{di_1}{dt} + 1 \frac{di}{dt} - 2 \frac{di_2}{dt}$$

$$e = 6 \frac{di}{dt} + 1 \frac{di_1}{dt} - 3 \frac{di_2}{dt} + 4 \frac{di_2}{dt} - 3 \frac{di}{dt} - 2 \frac{di_1}{dt}$$

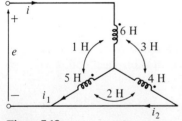

Figure 7.18

Also, of course,

$$i = i_1 + i_2$$

Solving for i from these three equations gives

$$e = \frac{48}{13}\frac{di}{dt}$$

Hence the equivalent inductance of Figure 7.18 is 48/13 henrys.

In ac analysis, it is sometimes more convenient to replace the effects of magnetic coupling by controlled sources. The controlled sources in Figure 7.19 take care of the magnetic coupling between the coils in Figure 7.17 branch for branch. We can verify this by checking the total voltage across

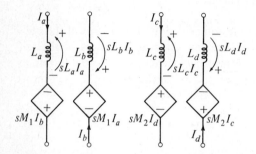

Figure 7.19 Controlled-source models of coupled coils.

each branch in both figures. Note that the directions of the controlled sources are *opposite* to the voltages caused by the self-inductances when the current directions are opposite with respect to the dots. They are in the *same direction* as the voltages caused by the self-inductances when the two currents are in the same direction with respect to the dots.

The impedance matrix of the two-ports of Figure 7.15 is

$$[z] = \begin{bmatrix} sL_1 & sM \\ sM & sL_2 \end{bmatrix} \tag{7.38}$$

The ratio

$$k = \frac{M}{\sqrt{L_1 L_2}} \tag{7.39}$$

is known as the *coefficient of coupling* and is a measure of how closely the two magnetic paths coincide with each other. In a physical coil, $k < 1$.

In a *unity-coupled coil*, $k = 1$. If we let

$$\frac{L_2}{L_1} = n^2 \tag{7.40}$$

then

$$M = nL_1 = \frac{1}{n}L_2 \tag{7.41}$$

Substituting (7.40) and (7.41) into (7.36) and (7.37), we get

$$e_1 = L_1\frac{di_1}{dt} + nL_1\frac{di_2}{dt} \tag{7.42}$$

$$e_2 = nL_1\frac{di_1}{dt} + n^2L_1\frac{di_2}{dt} \tag{7.43}$$

Equations (7.42) and (7.43) give

$$e_2 = ne_1 \tag{7.44}$$

Equation (7.44) is the direct consequence of the fact that the same flux links both coils. When this is true, the induced voltage in each coil is proportional to the number of turns in that coil. The ratio n is known as the *turns ratio*.

If, in addition to $k = 1$, we let $L_1 \to \infty$ and $L_2 \to \infty$, but hold (7.40) unchanged, then (7.42) and (7.43) also require that

$$i_2 = -\frac{i_1}{n} \tag{7.45}$$

Such a coupled coil is an *ideal transformer*. Its symbol is given in Figure 7.20. As its name implies, an ideal transformer is an idealized device much like an ideal diode. It is lossless since

$$e_1i_1 + e_2i_2 = 0 \tag{7.46}$$

must always hold. Alternatively, as we go from one side of an ideal transformer to the other, the voltage and the current are changed by the same factor, but in the opposite direction.

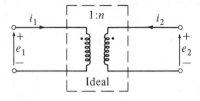

Figure 7.20   Symbol for the ideal transformer.

The $[z]$ and $[y]$ matrices of an ideal transformer are undefined. Its other matrices are

$$[g] = \begin{bmatrix} 0 & -n \\ n & 0 \end{bmatrix} \tag{7.47}$$

$$[h] = \begin{bmatrix} 0 & \dfrac{1}{n} \\[2ex] -\dfrac{1}{n} & 0 \end{bmatrix} \tag{7.48}$$

$$[F] = \begin{bmatrix} \dfrac{1}{n} & 0 \\[2ex] 0 & n \end{bmatrix} \tag{7.49}$$

In the preceding development, the turns ratio n may be either positive or negative. A change in the sign of n corresponds to the reversal of the terminals of one of the two ports. Also a change in the placement of one of the dots is equivalent to the reversal of the sign of n.

EXAMPLE 6   Find the input impedance Z_i of the circuit of Figure 7.21.

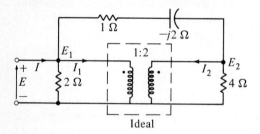

Figure 7.21

SOLUTION   Since

$$Z_i = \frac{E}{I} = E \Big|_{I=1}$$

we shall let $I = 1$ and find E. Using node analysis, we have

$$\frac{E_1}{2} + I_1 + \frac{E_1 - E_2}{1 - j2} = 1, \qquad \frac{E_2}{4} + I_2 + \frac{E_2 - E_1}{1 - j2} = 0$$

The ideal transformer requires that

$$E_2 = 2E_1 = 2E, \qquad \text{and} \qquad I_2 = -\frac{I_1}{2}$$

Substitution gives

$$\frac{E}{2} + I_1 - \frac{E}{1 - j2} = 1, \qquad \frac{E}{2} - \frac{I_1}{2} + \frac{E}{1 - j2} = 0$$

Elimination of I_1 gives

$$\frac{3}{2}E + \frac{E}{1-j2} = 1, \qquad E = \frac{1}{(3/2)+[1/(1-j2)]} = \frac{2-j4}{5-j6}$$

Hence

$$Z_i = 0.573 \underline{/-13.2°}\ \Omega$$

A real transformer can usually be represented accurately by an ideal transformer in conjunction with other basic two-terminal elements. For example, the circuit of Figure 7.22 is the usually accepted circuit model of an iron-core power transformer. Resistances R_1 and R_2 represent the resistances of the wires that make up the two windings. Resistance R_s represents the core loss. The combination of L_s and the ideal transformer is equivalent to a pair of unity-coupled coils, which represent the self- and mutual inductances resulting from the flux that links both coils. Inductances L_1 and L_2 are the equivalent series inductances due to fluxes that fail to link both coils and are known as *leakage inductances*.

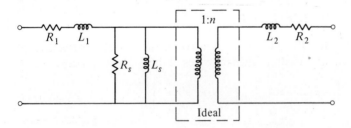

Figure 7.22   The equivalent circuit of a power transformer.

7.7   Interconnection of two-ports

Two-ports can be interconnected in several ways, so that certain matrices of the constituent networks combine very simply. These combinations can also be extended to more two-ports or to networks with more than two ports each. However, we shall deal here with the combination of only two two-ports. We shall denote the two individual two-ports by subscripts a and b, but the overall two-port will have no literal subscript.

Parallel-parallel combination   This combination is shown in Figure 7.23. The one-to-one ideal transformer is placed in the circuit to ensure that the two individual two-ports remain as two-ports (the currents entering and leaving the two terminals of the same port are the same). It may be located at any of the four ports of the network and only one such device is necessary.

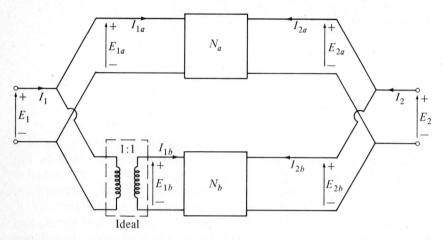

Figure 7.23 Parallel-parallel combination of two two-ports.

For such a combination,

$$E_1 = E_{1a} = E_{1b}, \qquad E_2 = E_{2a} = E_{2b}$$
$$I_1 = I_{1a} + I_{1b}, \qquad I_2 = I_{2a} + I_{2b}$$

(7.50)

It is easy to show that the admittance matrix of the parallel-parallel combination is the sum of the admittance matrices of the individual networks, or

$$\begin{bmatrix} y_{11} & y_{12} \\ y_{21} & y_{22} \end{bmatrix} = \begin{bmatrix} y_{11a} & y_{12a} \\ y_{21a} & y_{22a} \end{bmatrix} + \begin{bmatrix} y_{11b} & y_{12b} \\ y_{21b} & y_{22b} \end{bmatrix}$$

(7.51)

EXAMPLE 7 The two-port of Figure 7.24(a) is the parallel-parallel combination of the two two-ports of Figure 7.24, parts (b) and (c). For two-port N_a, we have

$$[y_a] = \begin{bmatrix} \dfrac{1}{R_f} & -\dfrac{1}{R_f} \\ -\dfrac{1}{R_f} & \dfrac{1}{R_f} \end{bmatrix}$$

(7.52)

For two-port N_b, from (7.11) we get

$$[y_b] = \begin{bmatrix} R_i & 0 \\ A_0 R_i & R_o \end{bmatrix}^{-1} = \begin{bmatrix} \dfrac{1}{R_i} & 0 \\ -\dfrac{A_0}{R_o} & \dfrac{1}{R_o} \end{bmatrix}$$

(7.53)

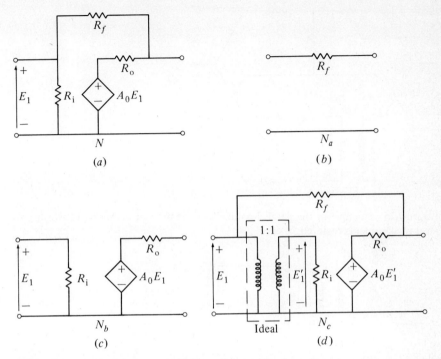

Figure 7.24 Example of the parallel-parallel combination of two two-ports.

Hence, for network N,

$$[y] = \begin{bmatrix} \dfrac{1}{R_f} + \dfrac{1}{R_i} & -\dfrac{1}{R_f} \\[3mm] -\dfrac{1}{R_f} - \dfrac{A_0}{R_o} & \dfrac{1}{R_f} + \dfrac{1}{R_o} \end{bmatrix} \qquad (7.54)$$

When we put N_a and N_b in the parallel-parallel combination according to Figure 7.23, the network of Figure 7.24(d) results. However, since the bottom terminals of the transformer are short-circuited, the ideal transformer can be eliminated altogether, resulting in the network of Figure 7.24(a). Figure 7.25 shows a different situation, in which the ideal transformer cannot be eliminated.

Series-series combination This combination is shown in Figure 7.26. For such a combination we have

$$E_1 = E_{1a} + E_{1b}, \qquad E_2 = E_{2a} + E_{2b}$$
$$I_1 = I_{1a} = I_{1b}, \qquad I_2 = I_{2a} = I_{2b} \qquad (7.55)$$

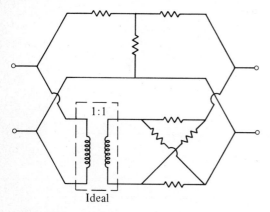

Figure 7.25 Example of the parallel-parallel combination of two-ports in which an ideal transformer is required.

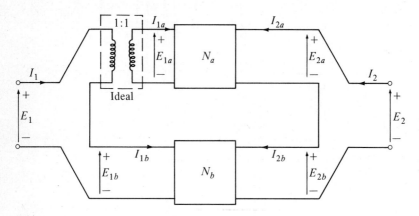

Figure 7.26 Series-series combination of two two-ports.

It is easy to show that

$$\begin{bmatrix} z_{11} & z_{12} \\ z_{21} & z_{22} \end{bmatrix} = \begin{bmatrix} z_{11a} & z_{12a} \\ z_{21a} & z_{22a} \end{bmatrix} + \begin{bmatrix} z_{11b} & z_{12b} \\ z_{21b} & z_{22b} \end{bmatrix} \tag{7.56}$$

Series-parallel combination   For the combination shown in Figure 7.27, we have

$$E_1 = E_{1a} + E_{1b}, \qquad E_2 = E_{2a} = E_{2b}$$
$$I_1 = I_{1a} = I_{1b}, \qquad I_2 = I_{2a} + I_{2b} \tag{7.57}$$

It is readily shown that

$$\begin{bmatrix} h_{11} & h_{12} \\ h_{21} & h_{22} \end{bmatrix} = \begin{bmatrix} h_{11a} & h_{12a} \\ h_{21a} & h_{22a} \end{bmatrix} + \begin{bmatrix} h_{11b} & h_{12b} \\ h_{21b} & h_{22b} \end{bmatrix} \tag{7.58}$$

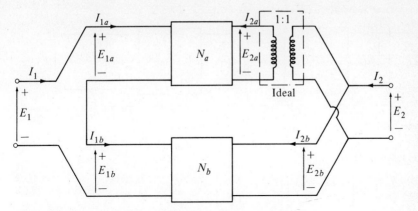

Figure 7.27 Series-parallel combination of two two-ports.

Parallel-series combination   This combination is shown in Figure 7.28. For such a combination,

$$E_1 = E_{1a} = E_{1b}, \qquad E_2 = E_{2a} + E_{2b}$$
$$I_1 = I_{1a} + I_{1b}, \qquad I_2 = I_{2a} = I_{2b}$$

(7.59)

And it is easy to show that

$$\begin{bmatrix} g_{11} & g_{12} \\ g_{21} & g_{22} \end{bmatrix} = \begin{bmatrix} g_{11a} & g_{12a} \\ g_{21a} & g_{22a} \end{bmatrix} + \begin{bmatrix} g_{11b} & g_{12b} \\ g_{21b} & g_{22b} \end{bmatrix}$$

(7.60)

Cascade connection   This arrangement is shown in Figure 7.29, and for such a combination

$$E_1 = E_{1a}, \qquad E_2 = E_{2b}$$
$$I_1 = I_{1a}, \qquad I_2 = I_{2b}$$
$$E_{2a} = E_{1b}, \qquad I_{2a} = -I_{1b}$$

(7.61)

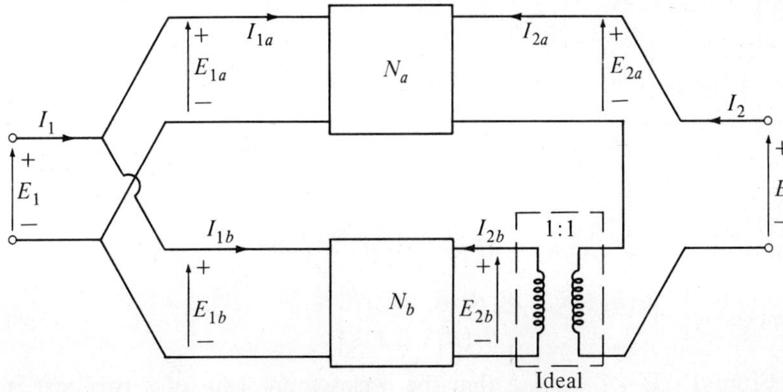

Figure 7.28 Parallel-series combination of two two-ports.

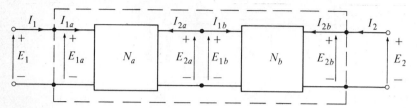

Figure 7.29 The cascade combination of two two-ports.

This implies that

$$\begin{bmatrix} A & B \\ C & D \end{bmatrix} = \begin{bmatrix} A_a & B_a \\ C_a & D_a \end{bmatrix} \begin{bmatrix} A_b & B_b \\ C_b & D_b \end{bmatrix} \tag{7.62}$$

EXAMPLE 8 Find the voltage gain of the cascade combination of two identical amplifiers of Figure 7.30, (a) when its output terminals are open-circuited and (b) when its output is terminated in a resistance of R_L ohms.

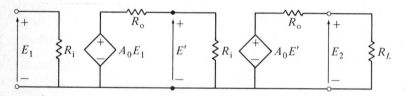

Figure 7.30 Two identical amplifiers connected in cascade.

SOLUTION From (7.11) and using Table 7.2, we obtain the chain matrix of each amplifier.

$$[F] = \begin{bmatrix} \dfrac{1}{A_0} & \dfrac{R_o}{A_0} \\[2ex] \dfrac{1}{A_0 R_i} & \dfrac{R_o}{A_0 R_i} \end{bmatrix}$$

The chain matrix of the cascade combination is

$$[F'] = [F][F] = \begin{bmatrix} \dfrac{1}{A_0^2} + \dfrac{R_o}{A_0^2 R_i} & \dfrac{R_o}{A_0^2} + \dfrac{R_o^2}{A_0^2 R_i} \\[2ex] \dfrac{1}{A_0^2 R_i} + \dfrac{R_o}{A_0^2 R_i^2} & \dfrac{R_o}{A_0^2 R_i} + \dfrac{R_o^2}{A_0^2 R_i^2} \end{bmatrix}$$

$$= \dfrac{1}{A_0^2 R_i^2} \begin{bmatrix} R_i(R_i + R_o) & R_i R_o(R_i + R_o) \\ R_i + R_o & R_o(R_i + R_o) \end{bmatrix} \tag{7.63}$$

(a) From Table 7.1, we see that the open-circuit gain of a two-port is equal to the reciprocal of its A parameter. Hence, for the cascaded amplifier, we get

$$\left. \frac{E_2}{E_1} \right|_{I_2=0} = \frac{1}{A} = \frac{R_i^2 A_0^2}{R_i(R_i+R_o)} \tag{7.64}$$

(b) From Table 7.3, with $Z_L = R_L$, we obtain

$$A_v = \frac{E_2}{E_1} = \frac{R_L}{B+AR_L}$$

$$= \frac{R_L R_i^2 A_0^2}{R_i R_o (R_i+R_o) + R_L R_i (R_i+R_o)}$$

$$= \frac{R_L R_i A_0^2}{(R_i+R_o)(R_o+R_L)} \tag{7.65}$$

7.8 The indefinite admittance matrix

There are situations in which it is more convenient to treat a network or a device on the terminal basis rather than on the port basis. A prime example of such a device is the transistor, which is a three-terminal device. A variety of orientations can be made out of such a single device. The advantage of treating a network or device on the terminal basis is that no commitment is made in advance as to how the terminals are paired or grouped. Although the impedance matrix may be used to characterize a multiterminal network, the admittance matrix is by far the more convenient one to use. The admittance matrix that characterizes a multiterminal network is known as the *indefinite admittance matrix* (IAM).

Let us look at an *n*-terminal network that is linear and contains no independent source. Let *n* external voltages ($E_1, E_2, ..., E_n$, with respect to ground) be applied to the network as shown in Figure 7.31. We can obtain a set of equations for the terminal currents in the form

$$I_1 = y_{11} E_1 + y_{12} E_2 + \cdots + y_{1n} E_n$$

$$I_2 = y_{21} E_1 + y_{22} E_2 + \cdots + y_{2n} E_n \tag{7.66}$$

$$\cdot \cdot \cdot \cdot \cdot \cdot \cdot \cdot \cdot \cdot \cdot \cdot \cdot \cdot \cdot \cdot \cdot \cdot \cdot \cdot \cdot \cdot$$

$$I_n = y_{n1} E_1 + y_{n2} E_2 + \cdots + y_{nn} E_n$$

The IAM of the network is

$$[y_i] = \begin{bmatrix} y_{11} & y_{12} & \cdots & y_{1n} \\ y_{21} & y_{22} & \cdots & y_{2n} \\ \cdot & \cdot & \cdot & \cdot \\ y_{n1} & y_{n2} & \cdots & y_{nn} \end{bmatrix} \tag{7.67}$$

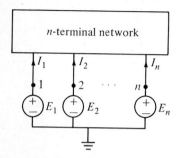

Figure 7.31 An n-terminal network excited by n voltage sources.

We may interpret each of the elements of (7.67) in much the same way as we interpret the two-port parameters when we know their defining equations. That is,

$$y_{ij} = \left. \frac{I_i}{E_j} \right|_{E_k = 0, \, k \neq j} \tag{7.68}$$

In other words, y_{ij} is the ratio of the current flowing into terminal i to the voltage at terminal j with all terminals except j grounded.

EXAMPLE 9 The network of Figure 7.32(a) is a three-terminal network. In order to obtain the elements of its IAM, we can excite the network

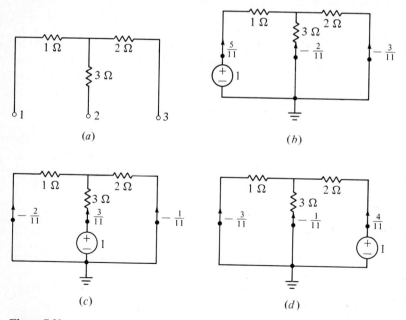

(a)

(b)

(c)

(d)

Figure 7.32

through one terminal at a time, with all other terminals grounded. Thus we have the situations of Figure 7.32(b) to (d), in which each exciting voltage is made to be unity. Thus each current value is equal to an admittance value defined by (7.68). From the current values in Figure 7.32 we may write for the network

$$[y_i] = \begin{bmatrix} \frac{5}{11} & -\frac{2}{11} & -\frac{3}{11} \\ -\frac{2}{11} & \frac{3}{11} & -\frac{1}{11} \\ -\frac{3}{11} & -\frac{1}{11} & \frac{4}{11} \end{bmatrix}$$

The elements in the IAM of a network are not independent. In Figure 7.31, it is clear that

$$I_1 + I_2 + \cdots + I_n = 0 \tag{7.69}$$

for any values of E's. If we set all voltages except one, say E_j, to zero, then we can conclude from (7.66) that

$$y_{1j} + y_{2j} + \cdots + y_{nj} = 0 \tag{7.70}$$

for $j = 1, 2, \ldots, n$.

Furthermore, if we let all the voltages be equal, then all the terminals are at the same potential and every terminal current will be zero. Each equation of (7.66) yields

$$y_{i1} + y_{i2} + \cdots + y_{in} = 0 \tag{7.71}$$

for $i = 1, 2, \ldots, n$.

Equations (7.70) and (7.71) state that the algebraic sum of the elements of any IAM along any row or column must vanish. Thus, to get an $n \times n$ IAM, we need only to find $(n-1) \times (n-1)$ elements. The remaining row and column are found simply by making each of their elements the negative of the sum of the row or column in which it appears.

If we take a three-terminal network and let $E_3 = 0$ as shown in Figure 7.33, we can regard the network as a three-terminal two-port. The $[y]$ matrix of the two-port is simply the upper left 2×2 submatrix of the IAM of the three-terminal network. On the other hand, if the $[y]$ matrix of a three-terminal two-port is known, then the IAM of this network is obtained

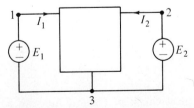

Figure 7.33 A three-terminal network as a two-port.

simply by bordering the $[y]$ matrix with an additional row and column in such a way that (7.70) and (7.71) are satisfied.

EXAMPLE 10   The small-signal circuit model of a transistor was given in Example 3 of Section 7.1 [Figure 7.7(a), Equation (7.16)]. This circuit is reproduced in Figure 7.34(a). If we treat this circuit as a three-terminal network, we simply augment the two-port admittance matrix by an additional row and column such that every row and column adds up to zero. Thus we get

$$[y_i]_{ecb} = \frac{1}{\Delta} \begin{bmatrix} r_b + r_c & -r_b & -r_c \\ -r_b - \alpha r_c & r_b + r_e & \alpha r_c - r_e \\ -(1-\alpha) r_c & -r_e & (1-\alpha) r_c + r_e \end{bmatrix} \tag{7.72}$$

Here the subscript ecb denotes that the first row and column correspond to the e (emitter) terminal, the second to the c (collector) terminal, and the third to the b (base) terminal.

Now, if we should need the two-port $[y]$ matrix of the transistor with the e terminal common to both ports, as shown in Figure 7.34(b), we simply set $E_1 = 0$ in the equations implied by (7.72). This is accomplished by deleting the first row and column. In other words, the $[y]$ matrix of the two-port of Figure 7.34(b) is

$$[y]_{cb} = \frac{1}{\Delta} \begin{bmatrix} r_b + r_e & \alpha r_c - r_e \\ -r_e & (1-\alpha) r_c + r_e \end{bmatrix} \tag{7.73}$$

Here the subscript cb denotes that terminal c is treated as the upper terminal of port 1 and b as that of port 2.

When two n-terminal networks are connected in parallel, the IAM of the parallel combination is simply the sum of the IAMs of the individual networks. Unlike the admittance matrices of networks treated on the port basis,

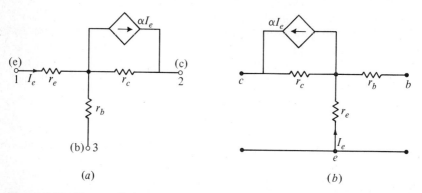

Figure 7.34   The small-signal transistor equivalent circuit of Figure 7.7(a) with a different orientation.

networks treated on the terminal basis can always be connected in parallel without using ideal transformers.

If a new $(n-1)$-terminal network is formed from an n-terminal network by combining terminals j and k, then

$$E_{j,k} = E_j = E_k, \qquad I_{j,k} = I_j + I_k \tag{7.74}$$

From (7.66) it is easy to see that we can obtain the IAM of the new $(n-1)$-terminal network from the IAM of the original n-terminal network by combining the jth and kth rows and the jth and kth columns.

If we obtain a new m-terminal network from an n-terminal network by leaving its last $n-m$ terminals (terminal $m+1$ through n) internal, then we have

$$I_{m+1} = I_{m+2} = \cdots = I_n = 0$$

and $E_{m+1}, E_{m+2}, ..., E_n$ are irrelevant. We may partition the IAM of the n-terminal network after the mth row and mth column, as shown.

$$
\begin{bmatrix}
y_{11} & \cdots & y_{1m} & y_{1(m+1)} & \cdots & y_{1n} \\
\cdots & \cdots & \cdots & \cdots & \cdots & \cdots \\
y_{m1} & \cdots & y_{mm} & y_{m(m+1)} & \cdots & y_{mn} \\
\hline
y_{(m+1)1} & \cdots & y_{(m+1)m} & y_{(m+1)(m+1)} & \cdots & y_{(m+1)n} \\
\cdots & \cdots & \cdots & \cdots & \cdots & \cdots \\
y_{n1} & \cdots & y_{nm} & y_{n(m+1)} & \cdots & y_{nn}
\end{bmatrix}
=
\begin{bmatrix}
[Y_{11}] & [Y_{12}] \\
[Y_{21}] & [Y_{22}]
\end{bmatrix}
\tag{7.75}
$$

Then we have

$$
\begin{bmatrix} I_1 \\ \vdots \\ I_m \end{bmatrix}
= [Y_{11}]
\begin{bmatrix} E_1 \\ \vdots \\ E_m \end{bmatrix}
+ [Y_{12}]
\begin{bmatrix} E_{m+1} \\ \vdots \\ E_n \end{bmatrix}
\tag{7.76}
$$

$$
[0] = [Y_{21}]
\begin{bmatrix} E_1 \\ \vdots \\ E_m \end{bmatrix}
+ [Y_{22}]
\begin{bmatrix} E_{m+1} \\ \vdots \\ E_n \end{bmatrix}
\tag{7.77}
$$

Solving for $[E_{m+1}, ..., E_n]_t$ from (7.77) and substituting into (7.76), we obtain

$$
\begin{bmatrix} I_1 \\ \vdots \\ I_m \end{bmatrix}
= \{[Y_{11}] - [Y_{12}][Y_{22}]^{-1}[Y_{21}]\}
\begin{bmatrix} E_1 \\ \vdots \\ E_m \end{bmatrix}
\tag{7.78}
$$

The quantity in the braces of (7.78) is the IAM of the new m-terminal network. This procedure is known as *pivotal condensation*.

EXAMPLE 11   The transistor circuit model of Figure 7.34(a) may be temporarily considered as a four-terminal network, as shown in Figure 7.35(a). Furthermore we may view the circuit for Figure 7.35(a) as the parallel

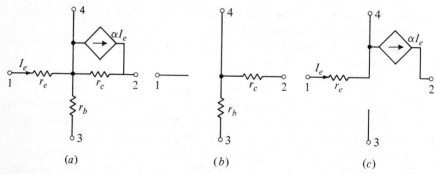

Figure 7.35

connection of two circuits, as shown in Figure 7.35(b) and (c). Now the IAM of the four-terminal network of Figure 7.35(a) is the sum of the IAMs of the networks of Figure 7.35(b) and (c) or

$$
[y_i]_4 = \begin{bmatrix} 0 & 0 & 0 & 0 \\[6pt] 0 & \dfrac{1}{r_c} & 0 & -\dfrac{1}{r_c} \\[10pt] 0 & 0 & \dfrac{1}{r_b} & -\dfrac{1}{r_b} \\[10pt] 0 & -\dfrac{1}{r_c} & -\dfrac{1}{r_b} & \dfrac{1}{r_c}+\dfrac{1}{r_b} \end{bmatrix}
$$

$$
+ \begin{bmatrix} \dfrac{1}{r_e} & 0 & 0 & -\dfrac{1}{r_e} \\[10pt] -\dfrac{\alpha}{r_e} & 0 & 0 & \dfrac{\alpha}{r_e} \\[10pt] 0 & 0 & 0 & 0 \\[10pt] -\dfrac{1-\alpha}{r_e} & 0 & 0 & \dfrac{1-\alpha}{r_e} \end{bmatrix}
$$

$$
= \begin{bmatrix} \dfrac{1}{r_e} & 0 & 0 & -\dfrac{1}{r_e} \\[10pt] -\dfrac{\alpha}{r_e} & \dfrac{1}{r_c} & 0 & -\dfrac{1}{r_c}+\dfrac{\alpha}{r_e} \\[10pt] 0 & 0 & \dfrac{1}{r_b} & -\dfrac{1}{r_b} \\[10pt] -\dfrac{1-\alpha}{r_e} & -\dfrac{1}{r_c} & -\dfrac{1}{r_b} & \dfrac{1}{r_b}+\dfrac{1}{r_c}+\dfrac{1-\alpha}{r_e} \end{bmatrix}
\qquad (7.79)
$$

From (7.78), the IAM of the three-terminal network of Figure 7.34(a) is

$$
[y_i]_3 =
\begin{bmatrix}
\dfrac{1}{r_e} & 0 & 0 \\[2mm]
-\dfrac{\alpha}{r_e} & \dfrac{1}{r_c} & 0 \\[2mm]
0 & 0 & \dfrac{1}{r_b}
\end{bmatrix}
\left(-
\begin{bmatrix}
-\dfrac{1}{r_e} \\[2mm]
-\dfrac{1}{r_c}+\dfrac{\alpha}{r_e} \\[2mm]
-\dfrac{1}{r_b}
\end{bmatrix}
\dfrac{1}{(1/r_b)+(1/r_c)+[(1-\alpha)/r_e]}\right)
$$

$$
\times
\begin{bmatrix}
-\dfrac{1-\alpha}{r_e} & -\dfrac{1}{r_c} & -\dfrac{1}{r_b}
\end{bmatrix}
$$

$$
= \dfrac{1}{\Delta}
\left\{
\begin{bmatrix}
\dfrac{\Delta}{r_e} & 0 & 0 \\[2mm]
-\dfrac{\alpha\Delta}{r_e} & \dfrac{\Delta}{r_e} & 0 \\[2mm]
0 & 0 & \dfrac{\Delta}{r_b}
\end{bmatrix}
-r_e r_b r_c
\begin{bmatrix}
\dfrac{1}{r_e} \\[2mm]
\dfrac{r_e-\alpha r_c}{r_e r_c} \\[2mm]
\dfrac{1}{r_b}
\end{bmatrix}
\begin{bmatrix}
\dfrac{1-\alpha}{r_e} & \dfrac{1}{r_c} & \dfrac{1}{r_b}
\end{bmatrix}
\right\}
$$

$$
= \dfrac{1}{\Delta}
\left\{
\begin{bmatrix}
\dfrac{\Delta}{r_e} & 0 & 0 \\[2mm]
-\dfrac{\alpha\Delta}{r_e} & \dfrac{\Delta}{r_c} & 0 \\[2mm]
0 & 0 & \dfrac{\Delta}{r_b}
\end{bmatrix}
-
\begin{bmatrix}
\dfrac{(1-\alpha)r_b r_c}{r_e} & r_b & r_c \\[2mm]
\dfrac{(1-\alpha)(r_e-\alpha r_c)r_b}{r_e} & \dfrac{(r_e-\alpha r_c)r_b}{r_c} & r_e-\alpha r_c \\[2mm]
(1-\alpha)r_c & r_e & \dfrac{r_e r_c}{r_b}
\end{bmatrix}
\right\}
$$

$$
= \dfrac{1}{\Delta}
\begin{bmatrix}
r_b+r_c & -r_b & -r_c \\[2mm]
-r_b-\alpha r_c & r_b+r_e & \alpha r_c-r_e \\[2mm]
-(1-\alpha)r_c & -r_e & (1-\alpha)r_c+r_e
\end{bmatrix}
\tag{7.80}
$$

which is identical to the matrix in (7.72).

7.9 Reciprocal and nonreciprocal networks

A network to which the reciprocity theorem applies is said to be a *reciprocal* network. For a reciprocal two-port,

$$
\left.\dfrac{E_2}{I_1}\right|_{I_2=0} = \left.\dfrac{E_1}{I_2}\right|_{I_1=0}
\tag{7.81}
$$

Therefore, for such a two-port,

$$z_{21} = z_{12} \tag{7.82}$$

Also

$$\left.\frac{I_2}{E_1}\right|_{E_2=0} = \left.\frac{I_1}{E_2}\right|_{E_1=0} \tag{7.83}$$

Hence

$$y_{21} = y_{12} \tag{7.84}$$

Thus a network containing LTI resistors, LTI capacitors, LTI inductors, and LTI mutual inductances, including ideal transformers, must have *symmetric* $[z]$ and $[y]$ matrices.

A network to which the reciprocity theorem does not necessarily apply is a *nonreciprocal* network. Thus we cannot expect a network containing controlled sources to have a symmetric $[z]$ or $[y]$ matrix.

The relationships of other parameters of reciprocal two-ports are left as exercises for the students. Some of these are included in the problems at the end of the chapter.

7.10 Concluding remarks

Having developed analysis techniques and methods of handling multiport or multiterminal devices or networks, we are now ready to apply some of these techniques to networks and electronic circuits that include multiterminal devices.

Problems

7.1 Find the z parameters of the two-port of Figure P7.1.

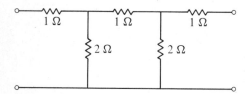

Figure P7.1

7.2 Find the y parameters of the two-port of Figure P7.2.

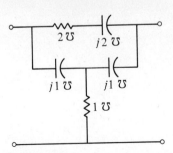

Figure P7.2

7.3 Find the z parameters of the two-port of Figure P7.3.

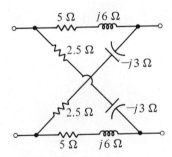

Figure P7.3

7.4 Find the y parameters of the two-port of Figure P7.4.

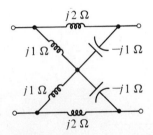

Figure P7.4

7.5 Determine z_{11} and z_{21} of the two-port of Figure P7.5.

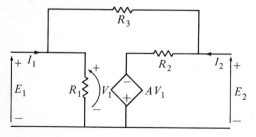

Figure P7.5

7.6 Derive the expressions for A, B, C, and D, in terms of (a) the z's, (b) the y's, (c) the g's, and (d) the h's.

7.7 Derive the expressions for the g's in terms of (a) the z's, (b) the h's, (c) $ABCD$, and (d) $\mathscr{ABCD}$.

7.8 Derive the expressions for the z's in terms of (a) the h's, (b) the g's and (c) $ABCD$.

7.9 Find the voltage ratio E_2/E_1 of the network of Figure P7.9 in terms of Y_s, Y_L, and the y's of the two-port.

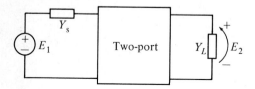

Figure P7.9

7.10 Obtain the y's of the two-ports of Figure P7.10. Then obtain the tee-to-pi transformation formulas by equating the corresponding y's and solving for y_1, y_2, and y_3 in terms of y_a, y_b, and y_c.

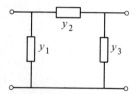 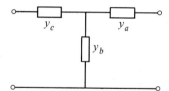

Figure P7.10

7.11 Obtain the z's of the two-ports of Figure P7.11. Then obtain the pi-to-tee transformation formulas by equating the corresponding z's and solving for z_a, z_b, and z_c in terms of z_1, z_2, and z_3.

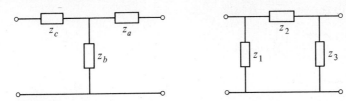

Figure P7.11

7.12 Find the $[y]$ matrix of the two-port of Figure P7.12.

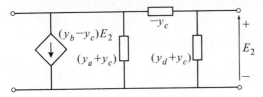

Figure P7.12

7.13 Find the $[z]$ matrix of each of the two-ports of Figure P7.13.

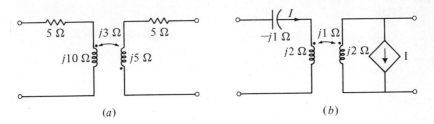

        (a)   (b)

Figure P7.13

7.14 Find the input impedance Z_i of the circuit of Figure P7.14. ($\omega = 100$.)

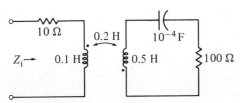

Figure P7.14

7.15 Write the KCL and KVL equations for the circuit of Figure P7.15.

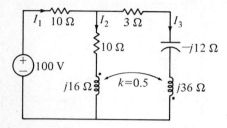

Figure P7.15

7.16 Find the $[z]$ matrix of the two-port of Figure P7.16.

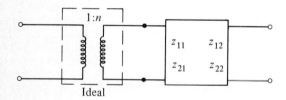

Figure P7.16

7.17 Find the $[z]$ matrix of the two-port of Figure P7.17.

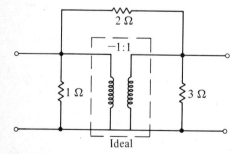

Figure P7.17

7.18 The [g] matrix of each of the two-ports of Figure P7.18 is

$$[g] = \begin{bmatrix} 0 & -\dfrac{1}{n} \\ -\dfrac{1}{n} & 0 \end{bmatrix}$$

What is the chain matrix of the cascade combination? Show that the cascade combination is equivalent to an ideal transformer.

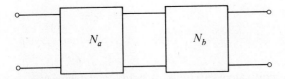

Figure P7.18

7.19 Find the [z] matrix of the parallel-tee two-port of Figure P7.19.

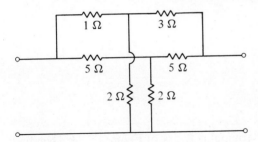

Figure P7.19

7.20 Find the y parameters of the bridged-tee two-port of Figure P7.20 as functions of the complex-frequency variable s.

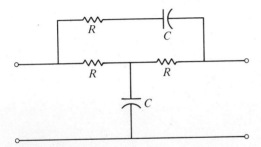

Figure P7.20

7.21 Find the IAM of the three-terminal network of Figure P7.21.

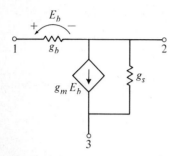

Figure P7.21

7.22 Find the IAM for the equivalent circuit of a field-effect transistor as shown in Figure P7.22.

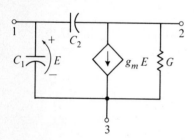

Figure P7.22

7.23 Find the IAM of the four-terminal network of Figure P7.23. Then find the IAM of the three-terminal network with terminal 4 considered internal. Then find the $[y]$ matrix of the two-port with terminals 1 and 3 as the terminal pair of port 1 and terminals 2 and 3 as the terminal pair of port 2.

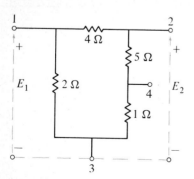

Figure P7.23

7.24 The IAM of a four-terminal network is known. A two-port is formed by considering terminals 1 and 4 as port 1 (with 1 as the upper terminal) and terminals 2 and 3 as port 2 (with 2 as the upper terminal). Derive the two-port y parameters in terms of the elements of the IAM.

7.25 Show that, if a two-port is reciprocal, then

$$g_{12} = -g_{21}, \qquad h_{12} = -h_{21}$$

$$AD - BC = 1, \qquad \mathcal{A}\mathcal{D} - \mathcal{B}\mathcal{C} = 1$$

7.26 Show that, for a reciprocal two-port,

$$\left.\frac{E_2}{E_1}\right|_{I_2 = 0} = -\left.\frac{I_1}{I_2}\right|_{E_1 = 0}$$

8 | FIELD-EFFECT TRANSISTOR CIRCUITS

Semiconductor electronic devices are the basic building blocks of modern electronic technology. The most important are the diode, the field-effect transistor (FET), and the junction transistor. These devices may be either discrete units or part of an integrated circuit that incorporates tens or even thousands of these components on one semiconductor chip. In either case it is important to know the characteristics of each individual component and how to analyze circuits containing them.

In Chapter 6 we discussed the diode and some diode circuits. In this and the following chapter we shall deal with the two types of transistor, their basic physical principles, and the analysis of circuits that use these devices.

8.1 The junction field-effect transistor (JFET)

The basic structure of a JFET is represented by the arrangement of Figure 8.1. Two *p-n* junctions are formed on two sides of a semiconductor bar.

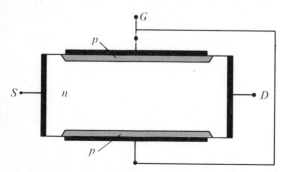

Figure 8.1 The basic structure of an *n*-channel junction FET.

The bar may be of either the p or the n type, and it becomes the *channel* of the JFET. We shall describe the operation of a JFET whose channel is formed by n-type material—an n-channel JFET. The p-channel JFET works in exactly the same way except for a polarity reversal.

When a potential difference is applied between the two ends of the bar, a current will flow, caused by the majority carriers in the channel. The end from which the carriers enter the channel is known as the *source* (S) and the end at which the carriers leave the bar is known as the *drain* (D). The outside surfaces of the p-n junctions are connected together and are known as the *gate* (G).

Figure 8.2 shows a typical arrangement for the application of an n-channel FET. The gate is biased negatively with respect to the channel. When a voltage is applied across the channel, electrons flow from the negative terminal to the positive terminal—in this case, from S to D—resulting in a positive i_D. For small values of v_{DS}, this current is determined by the resistivity and the size of the channel and is proportional to v_{DS}.

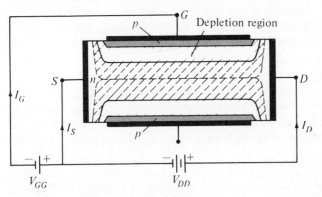

Figure 8.2 An FET whose gate is negatively biased with respect to the source and whose v_{DS} is small. (Dashed curves represent the boundaries of depletion regions at pinch-off.)

As the gate-to-source voltage v_{GS} is made more negative, the depletion region between the gate and the channel (shown shaded in Figure 8.2) widens. This results in a narrower channel and a higher channel resistance. A typical set of i_D-v_{DS} curves for several values of v_{GS} is shown in Figure 8.3. An FET operating in this region is a voltage-controlled resistor. The resistance increases as $|v_{GS}|$ is increased.

As $|v_{GS}|$ is increased and the depletion region widened, a situation is reached in which the two boundaries of the depletion region meet each other and the channel vanishes. This is indicated by the dashed curves in Figure 8.2. The FET is said to be "pinched off," and i_D is essentially zero. This corresponds to the curve $v_{GS} = -7$ V in Figure 8.3. The value of v_{GS} when pinch-off occurs is known as the *pinch-off voltage* of the FET and is denoted by V_{PO}.

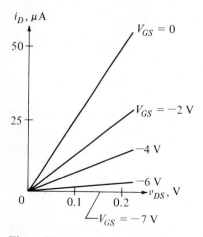

Figure 8.3 The i_D-v_{DS} characteristics of an FET for low values of v_{DS}.

An FET assumes the resistive characteristic only for low values of v_{DS}. As v_{DS} is increased, the linearity of the i_D-v_{DS} curves is soon lost, because the v_{DS} is being distributed along the channel. Figure 8.4 shows the boundaries of the depletion regions for several values of v_{DS} with $v_{GS} = 0$. For $v_{DS} = 7$ V, we have $v_{GD} = -7$ V $= V_{PO}$, and pinch-off occurs. For v_{DS} larger than this value, the channel becomes very constricted and the current flows through it in a very narrow stream. For a large range of v_{DS} beyond pinch-off, i_D remains essentially constant. At a certain very high value of v_{DS}, avalanche occurs in the channel, resulting in a very sharp increase in current for the same v_{DS}. The variation of i_D with respect to v_{DS} is summarized in the $v_{GS} = 0$ curve in Figure 8.5.

If v_{GS} is maintained at a negative value, the i_D-v_{DS} curve will start off at a slower rate for low values of v_{DS}, as was shown in Figure 8.3. Pinch-off

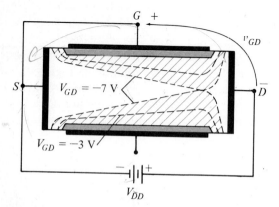

Figure 8.4 Widening of depletion regions or narrowing of the channel in an n-channel FET as v_{DS} is increased.

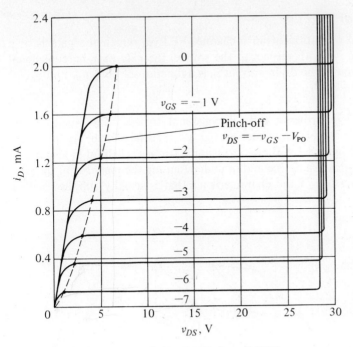

Figure 8.5 Drain characteristics of an n-channel FET.

will occur when $v_{GD} = V_{PO}$. Since $v_{GD} = v_{GS} - v_{DS}$, pinch-off will occur at $v_{DS} = -V_{PO} + v_{GS}$. For example, if $V_{PO} = -7$ V and $v_{GS} = -3$ V, then pinch-off will occur when $v_{DS} = 4$ V. Beyond pinch-off, i_D remains essentially constant until avalanche occurs.

A series of i_D-v_{DS} curves for several values of v_{GS} is shown in Figure 8.5. The symbol for an n-channel JFET is shown in Figure 8.6(a), and that for a p-channel one in Figure 8.6(b).

Since the gate-to-channel p-n junctions are reverse-biased, the gate-to-source current is the reverse saturation current of that junction. This current is usually very small, resulting in a very high gate-to-source resistance. A typical value for this resistance is 10^{12} ohms.

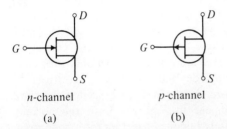

n-channel $\qquad$ p-channel

(a) $\qquad\qquad$ (b)

Figure 8.6 Symbols of the two types of FET.

8.2 JFET characteristics

In the normal operation of an n-channel FET, in which the gate is at a potential negative with respect to the source, the gate may be considered as an open circuit. The drain current i_D is a function of both v_{DS} and v_{GS} or

$$i_D = f(v_{DS}, v_{GS}) \tag{8.1}$$

Equation (8.1) describes a three-dimensional surface that quantitatively defines an FET. A portion of such an i_D-v_{DS}-v_{GS} surface in the useful octant is depicted in Figure 8.7. A three-dimensional surface is helpful in visualizing the characteristics of a device and in understanding the meaning of the two-dimensional version of the characteristics that is usually supplied with a specific FET.

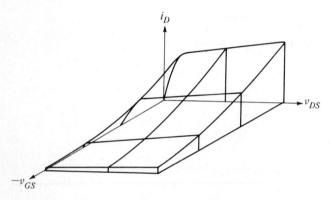

Figure 8.7 Three-dimensional relationship among i_D, v_{DS}, and v_{GS} in an FET.

The most commonly used characteristics are the *drain* (also known as the output) *characteristics*. These curves are the plots of i_D versus v_{DS} for various fixed values of v_{GS}. A typical set of such curves was shown in Figure 8.5. Each curve is the intersection of the plane corresponding to a constant v_{GS} and the three-dimensional i_D-v_{DS}-v_{GS} surface. The curve for $v_{GS} = 0$ is the i_D-v_{DS} curve when the gate is connected to the source. For a fixed v_{GS}, i_D is essentially independent of the value of v_{DS} as long as the latter is larger than the pinch-off voltage and below the avalanche breakdown.

Another set of two-dimensional curves based on (8.1) is the gate-to-drain *transfer (or mutual) characteristics*. These are the i_D-versus-v_{GS} curves for different values of fixed v_{DS}. These curves are usually shown only for values of v_{DS} in the current-saturation region. They indicate how v_{GS} controls the drain current i_D. Two such curves are shown in Figure 8.8 for the same FET whose drain characteristics appear in Figure 8.5. In the current-saturation region these curves are closely bunched together for a wide range of v_{DS}. The quantity I_{DSS} is the saturated drain current when the gate is *shorted* to the source ($v_{GS} = 0$). The transfer characteristic is given

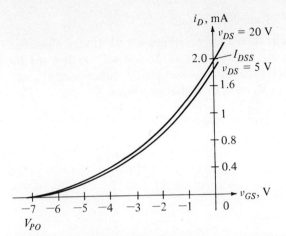

Figure 8.8 Transfer characteristics of an *n*-channel FET.

approximately by

$$i_D = I_{DSS}\left(1 - \frac{v_{GS}}{V_{PO}}\right)^2 \tag{8.2}$$

In theory, a third set of two-dimensional characteristics can also be drawn—the contours of v_{DS}-v_{GS} variation for various fixed values of i_D. Figure 8.9 shows such a set of curves. However, these curves are not very useful for FETs and are seldom given.

The operation of a *p*-channel FET is exactly like that of an *n*-channel one except that the polarity of every corresponding quantity is reversed.

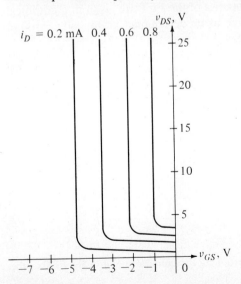

Figure 8.9 Constant-current characteristics of an *n*-channel FET.

8.3 dc Analysis of basic FET amplifier circuit

The basic FET amplifier circuit is shown in Figure 8.10. Under quiescent conditions, $v_i = 0$, and i_D, v_{GS}, and v_{DS} are all dc and will be denoted by I_D, V_{GS}, and V_{DS}, respectively. Analysis involves the determination of V_{DS} and I_D for a set of given V_{DD}, V_{GG}, R_L, and FET characteristics.

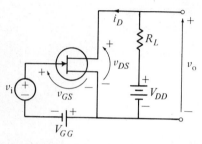

Figure 8.10 Basic FET amplifier circuit.

Analytical method If the transfer characteristic of the FET is given in analytical form, then we have

$$I_D = I_{DSS}\left(1 - \frac{V_{GG}}{V_{PO}}\right)^2 \tag{8.3}$$

Since I_{DSS} and V_{PO} are the parameters of the FET and are presumed to be known, we can calculate I_D from (8.3). Once we know I_D, we can find V_{DS} by

$$V_{DS} = V_{DD} - R_L I_D \tag{8.4}$$

Graphical method If the characteristics of the FET are given in a graphical form, the quiescent point will have to be determined graphically. Around the drain supply circuit KVL gives

$$V_{DS} = V_{DD} - R_L I_D \tag{8.5}$$

This is the equation of the *load line*, which is a straight line in the i_D-v_{DS}

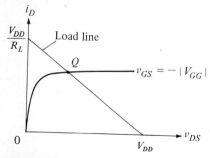

Figure 8.11 Graphical method of determining the quiescent point of the FET in the circuit of Figure 8.10.

plane, as shown in Figure 8.11. The other relationship the circuit must satisfy is the i_D-v_{DS} curve of the FET corresponding to the gate-to-source voltage V_{GS}. Hence the actual operating point is the intersection of the load line and the FET characteristic, i_D-v_{GS}. This point is marked Q in Figure 8.11.

8.4   Large-signal analysis of basic FET amplifier circuit

Suppose that a large time-varying sinusoidal signal is applied to the input of the FET amplifier of Figure 8.10. We then have

$$v_{GS}(t) = V_{GS} + v_i(t) = V_{GS} + V_{i\,max} \sin \omega t \qquad (8.6)$$

The drain current $i_D(t)$ and drain-to-source voltage v_{DS} at different times are found graphically by applying the dc analysis method of the previous section for a number of values of v_{GS}. For each value of v_{GS}, we obtain a pair of values of i_D and v_{DS}. The waveform of i_D or v_{DS} (or v_o) can then be plotted point by point. Figure 8.12 shows how a series of such points of dc analysis are used to obtain the output waveform.

Important note: In this volume, as far as possible, we shall use the IEEE standard notations to distinguish the following four classes of quantities: (1) A capital letter with capital subscripts implies a dc quantity. (2) A lower-case letter with lower-case subscripts implies an ac quantity as a function of

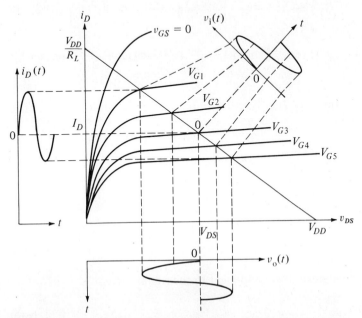

Figure 8.12   Large-signal operation of the basic FET amplifier circuit of Figure 8.10.

time. (3) A capital letter with lower-case subscripts represents the complex amplitude (effective value) of an ac quantity with the same letter designation. (4) A lower-case letter with capital subscripts represents any time-variant quantity. In particular, it frequently represents the sum of dc and ac quantities.

The transfer relationship between v_{GS} and i_D of the FET circuit for a given V_{DD} is more clearly displayed if we plot a curve of i_D versus v_{GS} for a given V_{DD} and a given R_L. We can do this easily by taking the readings of i_D and v_{GS} from the intersections of the load line and the constant-v_{GS} curves of Figure 8.12. The resulting curve is known as the *dynamic transfer characteristic* (as contrasted to the static transfer characteristics of Figure 8.8). Figure 8.13 shows an example of such a curve. Once we know $i_D(t)$, $v_o(t)$ is found easily.

We see from Figure 8.12 that, unless the spacing of the drain characteristics of an FET is fairly uniform for equally spaced values of v_{GS}, the drain current and the output voltage will be quite distorted. This fact is explained more clearly if we assume that the FET characteristics are approximately represented by (8.2).

Substituting (8.6) into (8.2), we get

$$
i_D = I_{DSS}\left(1 - \frac{V_{GG}+V_{i\,\max}\sin\omega t}{V_{PO}}\right)^2
$$

$$
= I_{DSS}\left[\left(1 - \frac{V_{GG}}{V_{PO}}\right)^2 - 2\left(1 - \frac{V_{GG}}{V_{PO}}\right)\frac{V_{i\,\max}}{V_{PO}}\sin\omega t + \frac{V_{i\,\max}^2}{V_{PO}^2}\sin^2\omega t\right]
$$

$$
= I_{DSS}\left[\left(1 - \frac{V_{GG}}{V_{PO}}\right)^2 + \frac{V_{i\,\max}^2}{2V_{PO}^2} - 2\left(1 - \frac{V_{GG}}{V_{PO}}\right)\frac{V_{i\,\max}}{V_{PO}}\sin\omega t - \frac{V_{i\,\max}^2}{2V_{PO}^2}\cos 2\omega t\right]
$$

$$(8.7)$$

The constant term in (8.7) is the dc component of the drain current. The signal component is

$$
i_d = -2I_{DSS}\left(1 - \frac{V_{GG}}{V_{PO}}\right)\frac{V_{i\,\max}}{V_{PO}}\sin\omega t
$$

$$(8.8)$$

But there is another component, whose frequency is twice that of the signal frequency. This represents a distortion in the waveform:

$$
i_{\text{dist}} = -I_{DSS}\frac{V_{i\,\max}^2}{2V_{PO}^2}\cos 2\omega t
$$

$$(8.9)$$

The ratio of the undesirable component to the signal current is

$$
\frac{i_{\text{dist}}}{i_d} = \frac{V_{i\,\max}}{4(V_{PO}-V_{GG})}
$$

$$(8.10)$$

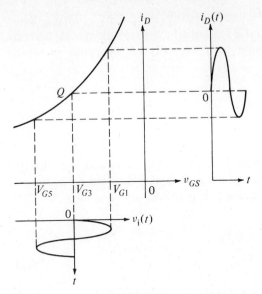

Figure 8.13 Dynamic transfer characteristic of the basic FET amplifier of Figure 8.10.

This distortion is seen to be proportional to the magnitude of the signal voltage. Hence, when $V_{i\,max}$ is a considerable fraction of V_{GG}, a sizable second harmonic can be expected from an FET amplifier.

8.5 Small-signal parameters of an FET

When the signal voltage $v_i(t)$ is small in comparison with V_{GG}, the distortion is small and the FET may be considered as a linear device for the signal component. This is equivalent to considering the characteristic surface of the FET as flat in the vicinity of the quiescent point. Three slopes of this surface are mathematically convenient for describing the quantitative behavior of the surface. They are the slopes of the curves on the surface parallel to the three coordinate planes. These slopes are also the partial derivatives obtained from the function that describes the surface:

The drain resistance

$$r_d = \frac{\partial v_{DS}}{\partial i_D}\bigg|_{v_{GS}=V_{GS}} \qquad (8.11)$$

is also the slope of the v_{DS}-i_D curve for a given value of v_{GS}. Most drain characteristics are plotted with i_D as the ordinate and v_{DS} as the abscissa, as shown in Figure 8.5. In that case r_d is the reciprocal of the slope of the i_D-v_{GS} curve. Frequently the reciprocal of r_d is preferred. This reciprocal is known as the *drain conductance* and is usually denoted by g_d or g_{os}. Since the drain characteristic of an FET is nearly horizontal in the current-saturation region, its r_d is quite high, typically in the range of 0.1 to several MΩ.

The transconductance

$$g_m = \left.\frac{\partial i_D}{\partial v_{GS}}\right|_{v_{DS}=V_{DS}} \tag{8.12}$$

is a measure of the amount of drain current change due to a change in gate-to-source voltage for a fixed value of v_{DS}. It is also denoted by g_{fs} and is equal to the slope of the i_D-v_{GS} curve of Figure 8.8.

The amplification factor

$$\mu = -\left.\frac{\partial v_{DS}}{\partial v_{GS}}\right|_{i_D=I_D} \tag{8.13}$$

is the ratio of the amount of drain voltage increase needed for a corresponding gate voltage decrease to maintain the source current constant. It is the negative of the slope of the constant-current characteristic of an FET.

If we first think of the i_D-v_{DS}-v_{GS} surface of Figure 8.7 as described by (8.1), then we have

$$di_D = \frac{\partial i_D}{\partial v_{DS}} dv_{DS} + \frac{\partial i_D}{\partial v_{GS}} dv_{GS} \tag{8.14}$$

$$= \frac{1}{r_d} dv_{DS} + g_m dv_{GS}$$

Now, if we let $di_D = 0$, then we have

$$\left.\frac{dv_{DS}}{dv_{GS}}\right|_{di_D=0} = -r_d g_m \tag{8.15}$$

Hence

$$\mu = r_d g_m \tag{8.16}$$

When not all three sets of characteristics of an FET are available, as is usually the case, we can estimate these parameters from the characteristics that are furnished. For example, suppose we have only the drain characteristics. We estimate the transconductance at an operating point Q by using the relationship

$$g_m \cong \left.\frac{\Delta i_D}{\Delta v_{GS}}\right|_{v_{DS}=\text{constant}} = \frac{i_{D2}-i_{D4}}{V_{G2}-V_{G4}} \tag{8.17}$$

The values in (8.17) are read off from the drain characteristic, as shown in Figure 8.14(a). Similarly we can estimate the amplification factor at the same operating point Q by using the relationship

$$\mu \cong -\left.\frac{\Delta v_{DS}}{\Delta v_{GS}}\right|_{i_D=\text{constant}} = \frac{v_{DS4}-v_{DS2}}{V_{G2}-V_{G4}} \tag{8.18}$$

The values in (8.18) can also be read off from the drain characteristics, as shown in Figure 8.14(b).

We can find the value of r_d at the quiescent point by first estimating the slope of the drain characteristic in the vicinity of the Q point. As Figure 8.14(a) shows,

$$r_d \cong \frac{\Delta v_{DS}}{\Delta i_D} \tag{8.19}$$

The three estimated values of r_d, g_m, and μ should satisfy (8.16) approximately. One usually obtains these parameters by direct measurement.

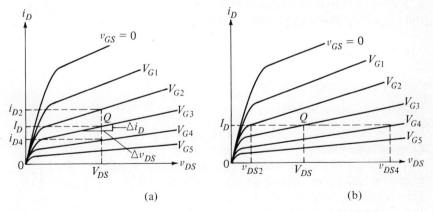

(a)   (b)

Figure 8.14 Graphical determination of small-signal parameters of an FET.

8.6 Relationships among small-signal components of quantities in an FET

For an FET operating in the vicinity of its quiescent point, we may represent its electric quantities as

$$v_{GS}(t) = V_{GS} + v_{gs}(t) \tag{8.20}$$

$$i_D(t) = I_D + i_d(t) \tag{8.21}$$

$$v_{DS}(t) = V_{DS} + v_{ds}(t) \tag{8.22}$$

where (V_{GS}, I_D, V_{DS}) is the state of the FET under quiescent conditions, and $v_{gs}(t)$, $i_d(t)$, and $v_{ds}(t)$ are the variational parts of the three FET quantities.

Frequently these variational parts are sinusoidal, or

$$v_{gs}(t) = \sqrt{2}V_1 \cos(\omega t + \psi_{gs})$$
$$i_d(t) = \sqrt{2}I_2 \cos(\omega t + \phi_d)$$
$$v_{ds}(t) = \sqrt{2}V_3 \cos(\omega t + \psi_{ds})$$

The ac analysis of an FET circuit is concerned with the relationships among $V_1, I_2, V_3, \psi_{gs}, \phi_d, \psi_{ds}$, as well as other ac quantities in other parts of the circuit outside the FET.

When the magnitudes of the variational parts of the electric quantities in an FET are small, that part of the characteristic surface of the FET can be regarded as a plane with sufficient accuracy. The slopes of the surface over the operating region may be regarded as constant. Hence the three quantities r_d, g_m, and μ as defined in (8.11), (8.12), and (8.13) become very useful in these analyses.

When the preceding assumptions are valid, we may treat an FET as a linear device as far as its ac components are concerned. Equation (8.14) then applies to the variational components of the electric quantities with or without the differential sign. In other words,

$$i_d(t) = \frac{v_{ds}(t)}{r_d} + g_m v_{gs}(t) \tag{8.23}$$

Applying (8.16) and rearranging, we get

$$v_{ds}(t) = -\mu v_{gs}(t) + r_d i_d(t) \tag{8.24}$$

Equation (8.24) is easily identified with the circuit branch of Figure 8.15(a). Keeping in mind that v_{gs} is the variational part of the source-to-gate voltage v_{GS}, as shown in Figure 8.15(b), we may therefore consider the FET as a three-terminal device, whose ac circuit model is shown in Figure 8.15(c). This model assumes that the gate current is either zero or negligible, an assumption that is usually valid when V_{GS} is negative and the ac signal is small. The model is equally applicable whether the FET is n-channel or p-channel.

The circuit model of Figure 8.15(c) is the Thévenin's equivalent circuit of an FET. An alternative circuit model may be obtained by replacing the branch of Figure 8.15(a) by its Norton's equivalent. This model is shown in Figure 8.15(d). Since r_d is usually quite high and is frequently omitted in the Norton's equivalent circuit, Figure 8.15(d) is the preferred model for an FET.

The ac indefinite admittance matrix (IAM) of an FET is therefore

$$[y_i]_{GDS} = \begin{bmatrix} 0 & 0 & 0 \\ g_m & g_d & -g_m-g_d \\ -g_m & -g_d & g_m+g_d \end{bmatrix} \tag{8.25}$$

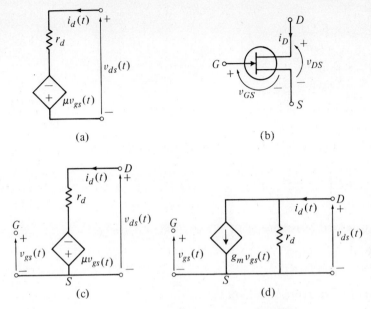

Figure 8.15 Small-signal ac equivalent circuits of an FET.

The first step in the small-signal ac analysis of an FET circuit is to replace each FET by its ac equivalent circuit. Other circuit elements are replaced by their respective impedances. A battery, which has no variational component in its voltage, is replaced by a short circuit. Then the circuit is analyzed by a suitable analysis technique to obtain the desired quantity or network function.

EXAMPLE 1   For the basic FET amplifier circuit of Figure 8.10, the small-signal ac equivalent circuit is as shown in Figure 8.16, where V_i, I_d, and V_o

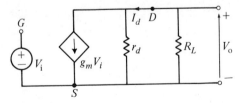

Figure 8.16 Small-signal ac equivalent circuit of the basic FET amplifier of Figure 8.10.

are the complex amplitudes of v_i, i_d, and v_o, respectively. Applying KCL to the output node, we have

$$\frac{V_o}{r_d} + \frac{V_o}{R_L} + g_m V_i = 0 \qquad (8.26)$$

Hence

$$V_o = -R_L I_d = -\frac{g_m r_d R_L V_i}{r_d + R_L} \qquad (8.27)$$

and the voltage ratio is

$$A_v = \frac{V_o}{V_i} = -\frac{g_m r_d R_L}{r_d + R_L} \qquad (8.28)$$

If $r_d \to \infty$, then $A_v = -g_m R_L$.

The circuit of Figure 8.16 may also be viewed as a two-port whose $[y]$ matrix is

$$[y] = \begin{bmatrix} 0 & 0 \\ g_m & g_d \end{bmatrix}$$

terminated in a load resistance of R_L. From Table 7.3, we get

$$A_v = \frac{-y_{21}}{y_{22} + Y_L} = \frac{-g_m}{g_d + (1/R_L)} \qquad (8.29)$$

which is equal to the expression in (8.28).

Since, as far as the ac signal is concerned, the output and the input share a common terminal—the source terminal of the FET—the basic amplifier arrangement of Figure 8.10 is also known as the *common-source amplifier*.

EXAMPLE 2 In the circuit of Figure 8.17(a), the parameters of the FET are $g_m = 1.6$ m℧ and $r_d = 50$ kΩ. Find the output voltage $v_o(t)$ for $v_i(t) = 0.01 \cos 2\pi \times 10^3 t$ volts.

SOLUTION The reactance of the capacitor is

$$X_C = \frac{1}{2\pi \times 10^3 \times 5 \times 10^{-9}} = 31.83 \text{ k}\Omega$$

Hence the ac equivalent circuit is as shown in Figure 8.17(b).

Combining the 50-kΩ and the 10-kΩ resistances and using mesh analysis, we have

$$I(58.333 \text{ k} - j31.83 \text{ k}) + 1.6 \times 10^{-3} \times 8.333 \text{ k} \times V_i = 0$$

where k represents the factor 10^3. Solving, we get

$$I = -\frac{13.333 \times 10^{-3}}{58.333 - j31.83} V_i$$

Since $V_o = 50 \text{ k}I$, we may write

$$V_o = -\frac{666.67}{58.333 - j31.83} V_i = -\frac{666.67}{66.45 \underline{/-28.62°}} V_i$$

$$= 10.03 \underline{/208.62°} V_i$$

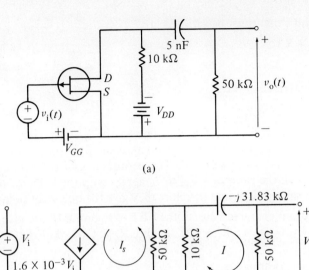

(a)

(b)

Figure 8.17

Thus

$$v_o(t) = 0.1003 \cos(2\pi \times 10^3 t + 208.62°) \text{ V}$$

8.7 Self-biased FET amplifier

The basic amplifier circuit of Figure 8.10 suffers from one major disadvantage in that it requires two power supplies. The arrangement of Figure 8.18 enables us to bias the gate at a potential negative with respect to the source without an extra power supply.

dc Analysis To determine the quiescent point, we wish to find the values of I_D, V_D, and V_{GS} for a set of given values of V_{DD}, R_L, and R_s with $v_i = 0$.

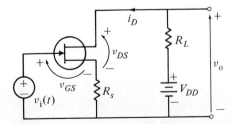

Figure 8.18 Self-biased FET amplifier circuit.

The three relationships that must be satisfied are

$$V_{DD} = V_{DS} + I_D(R_L + R_s) \tag{8.30}$$

$$V_{GS} = -I_D R_s \tag{8.31}$$

and the drain characteristic of the FET,

$$I_D = f(V_{DS}, V_{GS}) \tag{8.32}$$

Equation (8.30) is the equation of a load line in the i_D-v_{DS} plane. The intersection of this load line and the drain characteristics gives the points at which (8.30) and (8.32) are both satisfied. The coordinates of these intersection points, at which the ratio of $-V_{GS}$ to I_D agrees with the value of R_s of the circuit, would satisfy (8.31) and therefore they give the quiescent point.

EXAMPLE 3 The drain characteristics of the FET of Figure 8.18 are given in Figure 8.19(a); $V_{DD} = 20$ V, $R_s = 300$ Ω, and $R_L = 1700$ Ω. Find the quiescent point.

SOLUTION Equation (8.30) reads

$$20 = V_{DS} + 2000 I_D$$

Hence the load line intersects the axes at 20 volts and $20/2000 = 10$ mA, as shown in Figure 8.19(a). A series of (i_D, v_{GS}) points can now be read along the load line where it intersects the various constant-v_{GS} contours. These points are tabulated in Table 8.1 and entered as curve A in Figure 8.9(b). At the same time, (8.31), which reads

$$V_{GS} = -300 I_D$$

Table **8.1**

V_{GS}	I_D
-0.5	7.1
-1.0	6.2
-1.5	5.0
-2.0	3.8
-2.5	2.9

must also be satisfied. This equation is simply a straight line and is shown as line B in Figure 8.19(b). The intersect of these two curves gives the quiescent point, which corresponds to

$$I_D = 5.0 \text{ mA}, \qquad V_{GS} = -1.5 \text{ V}, \qquad V_{DS} = 10 \text{ V}$$

EXAMPLE 4 The FET of the previous example is replaced by one whose characteristic is given by (8.3), with $I_{DSS} = 10$ mA and $V_{PO} = -6$ volts. Find the quiescent point.

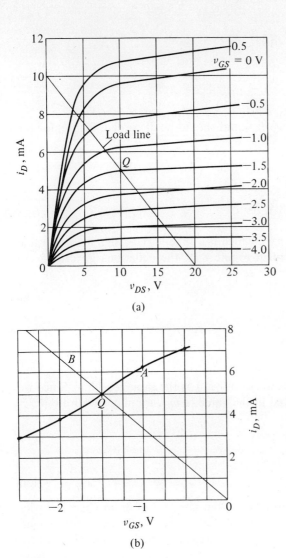

Figure 8.19 Example of the determination of the quiescent point of the self-biased circuit.

SOLUTION   In addition to (8.30) and (8.31), which read

$$20 = V_{DS} + 2000I_D \tag{8.33}$$

$$V_{GS} = -300I_D \tag{8.34}$$

we have (8.32) in analytical form, namely,

$$I_D = 10^{-2}\left(1 + \frac{V_{GS}}{6}\right)^2 \tag{8.35}$$

Elimination of V_{GS} between (8.34) and (8.35) gives

$$2500I_D^2 - 200I_D + 1 = 0$$

which yields

$$I_D = 74.64 \times 10^{-3} \quad \text{or} \quad 5.36 \times 10^{-3}$$

The larger value is way above I_{DSS} and should be discarded. Hence, for the Q point, we get

$$I_D = 5.36 \text{ mA}$$

$$V_{GS} = -5.36 \times 10^{-3} \times 300 = -1.61 \text{ V}$$

$$V_{DS} = 20 - 2 \times 5.36 = 9.28 \text{ V}$$

Large-signal analysis If a $v_i(t)$, which is a time-varying signal comparable in strength to V_{GS}, is present in Figure 8.18, the equations governing the behavior of this circuit are

$$V_{DD} = v_{DS} + i_D(R_L + R_s) \tag{8.36}$$

$$v_{GS} = v_i - i_D R_s \tag{8.37}$$

and the drain characteristics

$$i_D = f(v_{DS}, v_{GS}) \tag{8.38}$$

Equation (8.36), which is identical to (8.30), is the same load line. Since we are not particularly interested in the value of v_{GS}, we may substitute (8.37) into (8.38) to obtain

$$i_D = f(v_{DS}, v_i - i_D R_s) = f_1(v_{DS}, v_i) \tag{8.39}$$

in which

$$v_i = v_{GS} + i_D R_s \tag{8.40}$$

Equation (8.39) may be interpreted as the same set of drain characteristics of the FET, if every constant-gate voltage curve is relabeled to correspond to a constant-signal voltage (v_i). This is done according to (8.40), in which each i_D is the ordinate of the intersection of the load line and the drain characteristic. Hence, for each intersecting point along the load line, we can calculate from (8.40) a value for v_i that represents the status of the FET for that value of v_i. From a series of such points we can plot a dynamic transfer characteristic (i_D versus v_i).

EXAMPLE 5 Find the dynamic transfer characteristic of the circuit of Example 1.

SOLUTION A series of corresponding points between i_D and v_i is obtained from the intersecting points of the load line and the drain characteristics in Figure 8.16 according to (8.40). These values are tabulated in Table 8.2. The dynamic transfer characteristic is plotted in Figure 8.20.

Table **8.2**

v_{GS}	i_D (mA)	v_i (V)
0	7.8	2.34
−0.5	7.1	1.61
−1.0	6.2	0.86
−1.4	4.9	0
−1.5	4.8	−0.06
−2.0	3.8	−0.86
−2.5	2.9	−1.63
−3.0	2.1	−2.37

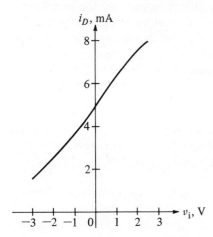

Figure 8.20 Dynamic transfer characteristic of the circuit of Figure 8.16.

Small-signal ac analysis   If $v_i(t)$ is small compared with V_{GG} and is sinusoidal, then the FET may be replaced by its ac equivalent circuit. The result is the ac equivalent circuit of Figure 8.21, in which V_{gs} is the complex amplitude of the ac component of v_{GS}. It is clear that

$$V_{gs} = -I_d R_s + V_i \tag{8.41}$$

$$I_d R_L + (I_d - g_m V_{gs}) r_d + I_d R_s = 0 \tag{8.42}$$

$$V_o = -R_L I_d \tag{8.43}$$

Solution of (8.41), (8.42), and (8.43) gives the voltage gain

$$A_v = \frac{V_o}{V_i} = -\frac{g_m r_d R_L}{r_d + R_L + (1 + g_m r_d) R_s} \tag{8.44}$$

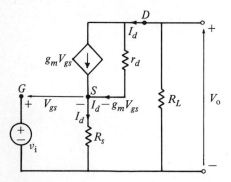

Figure 8.21 Small-signal ac equivalent circuit of the self-biased amplifier circuit.

A comparison of (8.44) with (8.28), which gives the voltage gain of the basic FET amplifier, shows that the voltage gain is reduced by the insertion of the resistance R_s. Thus the elimination of one battery is accomplished at the expense of a reduction in voltage gain. To restore this voltage gain, a *by-pass capacitor* is commonly placed in parallel with R_s, as shown in Figure 8.22. This capacitor does not affect the quiescent point of the FET. But the term R_s in the ac gain expression (8.44) is now replaced by the impedance of the parallel combination of R_s and C_s, which is

$$Z_s = \frac{1}{(1/R_s) + j\omega C_s} \qquad (8.45)$$

We can make this as small as necessary by making C_s sufficiently large.

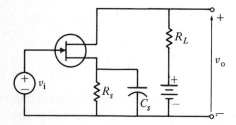

Figure 8.22 Self-biased circuit with a by-pass capacitor.

8.8 The source follower

The source follower circuit is shown in Figure 8.23(a). The arrangement is the same as the self-bias circuit of Figure 8.18 with $R_L = 0$, so that the dc analysis of this circuit is the same. The output, however, is taken at the source rather than the drain. So the ac equivalent circuit of the source follower is as shown in Figure 8.23(b). The drain is shorted to ground through the power supply, which is transparent to ac. The source follower is also known as the common-drain amplifier.

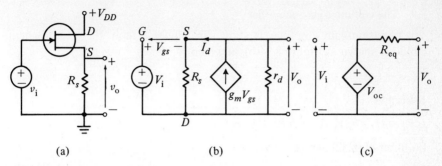

Figure 8.23 The source follower.

For ac

$$V_{gs} = V_i - I_d R_s = V_i - V_o \tag{8.46}$$

KCL requires that

$$\frac{V_o}{R_s} + \frac{V_o}{r_d} = g_m V_{gs} \tag{8.47}$$

These equations give

$$A_v = \frac{V_o}{V_i} = \frac{g_m}{g_m + (1/r_d) + (1/R_s)} \tag{8.48}$$

In (8.48), A_v approaches unity if r_d and R_s are both very large. This explains the name *source follower*.

Since the input and the remainder of the circuit of Figure 8.23(b) are completely isolated from each other, this circuit can be reduced to the form of Figure 8.23(c). The output branch is the Thévenin's equivalent at the output port. To get this equivalent we obtain from (8.48)

$$V_{oc} = \frac{g_m}{g_m + (1/r_d) + (1/R_s)} V_i \tag{8.49}$$

The short-circuit current at port 2 is

$$I_{sc} = g_m V_i \tag{8.50}$$

Hence

$$R_{eq} = \frac{V_{oc}}{I_{sc}} = \frac{1}{g_m + (1/r_d) + (1/R_s)} \tag{8.51}$$

The output impedance is seen to be equivalent to the parallel combination of g_m, R_s, and r_d. If R_s and r_d are both large compared with $1/g_m$, then $R_{eq} \cong 1/g_m$. For this reason, the source follower is frequently used to match a low-impedance load to a high-impedance source.

8.9 The common-gate amplifier

The common-gate amplifier is shown in Figure 8.24(a). Its ac equivalent circuit is shown in Figure 8.24(b), in which

$$V_{gs} = -I_d R_s - V_i \qquad (8.52)$$

KVL gives

$$I_d R_L + (I_d - g_m V_{gs}) r_d + I_d R_s + V_i = 0 \qquad (8.53)$$

Solution of (8.52) and (8.53) gives

$$I_d = -\frac{(g_m r_d + 1) V_i}{r_d + R_L + (1 + g_m r_d) R_s} \qquad (8.54)$$

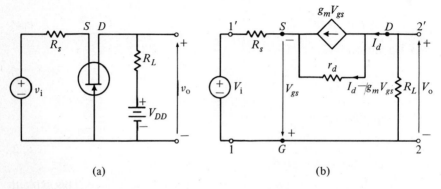

(a) (b)

Figure 8.24 The common-gate amplifier.

For an alternative solution that gives more complete information about this circuit, we regard the circuit of Figure 8.24(b) as a two-port with the terminal-pair designations shown (port 1 between terminals 1 and 1′ and port 2 between terminals 2 and 2′). The impedance parameters are

$$z_{11} = \frac{V_i}{-I_d} = \frac{r_d + R_L + (g_m r_d + 1) R_s}{g_m r_d + 1} \qquad (8.55)$$

$$z_{21} = \frac{V_o}{-I_d} = R_L = z_{22} \qquad (8.56)$$

$$z_{12} = \frac{R_L}{1 + g_m r_d} \qquad (8.57)$$

Hence for the two-port

$$[z] = \begin{bmatrix} \dfrac{r_d + R_L + (g_m r_d + 1) R_s}{1 + g_m r_d} & \dfrac{R_L}{1 + g_m r_d} \\[2mm] R_L & R_L \end{bmatrix} \qquad (8.58)$$

Since R_L is regarded as internal to the two-port, the voltage gain V_o/V_i is now the open-circuit voltage-transfer ratio of the two-port. From Table 7.3 and with $Z_L = \infty$, we have the voltage gain

$$A_v = \frac{z_{21}}{z_{11}} = \frac{(g_m r_d + 1) R_L}{r_d + R_L + (g_m r_d + 1) R_s} \tag{8.59}$$

the input impedance

$$Z_i = z_{11} = R_s + \frac{r_d + R_L}{g_m r_d + 1} \tag{8.60}$$

and the output impedance

$$Z_o = \left. \frac{E_2}{I_2} \right|_{E_1 = 0} = \frac{1}{y_{11}} = \frac{R_L [r_d + (g_m r_d + 1) R_s]}{r_d + (g_m r_d + 1) R_s + R_L} \tag{8.61}$$

The output impedance of a common-gate amplifier is equal to the parallel combination of two resistances—R_L and $r_d + (g_m r_d + 1) R_s$. If we think of R_s as the internal resistance of the source V_i, this amplifier can transform the source resistance from a low value to a high value. Also a grounded-gate amplifier has a relatively low input resistance compared with other FET amplifiers. If $r_d = \infty$, then we have

$$A_v = \frac{g_m R_L}{1 + g_m R_s} \tag{8.62}$$

$$Z_i = R_s + \frac{1}{g_m} \tag{8.63}$$

$$Z_o = R_L \tag{8.64}$$

8.10   The metal-oxide-semiconductor FET (MOSFET) or insulated-gate FET (IGFET)

The principle of operation of the MOSFET is slightly different from that of the JFET. There are two types of MOSFET—the depletion and the enhancement types.

The depletion-type MOSFET

The depletion-type MOSFET has characteristics very similar to those of the JFET. Its channel can be of either the n type or the p type. We shall describe the operation of an n-type MOSFET. For a p-type one, the types of carriers and the polarities of voltages and currents are reversed.

The cross section of an n-type depletion MOSFET is shown in Figure 8.25(a). We start with a lightly doped p-type silicon substrate. The channel

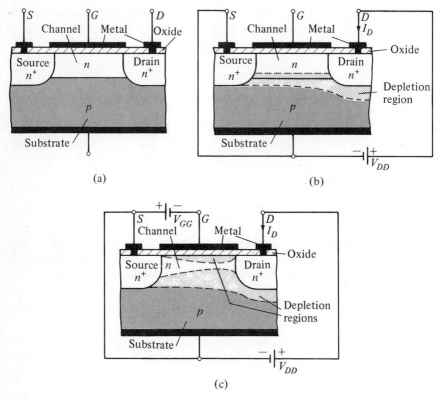

Figure 8.25 The cross section of an *n*-channel depletion-type MOSFET. (a) Basic structure. (b) Shaded region represents the depletion region between the *n*-type regions and the substrate. (c) Channel and depletion regions: v_{GS} is negative and v_{DS} is positive.

region is then doped to make it an *n*-type region. At the end of the channel, two heavily doped *n*-type regions, denoted as n^+, provide two high-conducting regions that link the channel to the two ohmic contacts connected to the source and drain terminals. The gate electrode is insulated from the channel by a layer of silicon oxide, which is an isulating material. The three electrodes are metallic, typically made of aluminum.

Usually the substrate is connected to the source, as shown in Figure 8.25(b). If the gate is floating and a positive v_{DS} is applied between the drain and the source, the *p-n* junction that exists between the *n* and n^+ regions and the *p* region is reverse-biased. A depletion region is created, as shown in Figure 8.25(b). Thus, in the normal operation of such a MOSFET, the substrate is relatively unimportant. In the channel, electrons flow from the source to the drain, resulting in a positive I_D.

Now if we make the gate negative and the drain positive with respect to the source, an additional depletion region is developed just under the gate because of the capacitive effect between the gate and the channel. This is illustrated in Figure 8.25(c). As v_{GS} is made more negative, the depletion region widens and the channel narrows. A depletion MOSFET is similar to a JFET and acts like a voltage-controlled resistor for low v_{DS}. As $|v_{GS}|$ becomes sufficiently high, the channel is pinched-off. Beyond pinch-off, the drain current is practically unchanged for a wide range of v_{DS}.

The symbols for n-channel depletion MOSFETs are shown in Figure 8.26. Figure 8.26(a) shows a three-terminal MOSFET whose substrate terminal is not accessible. Figure 8.26(b) represents a three-terminal MOSFET whose substrate terminal is internally connected to the source. This type is the most commonly used. The symbol of Figure 8.26(c) represents a four-terminal MOSFET whose substrate is available for external connection. For p-channel depletion MOSFETs, the symbols are the same as those for the n-channel ones except that the directions of the arrows are reversed.

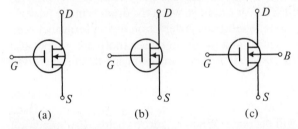

(a)   (b)   (c)

Figure 8.26 Symbols for n-channel depletion-type MOSFETs.

Enhancement-type MOSFET

An enhancement MOSFET differs from a depletion one in that the n-type region between the two n^+-type regions is omitted. The cross section of such a MOSFET is shown in Figure 8.27(a). If the gate is floating and a voltage

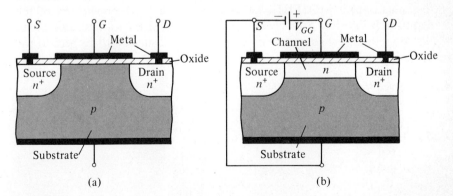

(a)   (b)

Figure 8.27 The cross section of an n-channel enhancement-type MOSFET. (a) Basic structure. (b) Formation of an n-type channel by a positive v_{GS} greater than V_{TH}.

is applied between the drain and the source, there will be negligible current flowing, since one or the other n^+ region will be reverse-biased with respect to the substrate and the only current that can flow is the reverse saturation current of one of the p-n junctions.

If the gate is made more positive with respect to the substrate and the source, the capacitive effect between the gate and the substrate will repel the p-type carriers away from and attract the n-type ones to the area just under the gate. As v_{GS} is gradually made more positive, the p-type carriers in this region will gradually diminish while the n-type will increase. At a certain value of v_{GS}, this region will have more n-type carriers than p-type ones. When this value of v_{GS} is reached, a channel is formed, as shown in Figure 8.27(b). This value of v_{GS} is known as the *threshold voltage* and is designated as V_{TH}. As v_{GS} is further increased, more n-type carriers are attracted to the channel and it becomes more conductive.

Once the channel is formed, this device has properties very similar to those of a depletion MOSFET. For example, when the drain is made positive with respect to the source and the substrate, a depletion region forms between the area that includes the channel and the drain region (both are n-type) and the substrate (p-type). The substrate is again insignificant in the operation of the device.

For $v_{GS} > V_{TH}$, and if v_{DS} is increased from zero in the positive direction, the channel is essentially a resistor for low values of v_{DS}. As v_{DS} is increased further, $v_{GD} = v_{GS} - v_{DS}$ will decrease. When v_{GD} drops below V_{TH}, pinch-off occurs and i_D remains essentially constant for a wide range of v_{DS}.

The symbols for n-channel enhancement MOSFETs are shown in Figure 8.28. As in the depletion-type ones, the substrate terminal may be unaccessible, internally connected, or available for external connection. The symbols for the p-channel ones are identical to the n-channel ones with the directions of the arrows reversed.

Having described the principles of operation of both the depletion and the enhancement MOSFETs, let us now return to the operation of the depletion MOSFET. An n-channel depletion MOSFET will also operate in the enhancement mode when its gate is made positive with respect to the

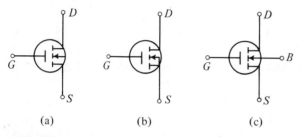

(a)　　　　　　(b)　　　　　　(c)

Figure 8.28 Symbols for n-channel enhancement-type MOSFETs.

source. As we make the gate more positive with respect to the substrate, more n-type carriers are drawn to the channel, thus increasing the conductivity of the channel. Hence a depletion MOSFET may have its gate biased either positively or negatively with respect to the source.

Figure 8.29(a) shows a set of drain characteristics of a typical n-channel depletion MOSFET. The MOSFET can operate in the depletion mode ($v_{GS} < 0$) or in the enhancement mode ($v_{GS} > 0$). The pinch-off voltage V_{PO} is -4 V. For $v_{GS} = 0$, pinch-off occurs at $v_{DS} = v_{GS} - V_{PO}$, which is shown as a dashed curve.

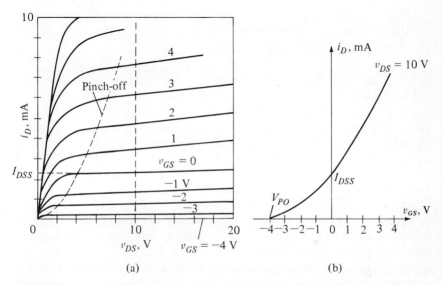

Figure 8.29   (a) Drain characteristics of an n-channel depletion MOSFET. (b) Transfer characteristic of an n-channel depletion MOSFET.

The gate-to-drain transfer characteristic for the same MOSFET is shown in Figure 8.29(b). This is simply a plot of i_D versus v_{GS} for a fixed v_{DS}. This curve also follows the square law of (8.2) as in an n-channel JFET. But the region for which this relationship is valid extends well into the positive part of the v_{GS} axis.

Figure 8.30(a) shows the drain characteristics of a typical n-channel enhancement MOSFET. The threshold voltage V_{TH} is approximately 1.5 V. The pinch-off points are shown as a dashed curve. The gate-to-drain transfer characteristic for $v_{DS} = 10$ V is shown in Figure 8.30(b). This characteristic also follows the square law or

$$i_D = K(v_{GS} - V_{TH})^2 \tag{8.65}$$

for $v_{GS} > V_{TH}$.

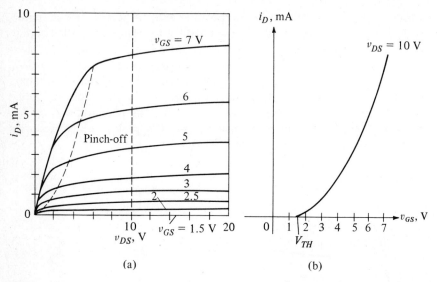

Figure 8.30 (a) Drain characteristics of an *n*-channel enhancement MOSFET. (b) Transfer characteristic of an *n*-channel enhancement MOSFET.

8.11 The biasing of the MOSFET

In the normal operation of an *n*-channel enhancement-type MOSFET, the drain is maintained at a potential that is positive with respect to the source. But the gate must also be biased at a potential positive with respect to the source. This is just opposite to the normal operation of an *n*-channel JFET.

Figure 8.31 shows two simple methods of biasing an *n*-channel enhancement MOSFET. Since the gate current in a MOSFET is even smaller than

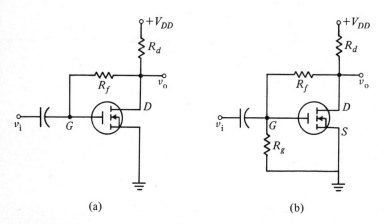

Figure 8.31 Biasing schemes for the enhancement MOSFET.

that in a JFET, the gate can be considered open-circuited. Hence, in the arrangement of Figure 8.31(a), the gate and the drain are maintained at the same potential or

$$V_{GS} = V_{DS} \tag{8.66}$$

This arrangement usually places the operating point quite close to the knees of the drain characteristics.

To move the operating point more to the current-saturation region, the arrangement of Figure 8.31(a) can be used. Here

$$V_{GS} = \frac{R_g}{R_f + R_g} V_{DS} \tag{8.67}$$

EXAMPLE 6   The characteristics of the MOSFET of Figure 8.31 are shown in Figure 8.32, with $V_{DD} = 20$ V, $R_d = 2$ kΩ, and $R_f = 10$ MΩ. Find the operating point if (a) $R_g = 10$ MΩ [Figure 8.31(b)] and (b) $R_g = \infty$ [Figure 8.31(a).].

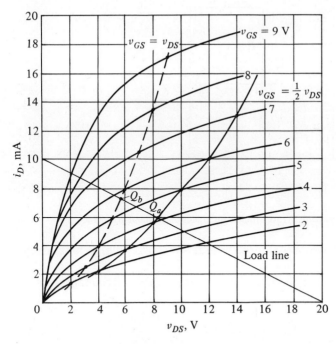

Figure 8.32 Example of the determination of the quiescent point for the circuit of Figure 8.31(b).

SOLUTION   (a) The relationships that must be satisfied are

$$V_{GS} = \tfrac{1}{2}V_{DS} \tag{8.68}$$

and

$$V_{DS} = V_{DD} - I_D R_D \tag{8.69}$$

We can easily locate points satisfying (8.68) on the drain characteristics. These points are joined on a curve in Figure 8.32. Equation (8.69) is the equation of a load line. The intersect of the load line and the $V_{GS} = \frac{1}{2}V_{DS}$ curve is the operating point Q_a.

(b) As in (a), the relationships to be satisfied are

$$V_{GS} = V_{DS} \tag{8.70}$$

and the same load line. The operating point is labeled Q_b in Figure 8.32.

An alternative scheme for biasing an enhancement MOSFET is shown in Figure 8.33(a). Since the gate draws no current, the gate-to-source voltage

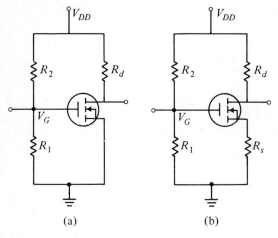

(a)   (b)

Figure 8.33 Other biasing arrangements for the enhancement MOSFET.

can be maintained independently of the drain-to-source voltage. In the circuit, $V_{GS} = V_G = R_1 V_{DD}/(R_1 + R_2)$.

Figure 8.33(b) shows another biasing circuit that is frequently used. In this circuit,

$$V_{GS} = \frac{R_1}{R_1 + R_2} V_{DD} - I_D R_s = V_G - I_D R_s \tag{8.71}$$

and

$$V_{DS} = V_{DD} - I_D(R_s + R_d) \tag{8.72}$$

To obtain the quiescent point graphically, we observe that V_{DD}, R_1, R_2, and R_s are known for a given circuit. The value of V_G is fixed. Thus for each value of V_{GS} there is only one value of I_D that will satisfy (8.71). A set of (i_D, v_{GS}) that satisfies (8.71) and (8.72) simultaneously is the quiescent point. The technique for locating the quiescent point is, in principle, similar to that used in Example 6 and is illustrated by Example 7.

EXAMPLE 7 The MOSFET whose drain characteristics are given in Figure 8.34(a) is used in the circuit of Figure 8.33(b) with $R_1 = R_2 = 10$ MΩ, $R_s = 400$ Ω, $R_d = 600$ Ω, and $V_{DD} = 20$ V. Determine the quiescent point. The equation for the load line is

$$20 = V_{DS} + 1000I_D \tag{8.73}$$

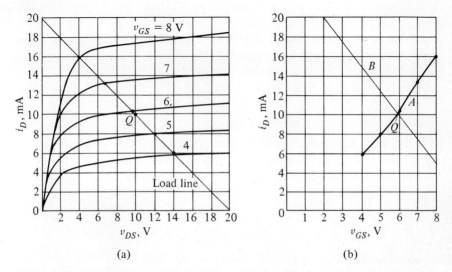

(a) (b)

Figure 8.34 Example of the determination of the quiescent point for the circuit of Figure 8.33(b).

and is readily constructed in Figure 8.34(a). A series of (i_D, v_{GS}) points along this load line can now be read off the various constant-v_{GS} contours. These points are tabulated in Table 8.3 and curve A in Figure 8.34(b) is drawn

Table **8.3**

v_{GS}	i_D
4	5.8
5	8
6	10.3
7	13.2
8	16

through them. Equation (8.71) reads

$$V_{GS} = 10 - 400I_D \tag{8.74}$$

This equation is a straight line in the i_D-v_{GS} plane. We can construct it by first locating two convenient points, for example, for $V_{GS} = 4$ V and $I_D = 15$ mA, or for $V_{GS} = 6$ V and $I_D = 10$ mA. From these points, line B is constructed in Figure 8.34(b). The intersect of curve A and line B gives the quiescent point, which is

$$I_D = 10.1 \text{ mA}, \qquad V_{GS} = 5.9 \text{ V}$$

From (8.72),

$$V_{DS} = 20 - 10.1 \times 1 = 9.9 \text{ V}$$

The gate of an n-channel depletion MOSFET may be biased either positively or negatively with respect to the source. It can use the biasing scheme for either the JFET or the enhancement MOSFET.

8.12 ac Analysis of MOSFET circuits

The ac small-signal equivalent circuit of a MOSFET is identical to that of a JFET. Hence the anlysis of the ac performance of a circuit involving MOSFETs is exactly like the analysis of a JFET circuit.

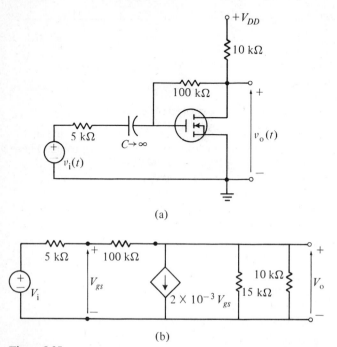

(a)

(b)

Figure 8.35

EXAMPLE 8 For the MOSFET of Figure 8.35(a) $g_m = 2\,\text{m}\mho$ and $r_d = 15\,\text{k}\Omega$. Find the small-signal voltage gain.

SOLUTION The ac equivalent circuit is shown in Figure 8.35(b). Using node analysis, we have

$$\frac{V_o}{15\,\text{k}} + \frac{V_o}{10\,\text{k}} + \frac{V_o - V_i}{105\,\text{k}} + 2 \times 10^{-3}V_{gs} = 0$$

$$V_{gs} = V_i + \tfrac{5}{105}(V_o - V_i)$$

Substituting, we get

$$\frac{V_o}{15\,\text{k}} + \frac{V_o}{10\,\text{k}} + \frac{V_o}{105\,\text{k}} + \frac{2 \times 10^{-3}}{21}V_o = -2 \times 10^{-3}V_i + \frac{2 \times 10^{-3}}{21}V_i + \frac{1}{105\,\text{k}}V_i$$

Hence

$$A_v = \frac{V_o}{V_i} = \frac{-2 + \frac{2}{21} + \frac{1}{105}}{\frac{1}{15} + \frac{1}{10} + \frac{1}{105} + \frac{1}{10.5}} = -6.98$$

8.13 Other FET circuit considerations

In this chapter, we have given a very brief account of the characteristics of FETs and the basic techniques for analyzing circuits containing these devices. What we are stressing here are only the fundamentals. There are many FET circuit topics that we did not even touch on, such as parameter variation, device fabrication, manufacturer's device specification, frequency response, biasing techniques, temperature effects, large-signal circuit analysis, and design aspects. Detailed treatments of these topics should be found in more advanced electronics courses, but we shall mention briefly just a few aspects.

In a practical FET circuit, there are usually many auxiliary components whose various functions enable the circuit to work. Two major types of auxiliary arrangements are the biasing circuit and blocking and by-passing capacitors. The biasing circuit ensures that the appropriate quiescent point is obtained and maintained during the operation. The capacitors serve to separate the quiescent (dc) and the signal (ac) quantities.

The circuit of Figure 8.36(a) is an example of an actual circuit that corresponds to the circuit of Figure 8.18. Capacitors C_1 and C_2 are blocking capacitors. They are open circuits for the dc and are large enough that, for the lowest frequency of interest, we may regard them as essentially short circuits. Since there is practically no current flowing through the gate, there is no dc current flowing through R_g and the gate is at ground potential under quiescent conditions. The value of R_g is usually quite high, so that it is practically open circuit for ac. It is possible to replace R_g by a reverse-biased junction diode, which also serves to protect the gate-to-source voltage from building up to an excessive value.

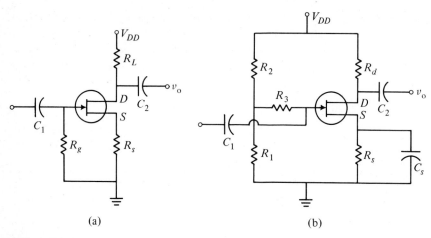

(a)   (b)

Figure 8.36 Two practical FET amplifier arrangements including auxiliary components.

The circuit of Figure 8.36(b) is a practical version of the circuit of Figure 8.33(b), in which a by-pass capacitor C_s is used to shunt R_s. The purpose of this by-pass capacitor was explained in Section 8.7. Both C_1 and C_2 are blocking capacitors, and R_3 is usually a resistor of very high resistance to increase the input resistance.

The small-signal model of FETs described in this chapter neglects the capacitances that are present between any two electrodes. Hence this model is only valid for low frequencies. Figure 8.37 shows a more complete circuit model for an FET, which includes interelectrode capacitances. The values

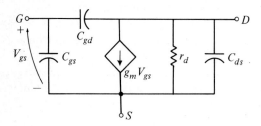

Figure 8.37 High-frequency circuit model of an FET.

of C_{gs} and C_{gd} are typically between 1 and 5 pF while that of C_{ds} is a fraction of a picofarad. Although these values tend to suggest that capacitive effects may be neglected for frequencies up to several tens of megahertz, they actually become quite significant at several hundred kilohertz because of the voltage amplification. The study of the effect of frequency on the response of an FET amplifier is, however, beyond the scope of this book.

Another aspect of FET circuit study is the relative merits of the various biasing schemes. Since the characteristics of a given FET type do vary from unit to unit and they are also altered by the temperature, the best biasing scheme should tolerate these variations. Other considerations for an FET circuit designer are the ratings of an FET. These include the total power dissipation ($i_D v_{DS}$), the maximum drain-to-source voltage (v_{DS}), and the maximum current (i_D).

Problems

8.1 In the circuit of Figure P8.1, $V_{DD} = 25$ V. For the JFET, $I_{DSS} = 5$ mA and $V_{PO} = -4$ V. Design a circuit such that, under quiescent conditions, $V_{DS} = 8$ V. The FET is assumed to be operating in the current-saturation region.

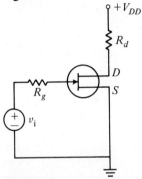

Figure P8.1

8.2 Repeat Problem 8.1 using the following new values: $I_{DSS} = 4$ mA, $V_{DS} = 7$ V.

8.3 Determine the quiescent values of V_{DS} and I_D in the circuit of Figure P8.3 with $V_{DD} = -25$ V, $I_{DSS} = -12$ mA, $V_{GG} = 1.75$ V, $V_{PO} = 5$ V, and

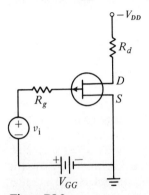

Figure P8.3

$R_d = 3.3$ kΩ. The FET is assumed to be operating in the current-saturation region.

8.4 The drain characteristics of the JFET of Figure P8.3 are given in Figure P8.4, with $V_{DD} = -30$ V and $V_{GG} = 0.4$ V. Locate the quiescent point for $R_d = 4$ kΩ.

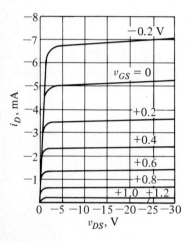

Figure P8.4

8.5 Construct the dynamic transfer characteristic of the FET amplifier circuit of Problem 8.4.

8.6 Estimate the small-signal parameters of the JFET whose drain characteristics are given in Figure P8.4 at the operating point of Problem 8.4.

8.7 What are the values of g_m, r_d, and μ of the FET of Problem 8.1 under the quiescent condition of the circuit of Figure P8.1? Give the small-signal ac equivalent circuit for this FET at this operating point.

8.8 Determine the values of g_m, r_d, and μ for the FET of Problem 8.3 at the quiescent point specified therein. Give the small-signal ac equivalent circuit of the amplifier circuit of Figure P8.3.

8.9 Find the ac small-signal gain (V_o/V_i) of the amplifier of Problem 8.1. Assume that there is infinite drain resistance and that the output signal (V_o) is taken at the drain.

8.10 Find the ac small-signal gain of the circuit of Problem 8.3. Assume that there is infinite drain resistance and that the output signal is taken at the drain.

8.11 The characterics of the FET in Figure P8.11 are given in Figure P8.4. (a) Determine the quiescent point. (b) Obtain the i_D-v_i dynamic transfer characteristic. Assume $C_s = 0$.

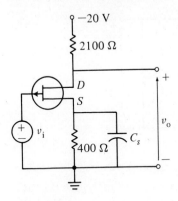

Figure P8.11

8.12 The parameters of the FET in Figure P8.11 are $\mu = 20$ and $r_d = 100$ kΩ. The signal frequency is 5 kHz. Find the small-signal gain V_o/V_i for: (a) $C_s = 0$, (b) $C_s = 50$ nF, and (c) $C_s \rightarrow \infty$.

8.13 For the FET in the circuit of Figure P8.13, $g_m = 5$ m$\mho$ and $r_d = 5$ kΩ. Find the voltage gain at 5 kHz.

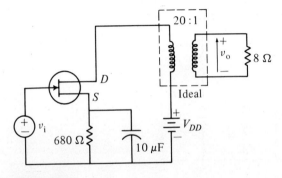

Figure P8.13

8.14 For the FET in the circuit of Figure P8.14, $\mu = 20$ and $r_d = 10$ kΩ. All capacitors have negligible impedance at the operating frequency. Find the ac voltage gain.

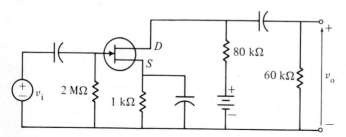

Figure P8.14

8.15 For the FET in the circuit of Figure P8.15, $g_m = 5$ m℧, $g_d = 0.1$ m℧, and $v_i(t) = 0.1 \cos 6280t$ V. (a) Draw the ac equivalent circuit. (b) Find the ac voltage gain. (c) Find the output impedance (Thévenin's equivalent impedance at the output port) of the amplifier.

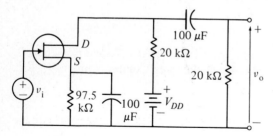

Figure P8.15

8.16 For the FET of Figure P8.16, $I_{DSS} = 6$ mA and $V_{PO} = -4$ V. The JFET is to operate at $I_D = 1.5$ mA and $V_{DS} = 6$ V. Find V_{GG} and R_d.

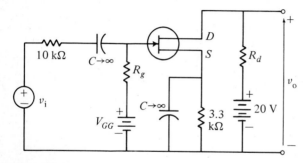

Figure P8.16

8.17 The circuit of Figure P8.17 is a dc electronic voltmeter. The resistance of the dc microammeter M is negligible. The FET has $I_{DSS} = 4$ mA and $V_{PO} = -3$ V. (a) What should the value of R_s be if $i_{max} = 0$ corresponds to $v_i = 0$? (b) The full-scale deflection of M corresponds to $i_{max} = 200$ μA. What is the value of v_i required to produce the full-scale deflection?

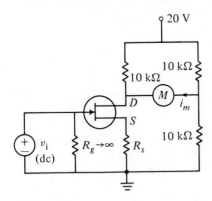

Figure P8.17

8.18 Calculate the ac small-signal gain of the amplifier of Problem 8.16.

8.19 The FET of Figure P8.19 has the following parameters: $I_{DSS} = 1$ mA, $V_{PO} = -1$ V. What is R_1 if the quiescent point has a drain-to-ground voltage of 10 V?

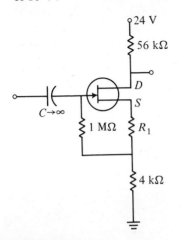

Figure P8.19

8.20 In the circuit of Figure P8.20, $V_{DD} = 60$ V, $R_1 = 1.3$ MΩ, $R_2 = 200$ kΩ, $R_d = 18$ kΩ, and $R_s = 4$ kΩ. For the FET, $|I_{DSS}| = 4$ mA and $V_{PO} = 4$ V. Find the quiescent I_D, V_{GS}, and V_{DS}.

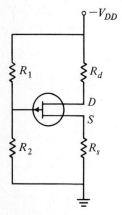

Figure P8.20

8.21 In the circuit of Figure P8.21, the JFET parameters are $\mu = 30$ and $r_d = 5$ kΩ. Neglecting capacitive impedances, find the ac small-signal gain.

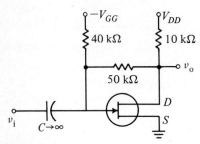

Figure P8.21

8.22 In the circuit of Figure P8.22, the FET parameters are $g_m = 2$ m℧ and $r_d = 10$ kΩ. Find the voltage gain at 1 kHz.

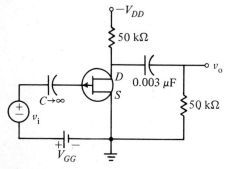

Figure P8.22

8.23 For the common-gate amplifier of Figure P8.23, neglect C_{ds} and show that the voltage gain is given by

$$A_v = \frac{g_m + g_d}{(G_d + g_d + j\omega C_{gd})[1 + (g_m + g_d + j\omega C_{gs})R_s] - (g_m + g_d)R_s g_d}$$

and the input admittance by

$$Y_i = \frac{g_m + g_d(1 - A_v) + j\omega C_{gs}}{1 + R_s(g_m + g_d + j\omega C_{gs})}$$

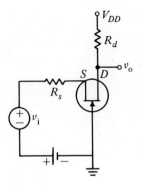

Figure P8.23

8.24 The transfer characteristic of a MOSFET in the current-saturation region can be approximately represented by the equation

$$I_{D(ON)} = K'\left(1 - \frac{V_{GS}}{V_{GS(TH)}}\right)^2 = K(V_{GS} - V_{GS(TH)})^2$$

For the MOSFET of Figure P8.24, $V_{GS(TH)} = 3$ V and $K = 0.1$ mA/V². Find R_d, given that the drain current is to be 2 mA under quiescent condition.

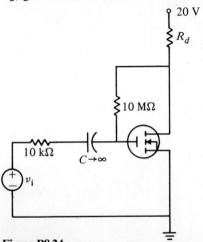

Figure P8.24

8.25 The output characteristics of the MOSFET of Figure P8.25(a) are given in Figure P8.25(b). (a) Find the quiescent point of the MOSFET. (b) Find the small-signal ac parameters of the MOSFET. (c) Calculate the ac voltage gain.

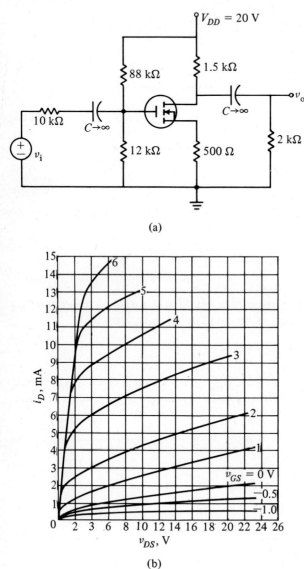

(a)

(b)

Figure P8.25

9 | BIPOLAR TRANSISTOR CIRCUITS

In this chapter we shall deal with the fundamentals of the bipolar junction transistor and circuits that use this device.

9.1 The bipolar junction transistor

A junction transistor is an arrangement of two *p-n* junctions back to back in one crystal. Two such arrangements are possible—the *p-n-p* and the *n-p-n*—as shown in Figure 9.1. Their corresponding circuit symbols are shown immediately below them.

The region sandwiched between the two junctions is known as the base (*B*). The region to one side of the base is the emitter (*E*) and the other is the collector (*C*). The two junctions are called the emitter junction J_E and the collector junction J_C.

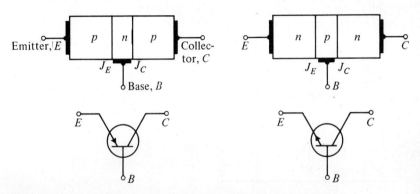

Figure 9.1 Arrangements for junction transistors and their symbols.

283

When a transistor is used in an amplifier circuit, the emitter junction is forward-biased and the collector junction is reverse-biased. Majority carriers in the emitter region are injected into the base region. These become minority carriers while they are in the base region. A large number of these minority carriers diffuse toward the collector region and are "collected" by the collector-to-base potential, which favors this diffusion process. Typically, 99% of the injected minority carriers end up in the collector region and contribute to the collector current. It is this diffusion of minority carriers that accounts for the amplification capability of the transistor.

Earlier transistors were of the point-contact and alloy types. More modern ones are fabricated from the grown junction or by the diffusion process. Transistors produced by the last process are usually of the planar form. Figure 9.2 shows a typical cross section of a planar *p-n-p* transistor.

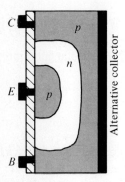

Figure 9.2   An arrangement for a planar junction transistor.

9.2   Current components in a transistor

To simplify our description of the current components in a transistor, we shall assume that the transistor is of the *p-n-p* type. For an *n-p-n* transistor, all types of carriers and voltage and current polarities are reversed.

In the arrangement of Figure 9.3, the emitter junction is forward-biased

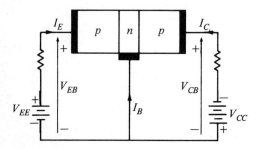

Figure 9.3   Notations for electric quantities associated with a transistor.

and the collector junction is reverse-biased. All currents are assumed to be directed into the transistor. By KCL, we have

$$I_B + I_C + I_E = 0 \tag{9.1}$$

Figure 9.4 shows the various components of the currents in a transistor under normal operation. Let us first focus our attention on the diffusion of the majority carriers as indicated in Figure 9.4(a). This takes place across

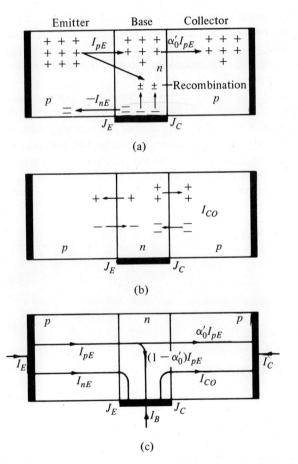

(a)

(b)

(c)

Figure 9.4 (a) Diffusion of majority carriers, (b) drift of minority carriers, and (c) component currents in a p-n-p transistor.

the emitter junction, with holes moving from the emitter region to the base region (I_{pE}) and electrons moving from the base region to the emitter region (I_{nE}). In a commercial transistor, the doping in the emitter is purposely made much larger than that in the base. Hence the diffusion current across the emitter junction is almost entirely made up of I_{pE}. Actually

$$I_E = I_{pE} + I_{nE} \tag{9.2}$$

The ratio between I_{pE} and I_E is known as the emitter efficiency and is denoted by γ_0:

$$\gamma_0 = \frac{I_{pE}}{I_E} = \frac{I_{pE}}{I_{pE} + I_{nE}} \tag{9.3}$$

Because the base region is usually relatively thin (typically 10^{-4} cm), most of the holes injected into the base region diffuse into the collector. This component of I_{pE} is labeled $\alpha_0' I_{pE}$ in Figure 9.4(a). In the base region a small amount of recombination does take place and this results in a contribution of $(1 - \alpha_0') I_{pE}$ to the base current $-I_B$.

At the same time, the drift of minority carriers across each p-n junction (holes from the n region to the p region and electrons from the p region to the n region) also takes place. The drift current across the emitter junction is negligible compared with the diffusion current because the junction is forward-biased. The drift current across the collector junction is the *reverse saturation current* of this junction. It is labeled I_{CO} in Figure 9.4(b).

All the significant components of the currents in a transistor are summarized in Figure 9.4(c). We see that

$$\begin{aligned}
I_C &= -\alpha_0' I_{pE} - I_{CO} \\
&= -\alpha_0' \gamma_0 I_E - I_{CO} \\
&= -\alpha_0 I_E - I_{CO}
\end{aligned} \tag{9.4}$$

in which

$$\alpha_0 = \alpha_0' \gamma_0 \tag{9.5}$$

is known as the *dc alpha* of the transistor. Since I_{CO} is almost constant, we see that

$$\alpha_0 = -\frac{dI_C}{dI_E} \tag{9.6}$$

Substituting I_E from (9.1) into (9.4) and rearranging we get

$$I_C = \frac{\alpha_0}{1 - \alpha_0} I_B - \frac{1}{1 - \alpha_0} I_{CO} = \beta_0 I_B - (1 + \beta_0) I_{CO} \tag{9.7}$$

in which

$$\beta_0 = \frac{\alpha_0}{1 - \alpha_0} = \frac{dI_C}{dI_B} \tag{9.8}$$

is approximately the ratio between the collector current change and the base current change.

Thus in a junction transistor both majority and minority carriers contribute to the conduction. Hence these transistors are known as *bipolar junction transistors* or *bipolar transistors*. In this chapter, a bipolar transistor will simply be called a transistor.

A transistor by itself is primarily a current-controlled current source. Except for I_{CO}, which ideally would be small, (9.4) indicates that I_C is proportional to I_E, or

$$-I_C \cong \alpha_0 I_E \tag{9.9}$$

and (9.7) indicates that I_C is also proportional to I_B, or

$$I_C \cong \beta_0 I_B \tag{9.10}$$

It is this property that makes a transistor capable of performing numerous amplification and other tasks in electronic circuits.

The foregoing description of transistor operations is valid only for the biasing polarities of Figure 9.3. A transistor operated under such a mode is said to be operating in its *active region*. For a *p-n-p* transistor, this region lies in the second quadrant of the v_{EB}-v_{CB} plane, as shown in Figure 9.5.

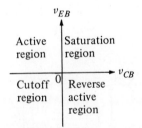

Figure 9.5 Terms used to describe the different operating regions of a transistor.

For most linear applications, the transistor is confined to operate in this region. For large-signal, pulse, or digital applications, a transistor operation may lie entirely or partially in other regions.

In the first quadrant, both junctions are forward-biased. The current I_C is greatly reduced in magnitude and may even become positive. This region is known as the *saturation region*.

In the third quadrant, both junctions are reverse-biased and they act as reverse-biased diodes. Currents I_E and I_C are the reverse saturation currents of the respective junctions. This is known as the *cutoff region*.

In the fourth quadrant, the emitter and collector reverse roles in theory and to some extent in reality. But because of the relative doping of the two *p* regions, the transistor generally does not perform satisfactorily in this region, which is known as the *reverse active region*.

9.3 Large-signal model for the junction transistor

Combining equations (9.4) and (6.1), we have

$$I_C = -\alpha_N I_E + I_{CO}(\epsilon^{V_{CB}/\eta V_T} - 1) \qquad (9.11)$$

Here the subscript of α_N connotes the *normal* operation of the transistor, I_{CO} is the reverse saturation current of the collector junction, and V_{CB} is the voltage across the collector junction. This formula is valid when the emitter junction is forward-biased, while the collector junction can be either forward- or reverse-biased, that is, in the first and second quadrants of the v_{EB}-v_{CB} plane of Figure 9.5.

When the collector junction is forward-biased, we may write an equation similar to (9.11).

$$I_E = -\alpha_R I_C + I_{EO}(\epsilon^{V_{EB}/\eta V_T} - 1) \qquad (9.12)$$

Here the subscript of α_R connotes the reversed operation of the transistor, I_{EO} is the reverse saturation current of the emitter junction, and V_{EB} is the voltage across the emitter junction. This formula is valid in the third and fourth quadrants of the plane of Figure 9.5.

The circuit model of a transistor with characteristic equations of (9.11) and (9.12) is shown in Figure 9.6(a). The two diodes in the circuit are *p-n* junction diodes with their respective values of reverse saturation currents indicated on the diagram. The circuit model of Figure 9.6(a) is now valid for all polarities of V_{EB} and V_{CB}.

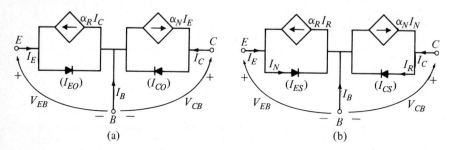

Figure 9.6 The Ebers-Moll models of a transistor. (Quantities in parentheses are the reverse saturation currents of the junction diodes.)

Solving for I_E and I_C in terms of I_{CO} and I_{EO} from (9.11) and (9.12), we get

$$I_E = -\frac{\alpha_R I_{CO}}{1 - \alpha_N \alpha_R}(\epsilon^{V_{CB}/\eta V_T} - 1) + \frac{I_{EO}}{1 - \alpha_N \alpha_R}(\epsilon^{V_{EB}/\eta V_T} - 1)$$

$$(9.13)$$

$$I_C = -\frac{\alpha_N I_{EO}}{1 - \alpha_N \alpha_R}(\epsilon^{V_{EB}/\eta V_T} - 1) + \frac{I_{CO}}{1 - \alpha_N \alpha_R}(\epsilon^{V_{CB}/\eta V_T} - 1)$$

Equations (9.13) may be represented by the circuit model of Figure 9.6(b), in which the two diodes are again *p-n* junction diodes with their equivalent reverse saturation currents given by

$$I_{ES} = \frac{I_{EO}}{1 - \alpha_N \alpha_R}, \qquad I_{CS} = \frac{I_{CO}}{1 - \alpha_N \alpha_R}$$

The two circuits of Figure 9.6 are known as the *Ebers-Moll models* of a transistor.

9.4 Transistor configurations

Since the transistor is a three-terminal device, there are three voltage variables and three current variables. Of course, only two of these three voltages or currents are independent. But there are altogether four independent variables—two voltages and two currents.

In an FET there are essentially only three variables: v_{GS}, i_D, and v_{DS}. The interrelationship among these three variables is a surface in a three-dimensional space (Figure 8.4). In a transistor, there are four interrelated quantities. This makes the three-dimensional surface visualization inadequate to describe their interrelationship. We have to rely on a combination of two three-dimensional surfaces, or their contours, to give the quantitative description of a transistor.

Furthermore, depending on the application, we may prefer to use different sets of two of the three voltages (or currents). The following are the three possible orientations and the preferred voltage and current variables:

1 *The common-base configuration* [*Figure 9.7(a)*]   Usually the emitter is regarded as the input terminal and the collector as the output. The terminal quantities of interest are i_E, i_C, v_{EB}, and v_{CB}.

2 *The common-emitter configuration* [*Figure 9.7(b)*]   Usually the base is regarded as the input terminal and the collector as the output. The terminal quantities of interest are i_B, i_C, v_{BE}, and v_{CE}.

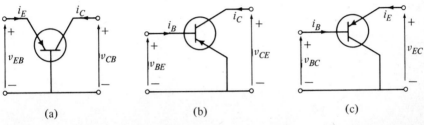

Figure 9.7 (a) The common-base, (b) the common-emitter, and (c) the common-collector configurations of a transistor.

3 *The common-collector configuration* [*Figure 9.7(c)*] Usually the base is regarded as the input terminal and the emitter as the output. The terminal quantities of interest are i_B, I_E, v_{BC}, and v_{EC}.

A transistor is primarily a current-to-current transducer. It is generally used in conjunction with other circuit elements to produce current, voltage, or power gains. The different configurations give different gains and different input and/or output impedances. The range of gains and input and output impedances allows us to find the configuration most suited for each particular application.

In presenting quantitatively the electrical characteristics of a transistor, we find it most convenient to use the input current and the output voltage as the independent variables. The input voltage and the output current are expressed as functions of these two independent variables. Curves describing these two functions are known as the input and output characteristics, respectively.

9.5 The common-base transistor characteristics

For the circuit of Figure 9.7(a), the output and input characteristics of a transistor in the common-base configuration are

$$i_C = f_1(v_{CB}, i_E) \tag{9.14}$$

$$v_{EB} = f_2(v_{CB}, i_E) \tag{9.15}$$

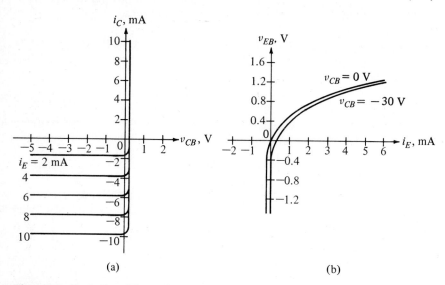

(a)   (b)

Figure 9.8 Examples of theoretical common-base transistor characteristics. (a) Output characteristics. (b) Input characteristics.

The output characteristic (9.14) was already expressed in the correct form in (9.11) and is repeated here.

$$i_C = -\alpha_N i_E + I_{CO}(\epsilon^{V_{CB}/\eta V_T} - 1) \tag{9.16}$$

This equation is usually displayed as i_C-v_{CB} curves for various fixed values of i_E. An example is shown in Figure 9.8(a). The third quadrant is the active region; the second quadrant is the cut-off region; the first and fourth quadrants correspond to the saturation region.

We can obtain the input characteristic (9.15) by eliminating I_C in (9.11) and (9.12). Figure 9.8(b) shows a typical set of v_{EB}-i_E curves for different fixed values of v_{CB}. The normal active region is the first quadrant.

The characteristics of Figure 9.8 are based on theoretical derivations and on the assumption that α_N and α_R are constant. Figure 9.9 shows a set of typical common-base input and output characteristics. Since for a p-n-p transistor the active region in the output characteristic is the third quadrant, it is usually more convenient to present this information with both axes inverted so that the active region falls in the first quadrant.

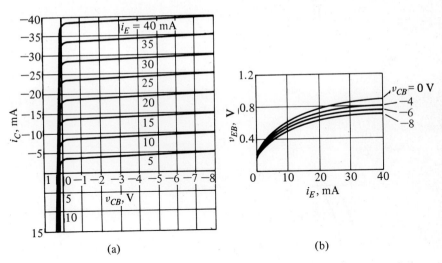

(a)   (b)

Figure 9.9 Example of practical common-base transistor characteristics. (a) Output characteristics. (b) Input characteristics.

One major discrepancy between the Ebers-Moll equations and an actual transistor characteristic is the fact that, for a fixed i_E, i_C does not remain constant as v_{CB} is varied. Figure 9.9 shows that α_N increases as $|v_{CB}|$ increases. This is because of the widening of the depletion region of the collector junction and the consequent narrowing of the effective base region as $|v_{CB}|$ is increased. This phenomenon is known as the *Early effect*. This effect also causes the input characteristic to shift downward as $|v_{CB}|$ is increased.

9.6 The common-emitter transistor characteristics

For the circuit of Figure 9.7(b) the output and input characteristics of a transistor in the CE configuration are

$$i_C = g_1(v_{CE}, i_B) \tag{9.17}$$

$$v_{BE} = g_2(v_{CE}, i_B) \tag{9.18}$$

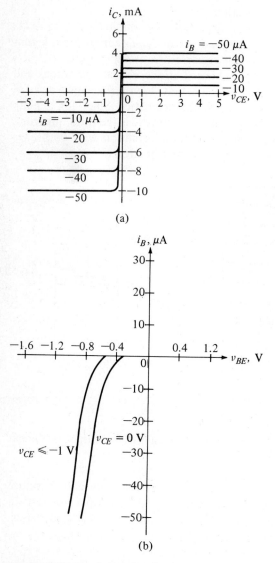

(a)

(b)

Figure 9.10 Example of theoretical common-emitter characteristics. (a) Output characteristics. (b) Input characteristics.

Explicit expressions for (9.17) and (9.18) may be found by solving for i_C and v_{BE} ($= -v_{EB}$) in terms of v_{CE} and i_B from (9.11) and (9.12). Characteristic (9.17) is usually displayed as i_C-v_{CE} curves for different values of i_B. An example of such a set of curves is shown in Figure 9.10(a). The input characteristics are usually displayed as v_{BE}-i_B curves for different values of v_{CE}. For a silicon transistor, these curves are indistinguishable from one another for $v_{CE} \leq -1$ V. Figure 9.10(b) shows a typical input characteristic based on (9.11) and (9.12).

A set of output and input common-emitter characteristics of a practical transistor is shown in Figure 9.11. We can see from this that the slopes of the output characteristics of the common-emitter configuration are much higher than those of the common-base configuration.

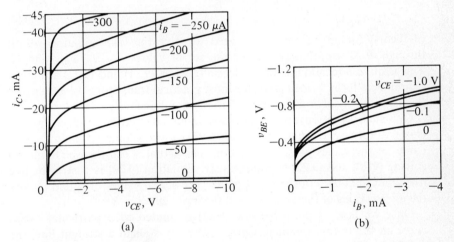

(a)   (b)

Figure 9.11   Example of practical common-emitter transistor characteristics. (a) Output characteristics. (b) Input characteristics.

9.7   dc Analysis of basic common-emitter transistor amplifier

Figure 9.12 shows the basic amplifier circuit using a junction transistor in the common-emitter configuration. The KVL equations to be satisfied are

$$v_o = v_{CE} = -V_{CC} - R_L i_C \tag{9.19}$$

$$v_i - V_{BB} = v_{BE} + i_B R_s \tag{9.20}$$

In the dc analysis of this circuit, we are interested in determining i_B and i_C for the fixed-bias voltage V_{BB} and the supply voltage V_{CC} with a given value of v_i.* The transistor characteristics are given by the output and input

---

* To find the quiescent point, set $v_i = 0$.

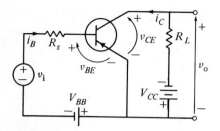

Figure 9.12 Basic common-emitter transistor amplifier circuit.

characteristics of the transistor. Analytically they may be represented by

$$i_C = g_1(v_{CE}, i_B) \tag{9.21}$$

$$v_{BE} = g_2(v_{CE}, i_B) \tag{9.22}$$

In theory, for any given v_i, we need to solve the four equations (9.19) through (9.22) simultaneously for the set of values v_{CE}, i_C, v_{BE}, and i_B. This is quite a formidable task, especially when (9.21) and (9.22) are given in graphical form. Fortunately, for most practical transistors, we are spared the necessity of solving the four equations simultaneously.

One such situation arises when the input characteristic curves are so clustered for a wide range of v_{CE} values that they become virtually a single curve for the values of v_{CE} in question. The actual i_B can then be found by solving (9.20) and (9.22) simultaneously. Equation (9.20) is a straight line (the input load line) in the v_{BE}-i_B plane. The actual values of i_B and v_{BE} are the intersections of the load line and the input curve.

Once we have i_B pinned down, (9.21) is limited to a particular i_C-v_{CE} curve on the output characteristics. But (9.19) is again a straight line (the output load line) in the i_C-v_{CE} plane. The actual values of i_C and v_{CE} are given by the intersection of the load line and the particular output curve.

EXAMPLE 1 The characteristics of the transistor of the circuit of Figure 9.12 are given in Figure 9.13, with $|V_{CC}| = 15$ volts, $|V_{BB}| = 9$ volts, $R_L = 250\ \Omega$, and $R_s = 30$ kΩ. Find the quiescent point.

SOLUTION For quiescent conditions, with $v_i = 0$, (9.20) reads

$$-9 = v_{BE} + 30\ \text{k}\ i_B$$

The input load line thus crosses the axes at $v_{BE} = -9$ V and $i_B = -300\ \mu$A. Since $v_{BE} = -9$ is not visible, the visible portion of the load line ought to have a slope of -30 k, or a change of 25 μA in i_B for every change of 0.75 V in v_{BE}. From Figure 9.13(b), we can estimate that $I_B = -0.28$ mA and $V_{BE} = -0.6$ V.

Equation (9.19) reads

$$v_{CE} = -15 - 250i_C$$

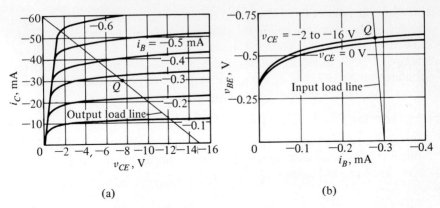

(a)   (b)

Figure 9.13 Input and output load lines of circuit of Figure 9.12.

The output load line thus crosses the axes at $v_{CE} = -15$ V and $i_C = -60$ mA. This load line is drawn on the output characteristics in Figure 9.13(a). The quiescent point of the output characteristic is on the load line just below the $i_B = -300$ μA curve. It is estimated that $I_C = 30$ mA and $v_{CE} = -7.4$ V.

Example 1 suggests that the value of v_{BE} is not at all critical in determining the output operating point of a transistor. The value of $|v_{BE}|$ is typically considerably smaller than $|V_{BB}|$. Also its variation is only over a very narrow range. Usually we simply estimate the value of $|v_{BE}|$ in order to determine i_B. This is the other approximation that is frequently made in a dc transistor circuit analysis. In fact, for many practical purposes we can assume that $|v_{BE}|$ is constant. The constant value is usually set at approximately 0.6 V for silicon transistors. Once we accept this assumption, we find that (9.20) gives

$$I_B = \frac{v_i - V_{BB} - V_{BE}}{R_s} \tag{9.23}$$

and I_B is known. The remainder of the procedure is unchanged.

For instance, in Example 1 we may assume that $V_{BE} = -0.6$ V and

$$I_B = \frac{-9 + 0.6}{30 \text{ k}} = -280 \ \mu\text{A}$$

This assumption is seen to be very good. If I_B was obtained on the assumption that $|V_{BE}|$ fell within the range between 0.5 and 0.7 V, its variation would not exceed the accuracy afforded by the resolution of the graphical data. Hence this assumption that $|v_{BE}|$ is constant frequently produces good results.

In the event that $v_i(t)$ is a large, slow-varying signal, and we want to find the output voltage $v_o(t)$, it is desirable to obtain the corresponding values of

v_o for several values of v_i and then to construct a v_o-v_i curve—the voltage-transfer curve. Then, for any input voltage waveform, we can easily determine the output. The voltage-transfer characteristic for the circuit of Example 1 is obtained as follows. Since $v_o = v_{CE}$, we read off the corresponding values of i_B and v_o along the output load line. Then we calculate the corresponding values of v_i according to the relationship

$$v_i = V_{BB} + v_{BE} + i_B R_s = 9 - 0.6 + i_B R_s$$

Following this sequence of steps, we obtain the values of v_o and v_i shown in Table 9.1. Finally we construct the dynamic transfer characteristic for this circuit, as shown in Figure 9.14.

Table **9.1**

i_B (mA)	v_o (V)	v_i (V)
-0.1	-12.2	5.4
-0.2	-9.6	2.4
-0.3	-7.0	-0.6
-0.4	-5.5	-3.6
-0.5	-3.5	-6.6
-0.6	-1.7	-9.6

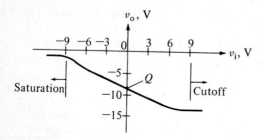

Figure 9.14   Voltage-transfer characteristic of the amplifier of Example 1.

EXAMPLE 2   The transistor of Figure 9.15 is an *n-p-n* silicon one with $v_{BE} \cong 0.7$ V and $\beta_0 = 50$. Neglecting I_{CO}, find the quiescent point of the transistor.

SOLUTION   In the input mesh, we have

$$I_B = \frac{2-0.7}{50\text{ k}} = 26\ \mu\text{A}$$

Hence

$$I_C = \beta_0 I_B = 50 \times 0.026 = 1.3\text{ mA}, \qquad V_{CE} = 25 - 15 \times 1.3 = 5.5\text{ V}$$

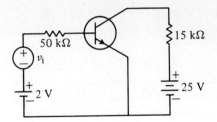

Figure 9.15

9.8   Other transistor circuit biasing schemes

The basic common-emitter amplifier circuit of Figure 9.12 is undesirable because it requires two separate power supplies. Another disadvantage of that circuit is the fact that v_i is located above ground. Many alternative biasing arrangements have been developed to avoid these two disadvantages. A few examples follow.

1 *The base-current bias*   The circuit of Figure 9.16(a) is called the base-current bias circuit. Two blocking capacitors are used to separate the dc and ac electric quantities. For dc analysis, the circuit is reduced to that shown in Figure 9.16(b). This circuit is identical to that of Figure 9.12 except that v_i is not in the dc circuit and that V_{CC} and V_{BB} are connected to the same power supply. (Also, of course, the polarity is reversed because of the difference in transistor types.) The dc analysis of this circuit is exactly the

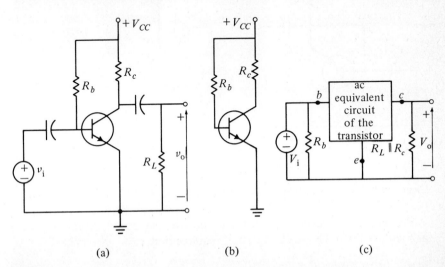

(a)   (b)   (c)

Figure 9.16 (a) Base-current bias circuit arrangement. (b) Circuit for dc analysis. (c) Circuit for ac analysis.

same as for the circuit in Figure 9.12. For a silicon transistor, we have

$$I_B = \frac{V_{CC} - 0.6}{R_b} \qquad (9.24)$$

This equation fixes the base current under quiescent conditions.

This biasing circuit is not practical, however, because (1) the quiescent point is fixed by I_B and (2) when the transistor is changed or when β changes as a result of an operating temperature change, the quiescent I_C and V_{CE} can vary widely. The circuit is included here primarily as an academic exercise.

For ac signals, the blocking capacitors should be large enough that their impedances may be neglected. Hence the ac equivalent circuit is that of Figure 9.16(c). We can carry out the analysis of this circuit straightforwardly, once we have the ac model of the transistor.

2 *Collector-to-base bias circuit* Some stability is gained by moving one end of R_b in Figure 9.16(a) from V_{CC} to the collector (see Section 9.10). This new arrangement is shown in Figure 9.17(a) and is known as the collector-to-base bias. This biasing arrangement appears to be the same as the MOSFET biasing circuit of Figure 8.27(a). However, since I_B in a transistor is not negligible (as the gate current is in a MOSFET), the dc analysis is slightly more complicated here.

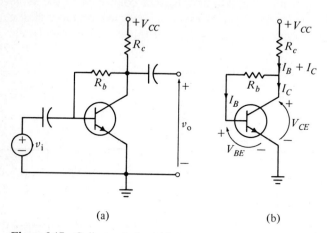

(a)   (b)

Figure 9.17 Collector-to-base bias arrangement.

We shall now concentrate on the dc part of the circuit, which is shown in Figure 9.17(b). The KVL equation requires that

$$V_{CE} = I_B R_b + V_{BE} \qquad (9.25)$$

$$V_{CC} = V_{CE} + (I_B + I_C) R_c \qquad (9.26)$$

The exact analysis of this circuit is quite difficult and is usually not necessary. As before, we may make the assumption that $V_{BE} \cong$ constant. In addition, we assume that I_B is negligible compared with I_C. With these assumptions, (9.26) becomes

$$V_{CC} = V_{CE} + I_C R_c \qquad (9.27)$$

This is the equation of the output load line in the $i_C\text{-}v_{CE}$ plane, as shown in Figure 9.18(b).

To locate the Q point, we need to find a set of values for I_B, I_C, and V_{CE} that satisfies (9.25) and (9.27) simultaneously. This can be done in either the $i_B\text{-}v_{CE}$ plane or the $i_C\text{-}v_{CE}$ plane. We shall illustrate this step by an example.

EXAMPLE 3   For the transistor whose characteristics are shown in Figure 9.18(a) and (b), find the quiescent point when it is used in the circuit of Figure 9.17 with $V_{CC} = 10$ V, $R_c = 125 \ \Omega$, and $R_b = 10$ kΩ.

SOLUTION   The intersects of the output load line with the V_{CE} and i_C axes are 10 V and 80 mA, respectively. The load line is readily constructed as shown in Figure 9.18(b). We can now read a series of (i_B, v_{CE}) points along the load line. Some of these values are tabulated in Table 9.2. We enter

Table **9.2**

i_B (mA)	v_{CE} (V)
1.1	1.4
1.0	1.9
0.9	2.6
0.8	3.3
0.7	4.0
0.6	4.8
0.5	5.6
0.4	6.4
0.3	7.3
0.2	8.3
0.1	9.2

these points in the $i_B\text{-}v_{CE}$ plane and draw curve A through them as shown in Figure 9.18(c). Assuming that $V_{BE} = 0.6$ V, we find that (9.25) becomes

$$V_{CE} = 10 \text{ k} \times I_B + 0.6 \qquad (9.28)$$

This equation represents a straight line passing through $(0, 0.6)$ and, say, $(0.7, 7.6)$ points in the $i_B\text{-}v_{CE}$ plane. It is drawn as line B in Figure 9.18(c). The intersection of A and B gives the Q point, which is at $I_B = 0.5$ mA and $V_{CE} = 5.6$ V. The corresponding value of I_C is $(10 - 5.6)/125 = 35.2$ mA.

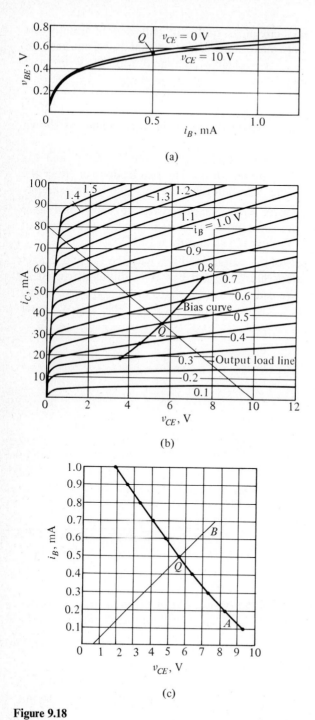

(a)

(b)

(c)

Figure 9.18

The quiescent point can be located on the output characteristic of Figure 9.18(b) as well. We can calculate a series of corresponding values of i_B and v_{CE} that satisfy (9.28). (Table 9.3 lists such a series of points.) We then locate these points on the output characteristics according to the constant-i_B

Table **9.3**

i_B (mA)	v_{CE} (V)
0.7	7.6
0.6	6.6
0.5	5.6
0.4	4.6
0.3	3.6

contour and the corresponding v_{CE} value. The curve joining these points is known as the *bias curve*, as shown in Figure 9.18(b). The intersection of the output load line and the bias curve is the quiescent point Q. In Figure 9.18(b), we see that the Q point is located at $I_C = 35.2$ mA and $V_{CE} = 5.6$ V. Knowing I_C, we can calculate I_B from (9.27) to be

$$I_B = \frac{5.6 - 0.6}{10 \text{ k}} = 0.5 \text{ mA}$$

Then, from the input characteristic of Figure 9.18(a), we determine that the more accurate value of V_{BE} is 0.56 V.

3 *The emitter bias circuit* Another fairly common bias scheme is shown in Figure 9.19(a). This might be compared to the MOSFET biasing arrangement of Figure 8.33. Both resistor R_c of Figure 9.19(a) and resistor R_d of Figure 8.33 serve as loads to their respective devices. Similarly, the source resistor R_s and the emitter resistor R_e produce like effects. In fact, these two circuits are very similar in many respects, especially in their ac behavior.

To analyze the dc components in the circuit of Figure 9.19(a), it is most convenient to replace the potentiometer arrangement of R_1 and R_2 by its Thévenin's equivalent. This is shown in Figure 9.19(b), in which

$$R_b = \frac{R_1 R_2}{R_1 + R_2} \tag{9.29}$$

$$V_{BB} = V_{CC} \frac{R_2}{R_1 + R_2} \tag{9.30}$$

In Figure 9.19(b), KVL requires that

$$V_{BB} = R_b I_B + V_{BE} + R_e(I_B + I_C) \tag{9.31}$$

$$V_{CC} = R_c I_C + V_{CE} + R_e(I_B + I_C) \tag{9.32}$$

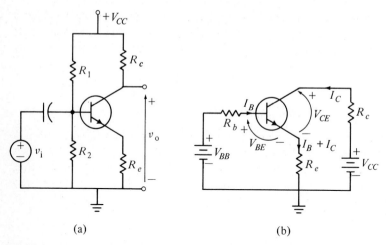

(a)   (b)

Figure 9.19 The emitter bias arrangement.

With the assumption that $|I_B| \ll |I_C|$, we may write (9.32) as

$$V_{CC} = V_{CE} + (R_e + R_c) I_C \tag{9.33}$$

This equation describes a load line on the output characteristics as shown in Figure 9.20. Eliminating I_C in (9.31) and (9.32), we get

$$V_{CE} = \left[V_{CC} - \frac{R_e + R_c}{R_e} V_{BB} + \frac{R_e + R_c}{R_e} V_{BE} \right] + \left[\frac{(R_e + R_b)(R_e + R_c)}{R_e} - R_e \right] I_B \tag{9.34}$$

If we now assume that $V_{BE} = $ constant, (9.31) takes the form

$$V_{CE} = k_1 + k_2 I_B \tag{9.35}$$

where k_1 and k_2 are constants. Equations (9.33) and (9.35) are identical to

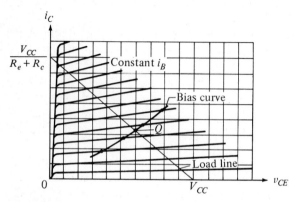

Figure 9.20 Graphical analysis of the emitter bias circuit.

(9.27) and (9.25) in form. Hence we can find the location of the quiescent point in exactly the same way as we did for the collector-to-base bias circuit. The scheme using the bias curve is shown in Figure 9.20.

9.9 Transistor ratings and biasing considerations

The ratings of a transistor usually contain the maximum collector power dissipation ($P_{C,\max}$), the maximum collector voltage ($V_{CE,\max}$), the maximum collector current ($I_{C,\max}$), and the maximum emitter-to-base voltage ($V_{EB,\max}$). Three of these limits are shown in Figure 9.21. The $P_{C,\max}$ curve is a hyperbola whose equation is $i_C v_{CE} = P_{C,\max}$.

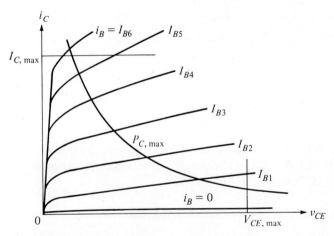

Figure 9.21 Maximum ratings of a transistor.

The choice of a quiescent point should be such that the operation of the transistor stays within these limits for the strongest signal the device is designed to handle. In addition, whenever possible, it is always desirable to place the operation in the region where the spacing of the output characteristics is most nearly uniform.

Two properties of the transistor should be borne in mind in the biasing of this device. One of these properties is the wide spread of characteristics among transistors of the same type. Despite the tremendous amount of research done in this area, the characteristics of transistors remain difficult to control and predict. Hence the "type" of a transistor usually indicates only a range of parameters rather than exact values. A biasing circuit that works well for one transistor may not be satisfactory for another one of the same type. This is illustrated in Figure 9.22. A good biasing circuit should therefore be satisfactory for a wide range of transistor parameters.

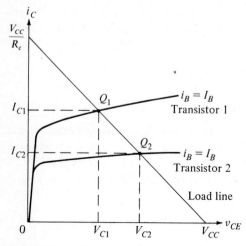

Figure 9.22 Shift of the quiescent point when the characteristics of a transistor are changed.

The other property is the fact that the characteristics of a transistor are highly temperature-dependent. Thus a biasing circuit that gives a satisfactory quiescent point when the transistor is at room temperature may give a quiescent point that is too close to the saturation region when the transistor is heated or too close to the cutoff region when its temperature drops sharply. This is illustrated in Figure 9.23.

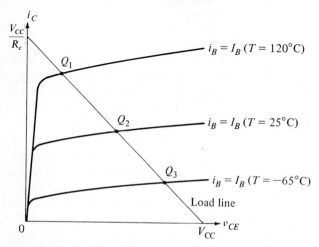

Figure 9.23 Shift of the quiescent point when the temperature of a transistor changes.

9.10 Stabilization of the operating point

In a practical transistor circuit, it is highly desirable to keep the operating or quiescent point relatively constant. This is usually achieved by circuit arrangements that tend to maintain I_C (or I_E, which is approximately equal to $-I_C$) unchanged.

As described in the previous sections, there are two major causes for changes in I_C. One is the fact that β_0 is a function of temperature. The other is that β_0 may vary from unit to unit among transistors bearing the same nominal type number. In either case, a good biasing circuit should make I_C immune to variations in β_0.

It was mentioned in Section 9.8 that the base-current biasing scheme of Figure 9.16(a) is impractical. As (9.24) reveals, I_B of that circuit is virtually constant. As a consequence, when β_0 changes, I_C will change proportionately. As I_C changes, $V_{CE} = V_{CC} - R_c I_C$ will also change. The quiescent point of such a biasing arrangement is usually quite unsatisfactory.

The collector-to-base circuit of Figure 9.17(a) offers some stabilization effect against β_0 change. Referring to Figure 9.17(b) and neglecting I_{CO}, we have

$$I_B = \frac{V_{CE} - V_{BE}}{R_b} \qquad (9.36)$$

$$V_{CE} = V_{CC} - (I_B + I_C) R_c \qquad (9.37)$$

and we can assume that

$$I_C = \beta_0 I_B \qquad (9.38)$$

Solution of these equations yields

$$I_C = \frac{V_{CC} - V_{BE}}{R_c + [(R_b + R_c)/\beta_0]} \qquad (9.39)$$

Since V_{CC} is constant and V_{BE} is almost constant, a change in β_0 only affects the second term of the denominator in (9.39). If $R_c \gg (R_b + R_c)/\beta_0$, then the effect of β_0 on I_C will be very small.

As an example, suppose we have $V_{CC} = 10$ V, $V_{BE} = 0.6$ V, $R_c = 500\ \Omega$, and $R_b = 10\ k\Omega$.

(a) For $\beta_0 = 50$, (9.39) gives

$$I_C = \frac{10 - 0.6}{500 + [(10{,}000 + 500)/50]} = 13.24 \text{ mA}$$

(b) For $\beta_0 = 100$, we have

$$I_C = \frac{10 - 0.6}{500 + [(10{,}000 + 500)/100]} = 15.54 \text{ mA}$$

Thus, for a 2-to-1 change in β_0, I_C changes by only about 17%. For larger β_0 and/or larger R_e, the quiescent I_C would be even more stable with respect to β_0 variation.

For the dc analysis of the emitter bias circuit of Figure 9.19(a), we use its equivalent circuit of Figure 9.19(b). Again, if we assume that I_{CO} is negligible and $I_C = \beta_0 I_B$, then around the base loop KVL requires that

$$V_{BB} = I_B R_b + V_{BE} + (I_B + I_C) R_e \tag{9.40}$$

which gives

$$I_C = \frac{\beta_0 (V_{BB} - V_{BE})}{R_b + (1 + \beta_0) R_e} \tag{9.41}$$

For $\beta_0 \gg 1$ and $(1 + \beta_0) R_e \gg R_b$, I_C is determined primarily by the value of R_e.

As an example, suppose that $R_1 = 25\ \text{k}\Omega$, $R_2 = 5\ \text{k}\Omega$, $V_{CC} = 20\ \text{V}$, and $R_e = 1\ \text{k}\Omega$. Then $V_{BB} = 3.33\ \text{V}$ and $R_b = 4.16\ \text{k}\Omega$.

(a) For $\beta_0 = 50$, we have

$$I_C = \frac{50(3.33 - 0.6)}{4166 + 51 \times 1000} = 2.48\ \text{mA}$$

(b) For $\beta_0 = 100$, we have

$$I_C = \frac{100(3.33 - 0.6)}{4166 + 101 \times 1000} = 2.60\ \text{mA}$$

Thus a 2-to-1 change in β_0 causes I_C to vary only by approximately 5%.

The foregoing analysis assumed that I_{CO} was negligible. This is quite realistic with silicon transistors. For germanium transistors, the variation in I_{CO} with temperature change is itself a serious problem, since at typical operating temperatures I_{CO} constitutes a noticeable part of I_C. Generally speaking, a biasing scheme that reduces the fluctuation of I_C due to β_0 change is also beneficial when the effects of I_{CO} change are considered.

Modern transistor circuits employ numerous specialty circuits to stabilize the operating point. Some of them take advantage of the nonlinear effects of semiconductors, so that a change in the transistor characteristics is counteracted by a similar change in the bias circuit. These special techniques are beyond the scope of this text.

9.11 Small-signal ac models for the bipolar transistor

As in the small-signal application of the FET, in which a small ac signal is superimposed on the quiescent condition, we can analyze the response of a transistor circuit to an ac signal by considering the transistor to be a linear device. This assumption is valid only when the ac signal is small enough that the operation of the transistor does not deviate too far from the quiescent point. If the ac signal is too large, the relationship among the four independent quantities of the transistor may no longer be considered linear. In that case, linear ac analysis is no longer valid.

The parameters most frequently used to describe the ac small-signal properties of a transistor are the h parameters defined in Chapter 7. Since the transistor is a three-terminal device, the h parameters are those of a three-terminal two-port. From Table 7.1 we have

$$E_1 = h_{11} I_1 + h_{12} E_2, \qquad I_2 = h_{21} I_1 + h_{22} E_2 \qquad (9.42)$$

The individual h parameters may be interpreted in an alternative notation as follows.

$$h_{11} = \left.\frac{E_1}{I_1}\right|_{E_2=0} = \text{short-circuit input impedance} = h_i$$

$$h_{21} = \left.\frac{I_2}{I_1}\right|_{E_2=0} = \text{short-circuit forward current gain} = h_f$$

$$\qquad (9.43)$$

$$h_{12} = \left.\frac{E_1}{E_2}\right|_{I_1=0} = \text{open-circuit reverse voltage gain} = h_r$$

$$h_{22} = \left.\frac{I_2}{E_2}\right|_{I_1=0} = \text{open-circuit output admittance} = h_o$$

The origin of these letter subscripts is also indicated in the verbal description of each h parameter. In transistor engineering, these subscripts are generally preferred by manufacturers and practitioners. (Usually lower-case subscripts are used for ac parameters and capital ones for dc.)

In addition, since there are three possible orientations for a transistor, a second subscript letter is introduced to indicate which of the three terminals of the transistor is common to both the input and the output. In theory, three sets of parameters can be found. They are as follows.

1 For the common-base configuration [Figure 9.7(a)]:

$$h_{ib} = \left.\frac{\partial v_{EB}}{\partial i_E}\right|_{v_{CB}} \qquad h_{fb} = \left.\frac{\partial i_C}{\partial i_E}\right|_{v_{CB}}$$

$$\qquad (9.44)$$

$$h_{rb} = \left.\frac{\partial v_{EB}}{\partial v_{CB}}\right|_{i_E} \qquad h_{ob} = \left.\frac{\partial i_C}{\partial v_{CB}}\right|_{i_E}$$

$$V_{eb} = h_{ib} I_e + h_{rb} V_{cb}, \qquad I_c = h_{fb} I_e + h_{ob} V_{cb} \qquad (9.45)$$

2 For the common-emitter configuration [Figure 9.7(b)]:

$$h_{ie} = \frac{\partial v_{BE}}{\partial i_B}\bigg|_{v_{CE}} \qquad h_{fe} = \frac{\partial i_C}{\partial i_B}\bigg|_{v_{CE}}$$

$$h_{re} = \frac{\partial v_{BE}}{\partial v_{CE}}\bigg|_{i_B} \qquad h_{oe} = \frac{\partial i_C}{\partial v_{CE}}\bigg|_{i_B} \tag{9.46}$$

$$V_{be} = h_{ie} I_b + h_{re} V_{ce}, \qquad I_c = h_{fe} I_b + h_{oe} V_{ce} \tag{9.47}$$

3 For the common-collector configuration [Figure 9.7(c)]:

$$h_{ic} = \frac{\partial v_{BC}}{\partial i_B}\bigg|_{v_{EC}} \qquad h_{fc} = \frac{\partial i_E}{\partial i_B}\bigg|_{v_{EC}}$$

$$h_{rc} = \frac{\partial v_{BC}}{\partial v_{EC}}\bigg|_{i_B} \qquad h_{oc} = \frac{\partial i_E}{\partial v_{EC}}\bigg|_{i_B} \tag{9.48}$$

$$V_{bc} = h_{ic} I_b + h_{rc} V_{ec}, \qquad I_e = h_{fc} I_b + h_{oc} V_{ec} \tag{9.49}$$

In equations (9.45), (9.47), and (9.49) the electric quantities are the complex amplitudes of the ac components of the corresponding quantities with the same but capitalized subscripts. For example, V_{eb} is the ac component of v_{EB}.

In practice, the common-emitter parameters are the most frequently used. Typical values of these parameters are

$$h_{ie} = 1\,k\Omega, \qquad h_{re} = 2 \times 10^{-4}, \qquad h_{fe} = 50, \qquad h_{oe} = 20\,\mu\mho \tag{9.50}$$

The factor h_{fe} is more commonly known as the beta (β) of the transistor.

When the input and output characteristics of a transistor are available in graphical form, its h parameters can be estimated from the characteristics. For example, for a common-emitter configuration with the characteristics given in Figure 9.24, we have

h_{ie} = slope of the input characteristic at the Q point (line AB),

$$h_{fe} \simeq \frac{i_{C2} - i_{C1}}{i_{B2} - i_{B1}} \tag{9.51}$$

$$h_{re} \simeq \frac{v_{B2} - v_{B1}}{v_{C2} - v_{C1}},$$

h_{oe} = slope of the output characteristic at the Q point (line CD)

In practice, these parameters are usually measured in the laboratory by various experimental techniques.

An examination of typical characteristics of the two types of transistor, p-n-p and n-p-n, reveals that their ac equivalent models are identical. Therefore we need make no distinctions in the ac model of a transistor because of its type.

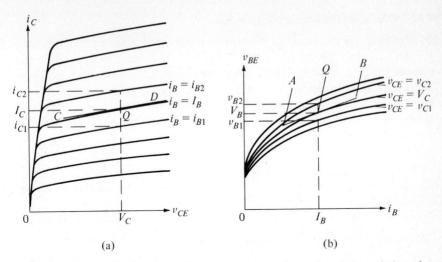

(a)   (b)

Figure 9.24 Obtaining the small-signal parameters from the characteristics of a transistor.

In Chapter 7 we showed that, when any one of the two-port parameters of a three-terminal two-port is known, the electrical properties of the two-port are completely determined. Thus, if the h parameters of a transistor are known for any one of the three configurations, it should be possible to obtain the h parameters (in fact, any of the six sets of parameters defined in Table 7.1) of the other orientations. This is most easily done through the indefinite admittance matrix (IAM) described in Section 7.8.

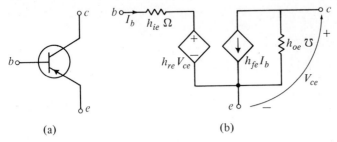

(a)   (b)

Figure 9.25 The h-parameter equivalent circuit of a transistor for small-signal analysis.

Once the h parameters of a transistor are known, its small-signal behavior is identical to that of a three-terminal two-port with these h parameters. Frequently this equivalent two-port is replaced by an equivalent circuit, particularly that of Figure 7.13(e) modified to form a three-terminal two-port. As an example, the transistor of Figure 9.25(a) can be replaced by the equivalent in Figure 9.25(b) for small-signal circuit analysis.

9.12 Other ac transistor circuit models

In the early development of transistor theory, the equivalent circuits of Figure 9.26 were proposed for the transistor. It is easy to appreciate the validity of these circuits. Figure 9.26(a) is almost a circuit replica of Figure 9.4(c), with a few resistors thrown in to represent the resistances of various parts of the semiconductors that form the transistor. These two circuits can be shown to be equivalent if $\beta = \alpha/(1-\alpha)$ and $r_d = r_c(1-\alpha)$ (Problem 9.25).

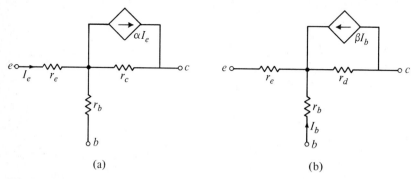

(a)   (b)

Figure 9.26   The T-equivalent circuits of a transistor.

As it turns out, these circuits are just as completely general in representing the ac behavior of a transistor as the h-parameter models derived in the previous section. We shall now show that the T-equivalent circuit of Figure 9.26(a) can be made equivalent to the circuit of Figure 9.25(b).

From (7.72) we have the IAM of the T-equivalent circuit of Figure 9.26(a).

$$[y_i]_{ecb} = \frac{1}{\Delta} \begin{bmatrix} r_b + r_c & -r_b & -r_c \\ -r_b - \alpha r_c & r_b + r_e & \alpha r_c - r_e \\ -(1-\alpha)r_c & -r_e & (1-\alpha)r_c + r_e \end{bmatrix} \qquad (9.52)$$

where $\Delta = r_e(r_b + r_c) + (1-\alpha)r_b r_c$. Hence the two-port $[y]$ with terminal b as the input, terminal c as the output, and e as the common terminal is

$$[y] = \frac{1}{\Delta} \begin{bmatrix} (1-\alpha)r_c + r_e & -r_e \\ \alpha r_c - r_e & r_b + r_e \end{bmatrix} \qquad (9.53)$$

Using Table 7.2, we get the $[h]$ of this two-port.

$$[h] = \frac{1}{(1-\alpha)r_c + r_e} \begin{bmatrix} \Delta & r_e \\ \alpha r_c - r_e & 1 \end{bmatrix} \qquad (9.54)$$

For the two circuits in Figure 9.25(b) and Figure 9.26(a) to be equivalent,

it is necessary that

$$h_{ie} = \frac{\Delta}{(1-\alpha)r_c + r_e}, \qquad h_{re} = \frac{r_e}{(1-\alpha)r_c + r_e}$$

$$h_{fe} = \frac{\alpha r_c - r_e}{(1-\alpha)r_c + r_e}, \qquad h_{oe} = \frac{1}{(1-\alpha)r_c + r_e} \tag{9.55}$$

Solving for the r's and α in (9.55), we obtain

$$r_b = h_{ie} - \frac{h_{re}(1+h_{fe})}{h_{oe}}, \qquad r_c = \frac{1+h_{fe}}{h_{oe}}$$

$$\alpha = \frac{h_{fe} + h_{re}}{1+h_{fe}} \cong \frac{h_{fe}}{1+h_{fe}}, \qquad r_e = \frac{h_{re}}{h_{oe}} \tag{9.56}$$

Substituting the typical h parameters of (9.50), we get

$$r_b = 490 \ \Omega, \qquad r_c = 2.55 \ \text{M}\Omega$$

$$\alpha = 0.9804, \qquad r_e = 10 \ \Omega \tag{9.57}$$

And for the circuit of Figure 9.26(b) we have, in addition to r_e and r_b of (9.57),

$$r_d = 50 \ \text{k}\Omega, \qquad \beta = 50 \tag{9.58}$$

In addition to the h-parameter equivalent circuit and the T-equivalent circuit, the most commonly used model for a transistor is probably the hybrid-π equivalent circuit of Figure 9.27. This cannot be made exactly equivalent to the T-equivalent circuit or the h-parameter model since it contains five elements as compared with the four of the other two models. The hybrid-π equivalent circuit is useful because its high-frequency version is more representative of the transistor's performance than are the other two circuits.

However, it is not too difficult to point out the similarities among the circuits in Figures 9.25, 9.26, and 9.27. The resistance r_x plays roughly the same role as r_b. The voltage V_π is approximately equal to $-I_e r_e$. Since $I_e \cong (1+\beta)I_b$, and since r_μ is usually a very large resistance, $V_\pi \cong I_b r_\pi$. Also, since r_π is usually very close to $(1+\beta)r_e$, $V_\pi \cong (1+\beta)r_e I_b$. The controlled current source $g_m V_\pi$ takes the place of $h_{fe} I_b$. Since $V_\pi \cong I_b r_\pi$, we usually

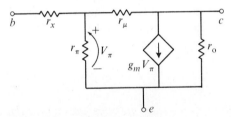

Figure 9.27 The hybrid-π circuit model of a transistor.

make $g_m = h_{fe}/r_\pi$. The resistance r_o, combined with r_μ, takes the place of $1/h_{oe}$. The reverse feedback factor h_{re} is accounted for by the resistance r_μ.

We can obtain hybrid-π element values by first computing

$$g_m = |I_C|/V_T \tag{9.59}$$

where I_C is the quiescent collector current and V_T is taken from (6.1a). Then we find the h parameters of the transistor, from which we obtain

$$r_\pi = \frac{h_{fe}}{g_m} \tag{9.60}$$

$$r_x = h_{ie} - r_\pi \tag{9.61}$$

$$r_\mu = \frac{r_\pi}{h_{re}} \tag{9.62}$$

$$\frac{1}{r_o} = h_{oe} - \frac{1+h_{fe}}{r_\mu} \tag{9.63}$$

As an example, if a transistor is biased at $I_C = 2$ mA and operated at 25°C ($V_T = 25.69$ mV), then we get

$$g_m = 78 \text{ m}\mho$$

For the transistor whose h parameters are given in (9.50), its hybrid-π model will have

$$r_\pi = 641 \ \Omega, \qquad r_x = 359 \ \Omega, \qquad r_\mu = 3.21 \ \text{M}\Omega, \qquad r_o = 243 \ \text{k}\Omega$$

Numerous other transistor equivalent circuits have been proposed before. Most of them are either simplified versions of the three circuits described here or they have been used so rarely that they are of no great importance.

9.13 Comparison of the three orientations of the transistor

As might be expected, the three orientations of the transistor serve very different functions when they are used in an amplifier circuit. We shall make a quantitative comparison of three versions of the basic amplifier, using the transistor with the typical h parameters given in (9.50) in the three different orientations. The three equivalent circuits are shown in Figure 9.28. The following quantities are usually of interest in an amplifier.

1 The current gain $A_i = I_L/I_i$

2 The voltage gain $A_v = V_o/V_s$

3 The input impedance of the amplifier $Z_i = V_i/I_i$. This does not include the source impedance R_s. The impedance seen by the source is $Z_g = V_s/I_i = Z_i + R_s$.

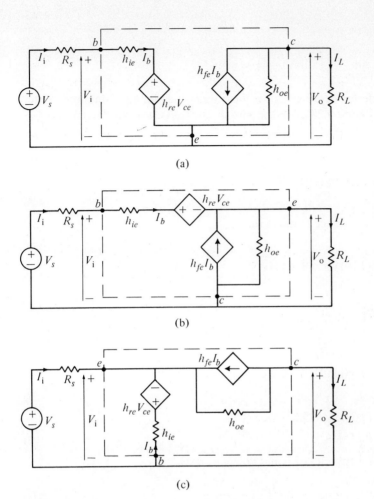

Figure 9.28 The ac equivalent circuits of three basic transistor amplifiers. (a) Common-emitter amplifier. (b) Common-collector amplifier. (c) Common-base amplifier.

4 The output impedance. The output impedance of an amplifier is the impedance seen between its output terminals with V_s set equal to zero. Since this is also the Thévenin's equivalent impedance, it can be found by calculating the ratio of the open-circuit voltage to the short-circuit current at the output. We find the open-circuit voltage from A_v by letting R_L approach infinity, or

$$V_{oc} = \lim_{R_L \to \infty} A_v V_s = V_s A_{vo} \qquad (9.64)$$

The short-circuit current is found from A_i by letting R_L equal zero. We have

$$I_{sc} = \lim_{R_L \to 0} I_L = \lim_{R_L \to 0} A_i I_i = \lim_{R_L \to 0} \frac{A_i V_s}{Z_g} = \frac{A_{is} V_s}{Z_{gs}} \qquad (9.65)$$

Hence we get

$$Z_o = \frac{V_{oc}}{I_{sc}} = \lim_{R_L \to \infty} (A_v) \bigg/ \lim_{R_L \to 0} \left(\frac{A_i}{Z_g}\right) = \frac{A_{vo} Z_{gs}}{A_{is}} \tag{9.66}$$

We shall derive expressions for these quantities for the common-emitter amplifier of Figure 9.28(a). In this circuit, the transistor parameters give

$$V_i = h_{ie} I_i + h_{re} V_o \tag{9.67}$$

$$-I_L = h_{fe} I_i + h_{oe} V_o \tag{9.68}$$

The source circuit requires that

$$V_i = V_s - R_s I_i \tag{9.69}$$

and the load resistance requires that

$$V_o = I_L R_L \tag{9.70}$$

Substituting (9.70) into (9.68) gives

$$-I_L = h_{fe} I_i + h_{oe} R_L I_L$$

whence we get

$$A_i = \frac{I_L}{I_i} = -\frac{h_{fe}}{1 + h_{oe} R_L} \tag{9.71}$$

Substituting (9.68) into (9.70), we get

$$V_o = -R_L h_{fe} I_i - R_L h_{oe} V_o \tag{9.72}$$

Substituting (9.69) into (9.67), we get

$$V_s - R_s I_i = h_{ie} I_i + h_{re} V_o \tag{9.73}$$

Eliminating I_i between (9.72) and (9.73), we get

$$A_v = \frac{V_o}{V_s} = -\frac{R_L h_{fe}}{(1 + R_L h_{oe})(R_s + h_{ie}) - R_L h_{re} h_{fe}} \tag{9.74}$$

Eliminating V_o between (9.72) and (9.73), we get

$$Z_g = \frac{V_s}{I_i} = R_s + h_{ie} - \frac{R_L h_{fe} h_{re}}{1 + R_L h_{oe}} \tag{9.75}$$

This is the impedance seen by the source. The input impedance of the amplifier is

$$Z_i = \frac{V_i}{I_i} = \frac{V_s}{I_i} - R_s = h_{ie} - \frac{R_L h_{fe} h_{re}}{1 + R_L h_{oe}} \tag{9.76}$$

To obtain the output impedance, we first obtain from (9.74)

$$A_{vo} = \lim_{R_L \to \infty} (A_v) = -\frac{h_{fe}}{h_{oe}(R_s + h_{ie}) - h_{re} h_{fe}} \tag{9.77}$$

From (9.71) we have

$$A_{is} = \lim_{R_L \to 0} (A_i) = -h_{fe} \tag{9.78}$$

and from (9.75) we have

$$Z_{gs} = \lim_{R_L \to 0} Z_g = R_s + h_{ie} \tag{9.79}$$

Substituting (9.77), (9.78), and (9.79) into (9.66) yields

$$Z_o = \frac{R_s + h_{ie}}{h_{oe}(R_s + h_{ie}) - h_{re}h_{fe}}$$

$$= \frac{R_s + h_{ie}}{h_{oe}R_s + |h_e|} \tag{9.80}$$

The derivation of these quantities for the other two transistor orientations is left as an exercise (Problems 9.18 and 9.19).

Using the typical transistor parameters given in (9.50) and with $R_L = R_s = 3 \text{ k}\Omega$, we obtain the quantities summarized in Table 9.4. We can then make the following observations, which are based on these typical values. The common-base configuration is almost a unity-gain current-to-current transducer with a very low input impedance and a very high output impedance. It is chiefly used as (1) a low-input impedance voltage amplifier, (2) an impedance-matching stage to match a high-impedance load to a low-impedance source or amplifier, or (3) an almost constant-current source.

The common-emitter configuration has a high voltage gain with a moderate input impedance and a high output impedance. This configuration is used extensively as voltage-amplification stages of transistor amplifiers.

Table **9.4** Typical transistor amplifier quantities

	Common-emitter	Common-collector	Common-base
A_i	-47.2	48.1	0.979
A_v	-35.6	0.973	0.919
Z_i	972 Ω	145 kΩ	20.2 Ω
Z_o	57.1 kΩ	78.3 Ω	2.19 MΩ

The common-collector configuration is mainly a unity-gain voltage amplifier with a low output impedance and a high input impedance. This configuration is often known as the emitter follower and is used chiefly as a stage to match a low-impedance load to a high-impedance source or amplifier.

In other words, it can be said that a transistor operating in the common-base configuration is somewhat similar to an FET operating in the grounded-gate mode, the common-emitter configuration is comparable to the grounded-source mode, and the common-collector configuration is comparable to the grounded-drain mode.

9.14 ac Analysis of transistor circuits

Once we have the ac small-signal mode of a transistor, the analysis of the signal portion of the circuit quantities follows the same procedure used to analyze FET circuits for ac. We first replace the transistor by its ac equivalent circuit. The latter can be the h-parameter equivalent circuit, the T-equivalent model, or the hybrid-π model. We then short-circuit the batteries. We also replace the capacitors and inductors by their impedances or admittances. If the impedance of a capacitor is relatively very small, we can replace it with a short circuit. This is frequently the case with blockings and by-pass capacitors. Similarly, if the impedance of an inductor is very high, we can remove it from the circuit and leave its terminals open-circuited. The following are a few examples.

1 *Common-emitter amplifier with collector-to-base bias* The circuit layout is shown in Figure 9.29(a). The transistor is assumed to have the h parameters given in (9.50). By using the h-parameter equivalent circuit of Figure 9.25(b) for the transistor and short-circuiting the capacitors, we get the ac equivalent circuit shown in Figure 9.29(b). In the I_b branch we can write

$$I_b = \frac{V_i - 2 \times 10^{-4} V_o}{1\,k}$$

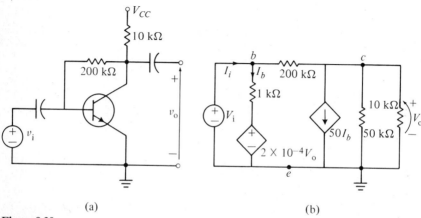

(a)　　　　　　　　　　　　　　(b)

Figure 9.29

Since this circuit has only two unconstrained nodes, node analysis should require only one equation. For node c, we write

$$\frac{V_o}{10\text{ k}} + \frac{V_o}{50\text{ k}} + 50I_b + \frac{V_o - V_i}{200\text{ k}} = 0$$

Substituting the expression for I_b into the preceding equation, we get

$$\frac{V_o}{10\text{ k}} + \frac{V_o}{50\text{ k}} + \frac{50V_i}{1\text{ k}} - \frac{0.01V_o}{1\text{ k}} + \frac{V_o}{200\text{ k}} - \frac{V_i}{200\text{ k}} = 0$$

Hence

$$A_v = \frac{V_o}{V_i} = \frac{-\frac{50}{1.0} + \frac{1}{200}}{\frac{1}{10} + \frac{1}{50} - \frac{0.01}{1} + \frac{1}{200}} = -434.74$$

To find the input impedance, we first find I_b:

$$I_b = \frac{1 + 2 \times 434.74 \times 10^{-4}}{1\text{ k}} V_i = 1.0869 \times 10^{-3}V_i$$

Then we get

$$I_i = I_b + \frac{V_i - V_o}{200\text{ k}} = 3.2656 \times 10^{-3}V_i$$

and

$$Z_i = \frac{V_i}{I_i} = 306.22\ \Omega$$

2 *The emitter-follower circuit* The pair of transistors in Figure 9.30(a) are arranged in what is commonly known as the *Darlington pair*. The combined transistor pair is equivalent to another transistor whose β is much higher than the β of each individual one. (You are left to find the relationship between the parameters of the composite arrangement and those of the individual transistors as an exercise in Problem 9.26.)

Of course, the two transistors may also be treated as individual devices. The ac equivalent circuit is shown in Figure 9.30(b). For variety, we shall use the T-equivalent circuit of Figure 9.26(a). Assuming that the transistor parameters of Q_1 and Q_2 are each given in (9.50), from (9.57) we have

$$\alpha = 0.9804, \qquad r_c = 2.55\text{ M}\Omega, \qquad r_e = 10\ \Omega, \qquad r_b = 490\ \Omega$$

Hence the details of the ac equivalent circuit are as indicated in Figure 9.30(c). Since this is a ladder network, we can assume a value for V_o (say, $V_o = 1$) and work back step-by-step toward the input. (Note that, when we assume V_o to be 1 V, we are not applying a 1-V source across it.)

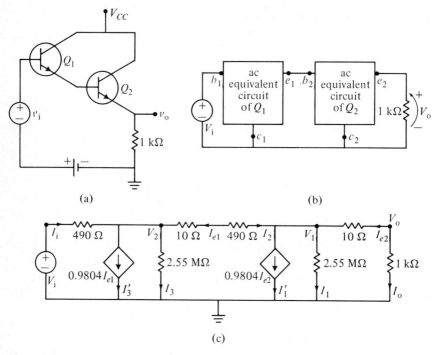

(a)

(b)

(c)

Figure 9.30 An emitter follower using a Darlington pair of transistors.

We proceed as follows:

$V_o = 1$ V

$I_o = 1$ mA

$V_1 = 1 + 0.01 = 1.01$ V

$$I_1 = \frac{1.01}{2.55\text{ M}} = 0.3961\ \mu\text{A}$$

$I_1' = 0.9804 \times (-10^{-3}) = -0.9804$ mA

$I_2 = I_o + I_1 + I_1' = 10^{-3} + 0.3961 \times 10^{-6} - 0.9804 \times 10^{-3} = 0.02$ mA

$V_2 = V_1 + 500 I_2 = 1.01 + 0.02 \times 0.5 = 1.02$ V

$$I_3 = \frac{1.02}{2.55\text{ M}} = 0.401\ \mu\text{A}$$

$I_3' = -\alpha I_2 = 0.9804 \times (-0.02 \times 10^{-3}) = -0.0196$ mA

$I_i = I_2 + I_3 + I_3'$

$\quad = 0.792\ \mu\text{A}$

$V_i = V_2 + 490 I_i = 1.02 + 0.388 \times 10^{-3} = 1.0204$ V

Since the circuit is linear, we have

$$A_v = \frac{V_o}{V_i} = 0.98$$

$$A_i = \frac{I_o}{I_i} = 1262.6$$

$$Z_i = \frac{V_i}{I_i} = 1.288 \text{ M}\Omega$$

3 *The cascode amplifier* A cascode amplifier is the cascade connection of a common-emitter stage and a common-base stage. As well as a relatively high input impedance and a relatively high output impedance, this combination offers high gain, wide bandwidth, and good isolation between the input and the output. We shall analyze its low-frequency properties.

One arrangement of such an amplifier is shown in Figure 9.31(a), and the ac equivalent circuit is shown in Figure 9.31(b). Using the *h*-parameter equivalent circuit of Figure 9.25(b) for the transistor and with the parameters of the transistor given in (9.50), we obtain the circuit of Figure 9.31(c). This is basically a three-node circuit, for which the node equations are

$$\frac{V_i}{1 \text{ k}} + I_{b1} = I_i$$

$$50I_{b1} + \frac{V_1}{50 \text{ k}} - I_{b2} - 50I_{b2} - \frac{V_2}{50 \text{ k}} = 0$$

$$\frac{V_o}{5 \text{ k}} + 50I_{b2} + \frac{V_2}{50 \text{ k}} = 0$$

in which

$$I_{b1} = \frac{V_i - 2 \times 10^{-4}V_1}{1 \text{ k}}$$

$$I_{b2} = -\frac{V_1 + 2 \times 10^{-4}V_2}{1 \text{ k}}$$

$$V_2 = V_o - V_1$$

Substituting these relationships into the node equations, we get

$$V_i + V_i - 2 \times 10^{-4}V_1 = I_i \times 10^3$$

$$\frac{50(V_i - 2 \times 10^{-4}V_1)}{1 \text{ k}} + \frac{V_1}{50 \text{ k}} + \frac{51(V_1 + 2 \times 10^{-4}V_o - 2 \times 10^{-4}V_1)}{1 \text{ k}}$$

$$+ \frac{V_1 - V_o}{50 \text{ k}} = 0$$

$$-\frac{50(V_1 + 2 \times 10^{-4}V_o - 2 \times 10^{-4}V_1)}{1 \text{ k}} + \frac{V_o - V_1}{50 \text{ k}} + \frac{V_o}{5 \text{ k}} = 0$$

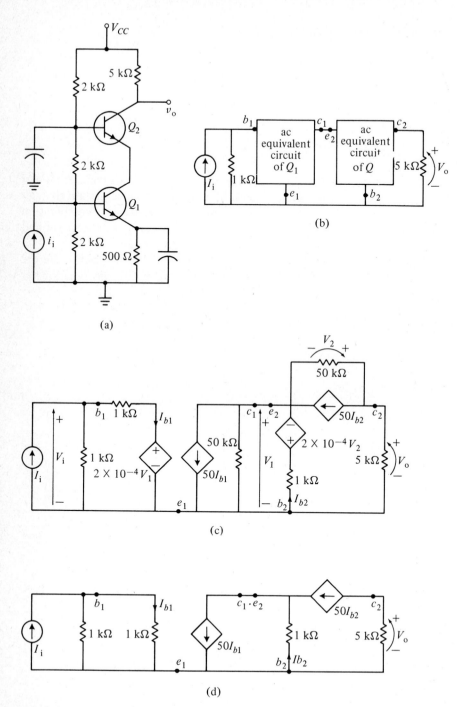

Figure 9.31 A cascode amplifier.

Rearranging, we get

$$2V_i - 2 \times 10^{-4}V_1 = I_i \times 10^3$$

$$2500V_i + 2550.99V_1 - 0.49V_0 = 0$$

$$-2500.5V_1 + 10.5V_0 = 0$$

Solution of these equations gives

$$V_i = 500.0I_i, \qquad V_1 = -513.4I_i, \qquad V_0 = -122.3 \times 10^3 I_i$$

Alternatively, we have

$$Z_i = \frac{V_i}{I_i} = 500.0 \ \Omega, \qquad Z_{21} = \frac{V_0}{I_i} = -122.3 \ \text{k}\Omega$$

The analysis of the circuit of Figure 9.31(c) is seen to be quite lengthy. Electronic circuits any more complicated than this are typically analyzed by a computer-aided analysis program. Sometimes we can find approximate answers by simplifying the model used for the transistor. For example, if we neglect h_{re} and h_{oe} of each transistor, the cascode amplifier equivalent circuit is reduced to that of Figure 9.31(d). In this circuit,

$$I_{b1} = \frac{I_i}{2}$$

KCL requires that

$$50I_{b1} = I_{b2} + 50I_{b2}$$

Hence we have

$$I_{b2} = \frac{50}{102}I_i, \qquad V_0 = -50I_{b2} \times 5\,\text{k} = -122.6\,\text{k}\,I_i$$

Thus

$$Z_i = 1\,\text{k} \,\|\, 1\,\text{k} = 500 \ \Omega, \qquad Z_{21} = -122.6 \ \text{k}\Omega$$

We see that there is practically no difference in the values for Z_i. The discrepancy in Z_{21} is also very small when the simplified equivalent circuit of the transistor is used. Although the results may not always be this close, when a quick, ball-park type of answer is desired, the simplified circuit model will save a great deal of analytical effort.

9.15 High-frequency equivalent circuits of a transistor

So far, we have neglected two secondary effects in a transistor. One is the fact that, as carriers are being transported from region to region, there is a definite time lapse during which each motion takes place. The other is the capacitance effects between two regions of unequal potentials. These two effects are not significant at low frequencies, such as the low audio-frequency range, but at higher frequencies they can be extremely important.

Usually we take these two effects into account by modifying the low-frequency equivalent circuit of the transistor. The complexity of the modified equivalent circuits depends somewhat on the frequency range for which the transistor is to be utilized.

High-frequency effects are usually accounted for by placing equivalent capacitances across the various resistors or other appropriate places in the equivalent circuit. The most commonly used model is the modified hybrid-π model of Figure 9.32, in which two capacitances are added to the model of Figure 9.27. Capacitance C_μ represents the depletion-region capacitive effect

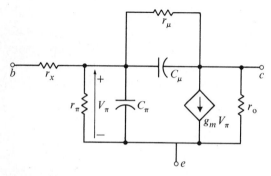

Figure 9.32 Hybrid-π transistor circuit model valid for wider ranges of frequency.

of the collector junction; it is usually obtained by measuring the output capacitance of the transistor in the common-base configuration and is customarily denoted by C_{ob}. The capacitance C_π represents the depletion-region capacitive effect of the emitter junction, and is usually calculated from its effect on the frequency characteristic of the current gain at high frequencies.

Problems

9.1 Both the emitter and the collector junctions of a transistor are reverse-biased, with $|V_{CB}| \gg V_T$ and $|V_{EB}| \gg V_T$. Show that the currents are given by

$$I_E = \frac{I_{EO}(1-\alpha_N)}{1-\alpha_N \alpha_R}, \qquad I_C = -\frac{I_{CO}(1-\alpha_R)}{1-\alpha_N \alpha_R}$$

It is known that $\alpha_R I_{CO} = \alpha_N I_{EO}$.

9.2 Find the collector and emitter currents of a transistor with $I_{CO} = -6$ μA, $I_{EO} = -5$ μA, and $\alpha_N = 0.98$, when it is operating in the cutoff region.

9.3 The collector current I_C of an *n-p-n* transistor increases from 200 μA to 500 μA as the base current I_B increases from 5 μA to 15 μA. Find β_0 and I_{CO} of this transistor.

9.4 Derive the equations in (9.13) from (9.11) and (9.12).

9.5 In the circuit of Figure P9.5, find V_{CE}, neglecting the reverse saturation current and assuming that $\alpha_0 = 0.98$ and $V_{BE} = 0.6$ V.

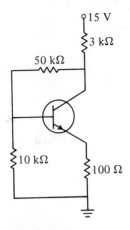

Figure P9.5

9.6 In the circuit of Figure P9.6, locate the Q point for $I_B = 200$ μA.

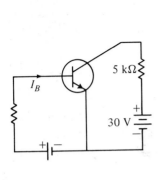

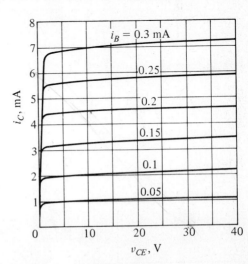

Figure P9.6

9.7 In the circuit of Figure P9.7, $\beta_0 = 120$ and $I_{co} = 1$ μA. Find I_C and V_{CB} for $I_E = 4$ mA.

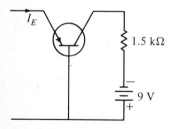

Figure P9.7

9.8 Suppose that, for the arrangement shown in Figure P9.8, the dc beta (β_0) of the silicon transistor is 50. Find its I_C, I_B, and V_{CE}.

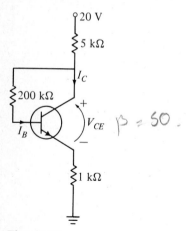

Figure P9.8

9.9 The transistor in the circuit of Figure P9.9 has $\alpha_0 = 0.98$, $I_{co} = 1$ μA, and $V_{BE} = 0.6$ V. What is the value of v_i such that the transistor is in the saturation region ($v_{CE} = 0$)?

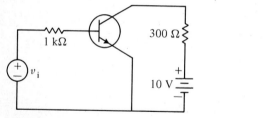

Figure P9.9

9.10 The transistor in the circuit of Figure P9.10 has $\beta_0 = 140$, $I_{co} = 1.4\,\mu A$, and $V_{BE} = 0.6$ V. Select a value for the resistance R_b so that $I_C = 4$ mA. What will be the value of V_{CE} under this condition?

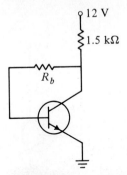

Figure P9.10

9.11 Determine the Q point of the silicon transistor in the circuit of Figure P9.11.

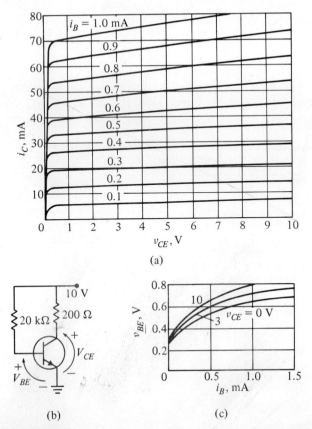

(a)

(b)   (c)

Figure P9.11

9.12 In the circuit of Figure P9.12, locate the quiescent point.

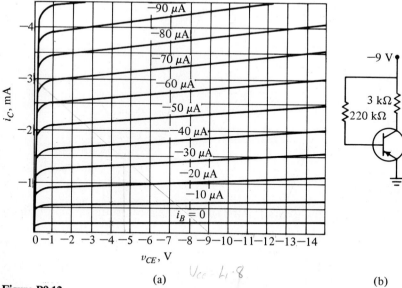

(a) $V_{CC} = 4.8$ (b)

Figure P9.12

9.13 For the collector-to-base bias circuit of Figure 9.17(b), the characteristics of the transistor are given in Figure P9.13, with $V_{CC} = -15$ V, $R_b = 50$ kΩ, and $R_c = 1$ kΩ. Assuming that $|I_C| \gg |I_B|$, locate the quiescent point.

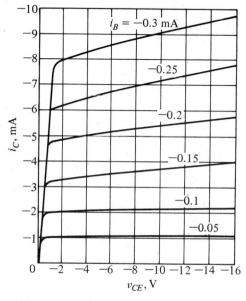

Figure P9.13   (a)

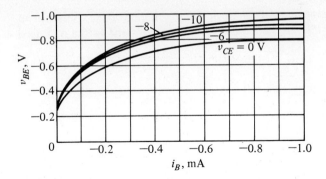

(b)

Figure P9.13 (continued)

9.14 Locate the quiescent point on both characteristics of the transistor in the circuit of Figure P9.14.

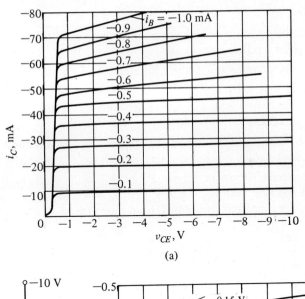

(a)

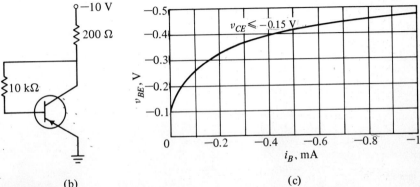

(b)

(c)

Figure P9.14

9.15 Locate the quiescent point on both characteristics of the transistor in the circuit of Figure P9.15. The transistor used is the same as the one used in Problem 9.11.

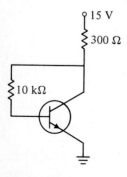

15 V

300 Ω

10 kΩ

Figure P9.15

9.16 Derive the common-base h parameters of a transistor in terms of its common-emitter h parameters.

9.17 Derive the common-collector h parameters of a transistor in terms of its common-emitter h parameters.

9.18 Derive the expressions for A_v, A_i, Z_i, and Z_o for the basic amplifier circuit of Figure 9.28(b).

9.19 Derive the expressions for A_v, A_i, Z_i, and Z_o for the basic amplifier of Figure 9.28(c).

9.20 In the circuit shown in Figure P9.20, $V_{CC} = 20$ V, $R_c = 10$ kΩ, and $R_e = 300$ Ω. Assume that $V_{BE} = 0.6$ V and $\beta_0 = 45$ and it is desired that $V_{CE} = 5$ V under quiescent conditions. Find the value of R.

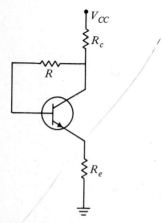

V_{CC}

R_c

R

R_e

Figure P9.20

9.21 Determine h_{fe} and h_{oe} of the transistor of Problem 9.12 at $V_{CE} = -10$ V and $I_B = -70$ μA.

9.22 Determine $[h_e]$ for the transistor of Problem 9.13 at the operating point $I_B = -300$ μA and $V_{CE} = -10$ V.

9.23 Determine $[h_e]$ for the transistor of Problem 9.14 at the operating point $I_C = -50$ mA and $I_B = -0.6$ mA.

9.24 Determine $[h_b]$ for the transistor of Problem 9.11 at the operating point $I_C = 40$ mA and $V_{CE} = 3$ V.

9.25 Prove that the two three-terminal circuits of Figure 9.26 are equivalent if $\beta = \alpha/(1-\alpha)$ and $r_d = r_c(1-\alpha)$.

9.26 Show that the h parameters for the two-port of the Darlington pair of transistors shown in Figure P9.26 are as follows.

$$h_{ie} = h_{ie1} + \frac{(1-h_{re1})(1+h_{fe1})h_{ie2}}{1+h_{oe1}h_{ie2}}$$

$$h_{fe} = h_{fe1} + \frac{(h_{fe2}-h_{oe1}h_{ie2})(1+h_{fe1})}{1+h_{oe1}h_{ie2}}$$

$$h_{oe} = h_{oe2} + \frac{(1+h_{fe2})(1-h_{re2})h_{oe1}}{1+h_{oe1}h_{ie2}}$$

$$h_{re} = h_{re2} + \frac{(h_{ie2}h_{oe1}+h_{re1})(1-h_{re2})}{1+h_{oe1}h_{ie2}}$$

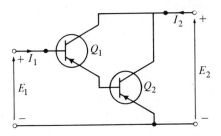

Figure P9.26

9.27 Find the h parameters of the composite transistor of Figure P9.26 by assuming identical transistors and using the values in (9.50) for each transistor.

9.28 The transistor in the circuit of Figure P9.28 has the parameters given in (9.50). Calculate its small-signal voltage gain V_o/V_i, input impedance Z_i, and output impedance Z_o.

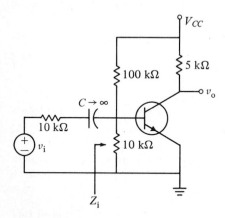

Figure P9.28

9.29 For the transistor of the circuit of Figure P9.29, $h_{ie} = 100$ Ω, $h_{re} = 0.1$, $h_{fe} = 10$, and $h_{oe} = 10$ $\mu\mho$. Find the ac small-signal voltage gain $A_v = V_o/V_i$, the input impedance Z_i, and the output impedance Z_o.

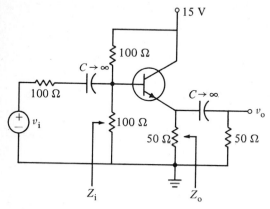

Figure P9.29

9.30 The transistor in the circuit of Figure P9.30 has the following parameters:

$$h_{ie} = 1.1 \text{ k}\Omega, \qquad h_{re} = 2.5 \times 10^{-4}, \qquad h_{fe} = 50, \qquad h_{oe} = 1/(40 \text{ k}) \mho$$

Find the ac small-signal voltage gain V_o/V_i and the input impedance Z_i.

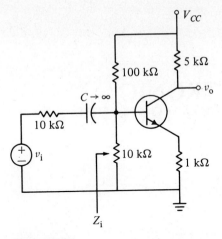

Figure P9.30

9.31 The transistor in the circuit of Figure P9.31 has the parameters given in (9.50). Find the small-signal voltage gain $A_v = V_o/V_i$.

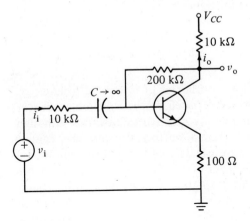

Figure P9.31

10 | OTHER ELECTRONIC DEVICES AND CIRCUITS

In this chapter we shall briefly describe three other groups of electronic devices—vacuum tubes, integrated circuits, and operational amplifiers. Some circuits using these devices are also introduced.

10.1 Vacuum tubes

Historically, vacuum tubes were the workhorses of electronic technology. Since the invention of solid-state devices such as the junction transistor and the field-effect transistor, their role has greatly declined. But, although current practice seeks to avoid using them altogether, vacuum tubes cannot yet be dismissed as out-of-date historical devices for several reasons. (1) Much of the equipment constructed after World War II used vacuum tubes and some of it is still in use. (2) For some ground-based high-power equipment, such as radar systems and radio transmitters, vacuum tubes remain the best devices to use. (3) Many special-purpose devices, especially those for high-frequency applications, such as the traveling-wave tubes (klystrons), are basically vacuum tubes. We'll describe several basic vacuum-tube devices here.

1 The vacuum triode

The current through a thermionic vacuum diode can be controlled by introducing a third electrode—the grid—between the cathode and the anode. The grid is usually made of either a thin wire or a meshed screen. It is placed closer to the cathode than the anode is. Thus the voltage of the grid has a much larger effect on the number of electrons leaving the cathode than does the anode voltage. Because of the low net metallic area of the grid, most of the electrons leaving the cathode pass through the surface occupied by the grid and proceed to the anode. Such a device is called a *vacuum triode*.

In the typical operation of a triode, the grid is maintained at a negative voltage with respect to the cathode. This greatly reduces the plate current. By changing the potential of the grid, we can control the plate current and thereby effect amplification. The essential components of the interior of a typical receiving tube are shown in Figure 10.1(a). The symbol for a vacuum triode is shown in Figure 10.1(b). In most circuit diagrams, the heaters of vacuum tubes are either omitted or grouped separately.

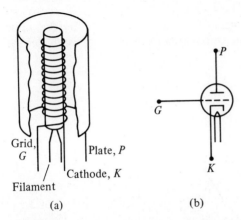

(a)   (b)

Figure 10.1   (a) The interior of a vacuum triode. (b) Symbol for a vacuum triode.

In the normal operation of a vacuum triode, in which the grid potential is negative with respect to the cathode, as shown in Figure 10.2, it is justifiable to assume that $i_G = 0$. Thus, as far as its external characteristics are concerned, a vacuum triode acts very much like an n-channel FET; the grid may be compared to the gate, the cathode to the source, and the plate to the drain. In fact, all the principles of analysis and circuit functions

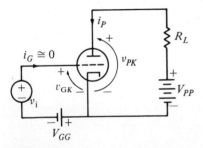

Figure 10.2   A basic vacuum triode amplifier circuit.

developed for the junction FET can be directly transplanted to vacuum-triode applications. The chief difference between these two devices is the manner in which the plate (or drain) current is dependent on the grid (or gate) voltage and the plate (or drain) voltage. Instead of (8.2), for a vacuum triode we have

$$i_P = G\left(v_{GK} + \frac{v_{PK}}{\mu}\right)^n = G'(\mu v_{GK} + v_{PK})^n \tag{10.1}$$

where n depends on the geometry of the electrodes and varies in the neighborhood of 1.5.

The *output characteristics* of a triode, like those of FETs, are a plot of i_P versus v_{PK} for different fixed values of v_{GK}. A typical set is shown in Figure 10.3. These are also known as *plate characteristics*. By the same token, transfer characteristics and constant-current characteristics can be constructed for vacuum triodes.

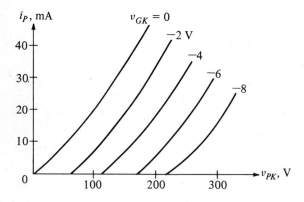

Figure 10.3 The plate characteristics of a triode.

The biasing of vacuum tubes is exactly like that of n-channel FETs. Of course, vacuum tubes have no counterpart to a p-channel FET.

For small-signal applications, the pertinent parameters are:

(*a*) *The plate resistance:*

$$r_p = \frac{\partial v_{PK}}{\partial i_P} \tag{10.2}$$

(*b*) *The transconductance:*

$$g_m = \frac{\partial i_P}{\partial v_{GK}} \tag{10.3}$$

(c) *The amplification factor:*

$$\mu = -\frac{\partial v_{PK}}{\partial v_{GK}} \tag{10.4}$$

Several small-signal vacuum-triode ac equivalent circuits are shown in Figure 10.4.

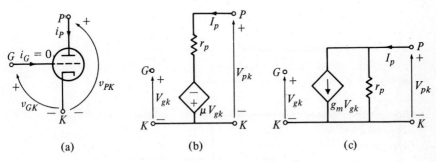

| (a) | (b) | (c) |

Figure 10.4 Small-signal ac equivalent circuits of a vacuum triode.

2 The vacuum tetrode

Of historical interest in the development of vacuum tubes is the *tetrode*, in which an extra grid is interposed between the plate and the grid of a triode. This extra grid, known as the screeen grid, is maintained at a constant potential that is positive with respect to the cathode. Figure 10.5 shows a tetrode in typical operation. The presence of the screen grid has three important effects.

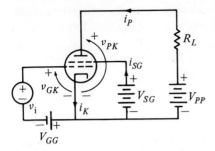

Figure 10.5 A vacuum tetrode and its biasing arrangement.

First, the ability of the plate to attract electrons away from the cathode is almost completely shielded by the screen grid. The cathode current is almost constant for a wide range of plate voltages. This cathode current is divided between the plate and the screen grid for low plate voltages. When the plate voltage is higher than the screen-grid voltage, most of the cathode current flows directly to the plate. A typical v-i characteristic of a tetrode is shown in Figure 10.6.

The second effect of the screen grid is that, since it is maintained at a constant potential, it is grounded for ac. Hence the capacitive (electrostatic) effect between the plate and the grid is much reduced (by a factor of 1000 or more). A tetrode may be operated at a much higher frequency than a triode.

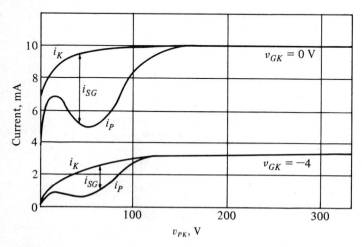

Figure 10.6 Plate characteristics of a vacuum tetrode.

The third effect is the negative slope of the plate current in the range in which the screen-grid potential exceeds the plate potential. This may be attributed to the secondary emission of the plate. When electrons from the cathode arrive at the plate with sufficient energy, they cause electrons in the atoms of the plate material to become free electrons. These free electrons are attracted by the screen grid, which has a higher potential, resulting in a reduction in plate current. This negative slope in the plate characteristic makes the tetrode undesirable for many applications.

3 The vacuum pentode

In order to eliminate the negative slope part of the tetrode characteristics, another grid is introduced between the plate and the screen grid. This is known as the *suppressor grid* and it is maintained at the same potential as the cathode, usually by a direct connection, as shown in Figure 10.7. The presence of this third grid prevents the plate secondary electrons from being attracted by the screen grid and results in a much smoother plate characteristic. A typical set of pentode plate characteristics is shown in Figure 10.8.

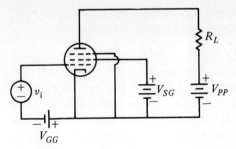

Figure 10.7 A vacuum pentode and its biasing arrangement.

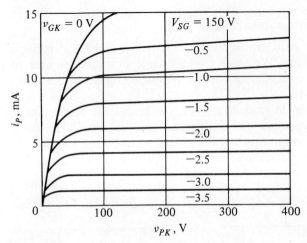

Figure 10.8 Plate characteristics of a vacuum pentode.

Although a pentode is a five-electrode tube, we can treat it as a three-terminal device just like a triode. This is because we do not use the screen grid or the suppressor grid for the injection or extraction of signals. The screen-grid battery may be considered internal to the tube. The short circuit between the suppressor grid and the cathode is actually supplied internally in some tubes. The difference between a triode and a pentode lies mainly in the shape of their characteristics.

The comparison between the triode and the pentode may be summarized as follows:

1 They have comparable transconductances. Typical values fall between 0.5 and 10 m℧.

2 Pentodes have much higher plate resistances (0.1 to 2 MΩ) than triodes (0.5 to 100 kΩ).

3 Pentodes have much higher amplification factors (100 to 10,000) than triodes (2.5 to 100).

4 The plate-to-grid capacitance in a pentode (sometimes as low as 0.01 pF) is much smaller than in a triode (sometimes as high as 15 pF).

This comparison also shows that the pentode resembles the *n*-channel FET even more than the triode, inasmuch as the pentode's plate characteristics display a more nearly constant-current feature, like the FET in the current-saturation region. However, apart from the differences in their characteristics and therefore in their small-signal parameters, these three devices (triode, tetrode, and pentode) can be treated exactly alike analytically.

10.2 ac Analysis of vacuum-tube circuits

Since a vacuum-tube circuit can be treated exactly like an FET circuit, no new principle is involved. We shall give a couple of examples here to illustrate the analysis of vacuum-tube circuits for small-signal applications.

1 *The cascode amplifier* A cascode amplifier is the cascade connection of a grounded-cathode amplifier and a grounded-grid amplifier. The basic arrangement of such a composite amplifier is shown in Figure 10.9(a). The ac equivalent of this circuit is shown in Figure 10.9(b), in which

$$V_{gk2} = -I_p r_{p1} + \mu_1 V_i \tag{10.5}$$

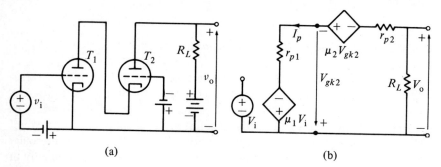

(a)   (b)

Figure 10.9 A cascode amplifier.

KVL requires that

$$I_p(r_{p1} + r_{p2} + R_L) = \mu_1 V_i + \mu_2 V_{gk2} \tag{10.6}$$

Equations (10.5) and (10.6) give

$$I_p = \frac{(\mu_1 + \mu_1 \mu_2) V_i}{r_{p1}(1 + \mu_2) + r_{p2} + R_L} \tag{10.7}$$

The voltage gain is

$$A_v = \frac{-I_p R_L}{V_i} = -\frac{\mu_1(1+\mu_2)R_L}{r_{p1}(1+\mu_2)+r_{p2}+R_L} \tag{10.8}$$

If $r_{p1}(1+\mu_2) \gg r_{p2}+R_L$, then we have

$$A_v \cong -g_{m1}R_L \tag{10.9}$$

2 *Triode amplifier at a high frequency* At high frequencies, the inter-electrode capacitances can no longer be ignored. Take the amplifier of Figure 10.10(a). For the triode, $\mu = 20$ and $r_p = 5$ kΩ. The interelectrode

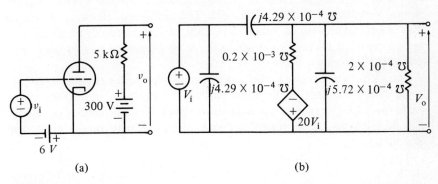

(a)   (b)

Figure 10.10 A vacuum triode amplifier with its interelectrode capacitances taken into account.

capacitances are $C_{GP} = 3$ pF, $C_{GK} = 3$ pF, and $C_{PK} = 4$ pF. To find the voltage gain at 22.76 MHz, we have the equivalent circuit of Figure 10.10(b), which shows the admittance of each interelectrode capacitance. Using node analysis, we have

$$(2+j5.72) \times 10^{-4}V_o + 2 \times 10^{-4}(V_o+20V_i) + j4.29 \times 10^{-4}(V_o - V_i) = 0$$

which gives

$$\frac{V_o}{V_i} = \frac{-40+j4.29}{4+j10.01} = \frac{40.23\ \underline{/173.9°}}{10.78\ \underline{/68.2°}} = 3.73\ \underline{/105.7°} \tag{10.10}$$

10.3 Integrated electronics

In Chapters 6, 8, and 9 we discussed the electric properties of several important *discrete* semiconductor devices and the analysis of circuits using these devices. A familiarity with semiconductors is essential in modern electronics. Not only are these devices commonly found as individual units in electronic circuits. They are also the basic components of functional modules that may range from the electronic portion of a complete radio set on a single printed-circuit board to a miniaturized video amplifier encapsulated in a TO or DIP package. Hence a basic knowledge of discrete electronic components—junction diodes, bipolar transistors, field-effect transistors—is the foundation necessary to an understanding of modern integrated electronics.

The heart of integrated electronics is the monolithic *integrated circuit* (IC). The development of this area, also known as microelectronics, since the early fifties has completely revolutionized electronic technology. A number of circuit elements (transistors, diodes, resistors, capacitors) can be produced on a single piece of semiconductor, usually a silicon chip, in several simultaneous fabrication steps. The number of elements produced may be several tens on an ordinary IC chip, several hundreds on a medium-scale integrated (MSI) circuit, and over a thousand in a large-scale integrated (LSI) circuit.

The technology of ICs is still a developing area with new improvements being made constantly. We shall outline the most common fabrication techniques to give you some idea of the processes involved. The figures and descriptions are representative and, of course, may vary a great deal in practice.

The process usually starts with a *p*-type silicon wafer about 0.2 mm thick and 50 mm in diameter as the substrate. An *n*-type layer of crystal of the right thickness, say 0.05 mm, is grown on the substrate by a gas mixture that contains silicon chloride, the right amount of impurities, and other agents. This process is known as the epitaxial growth. Various components are produced in this layer.

We shall first describe a typical method of producing bipolar transistors. This is done by a series of masks and diffusion processes that change the type, depth, and concentration of majority carriers in the epitaxial layer. The steps are illustrated in Figure 10.11.

In Figure 10.11(a), a thin layer of silicon oxide is formed over the wafer by oxidation. Openings are made in this oxide layer by etching over the area that surrounds the transistor to be produced, as shown in Figure 10.11(b). Then the wafer is subjected to a *p*-type diffusion through these openings. In this process, a number of box-shaped *n*-type islands are formed. Now, if we keep the substrate at a potential lower than the *n*-type islands, we have a reverse-biased *p-n* junction at the boundaries of the islands. Hence the newly diffused *p* regions act as isolation regions.

The next step is to remove the first oxide layer, form a new oxide layer, and etch out a new pattern of openings, as illustrated in Figure 10.11(c). The *p*-type diffusion is repeated to form the base region. The remaining *n* region of the island is to become the collector region. It is important that the depth of this *p*-type base region be shallower than the epitaxial layer.

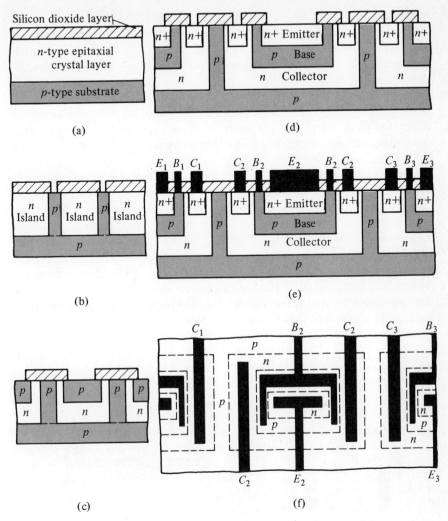

Figure 10.11 Series of steps in IC fabrication. (Drawings are not to scale.)

The emitter-region diffusion of n-type impurities again follows the formation of a new oxide-layer pattern. The result is the emitter regions labeled n^+ in Figure 10.11(d). During this step, the collector regions adjacent to the wafer surface are also exposed to allow them to be heavily doped with the n-type impurities. This improves their conductivity with the metallic contact of the collector electrodes.

The last step is to interconnect the various electrodes. Again a new oxide-layer pattern is formed and each electrode is exposed. A layer of thin aluminum is deposited on the wafer. Then a photoresist process is applied

to etch away the undesired aluminum and leave the desired interconnections. Figure 10.11(e) shows only the base, collector, and emitter electrodes.
The top view of these transistors is shown in Figure 10.11(f). In an actual
IC, these electrodes would be connected to other points on the same chip,
as dictated by the circuit design.

We have described briefly the fabrication of a bipolar transistor in an
integrated circuit because it involves all the typical steps in producing an
integrated circuit. By omitting some of these steps and/or appropriately
connecting certain terminals, many other elements can be produced at the
same time.

For example, resistors are formed by leaving out the emitter-diffusion
step. The same p-type semiconductor layer that forms the base region of the
transistor now serves as the resistor channel. However, since the same
material must also serve as the transistor base region, the resistivity of the
resistor is fixed. Only the channel length and width can be used to produce
different resistance values. Frequently the channel has to be doubled back
several times to provide enough resistance. Figure 10.12 shows the cross
section of a representative diffused resistor in an IC. The isolation of such
a resistor from the area surrounding it is achieved by connecting the n region
outside the channel to the most positive potential in the circuit.

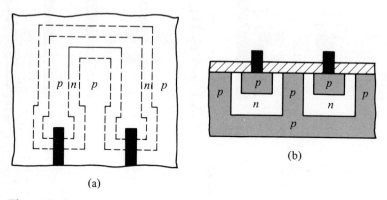

(a)

(b)

Figure 10.12   Top and cross-sectional views of an IC resistor.

There are two major types of IC capacitors: the diffused or junction
capacitor, and the MOS capacitor. The junction capacitor makes use of the
reverse-biased p-n junction that exists between the collector-diffusion and
the base-diffusion steps. Figure 10.13 shows a representative cross-sectional
diagram of such a capacitor. The MOS capacitor is somewhat like an
ordinary capacitor in that it has two plate electrodes and a dielectric
between these electrodes. A representative cross-sectional diagram is shown
in Figure 10.14. One of the electrodes is the metallic surface. The other is

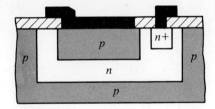

Figure 10.13 Cross-sectional view of an IC junction capacitor.

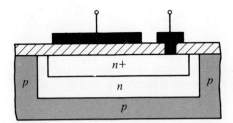

Figure 10.14 Cross-sectional view of an MOS capacitor.

the n^+ region formed during the emitter-diffusion step just below the metallic surface. The silicon dioxide layer is the dielectric material.

The capacitance values obtainable in ICs are severely limited. A large capacitor will take up a large area, which is always at a premium. For this reason, capacitances of large values must be avoided within an IC.

Since a *p-n* junction exists between the base and the collector or the emitter, either junction can be used to provide a junction diode. In addition, transistor terminals can be connected to form diodes. There are three modes of connection possible, as shown in Figure 10.15.

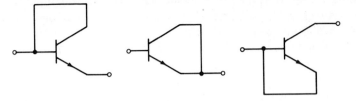

Figure 10.15 Bipolar transistors connected to form diodes.

The series of steps presented in Figure 10.11 are also used to fabricate the JFET and the MOSFET. Figure 10.16 is a cross-sectional view of a *p*-channel JFET. It is easy to see that MOS-type FETs can be fabricated at the same time that other elements are being produced.

We have outlined the typical steps in the fabrication of monolithic IC components. A well-planned program is obviously required so that the

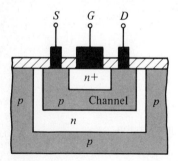

Figure 10.16 Cross-sectional view of an IC JFET.

design, layout, and diffusion for all the components are done at the same time. For an ordinary IC, with 20 to 60 elements in each unit, the unit is repeated many times on the same wafer. A wafer may contain several hundreds of such IC chips, all produced in the same series of processes.

The main advantages of ICs are their small size, low cost (because of large production volume), high reliability, and good performance (because of the availability of cheap active components).

Monolithic ICs also have some drawbacks, the chief of which is their low power-handling capacity, primarily because of limited size. Another is their inability to produce large capacitances. No practical inductors or transformers can be produced in monolithic form. The proximity of components also causes many unwanted parasitic effects, which limit their high-frequency performance. Monolithic ICs are only economical when the volume of production is very high.

Modern electronics often uses monolithic ICs in conjunction with discrete components, enabling us to take advantage of the superior features of both. This is known as *hybrid integrated circuit* technology. There are two major types of hybrid IC technology; the thin-film and the thick-film techniques.

In *thin-film techniques*, the substrate is usually glass. Conductors and resistors are formed from materials deposited on the substrate with appropriate masks. Conductors are usually made of aluminum, tantalum, silver, or gold. Resistors can be made from aluminum, tantalum, or a nickel-chromium alloy. Capacitors may be discrete or formed on the substrate by superimposing two metallic films on top of each other before the lower one is partially anodized to form the dielectric between the two films. In addition to these basic components, discrete inductors, capacitors, resistors, diodes, transistors, and ICs are bonded or soldered to the circuit. Thin-film element values can usually be very accurately controlled. Also, after fabrication, these elements can be adjusted or trimmed by several techniques, such as laser trimming.

In *thick-film techniques*, the substrate is usually made of some ceramic material. Conductors or resistors are formed on the substrate by silk-screening of conductive or resistive pastes or inks and subsequent firing.

The resistances of the resistors can also be trimmed by a laser beam or by sandblasting. Discrete components and IC chips are then attached to the circuit by bonding techniques. A thick-film circuit is actually a miniaturized printed circuit.

Modern electronics uses all four types of technology: (1) monolithic IC; (2) thin-film hybrid IC; (3) thick-film hybrid IC; (4) discrete. They decrease in developmental cost in this order. Hence a monolithic IC is only economical when the production volume is extremely high, say on the order of 10^7. Thin-film technology is attractive when the volume is of the order of 10^5 to 10^6. Thick-film techniques are used in the range of 10^3 to 10^4 units.

10.4 Operational amplifier

The rapidly developing IC technology has added a very versatile electronic functional block—the operational amplifier, or op amp—to the list of basic electronic devices along with discrete electronic components. Although an op amp is actually a series of stages of amplifiers, the IC version of the device is so cheap and so small that we may in many cases regard it as a single functional module and pay no attention to its internal details. That is what we will do here. Of course, someone still has to design and fabricate these devices. Also, there are many finer points about this device, which we shall leave to more specialized courses.

There are five principal terminals in an op amp. These are shown in Figure 10.17. Two of these terminals are for dc power supply, one positive

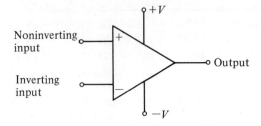

Figure 10.17 Block diagram of an operational amplifier.

and one negative. These terminals also provide a path for ac current to flow to ground. In most ac applications, this path is omitted in the diagram and its presence is understood.

The working model of an op amp comprises the remaining three terminals, as shown in Figure 10.18. The terminal marked plus (+) is known as the *noninverting* terminal. That marked minus (−) is known as the *inverting* terminal. The third is the *output* terminal. The basic function of an op amp is equivalent to the circuit diagram shown in Figure 10.19. The device is basically a high-gain amplifier whose input voltage is the voltage

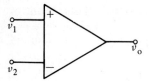

Figure 10.18 Block diagram of an operational amplifier with the dc supply terminals omitted but implied.

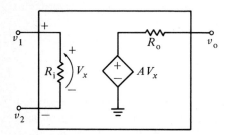

Figure 10.19 Small-signal equivalent circuit of the op amp.

difference between the two input terminals. The input resistance R_i is extremely high and the output resistance R_o is very low. A few sets of typical values are shown in Table 10.1.

Table **10.1**

Type of circuit	Gain	R_i (MΩ)	R_o (Ω)	Supply voltage
Discrete bipolar transistor circuit	10^5	1	500	±25 V
Monolithic IC	10^4	2	25	±15 V
Monolithic IC with FET input	10^5	10^6	75	±15 V

An op amp used in conjunction with other circuit elements and devices can usually be regarded as ideal, if the circuit is properly arranged so that it is stable, and if the op amp is operating in the linear portion of its characteristic. In an ideal op amp, we assume that

$$R_i = \infty, \qquad R_o = 0, \qquad A = \frac{v_o}{V_x} = \frac{v_o}{v_1 - v_2} = \infty$$

The last requirement (that $A = \infty$) is better stated as

$$v_1 - v_2 = \epsilon \to 0$$

In other words, in a properly arranged op amp circuit, v_1 and v_2 are virtually the same. At the same time, $i_1 = 0$ and $i_2 = 0$. Thus the input terminals of an op amp are constrained in such a way that they are both short-circuited ($v_1 = v_2$) and open-circuited ($i_1 = 0$, $i_2 = 0$) at the same time. We speak of this phenomenon as a *virtual short circuit** (one terminal is a virtual ground when the other terminal is permanently grounded). Figure 10.20 shows the equivalent circuit of an ideal op amp.

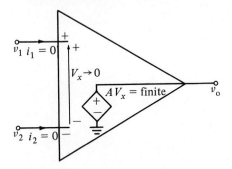

Figure 10.20 Equivalent circuit of the ideal op amp.

10.5 Operational amplifier circuits

We shall now analyze several circuits using op amps with the assumption that each op amp is ideal.

1 *Inverting amplifier*   In the circuit of Figure 10.21, the minus terminal is a virtual ground. Hence the currents in R_1 and R_2 are, respectively,

$$i_1 = \frac{v_i}{R_1}, \qquad i_2 = \frac{v_o}{R_2} \tag{10.11}$$

But since no current can flow into the minus terminal, we have

$$\frac{v_i}{R_1} + \frac{v_o}{R_2} = 0 \tag{10.12}$$

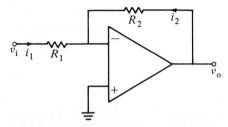

Figure 10.21   An inverting amplifier.

* In active network theory, we would say that a *nullator* is connected between these two terminals.

Hence

$$A_v = \frac{v_o}{v_i} = -\frac{R_2}{R_1}$$

(10.13)

2 *Noninverting amplifier*   In the circuit of Figure 10.22, we have

$$i_2 = \frac{v_o - v_i}{R_2} \quad \text{and} \quad i_1 = \frac{v_i}{R_1}$$

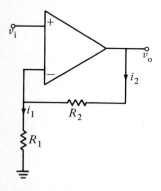

Figure 10.22   A noninverting amplifier.

Since $i_1 = i_2$, we have

$$\frac{v_o - v_i}{R_2} = \frac{v_i}{R_1}$$

(10.14)

or

$$A_v = \frac{v_o}{v_i} = \frac{R_1 + R_2}{R_1} = 1 + \frac{R_2}{R_1}$$

(10.15)

3 *The voltage follower*   In (10.15), if we let $R_1 = \infty$, we have

$$A_v = \frac{v_o}{v_i} = 1$$

(10.16)

The result is the unity-gain voltage amplifier. We can simplify the circuit to that of Figure 10.23. This circuit can be used to buffer two stages of

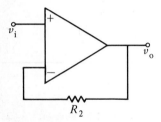

Figure 10.23   A voltage follower.

amplifiers, so that the input of the second stage does not load the output of the first stage. Since the value of R_2 is arbitrary, we may replace it by a short circuit.

4 Current-to-voltage converter The circuit of Figure 10.24 is the same as that in Figure 10.21 with R_1 set to zero. Equation (10.12) becomes

$$i_1 + \frac{v_o}{R_2} = 0 \qquad \text{or} \qquad v_o = -R_2 i_1 \qquad\qquad (10.17)$$

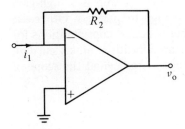

Figure 10.24 A current-to-voltage converter.

We can use this circuit to measure a current. First convert it into a voltage, then amplify the voltage and read it.

5 Integrator In the circuit of Figure 10.25 we have

$$i_1 = \frac{v_1}{R}, \qquad i_2 = C\frac{dv_o}{dt} \qquad\qquad (10.18)$$

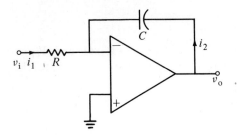

Figure 10.25 An op-amp integrator.

Since $i_1 + i_2 = 0$, we have

$$v_o(t) = -\frac{1}{RC}\int v_i(t)\, dt \qquad\qquad (10.19)$$

Hence the output voltage v_o is proportional to the time integral of the input voltage v_i.

The preceding examples demonstrate the versatility and simplicity of op amp circuits. This is precisely what makes op amps attractive for many applications, such as electronic instruments, digital circuits, oscilloscopes, analog computers, instrumentation systems, active filters, and amplifiers.

On the other hand they have also several limitations. The maximum output voltage swing is obviously limited by the power supply voltages. Although op amps made for instrumentation purposes can supply a very large output current and they are well protected against accidental misuse, IC op amps are basically low-signal, low-power devices. Another severe limitation is their frequency bandwidth. Since the op amp is a high-gain amplifier, it is necessary to reduce its gain at high frequencies. Otherwise it will be unstable and begin to oscillate. Other practical considerations for the use of an op amp are the common-mode amplification, off-set current, off-set voltage, slew rate, and so on. These topics are beyond the scope of this text.

10.6 Concluding remarks

The coverage in this chapter is meant only to introduce these three groups of electronic devices. It is more of an acknowledgement of their existence than an in-depth presentation. To provide the latter, a separate volume could be devoted to each topic. Students should take further courses or search out additional references if they are interested in devoting more time to these areas.

Problems

10.1 In the circuit of Figure P10.1, $R_k = 2 \text{ k}\Omega$, $R_L = 18 \text{ k}\Omega$, and $V_{PP} = 300$ V. (a) Draw the load line. (b) Draw the bias curve. (c) Locate the quiescent point.

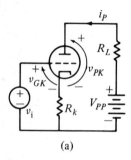

(a)

Figure P10.1

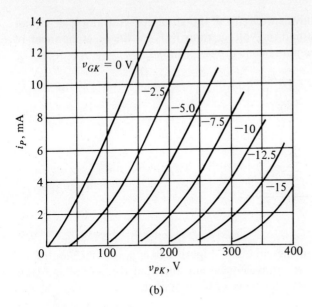

(b)

Figure P10.1 (continued)

10.2 In the circuit of Figure P10.2, find the value of V_i that will give a value of $V_o = 50$ V.

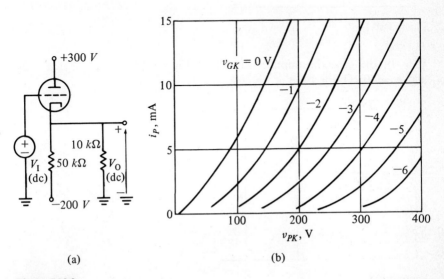

(a) (b)

Figure P10.2

10.3 Draw the ac equivalent circuit of the grounded-grid amplifier circuit of Figure P10.3. Then find the voltage ratio V_o/V_i for the ac component of the amplifier. The tube parameters are μ, r_p, and g_m.

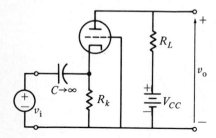

Figure P10.3

10.4 For the triode in the circuit of Figure P10.4, $g_m = 5$ m℧ and $g_p = 0.1$ m℧. (a) Draw the ac equivalent circuit. (b) Find the ac voltage gain V_o/V_i. (c) Find the output impedance of the amplifier.

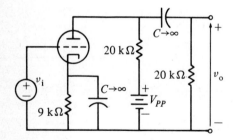

Figure P10.4

10.5 In the cascode amplifier circuit of Figure P10.5, $T_1 = T_2$, $\mu = 20$, and $r_p = 10$ kΩ. Find the ac voltage gain V_o/V_i.

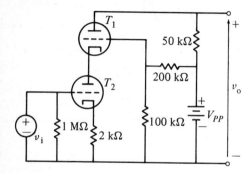

Figure P10.5

10.6 In the amplifier circuit of Figure P10.6, $T_1 = T_2$, $\mu = 20$, and $r_p = 10\ k\Omega$. The input signal has an rms value of 0.1 V. Find the rms values of the two output voltages, V_{o1} and V_{o2}, and their phase relationship with V_i.

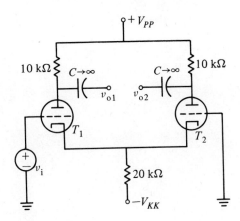

Figure P10.6

10.7 In the circuit of Figure P10.7, $\mu = 50$ and $r_p = 40\ k\Omega$ for each tube. Calculate the ac small-signal gain V_o/V_i.

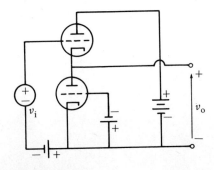

Figure P10.7

10.8 In the circuit of Figure P10.8, $\mu = 70$ and $r_p = 44$ kΩ for each tube. Find the signal component of i_p in terms of those of the input voltages, v_1 and v_2.

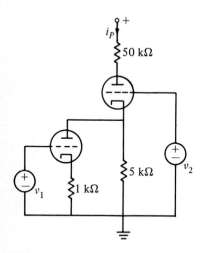

Figure P10.8

10.9 Suppose that a 5-kΩ resistor is needed in an IC. If the channel width is 0.05 mm, the thickness is 0.002 mm, and the average resistivity of the channel is 0.1 Ω-cm, what is the required channel length? [*Note:* Resistance = resistivity × length/cross-sectional area.]

10.10 An MOS capacitor in an IC has electrodes that are each 0.1×0.1 mm in dimension. The thickness of the dielectric material is 5×10^{-8} m. If the permittivity of the oxide material is 3×10^{-11} F/m, what is the capacitance of the capacitor? [*Note:* Capacitance = permittivity × area/thickness.]

10.11 Find the transfer impedance v_o/i_s of the circuit in Figure P10.11.

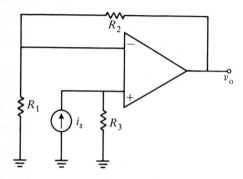

Figure P10.11

10.12 The circuit of Figure P10.12 can be made to convert a voltage into a current. Show that i_L is proportional to v_i regardless of the value of R_L, if $R_2 R_4 = R_1 R_3$.

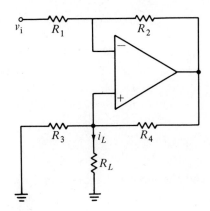

Figure P10.12

10.13 The circuit of Figure P10.13 is a summer circuit. Show that $v_o = -(R_3/R_1)v_1 - (R_3/R_2)v_2$.

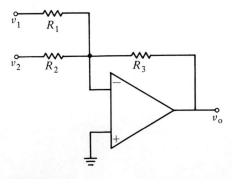

Figure P10.13

10.14 The circuit of Figure P10.14 is that of a differential amplifier. That is, $v_o = Av_2 - Bv_1$. Find A and B in terms of the R's.

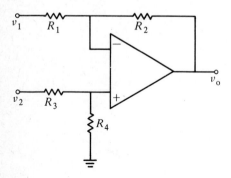

Figure P10.14

10.15 Find the relationship between v_o and the input voltages, v_1 and v_2, in the circuit of Figure P10.15.

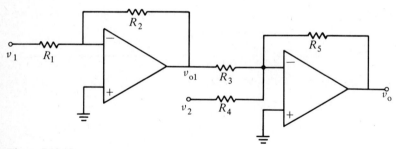

Figure P10.15

11 | NETWORK ANALYSIS IN THE FREQUENCY DOMAIN

In Section 5.2, we introduced the steady-state analysis of a network when its excitation is of the form $C\epsilon^{st}$, in which both C and s may be complex. At first, this approach was justified solely on the basis that it is a mathematically legitimate move. Then we identified a few physical situations that were actually included in the generic problem we had initially posed. One of these was the ac circuit analysis, in which C is identified as the complex amplitude of a sinusoid and s is limited to being imaginary ($s = j\omega$ or $\sigma = 0$).

When we treat a circuit problem as an ac analysis problem, we assume ω to have a definite value. Then we use that value to compute the impedance or admittance of each element and proceed to analyze the circuit. In many cases, this is only a small part of the entire solution.

One example of a network in which ω assumes only one fixed value is the power system (in which, for example, it may be 60, 50, or 25 Hz). Another is the dc circuit of certain applications such as automobiles. In almost all other networks or systems of any usefulness, we are more interested in knowing how the networks perform at more than one frequency. More often than not, we are interested in their performance over a range of frequencies.

In this chapter we shall extend the ac analysis to allow ω to vary. Indeed, as we shall soon see, it is sometimes more advantageous to leave the frequency variable as complex. This is exactly what we shall do.

11.1 Network functions in the complex-frequency domain

In Section 5.2 we saw how the electrical behavior of LTI elements may be characterized by their impedances or admittances. Whenever we talk about the impedance or admittance of an element, certain assumptions are automatically implied. Referring to the element of Figure 11.1, if we say that the

Figure 11.1 The representation of an LTI element by its impedance for analysis in the frequency domain.

element has an impedance of Z ohms, we are saying that the current-voltage pair associated with the element is

$$i(t) = I\epsilon^{st} \tag{11.1}$$

$$e(t) = E\epsilon^{st} \tag{11.2}$$

and, in addition, that their complex amplitudes must be related in such a way that

$$E = IZ \tag{11.3}$$

is always satisfied. If the element is a resistor, then Z is a real number ($Z = R$). If the element is an inductor, then $Z = sL$. If the element is a capacitor, then $Z = 1/sC$. In general, Z is a function of s.

The physical significance of the variable s was explained to some extent in Section 5.3. When $s = j\omega$, the quantity can be readily identified with the angular frequency (usually in radians per second) of the excitation (and hence that of the forced response). When s is complex, its significance can still be identified with an exponentially decreasing or increasing sinusoid. When $s = \sigma$, the excitation and response are exponential. When $s = 0$, the situation is dc.

You are all familiar with the term *frequency* ($f = \omega/2\pi$) of a periodic quantity. In a way, the variable s is a generalized frequency variable, since $\text{Im}(s) = \omega$ is the *real* angular frequency. Hence the variable s is referred to as the *complex frequency variable*.

When we speak of analyzing a system in the frequency domain, we are saying that we want to find out how the system behaves as the variable s is varied. For example, suppose we take the circuit of Figure 11.2. We want to find $I_2(s)$ for a given complex amplitude E. The problem implies* that

$$e(t) = E\epsilon^{st} \tag{11.4}$$

and the value of s is purposely unspecified. In other words, we are deliberately leaving the quantity s as a variable. The problem is to find I_2 as a function of s.

To find an analytical answer to this problem is not a difficult task. In fact

---

* In the case of sinusoidal excitations, a scaling factor of $\sqrt{2}$ is also implied.

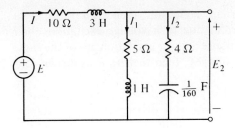

Figure 11.2

it is no more difficult than when the value of s or ω is specified. All we need to do is to leave s in literal form rather than setting it equal to a particular value. First let us find the impedance as seen by the voltage source E:

$$Z = 10 + 3s + \frac{(5+s)[4+(160/s)]}{s+9+(160/s)} \tag{11.5}$$

The current I is

$$I = \frac{E}{Z} = \frac{100}{Z}$$

and by the current-division rule we get

$$I_2 = \frac{5+s}{s+9+(160/s)} I$$

Hence

$$I_2(s) = \frac{100(5+s)}{[s+9+(160/s)](10+3s)+(5+s)[4+(160/s)]}$$

$$= \frac{100s(s+5)}{(s^2+9s+160)(3s+10)+(s+5)(4s+160)}$$

$$= \frac{100s(s+5)}{3s^3+41s^2+750s+2400} \tag{11.6}$$

Equation (11.6) is the mathematical description of how I_2 varies as the value of s in (11.4) is varied.

This chapter is mainly directed toward the handling and extraction of pertinent information from functions of the type of (11.6). Generally, a network function is the ratio of a response to an excitation in the same network, assuming both are of the form $A\epsilon^{st}$. As in ac circuits, depending on the localities and the types of electric quantities in question, network functions carry various names. If both the response and the excitation are located at the same terminal pair, their ratio is of the *driving-point* type. If they are at two different localities, their ratio is the *transfer* type. If the response is a voltage due to a current excitation, then their ratio is an *impedance*. If the response is a current due to a voltage excitation, their ratio is an *admittance*. If both the response and the excitation are of the same type (both are currents or both are voltages), then their ratio is demensionless and is simply termed a *ratio*.

For example, in Figure 11.2, $E/I = Z$ is a driving-point impedance; $I_2/E = Y_t$ is a transfer admittance; $I/E = Y$ is a driving-point admittance; $I_2/I = A_i$ is a (current) transfer ratio or a current gain; and $E_2/E = A_v$ is a (voltage) transfer ratio or a voltage gain.

Other adjectives are often attached to these functions either to indicate the localities of the assumed quantities or to qualify the network in question. We have already met some of these in Chapter 7. For example, we call

$$z_{21} = \left. \frac{E_2}{I_1} \right|_{I_2 = 0}$$

the open-circuit transfer impedance between port 1 and port 2. The main difference between the emphasis here and that in Chapters 5 and 7 is that these ratios are now viewed as functions of s rather than as a quantity.

EXAMPLE 1   In the FET amplifier circuit of Figure 11.3(a), $R_1 = 100 \text{ k}\Omega$, $R_s = 1.5 \text{ k}\Omega$, $R_L = 10 \text{ k}\Omega$, $C_s = 10 \text{ }\mu\text{F}$, $g_m = 2 \text{ m}\mho$, and $r_d = 20 \text{ k}\Omega$. Find the small-signal voltage gain as a function of s.

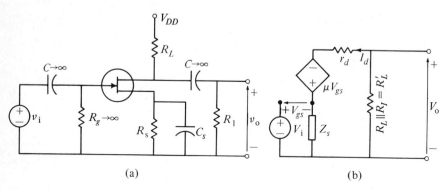

(a)   (b)

Figure 11.3   (a) An FET amplifier circuit. (b) The ac equivalent circuit of (a).

SOLUTION   The small-signal equivalent circuit is shown in Figure 11.3(b), where

$$\mu = g_m r_d = 40$$

$$R_L' = R_L \| R_1 = \frac{100 \text{ k} \times 10 \text{ k}}{110 \text{ k}} = 9.091 \times 10^3$$

$$Z_s = \frac{1}{10^{-5}s + (1/1.5 \text{ k})} = \frac{1.5 \text{ k}}{1 + 0.015s}$$

$$V_{gs} = V_i - I_d Z_s$$

$$(R_L' + r_d + Z_s)I_d = \mu V_{gs} = \mu(V_i - I_d Z_s)$$

$$I_d = \frac{\mu V_i}{R_L' + r_d + (1+\mu)Z_s}$$

$$V_o = -I_d R_L' = -\frac{\mu R_L' V_i}{R_L' + r_d + (1+\mu)Z_s}$$

$$A_v(s) = \frac{V_o}{V_i} = -\frac{\mu R_L'}{R_L' + r_d + (1+\mu)Z_s}$$

$$= -\frac{40 \times 9.091 \text{ k}}{9.091 \text{ k} + 20 \text{ k} + [(41 \times 1.5 \text{ k})/(1+0.015s)]}$$

$$= -\frac{363.6 \text{ k}}{29.091 \text{ k} + [61.5 \text{ k}/(1+0.015s)]} = -\frac{363.6(0.015s+1)}{0.436s + 90.591}$$

$$\tag{11.7}$$

11.2 Poles and zeros

One of the most compelling reasons to study the behavior of network functions in the complex-frequency domain is that a great deal is known about the functions of a complex variable. It is a well-established area in mathematics. When an LTI system is made up of lumped elements only (R, L, C, and controlled sources), its network function is always a rational function in s. This means that every network function is expressible as the ratio of two polynomials in s. Furthermore the coefficients of these polynomials are all real. These conclusions are easily appreciated if we observe that, in solving for any voltage or current in a network, we can always use node or mesh analysis. Each of the coefficients of the node or mesh equations will be of the form $as+b+c/s$, where a, b, and c are all real. When we solve for any of the unknowns in the node or mesh equations, we can express it as the ratio of two determinants whose elements are no more complicated than $as+b+c/s$. Such a ratio is always a real rational function in s.

A real rational function

$$F(s) = \frac{a_n s^n + a_{n-1} s^{n-1} + \cdots + a_1 s + a_0}{b_m s^m + b_{m-1} s^{m-1} + \cdots + b_1 s + b_0} \tag{11.8}$$

can always be expressed in the form

$$F(s) = K\frac{(s-z_1)(s-z_2)\cdots(s-z_n)}{(s-p_1)(s-p_2)\cdots(s-p_m)} = K\frac{N(s)}{D(s)} \tag{11.9}$$

where z_i are the roots of $N(s) = 0$ and p_i are the roots of $D(s) = 0$, and $K = a_n/b_m$. The z's are the values of s at which $F(s) = 0$ and are known as the *zeros of* $F(s)$. The p's are the values of s at which $F(s)$ is infinite and are known as the *poles of* $F(s)$. Since the coefficients of $F(s)$ are real, the complex poles and zeros of a network function must occur in conjugate pairs.

For the circuit of Figure 11.2, we have

$$Y_t(s) = \frac{I_2}{E} = \frac{s(s+5)}{3s^3 + 41s^2 + 750s + 2400}$$

$$= \frac{1}{3} \cdot \frac{s(s+5)}{(s+3.76)(s^2 + 9.907s + 212.75)}$$

$$= \frac{1}{3} \frac{(s-0)(s+5)}{(s+3.76)(s+4.95+j13.72)(s+4.95-j13.72)} \qquad (11.10)$$

Thus $Y_t(s)$ of (11.10) has zeros at $s = 0$ and $s = -5$ and poles at $s = -3.76$, $s = -4.95 - j13.72$, and $s = -4.95 + j13.72$.

For the circuit of Figure 11.3, its transfer voltage ratio $A_v(s)$ has a zero at $-1/0.015$ and a pole at $-90.591/0.436 = -207.8$.

Actually, a rational function must have the same number of poles and zeros. If $n > m$, the function has $n - m$ poles at the point at infinity. If $m > n$, it has $m - n$ zeros at the point at infinity. Hence, in addition to the finite zeros and poles mentioned for the $Y_t(s)$ of (11.10), it also has a zero at infinity. Both the pole and the zero of the function of (11.7) are finite and visible. For all purposes, however, we need mention only finite poles and zeros, as their numbers automatically tell us how the function behaves at infinity.

A *pole-zero pattern* is simply a diagram that displays the locations of all the finite poles and zeros of a function. A zero is usually shown as a small circle and a pole as a cross. The pole-zero pattern of the network function of (11.10) is shown in Figure 11.4. In many situations such diagrams enable us to gain at a glance a great deal of insight into the properties of network functions.

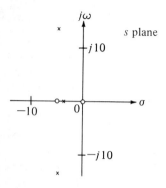

Figure 11.4 Pole-zero pattern of the transfer admittance of Equation (11.10).

Except for the proportionality constant K, the poles and zeros of a network function completely describe the function mathematically. Hence, if we know the poles and zeros of a network, we should be able to find out everything about the network to within a constant multiplier. This is one of the reasons why the poles and zeros of network functions are convenient to use when we are studying a system from the frequency-domain point of view. One example of the usefulness of the poles-and-zeros concept is provided in the next section.

11.3 Frequency characteristics of network functions

Mathematically, a network function assumes a unique value at any point throughout the s plane. Frequently the values of a function at certain chosen points are of interest for various reasons, for example, the points at which a function vanishes (zeros) or the points at which the values of the function are unbounded (poles).

However, the values of a network function for complex values of s are generally difficult to measure. Although we can give physical interpretations to these values (as was done in Section 5.3), these are usually only of theoretical interest. For practical purposes, we are mostly interested in the behavior of a network function along the j axis. Each point on the j axis corresponds to a real frequency. For instance, if we want to measure the driving-point impedance of a network at 1000 Hz, we are interested in the value of the impedance function $Z(s)$ of that network at $s = j2\pi \times 1000$, or $Z(j6283.2)$. We can go into a laboratory, set up our signal generator frequency at 1000 Hz, and, maybe, measure the voltage and current at the terminals of the network and the phase angle between them. Then we can compute the complex impedance. The behavior of a network function along the j axis of the s plane is known as the frequency characteristic of the network.

Generally, the value of a network function at any value of $s = j\omega$ is a complex quantity. Therefore, to display the variation of a network function along the j axis, we need two graphs. In the case of driving-point functions, graphs showing the real (resistance or conductance) and imaginary (reactance or susceptance) parts are usually preferred. In the case of transfer functions, we prefer graphs showing the magnitude (absolute value) and phase (angle). Of course, these two types of graph are convertible from one to the other. Here we shall dwell on the magnitude and phase characteristics.

Given a network funtion, we can find the variation of its magnitude and phase along the j axis straightforwardly, by directly computing these quantities at a number of frequencies and then plotting their variations. However, the following concept can sometimes help us to "get a feel" for what a network function does.

Suppose a given network function is in the form of (11.9). To obtain the magnitude of $F(s)$ at a particular value of s, we see that

$$|F(s)| = K \frac{|s-z_1||s-z_2| \cdots |s-z_n|}{|s-p_1||s-p_2| \cdots |s-p_m|} \tag{11.11}$$

Each of the factors $|s-p_i|$ and $|s-z_i|$ has a simple geometric interpretation. It is the distance from the point s to either z_i or p_i, as shown in Figure 11.5(a). Thus, if the pole-zero pattern of a network function is given and

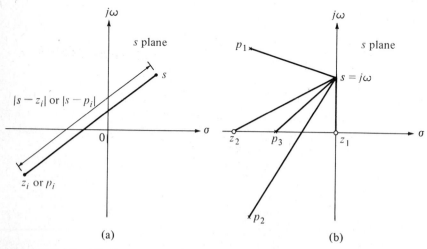

(a)   (b)

Figure 11.5 Contribution of poles or zeros to the magnitude of a network function.

we wish to obtain its magnitude along the j axis, we can imagine that a rubber band is connected between a point on the j axis and each of the poles and zeros. Then the value of $|F(s)|$ at that $j\omega$ is K times the ratio of the appropriate products of all the lengths of the rubber bands, as required by (11.11). As the $j\omega$ point moves along the j axis, the lengths of these rubber bands change and, of course, so does the value of $|F(j\omega)|$ [Figure 11.5(b)]. Sometimes this method of visualization will give us a pretty good idea as to how $|F(j\omega)|$ varies as ω is varied from 0 to ∞.

Similarly, if we want to obtain the phase angle of $F(s)$ at a particular value of s, we have

$$\arg[F(s)] = \arg(s-z_1) + \arg(s-z_2) + \cdots + \arg(s-z_n) - \arg(s-p_1)$$
$$- \arg(s-p_2) - \cdots - \arg(s-p_m) \tag{11.12}$$

where "arg" denotes "the argument or angle of [the quantity following it]." Each term $\arg(s-z_i)$ or $\arg(s-p_i)$ is the angle from the horizontal reference to the line joining the point s and the point z_i or p_i, as shown in Figure 11.6(a). (The angle is positive if counterclockwise and negative if clockwise.) Now, if we imagine that a set of rubber bands are connected between each of the poles and zeros and a point on the j axis, then we can determine an angle between each rubber band and the horizontal reference, as shown

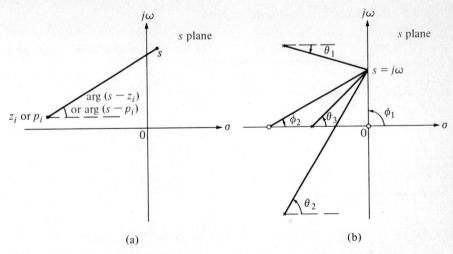

Figure 11.6   Contribution of poles or zeros to the phase of a network function.

in Figure 11.6(b). Then the angle of $F(j\omega)$ at that particular value of $j\omega$ is simply the appropriate algebraic sum of all the angles, as required in (11.12). [In Figure 11.6(b), $\arg[F(j\omega)] = \phi_1 + \phi_2 - \theta_1 - \theta_2 - \theta_3$. The numerical value of θ_1 is itself negative.] Thus, as the point $s = j\omega$ is moved along the j axis, the inclination of these rubber bands will change accordingly. Sometimes this scheme of visualization can give us an idea of the general shape of the phase characteristic as ω is varied from 0 to ∞.

These schemes of visualization are helpful only in giving us some qualitative information. However, there is no reason why we cannot obtain fairly accurate quantitative information, if we draw an accurate diagram, use a scale and a protractor, and perform some simple computations.

With the aid of this concept, you should be able to convince yourself that the magnitude and phase characteristics of the network function of $Y_t(s)$ of (11.10), with its pole-zero pattern shown in Figure 11.4, have the general shapes shown in Figure 11.7.

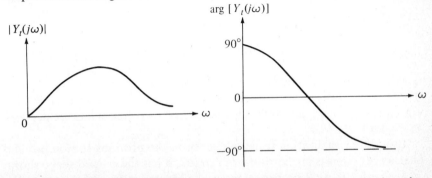

Figure 11.7   Magnitude and phase functions of the network function with the pole-zero pattern of Figure 11.4.

11.4 Resonance in second-order circuits

Series resonance Let us now look at the series RLC circuit of Figure 11.8 in detail. The voltage-current relationship is

$$\frac{I}{E} = Y(s) = \frac{1}{sL + R + (1/sC)} = \frac{1}{L} \frac{s}{s^2 + (R/L)s + (1/LC)}$$

$$= \frac{1}{L} \frac{s}{(s + R/2L + \sqrt{R^2/4L^2 - 1/LC})(s + R/2L - \sqrt{R^2/4L^2 - 1/LC})}$$

$$(11.13)$$

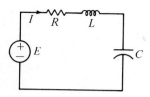

Figure 11.8 An RLC series circuit.

As in Chapter 5 [Equation (4.53) and Problem 4.17], we write

$$Y(s) = \frac{1}{L} \cdot \frac{s}{(s + \alpha + \gamma)(s + \alpha - \gamma)} \qquad (11.14)$$

if $(R^2/4L^2) > (1/LC)$ and

$$Y(s) = \frac{1}{L} \cdot \frac{s}{(s + \alpha + j\beta)(s + \alpha - j\beta)} \qquad (11.15)$$

if $(R^2/4L^2) < (1/LC)$, where $\alpha = R/2L$, $\gamma = \sqrt{(R^2/4L^2) - (1/LC)}$, and $\beta = \sqrt{(1/LC) - (R^2/4L^2)}$. Thus $Y(s)$ of (11.13) has two finite poles, $-\alpha \pm \gamma$ or $-\alpha \pm j\beta$, one zero at the origin, and one zero at infinity. It is also easy to show that

$$\alpha^2 - \gamma^2 = \alpha^2 + \beta^2 = \frac{1}{LC} = \omega_0^2$$

is independent of R. Thus, if we let R vary from 0 to a very large value, the loci of these poles will start at $\pm j\omega_0$. They move along the circle whose radius is ω_0 and they become coincident when $\beta = 0$ (or $\alpha = \omega_0$). Then they move along the negative real axis in a reciprocal fashion $[(\alpha + \gamma)(\alpha - \gamma) = \omega_0^2]$ until they approach 0 and $-\infty$. These loci are depicted in Figure 11.9.

Using the visualization technique given in the previous section, we find that, since $|Y(j\omega)|$ is proportional to $\ell_3/\ell_2 \ell_1$, it has the general shape shown in Figure 11.10. As R decreases, the peaks become taller and narrower. We

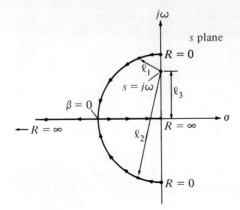

Figure 11.9 Loci of poles of the admittance of the *RLC* circuit as *R* is varied.

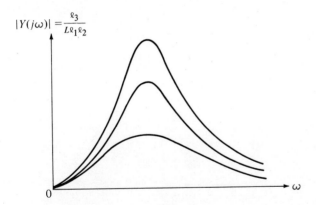

Figure 11.10 Magnitude functions of the admittance of the *RLC* circuit.

shall now look into this phenomenon quantitatively. From (11.13) we obtain

$$|Y(j\omega)| = \frac{1}{\sqrt{R^2 + (\omega L - 1/\omega C)^2}} \qquad (11.16)$$

The term $|Y(j\omega)|$ is maximum if

$$\omega L = \frac{1}{\omega C} \qquad (11.17)$$

or

$$\omega = \frac{1}{\sqrt{LC}} = \omega_0 \qquad (11.18)$$

that is to say, that the peak of the $|Y(j\omega)|$-versus-ω curve is situated at $\omega = \omega_0$, as given by (11.18), regardless of the value of *R*. This happens when the source frequency coincides with ω_0. When this occurs, resonance (specifically, series resonance) is said to take place. Other than the fact that $|Y(j\omega)|$ is maximum, we also have the following

1 The reactance of the series combination is zero.

2 The voltages across the capacitor and the inductor are equal in magnitude and opposite in polarity.

3 The impedance of the series combination is equal to the resistance R.

So far, we have determined that the value of R fixes the peak value of $|Y(j\omega)|$. The value of $1/\sqrt{LC}$ fixes the position of that peak. (See Figure 11.11.) Since there are only three elements in the circuit, there is only one

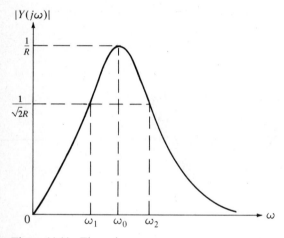

Figure 11.11 The series resonance curve.

other degree of freedom. This third degree of freedom can be used as a measure of the sharpness of the $|Y(j\omega)|$-versus-ω curve. This is usually done by first locating the two points on the curve whose values are $1/\sqrt{2}$ of the peak value. They are known as half-power points because the power delivered to R at these points is exactly one-half of that delivered at $\omega = \omega_0$. We shall denote these points by ω_1 and ω_2. Their values are the solution to the equation

$$\sqrt{R^2 + \left(\omega L - \frac{1}{\omega C}\right)^2} = \sqrt{2}\,R \tag{11.19}$$

or

$$\omega_1, \omega_2 = \sqrt{\frac{R^2}{4L^2} + \frac{1}{LC}} \pm \frac{R}{2L} \tag{11.20}$$

The half-power bandwidth is

$$BW = \omega_2 - \omega_1 = \frac{R}{L}$$

The measure of sharpness is the ratio of ω_0 to the half-power bandwidth, commonly known as the Q factor (Q connotes "quality").

$$Q = \frac{\omega_0}{\omega_2 - \omega_1} = \frac{\omega_0 L}{R} \tag{11.21}$$

Thus, the higher Q is, the sharper the resonance curve will be.

Normalized resonance curve   Expressing the admittance function in terms of R, ω_0, and Q, we have

$$Y(s) = \frac{1}{L} \cdot \frac{s}{s^2 + (R/L)s + 1/LC} = \frac{\omega_0}{L} \cdot \frac{s/\omega_0}{s^2 + (\omega_0/Q)s + \omega_0^2}$$

$$= \frac{1}{\omega_0 L} \cdot \frac{s/\omega_0}{(s/\omega_0)^2 + (1/Q)(s/\omega_0) + 1}$$

$$= \frac{1}{QR} \cdot \frac{s/\omega_0}{(s/\omega_0)^2 + 1/Q(s/\omega_0) + 1}$$

At $s = j\omega_0$, we have

$$Y(j\omega_0) = \frac{1}{R} = G$$

Hence

$$\frac{Y(s)}{G} = \frac{1}{Q} \frac{s/\omega_0}{(s/\omega_0)^2 + (1/Q)(s/\omega_0) + 1} \tag{11.22}$$

Equation (11.22) is the expression of the normalized admittance variation. The peak value is unity and it occurs at $\omega/\omega_0 = 1$. The half-power points occur $1/Q$ apart. Such a normalized resonance curve is shown in Figure 11.12. All series RLC circuits with the same Q have the same normalized resonance curve.

Parallel resonance   In the GLC parallel resonance circuit of Figure 11.13, we have

$$Z(s) = \frac{E}{I} = \frac{1}{sC + G + (1/sL)} \tag{11.23}$$

This equation is seen to be similar to the $Y(s)$ of (11.13). In fact, they are identical, except that the roles of the following quantities are interchanged.

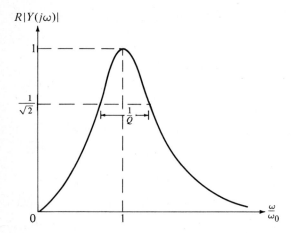

Figure 11.12 The normalized resonance curve.

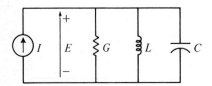

Figure 11.13 The GLC parallel circuit.

$$I \leftrightarrow E$$

$$L \leftrightarrow C$$

$$R \leftrightarrow G$$

$$Z \leftrightarrow Y$$

These two circuits are thus *dual* to each other. Everything we said about the circuit of Figure 11.8 is equally applicable to the circuit of Figure 11.13, provided dual statements are made for the latter. The following sample statements are dual to similar statements made earlier for the series circuit.

1 The maximum value of $|Z(j\omega)|$ is $1/G$ and it occurs at $\omega = 1/\sqrt{CL}$.

2 If $\omega = 1/\sqrt{CL}$, the current in L and the current in C are equal in magnitude and opposite in polarity. The circuit is in *parallel resonance*.

3 The dual of (11.16) is

$$|Z(j\omega)| = 1/\sqrt{G^2 + [\omega C - (1/\omega L)]^2} \tag{11.24}$$

Alternative definition of Q A more general definition for Q that is applicable to more complex systems is based on the energy consideration. Take the series *RLC* circuit of Figure 11.8 and let the current be expressed as

$$i(t) = I_m \cos \omega t \qquad (11.25)$$

The energy stored in the inductance at any instant is

$$w_L = \tfrac{1}{2}Li^2 = \tfrac{1}{2}LI_m^2 \cos^2 \omega t \qquad (11.26)$$

The energy stored in the capacitance is

$$w_C = \frac{1}{2}C\left(\frac{1}{C}\int I_m \cos \omega t \, dt\right)^2 = \frac{1}{2}\frac{I_m^2}{\omega^2 C}\sin^2 \omega t \qquad (11.27)$$

At $\omega = \omega_0$, $\omega_0^2 CL = 1$ and

$$w_L + w_C = \tfrac{1}{2}LI_m^2(\cos^2 \omega t + \sin^2 \omega t) = \tfrac{1}{2}I_m^2 L \qquad (11.28)$$

Equation (11.28) indicates that the *stored energy* in the series combination is constant. From (11.21) we have

$$Q = \frac{\omega_0 L}{R} = \frac{2\pi L}{T_0 R} = \frac{2\pi}{T_0} \times \frac{I_m^2 L/2}{I_m^2 R/2} \qquad (11.29)$$

where $T_0 = 1/f_0 = 2\pi/\omega_0$ is the period corresponding to the resonance frequency. But $I_m^2 R/2$ is the average power dissipated in the resistor. Hence we may say that

$$Q = 2\pi \times \frac{\text{stored energy}}{\text{energy dissipated per cycle}} \qquad (11.30)$$

This is a more general definition for Q than (11.21).

11.5 Bode diagrams

In practice, the frequency characteristics of a network function are often expressed in logarithmic scales in both directions. When we take the logarithm of a network function, we get

$$\ln[F(j\omega)] = \ln[A(\omega)\epsilon^{j\beta(\omega)}] = \ln(A) + j\beta(\omega) \qquad (11.31)$$

where $A(\omega) = |F(j\omega)|$ and $\beta(\omega) = \arg[F(j\omega)]$. In (11.31), the real part is the logarithm of its magnitude and the imaginary part is its phase angle. When network frequency characteristics are expressed logarithmically, they are shown in graphs of $\ln(A)$ and β. We shall denote $\ln(A)$ by α, or

$$\alpha(\omega) = \ln[A(\omega)] \qquad (11.32)$$

In (11.32), the logarithm is taken with respect to the base ϵ ($= 2.718$). The quantity $\alpha(\omega)$ obtained on this basis has a unit of *neper*. A more commonly used unit is the *decibel*, or dB. The decibel differs from the neper by not only a base but also a proportionality constant, that is,

$$\alpha = 20 \log_{10} A \text{ dB} \tag{11.33}$$

Thus, if the gain of a network is N nepers, this gain may also be said to be 8.686 N dB (8.686 = 20/ln 10).

The phase angle function $\beta(\omega)$ also has two popular units—the radian and the degree. This should not require any elaboration.

When the points along the horizontal axis are arranged logarithmically, usually the values of ω corresponding to various points are labeled rather than their logarithms. As a result, frequencies that have the same ratios are spaced uniformly. An example of such a scale, as well as its true logarithmic scale ($u = \log_{10} \omega$), is shown in Figure 11.14. Two frequencies whose ratio

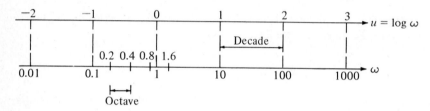

Figure 11.14 The logarithmic frequency scale.

is 10 to 1 are said to be a *decade* apart. Those whose ratio is 2 to 1 are said to be an *octave* apart. The manner in which the values of ω are labeled is exactly the way grids are spaced on logarithmic graph paper.

When network characteristics are presented in logarithmic scales along both their ordinates and abscissas, they are known as *Bode diagrams* or *Bode plots.*

The Bode diagrams of a network function can frequently be constructed approximately by looking at the asymptotic behavior of the individual factors that make up the function. Let us first look at an individual factor of the form

$$F_i = \left(1 + j\frac{\omega}{\sigma_i}\right) \tag{11.34}$$

The magnitude of such a factor is

$$A_i = \left|1 + j\frac{\omega}{\sigma_i}\right| = \sqrt{1 + \frac{\omega^2}{\sigma_i^2}} \tag{11.35}$$

The contribution of this factor to $\alpha(\omega)$ is

$$\alpha_i = 20 \log\left|1 + j\frac{\omega}{\sigma_i}\right| = 10 \log\left(1 + \frac{\omega^2}{\sigma_i^2}\right) \tag{11.36}$$

For $\omega \ll \sigma_i$, $\alpha_i \cong 0$. This asymptote is shown as a solid half-line in Figure

11.15. For $\omega \gg \sigma_i$,

$$\alpha_i \cong 10 \log\left(\frac{\omega^2}{\sigma_i^2}\right) = 20(\log \omega - \log \sigma_i) \, \text{dB} \tag{11.37}$$

This asymptote is another half-line, also shown in Figure 11.15. The slope of this half-line is such that α_i increases by $20 \log(2) = 6.020$ dB every time ω is doubled or by $20 \log(10) = 20$ dB every time ω increases tenfold. Such a slope is frequently termed "6 db per octave" or "20 dB per decade."

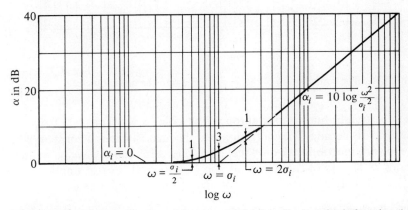

Figure 11.15 The contribution of the term of (11.34) to the magnitude function (in dB).

In the vicinity of $\omega = \sigma_i$, these half-lines are no longer a good approximation of (11.36). At $\omega = \sigma_i$, $\alpha_i = 10 \log (2) = 3.0103$; at $\omega = 2\sigma_i$, $\alpha_i = 10 \log (5) = 6.9897$, which is 0.9691 dB above the extension of the inclined half-line; at $\omega = \sigma_i/2$, $\alpha_i = 10 \log (1.25) = 0.9691$ dB, which is 0.9691 dB above the $\alpha_i = 0$ line. The true value of α_i in the vicinity of $\omega = \sigma_i$ is shown as a solid curve in Figure 11.15 with the decibel clearances shown in rounded-off figures. When these three segments of solid curve and lines are joined, the entire curve is a very good approximation of α_i of (11.36).

The curve of the phase angle associated with the factor of (11.34) is easy to construct since

$$\beta_i = \arg[F_i] = \tan^{-1} \frac{\omega}{\sigma_i} \tag{11.38}$$

The variation of β_i with respect to ω/σ_i is shown in Figure 11.16. Sometimes, as an approximation to this phase variation, we use the broken-line variation of Figure 11.16. This is not very accurate, as a maximum error of approximately 6° per factor is present.

For the factor s, its contribution to α is

$$\alpha_i = 20 \log \omega$$

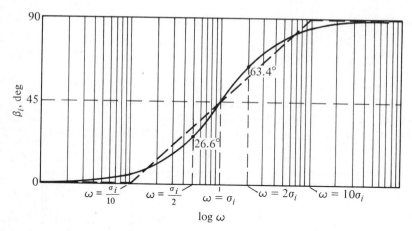

Figure 11.16 The contribution of the term of (11.34) to the phase function.

This is a straight line passing through the point $\alpha = 0$ and $\omega = 1$ with a slope of 20 dB/decade. The contribution to the phase angle is a constant 90°.

A network function with only real poles and zeros can always be written in terms of factors of the forms ω^k and $[1 + j(\omega/\sigma_i)]$. For example, if the function has only real poles and zeros away from the origin, then

$$F(s) = \frac{K(s+\sigma_{z1})(s+\sigma_{z2})\cdots(s+\sigma_{zn})}{(s+\sigma_{p1})(s+\sigma_{p2})\cdots(s+\sigma_{pm})}$$

For $s = j\omega$, it can always be written in the form

$$F(j\omega) = \frac{K\sigma_{z1}\sigma_{z2}\cdots\sigma_{zn}}{\sigma_{p1}\sigma_{p2}\cdots\sigma_{pm}} \times \frac{\left(1+j\dfrac{\omega}{\sigma_{z1}}\right)\left(1+j\dfrac{\omega}{\sigma_{z2}}\right)\cdots\left(1+j\dfrac{\omega}{\sigma_{zn}}\right)}{\left(1+j\dfrac{\omega}{\sigma_{p1}}\right)\left(1+j\dfrac{\omega}{\sigma_{p2}}\right)\cdots\left(1+j\dfrac{\omega}{\sigma_{pm}}\right)} \qquad (11.39)$$

If a zero or a pole of order k is present at the origin, the factor corresponding to this zero or pole need not be modified. The contribution of this factor is simply a straight line with a slope of $\pm 20k$ dB/decade passing through the point $\alpha = 0$ and $\omega = 1$.

Once a network function is in the form of (11.39), with possibly an additional ω^k or $1/\omega^k$ factor, the contribution by various factors, including the proportionality constant, is easily summed up. We can best illustrate this by some examples.

EXAMPLE 2 Suppose we have

$$F(s) = \frac{s+2}{s(s+20)} \qquad (11.40)$$

Then we have

$$F(j\omega) = \frac{2[1+j(\omega/2)]}{20j\omega[1+j(\omega/20)]}$$

The α characteristic is given by

$$\alpha(\omega) = -20 + 20\log\left|1 + j\frac{\omega}{2}\right| - 20\log\omega - 20\log\left|1 + j\frac{\omega}{20}\right| \qquad (11.41)$$

The asymptotes and actual contributions of each of these terms are shown in Figure 11.17(a). When all the contributions are summed, the characteristic of Figure 11.17(b) results.

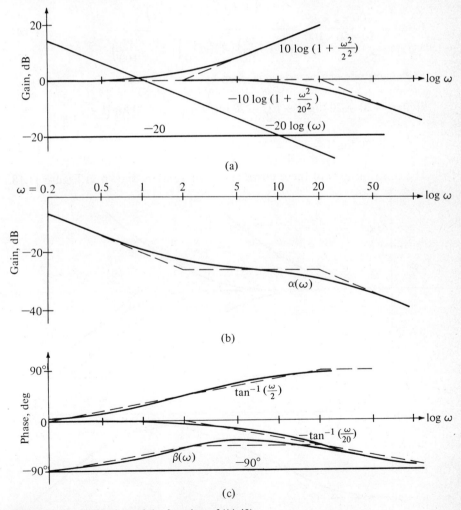

Figure 11.17 Bode plots of the function of (11.40).

The phase characteristic is given by

$$\beta(\omega) = \tan^{-1}\left(\frac{\omega}{2}\right) - 90° - \tan^{-1}\left(\frac{\omega}{20}\right) \tag{11.42}$$

The contribution of each term and the sum are given in Figure 11.17(c). The broken-line approximations of these curves are also given in the figure. The error is seen to be quite large near $\omega = 5$.

EXAMPLE 3   Suppose we have

$$F(s) = \frac{100(s+2)(s+25)}{(s+10)(s+50)(s+100)} \tag{11.43}$$

$$F(j\omega) = \frac{100 \times 2 \times 25}{10 \times 50 \times 100} \cdot \frac{\left(1 + j\dfrac{\omega}{2}\right)\left(1 + j\dfrac{\omega}{25}\right)}{\left(1 + j\dfrac{\omega}{10}\right)\left(1 + j\dfrac{\omega}{50}\right)\left(1 + j\dfrac{\omega}{100}\right)} \tag{11.44}$$

The magnitude characteristic is given by

$$\alpha(\omega) = -20 + 20\log\left|1 + j\frac{\omega}{2}\right| + 20\log\left|1 + j\frac{\omega}{25}\right| - 20\log\left|1 + j\frac{\omega}{10}\right|$$

$$- 20\log\left|1 + j\frac{\omega}{50}\right| - 20\log\left|1 + j\frac{\omega}{100}\right| \tag{11.45}$$

The contributions of these terms and their sum are shown in Figure 11.18.

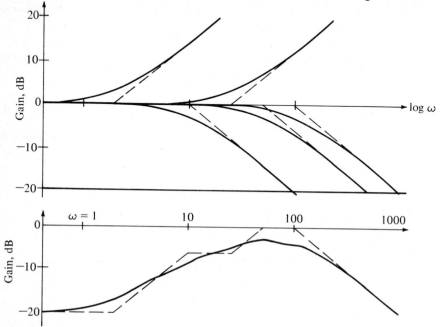

Figure 11.18   Bode magnitude plot of the function of (11.45).

EXAMPLE 4   In the circuit of Figure 11.19(a) the parameters of the FET are

$$g_m = 2 \text{ m}\mho, \qquad r_d = 20 \text{ k}\Omega$$

Find the magnitude and phase characteristics of the voltage-gain function V_o/V_i.

SOLUTION   The ac equivalent circuit of Figure 11.19(a) is shown in Figure 11.19(b), where

$$E_1 = \frac{500 \text{ k}}{500 \text{ k} + (1/10^{-5}s)} V_i \tag{11.46}$$

$$V_{gs} = -E_2 + E_1 \tag{11.47}$$

$$\frac{E_2}{15 \text{ k}} + 10^{-5}sE_2 + \frac{E_2 - V_o}{20 \text{ k}} - 2 \times 10^{-3}V_{gs} = 0 \tag{11.48}$$

$$\frac{V_o - E_2}{20 \text{ k}} + \frac{V_o}{55 \text{ k}} + 2 \times 10^{-3}V_{gs} = 0 \tag{11.49}$$

Adding (11.48) and (11.49), we get

$$\frac{E_2}{15 \text{ k}} + 10^{-5}sE_2 + \frac{V_o}{55 \text{ k}} = 0$$

or

$$E_2 = -\frac{3}{11(1+0.15s)}V_o \tag{11.50}$$

Substituting (11.46), (11.47), and (11.50) into (11.49), we get

$$\frac{V_o}{20 \text{ k}} + \frac{V_o}{55 \text{ k}} + \frac{3[(1/20 \text{ k}) + 2 \times 10^{-3}]}{11(1+0.15s)}V_o + \frac{1000}{500 \text{ k} + (1/10^{-5}s)}V_i = 0$$

$$\frac{(6.9+0.1125s) \times 10^{-3}}{11(1+0.15s)}V_o = -\frac{10^{-2}s}{1+5s}V_i$$

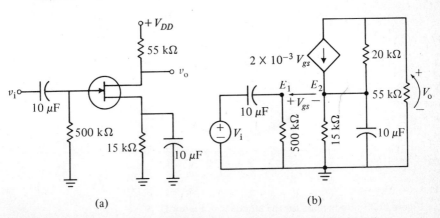

(a)   (b)

Figure 11.19   (a) An FET amplifier. (b) Its small-signal ac equivalent circuit.

Thus we get

$$\frac{V_o}{V_i} = -\frac{11 \times 10^{-2} s(1+0.15s)}{6.9 \times 10^{-3}(1+5s)(1+0.0163s)}$$

$$= -\frac{15.94s[1+(s/6.667)]}{[1+(s/0.2)][1+(s/61.33)]} \qquad (11.51)$$

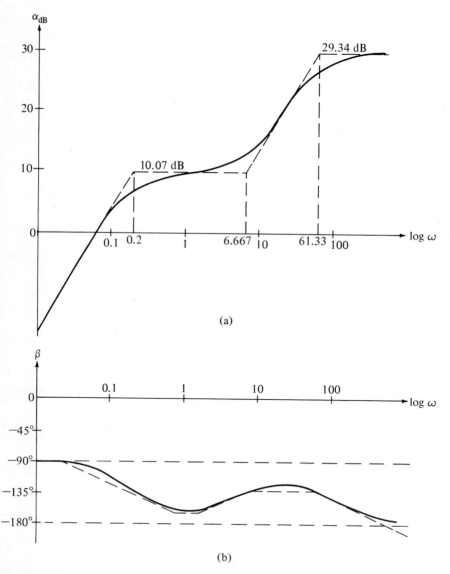

(a)

(b)

Figure 11.20 Bode plots for the amplifier of Figure 11.19.

Equation (11.51) gives

$$\alpha_{dB}(\omega) = 24.05 + 20 \log \omega - 20 \log \left|1 + j\frac{\omega}{0.2}\right| + 20 \log \left|1 + j\frac{\omega}{6.667}\right|$$

$$- 20 \log \left|1 + j\frac{\omega}{61.33}\right| \tag{11.52}$$

$$\beta(\omega) = -90° - \tan^{-1}\left(\frac{\omega}{0.2}\right) + \tan^{-1}\left(\frac{\omega}{6.667}\right) - \tan^{-1}\left(\frac{\omega}{61.33}\right) \tag{11.53}$$

These two functions are plotted in Figure 11.20.

When a network function has complex poles or zeros, their contribution is slightly more complicated to handle. However, the principle is still the same. Since complex poles must occur in conjugate pairs, we shall look at one typical pair of poles or zeros stemming from the factor of the type $F_i = (as^2 + bs + c)$. Such a factor can always be normalized to read

$$\frac{F_j(j\omega)}{c} = 1 + \frac{b}{c}j\omega - \frac{a\omega^2}{c} = 1 + j\frac{1}{Q}\left(\frac{\omega}{\omega_i}\right) - \left(\frac{\omega}{\omega_i}\right)^2 \tag{11.54}$$

where $\omega_i = \sqrt{c/a}$ and $Q = \sqrt{ac}/b$.* The contribution of such a factor is

$$\alpha_i(\omega) = 10 \log \left[\left(1 + \frac{\omega^2}{\omega_i^2}\right)^2 + \frac{1}{Q^2}\left(\frac{\omega}{\omega_i}\right)^2\right] \tag{11.55}$$

The asymptotic behavior of $\alpha_i(\omega)$ is as follows: For $\omega \ll \omega_i$, $\alpha_i \cong 0$; for $\omega \gg \omega_i$,

$$\alpha_i(\omega) \cong 40 \log \left(\frac{\omega}{\omega_i}\right) \text{ dB} \tag{11.56}$$

The function of (11.56) is exactly twice that of (11.37). Hence the asymptote of $\alpha_i(\omega)$ at high values of ω is a half-line with a slope of 12 dB-per-octave or 40 dB-per-decade. If this half-line were extended, it would intersect the $\alpha = 0$ line at $\omega = \omega_i$, as shown in Figure 11.21.

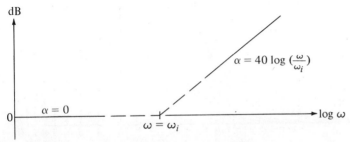

Figure 11.21 Asymptotes of the magnitude of the term in (11.54).

* In many textbooks, the parameter $\zeta = 1/2Q$ is used.

The behavior of $\alpha_i(\omega)$ of (11.55) in the vicinity of $\omega = \omega_i$ is highly dependent on the value of Q. Figure 11.22(a) gives a set of curves for various values of Q. Armed with this set of standard curves, one can give a good estimate of $\alpha_i(\omega)$ for a large range of Q values.

At the same time, the contribution of the factor of (11.54) to the phase characteristic is given by

$$\beta_i(\omega) = \tan^{-1}\frac{\omega/\omega_i}{Q[1-(\omega^2/\omega_i^2)]} \tag{11.57}$$

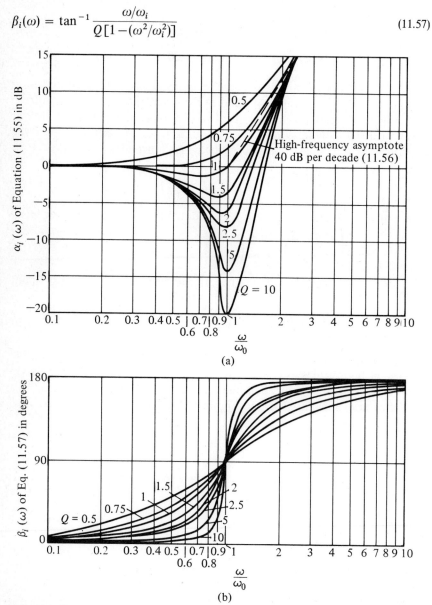

Figure 11.22 Contribution of the term of (11.54) for different values of Q.

The asymptotic values of $\beta_i(\omega)$ are $0°$ for $\omega \ll \omega_i$ and $180°$ for $\omega \gg \omega_i$. At $\omega = \omega_i$, $\beta_i(\omega_i) = 90°$. The variation of $\beta_i(\omega)$ for other values of ω depends on the value of Q. Figure 11.22(b) gives a set of curves for $\beta_i(\omega)$ for several values of Q.

11.6 Concluding remarks

In this chapter we have delineated the method of describing the behavior of networks in the frequency domain through network functions as functions of the complex variable s. We can then obtain the behavior of these networks along the ω axis.

Once we know the magnitude and phase characteristics of a network along the ω axis, we are able to tell what the network response will be when either the frequency of the excitation is varied or the excitation contains more than one frequency. The latter situation will be taken up in Chapter 13.

Problems

11.1 Find the driving-point impedance $Z(s)$ of the network of Figure P11.1 as a function of the complex frequency s. Find the poles and zeros of this function.

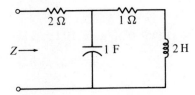

Figure P11.1

11.2 Find the transfer ratio E_2/E_1 of the network of Figure P11.2 as a function of s.

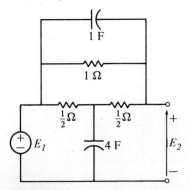

Figure P11.2

11.3 Find the transfer impedance E_2/I_1 of the network of Figure P11.3 as a function of s.

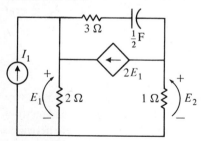

Figure P11.3

11.4 Find the $[z(s)]$ matrix of each of the two-ports of Figure P11.4.

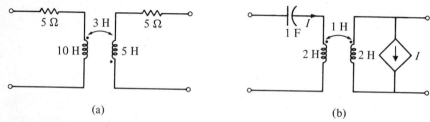

(a)   (b)

Figure P11.4

11.5 Find the input impedance $Z(s)$ of the circuit of Figure P11.5. Then find its poles and zeros.

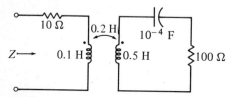

Figure P11.5

11.6 Find the poles and zeros of the transfer function E_o/E_i of the network of Figure P11.6.

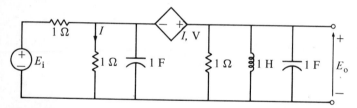

Figure P11.6

11.7 Determine the small-signal voltage gain of the amplifier in Figure P11.7 as a function of s. For the JFET, $C_{gd} = 3$ pF, $C_{gs} = 3$ pF, $C_{ds} = 4$ pF, $g_m = 4$ m℧, and $r_d = 5$ kΩ.

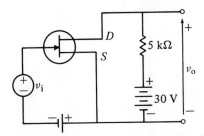

Figure P11.7

11.8 For the JFET in the circuit of Figure P11.8, $g_m = 5$ m℧ and $g_d = 0.1$ m℧. (a) Draw the ac equivalent circuit. (b) Find the small-signal voltage gain V_o/V_i as a function of s. (c) Find the output impedance of the amplifier as a function of s.

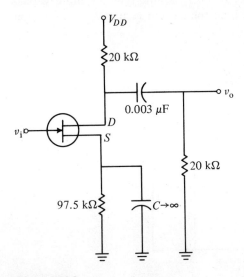

Figure P11.8

11.9 For the circuit of Figure P11.9, the transistor has the following parameters: $h_{ie} = 2\ k\Omega$, $h_{re} = 300 \times 10^{-6}$, $h_{fe} = 50$, $h_{oe} = 10 \times 10^{-6}\ \mho$. The circuit elements are $R_E = 1\ k\Omega$, $R_c = 1\ k\Omega$, $R_d = 10\ k\Omega$, $R_B = 10\ k\Omega$, $R_i = 2.5\ k\Omega$, $C_E \to \infty$, $C_c = 1\ \mu F$, $C_d = 2\ \mu F$. Find the current gain I_2/I_1 as a function of s.

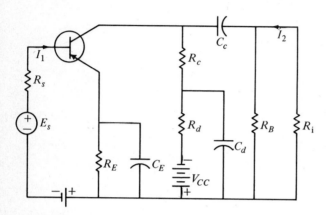

Figure P11.9

11.10 For the circuit of Figure P11.10, the transistor is identical to that given in Problem 11.9. The circuit elements are: $R_c = 10\ k\Omega$, $R_i = 5\ k\Omega$, $R_B = 15\ k\Omega$, $C_c = 0.01\ \mu F$, $C_E \to \infty$, $L \to \infty$. Assume that the input capacitance of the next stage is 100 pF. Find the current gain I_2/I_1 as a function of s.

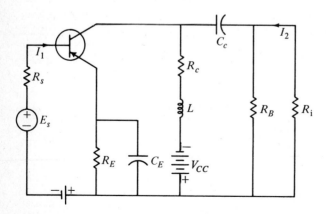

Figure P11.10

11.11 For the common-base transistor amplifier of Figure P11.11, find the voltage gain E_2/E_s. The circuit elements are: $R_c = 10 \text{ k}\Omega$, $R_B = 1.5 \text{ k}\Omega$, $R_i = 40 \Omega$, $C_c = 5 \mu\text{F}$, and $R_s = 100 \Omega$. The transistor parameters are $h_{ib} = 40 \Omega$, $h_{rb} = 4 \times 10^{-6}$, $h_{fb} = -0.99$, $h_{ob} = 10^{-6} \text{ \TH}$.

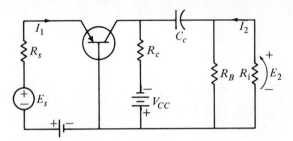

Figure P11.11

11.12 Given the series RLC circuit shown in Figure P11.12, (a) find $f_0 \, (= \omega_0/2\pi)$ of this circuit; (b) find Q of this circuit; (c) find the values of ω at which the half-power occurs.

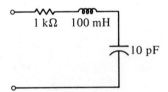

Figure P11.12

11.13 A coil has a resistance of 2Ω and an inductance of 0.1 H. It is desired to use this coil in series with a capacitor to show the phenomena of resonance. If the only source available is 115 V, 60 Hz, what is the necessary capacitance of the capacitor? If the capacitor is designed for a maximum rms voltage of 700 V, what resistance must be inserted in the circuit in order that the voltage across the capacitor at resonance shall not exceed this amount?

11.14 If ω_0/BW, where BW is the half-power bandwidth, is defined as the Q of an RLC parallel circuit, what is Q in terms of: (a) R, L, and C; (b) R, C, and ω_0; (c) R, L, and ω_0.

11.15 A series RLC circuit has the following constants: $Q = 10$; $BW = \omega_2 - \omega_1 = 20$ radians per second; the magnitude of the impedance at half-power points $= 2 \Omega$. Find the parameters of this circuit.

11.16 Derive an expression in terms of Q, ω_0, and a for the bandwidth, $BW = \omega_b - \omega_a$, of an RLC series circuit with ω_b and ω_a representing the points where $R|Y(j\omega)|$ is equal to a. Check your answer for $a = 0.707$. Also show that for any value of a, $\omega_a \omega_b = \omega_0^2$. (See Figure P11.16.)

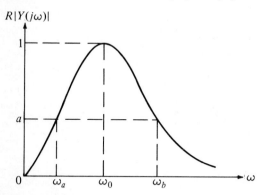

Figure P11.16

11.17 Give the Bode magnitude plot of the function

$$H(s) = \frac{10s}{(s+1)(s+2)}$$

11.18 Give the Bode straight-line magnitude plot of the function

$$H(s) = \frac{1000s}{(1+0.01s)(1+0.005s)}$$

Show the coordinates of all key points.

11.19 Sketch the magnitude part of the Bode diagram for the network function

$$T(s) = \frac{100}{(1+100/s)(1+s/10^5)}$$

Give both the broken-line and the smooth-varying versions. Indicate the ordinates of key points along both curves.

11.20 A network function $H(s)$ has only real poles. Its asymptotic part of the Bode magnitude plot is shown in Figure P11.20. Construct $H(s)$.

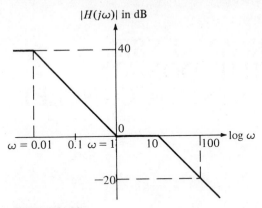

Figure P11.20

11.21 Obtain the Bode diagram for the network function obtained in Problem 11.7.

11.22 Obtain the Bode diagram for the network function obtained in Problem 11.8(b).

11.23 Obtain the Bode diagram for the network function obtained in Problem 11.9.

11.24 Obtain the Bode diagram for the network function obtained in Problem 11.10.

11.25 Obtain the Bode diagram for the network function obtained in Problem 11.11.

12 | NETWORK ANALYSIS IN THE TIME DOMAIN AND THE SYSTEM CONCEPT

In this chapter we shall develop some basic concepts on how to handle a circuit-analysis problem entirely in the time domain—in other words, in such a way that all quantities are real functions of time. We shall limit our scope to LTI networks.

There are two approaches to the time-domain analysis of a network. One is to rely solely on the solution of the differential equation that governs the behavior of the network, as described in Section 4.5. This technique is not particularly attractive for practical problems, especially when the network is complex. The other approach—through the impulse response of a network— is the one that we shall dwell on in this chapter.

We are interested in the solution of circuit problems in the time domain because, basically, every signal is a function of time. It is true that some signals are functions of time in a definite way, such as sinusoids and exponentials; and, for these signals, we might be interested in their behavior as ω and σ are varied. But even then the signals really exist as functions of time. Yet other signals are not found as simple mathematical functions. In any case, there are situations in which we are primarily interested in the response of a network as a function of time.

Furthermore, with the availability of computers, we can handle many network-analysis and design problems quite naturally and conveniently in the time domain with as much accuracy as we wish. There is no reason why some of these problems should not be dealt with entirely in the time domain. Then there are systems whose inputs and outputs are specified in the time domain. Analysis techniques relating quantities in these systems would be very desirable.

As we shall see in Chapters 14 and 15, there is a parallelism between the time-domain and the frequency-domain analyses of an LTI system.

Furthermore, signals in these two domains are related to each other. Hence it makes no theoretical difference whether a circuit-analysis problem is handled in one domain or the other. The difference is either in the point of view or as a matter of convenience or necessity.

12.1 The impulse response

The block diagram of Figure 3.1 is a symbolic representation of the response–excitation (output–input) relationship of a network and it is reproduced in Figure 12.1. The rectangular block represents the interconnection of a

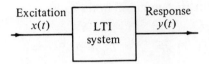

Figure 12.1 Input–output relationship of an LTI system.

number of LTI elements. A certain quantity in the circuit is designated as the response, represented by $y(t)$, that occurs when a certain excitation $x(t)$ is applied to the circuit. In a network, $x(t)$ or $y(t)$ could be either a current or a voltage. For example, in the circuit of Figure 12.2 the input is the source voltage $e_s(t)$. The output could be the current $i(t)$ or any one of the three voltages across the three elements.

For many applications, an LTI system is most conveniently characterized by its *impulse response* $h(t)$. This is simply the response of the system when the excitation applied is a unit impulse, $u_0(t)$, and the system is initially idle. Thus, for the circuit of Figure 12.2, if $y(t) = i(t)$, then its impulse response is

$$h(t) = \frac{1}{L} \epsilon^{-\alpha t} \left(\cos \beta t - \frac{\alpha}{\beta} \sin \beta t \right) u_{-1}(t) \tag{12.1}$$

where $\alpha = R/2L$ and $\beta = \sqrt{(1/LC)-(R^2/4L^2)}$, as was derived in Section 4.7.

For other applications, the *step response*, herein denoted by $g(t)$, is slightly

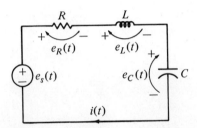

Figure 12.2 An *RLC* series circuit.

more convenient to use. The step response of an LTI system is simply the response of the system when the excitation is a unit step, $u_{-1}(t)$, and the system is initially idle. Since the derivative of a unit step is a unit impulse, the impulse response of a system is the derivative of its step response, or

$$h(t) = \frac{d}{dt} g(t)$$

Hence, for the circuit of Figure 12.2, we have

$$g(t) = \frac{1}{L} \int_0^t \epsilon^{-\alpha t} \left(\cos \beta t - \frac{\alpha}{\beta} \sin \beta t \right) dt = \frac{1}{\beta L} \epsilon^{-\alpha t} \sin \beta t \, u_{-1}(t)$$

As was mentioned in Section 4.5, to find the response of a network, it is generally necessary to solve a linear differential equation in the form

$$a_n \frac{d^n y}{dt^n} + a_{n-1} \frac{d^{n-1} y}{dt^{n-1}} + \cdots + a_1 \frac{dy}{dt} + a_0 y = b_m \frac{d^m x}{dt^m} + b_{m-1} \frac{d^{m-1} x}{dt^{m-1}} + \cdots$$

$$+ b_1 \frac{dx}{dt} + b_0 x \tag{12.2}$$

To obtain the impulse response, we would set $x(t) = u_0(t)$. To obtain the step response, we would set $x(t) = u_{-1}(t)$. In either case we assume that no energy is stored in any inductance or capacitance prior to $t = 0$.

For example, suppose that we desire to find the impulse response of the network of Figure 12.3, with $e_2(t)$ as the response. Node analysis gives

$$(e_1 - e_2) + (e_1 - e_s) + \int_0^t (e_1 - e_3) \, dt = 0 \tag{12.3}$$

$$\frac{de_2}{dt} + (e_2 - e_1) = 0 \tag{12.4}$$

$$e_3 + \int_0^t (e_3 - e_1) \, dt = 0 \tag{12.5}$$

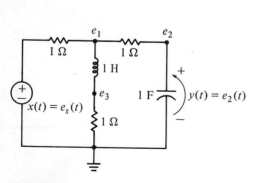

Figure 12.3

From (12.4) we have

$$e_1 = \frac{de_2}{dt} + e_2$$

Integrating, we get

$$\int_0^t e_1 \, dt = e_2 + \int_0^t e_2 \, dt$$

Substituting these relationships into (12.3) and solving, we get

$$\int_0^t e_3 \, dt = 2e_1 + \int_0^t e_1 \, dt - e_2 - e_s = 2\frac{de_2}{dt} + 2e_2 + \int_0^t e_2 \, dt - e_s$$

Differentiating yields

$$e_3 = 2\frac{d^2e_2}{dt^2} + 2\frac{de_2}{dt} + e_2 - \frac{de_s}{dt}$$

Substituting the appropriate expressions into (12.5) gives

$$2\frac{d^2e_2}{dt^2} + 4\frac{de_2}{dt} + 2e_2 = e_s + \frac{de_s}{dt} \tag{12.6}$$

We then set $e_s(t) = u_0(t)$ and solve this differential equation.

The solution of (12.6) with the system initially idle is not out of reach with the knowledge we have acquired so far, since it is only of the second order and we can take advantage of the superposition properties of LTI systems. However, the solution of the differential equation of a more complex system is, in general, quite laborious. Fortunately we do not have to rely on the solution of a differential equation to obtain the impulse or step response of a network. There are several means by which these responses can be determined. Experimentally, they can be measured in the laboratory, at least approximately. Mathematically, they are most easily found through the transform methods, one of which will be presented in Chapter 15. For our current purposes, we shall assume that the impulse or step response of a network is somehow known. Our attention will focus on the problem of how to determine the response of a network whose impulse or step response is known, when an excitation of any shape is applied to it.

12.2 The convolution integral

Let us assume that we know the impulse response of a system. We can first obtain an approximate solution by approximating the excitation with a series of pulses each of which is, in turn, approximated by an impulse function. Specifically, referring to $x(\lambda)$ of Figure 12.4(a), we make these pulses uniformly

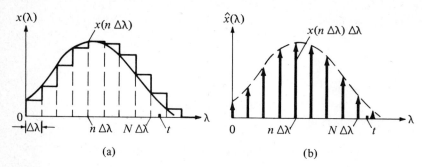

Figure 12.4 Rectangular pulse and impulse approximation of a continuous function.

spaced. Call this spacing $\Delta\lambda$. The area of each rectangular pulse is then $x(n\,\Delta\lambda)\,\Delta\lambda$, and the impulse approximation of $x(t)$ is a series of impulses. The strength of each is $x(n\,\Delta\lambda)\,\Delta\lambda$, as shown in Figure 12.4(b), in which the height of each impulse indicates its relative strength and the approximating function is denoted by

$$\hat{x}(\lambda) = \sum_{n=0}^{\infty} x(n\,\Delta\lambda)\,\Delta\lambda u_0(\lambda - n\,\Delta\lambda) \tag{12.7}$$

Now, since the system is LTI, we know that the law of superposition applies. Since we also know the response of the system due to each impulse, we can write out the response of the system corresponding to the series of impulses at any value of λ. At $\lambda = t$,

$$\hat{y}(t) = x(0)\,\Delta\lambda h(t-0) + x(\Delta\lambda)\,\Delta\lambda h(t-\Delta\lambda) + x(2\,\Delta\lambda)\,\Delta\lambda h(t-2\,\Delta\lambda) + \cdots$$
$$+ x(N\,\Delta\lambda)\,\Delta\lambda h(t-N\,\Delta\lambda) \tag{12.8}$$

where N is the largest integer that satisfies $N\,\Delta\lambda < t$. Alternatively we may write (12.8) as

$$\hat{y}(t) = \sum_{n=0}^{N} x(n\,\Delta\lambda)h(t-n\,\Delta\lambda)\,\Delta\lambda \tag{12.9}$$

As we let $\Delta\lambda$ get smaller and smaller, $\Delta\lambda \to d\lambda$, $N \to \infty$, and $n\,\Delta\lambda \to \lambda$. The summation of (12.9) approaches an integral with respect to λ, with its upper limit $N\,\Delta\lambda \to t$. Or

$$y(t) = \lim_{\Delta\lambda \to 0} \hat{y}(t) = \int_0^t x(\lambda)h(t-\lambda)\,d\lambda \tag{12.10}$$

Equation (12.10) is known as the *convolution integral*. Other names for it are the superposition integral, the Carson integral and the DuHamel integral.

In the derivation of (12.10), we assumed that $x(\lambda) = 0$ for $\lambda < 0$. This assumption is not necessary. Indeed it is easy to see that, if $x(\lambda)$ is nonzero for any $\lambda < 0$, we merely have to extend the lower limit of λ in (12.10) to include that part of the axis. In general, it certainly would make no difference if the interval also included that part of the negative λ axis over which $x(\lambda)$ is zero. Hence a more general form of (12.10) is

$$y(t) = \int_{-\infty}^{t} x(\lambda) h(t - \lambda) \, d\lambda \tag{12.11}$$

Also, since we are dealing with an LTI system with no initial energy, it must be causal. (A system is *causal* if its response is zero before an excitation is applied.) Hence $h(t - \lambda) = 0$ for $\lambda > t$. The integrand in either (12.10) or (12.11) is zero for $\lambda > t$. For this reason, the convolution integral is sometimes written as

$$y(t) = \int_{-\infty}^{\infty} x(\lambda) h(t - \lambda) \, d\lambda \tag{12.12}$$

EXAMPLE 1 Suppose that we have

$$e_s(t) = \epsilon^{-2t} u_{-1}(t) \tag{12.13}$$

in the circuit of Figure 12.5. Find $i(t)$.

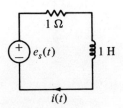

Figure 12.5

SOLUTION Considering $i(t)$ as the response, from Figure 4.10, we have

$$h(t) = \epsilon^{-t} u_{-1}(t) \tag{12.14}$$

Equation (12.10) gives

$$i(t) = \int_{0}^{t} \epsilon^{-2\lambda} \epsilon^{-(t - \lambda)} \, d\lambda \tag{12.15}$$

In (12.15) the unit steps are not necessary, since the limits of integration do not allow the argument of either $e_s(\lambda)$ or $h(t - \lambda)$ to assume negative values. Integration of (12.15) yields

$$i(t) = (\epsilon^{-t} - \epsilon^{-2t}) u_{-1}(t) \tag{12.16}$$

The unit step in (12.16) is artificially inserted so that the expression is valid for all t.

It would be instructive to see graphically what is happening in the integral of (12.15). The various functions for a particular value of t are depicted in Figure 12.6. The function $h(t - \lambda)$ is the mirror image of $h(\lambda)$ about the vertical axis, translated to the right by the distance t. The value of y at the instant t is the shaded area under the curve representing the integrand in the range from 0 to t.

We should point out that in the integral of (12.10) or (12.15) the integration is with respect to the variable λ. The variable t is a parameter that should be considered constant for the integration. As the value of t changes, so does the integral, or $y(t)$.

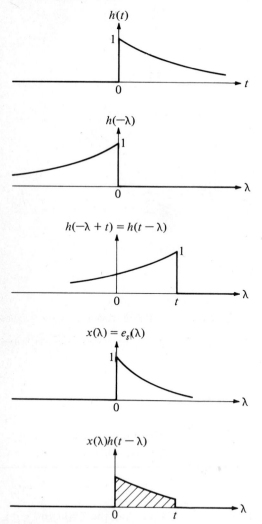

Figure 12.6 Example of the evaluation of a convolution integral at a particular value of t.

The solution to Example 1 is rather simple because both $x(t)$ and $h(t)$ are expressible in the form of a single function for all $t > 0$. When this is not the case, one must handle the convolution integral very carefully.

EXAMPLE 2   Find the convolution integral of $x(t)$ and $h(t)$ shown in Figure 12.7, (a) and (b), respectively.

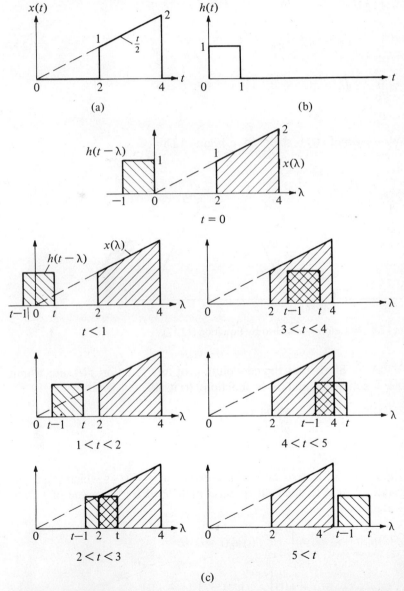

Figure 12.7 Example of the relative positions of the two factors of the integrand of a convolution integral.

SOLUTION   Figure 12.7(c) depicts the two functions that multiply to form the integrand of the convolution integral for various ranges of value of t. With the aid of these sketches we see that

$$y(t) = 0, \qquad t < 2$$

$$y(t) = \int_{2}^{t} \frac{\lambda}{2} d\lambda = \tfrac{1}{4}(t^2 - 4), \qquad 2 < t < 3$$

$$y(t) = \int_{t-1}^{t} \frac{\lambda}{2} d\lambda = \tfrac{1}{4}(2t - 1), \qquad 3 < t < 4 \tag{12.17}$$

$$y(t) = \int_{t-1}^{4} \frac{\lambda}{2} d\lambda = \tfrac{1}{4}(15 + 2t - t^2), \qquad 4 < t < 5$$

$$y(t) = 0, \qquad 5 < t$$

The waveform of $y(t)$ is sketched in Figure 12.8.

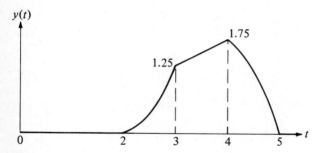

Figure 12.8   Waveform described by Equation (12.17).

EXAMPLE 3   Show that the convolution of any function $f(t)$ and a unit impulse function is equal to the function $f(t)$ itself.

SOLUTION   By (12.12) we have

$$f(t) * u_0(t) = \int_{-\infty}^{\infty} f(\lambda) u_0(t - \lambda) \, d\lambda$$

But the integrand is zero everywhere except at $\lambda = t$, at which point the integrand is equal to the unit impulse multiplied by the value of $f(\lambda)$ at $\lambda = t$. Hence we have

$$\int_{-\infty}^{\infty} f(\lambda) u_0(t - \lambda) \, d\lambda = \int_{\lambda = t^-}^{\lambda = t^+} f(t) u_0(t - \lambda) \, d\lambda$$

$$= f(t) \int_{\lambda = t^-}^{\lambda = t^+} u_0(t - \lambda) \, d\lambda = f(t)$$

EXAMPLE 4   Find

$$q(t) = \int_0^t f_1(\lambda) f_2(t - \lambda)\, d\lambda$$

with $f_1(t)$ and $f_2(t)$ as given in Figure 12.9. The function $f_2(t)$ is the super-position of a rectangular pulse and a two-unit impulse function.

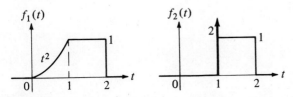

Figure 12.9

SOLUTION   Figure 12.10 shows the functions used in the convolution for various values of t. With the help of these sketches and the result of the previous example, we get for $0 < t < 1$,

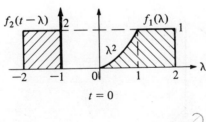

$$q(t) = 0$$

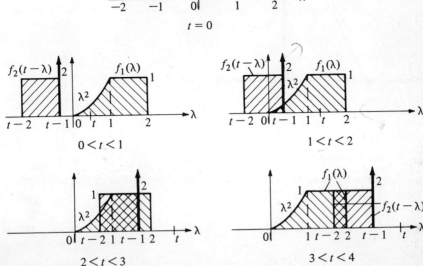

Figure 12.10

for $1 < t < 2$,

$$q(t) = \int_0^{t-1} \lambda^2 \, d\lambda + 2(t-1)^2 = \tfrac{1}{3}\lambda^3 \Big|_0^{t-1} + 2(t-1)^2$$

$$= \tfrac{1}{3}(t-1)^3 + 2(t-1)^2 = \tfrac{1}{3}t^3 + t^2 - 3t + \tfrac{5}{3}$$

for $2 < t < 3$,

$$q(t) = \int_{t-2}^1 \lambda^2 \, d\lambda + \int_1^{t-1} d\lambda + 2$$

$$= \tfrac{1}{3}\lambda^3 \Big|_{t-2}^1 + \lambda \Big|_1^{t-1} + 2$$

$$= \tfrac{1}{3} - \tfrac{1}{3}(t-2)^3 + t - 1 - 1 + 2$$

$$= -\tfrac{1}{3}t^3 + 2t^2 - 3t + 3$$

and, for $3 < t < 4$,

$$q(t) = \int_{t-2}^2 d\lambda = 2 - (t-2) = 4 - t$$

The variation of $q(t)$ is shown in Figure 12.11.

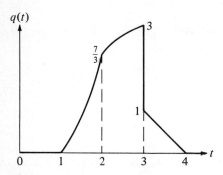

Figure 12.11

12.3 Some properties of the convolution integral

In this section, we shall present several useful properties of the convolution integral. Starting with (12.10), we have

$$y(t) = \int_{\lambda=0}^{\lambda=t} x(\lambda)h(t-\lambda) \, d\lambda \tag{12.18}$$

If we now make a change of variable, $t - \lambda = \lambda'$, we have

$$x(\lambda) = x(t - \lambda'), \qquad h(t - \lambda) = h(\lambda'), \qquad d\lambda = -d\lambda'$$

When $\lambda = t$, $\lambda' = 0$. When $\lambda = 0$, $\lambda' = t$. Hence we get

$$y(t) = -\int_{\lambda'=t}^{\lambda'=0} x(t - \lambda')h(\lambda')\,d\lambda' \tag{12.19}$$

Reversing the upper and lower limits and dropping the prime, we have

$$y(t) = \int_{\lambda=0}^{\lambda=t} h(\lambda)x(t-\lambda)\,d\lambda \tag{12.20}$$

Comparing (12.18) and (12.20), we see that the two functions h and x have exchanged roles. Thus the convolution of two functions is commutative. The operations given by (12.18) or (12.20) are frequently denoted by

$$y(t) = h(t) * x(t) = x(t) * h(t) \tag{12.21}$$

and $y(t)$ is said to be the convolution of $x(t)$ and $h(t)$.

From the differentiability property of an LTI system and the commutativeness of the convolution integral we may conclude that

$$\frac{dy}{dt} = \int_0^t x(\lambda)\frac{dh(t-\lambda)}{d(t-\lambda)}\,d\lambda = \int_0^t \frac{dx(\lambda)}{d\lambda}h(t-\lambda)\,d\lambda \tag{12.22}$$

or*

$$y^{(1)}(t) = x(t) * h^{(1)}(t) = x^{(1)}(t) * h(t) \tag{12.23}$$

Similarly, from the integrability property of an LTI system, we may say that

$$\int_{-\infty}^t y(t)\,dt = \int_0^t x(\lambda)h^{(-1)}(t-\lambda)\,d\lambda = \int_0^t x^{(-1)}(\lambda)h(t-\lambda)\,d\lambda \tag{12.24}$$

or

$$y^{(-1)}(t) = x(t) * h^{(-1)}(t) = x^{(-1)}(t) * h(t) \tag{12.25}$$

Successive application of (12.23) and (12.25) will lead to

$$y^{(n)}(t) = x^{(a)}(t) * h^{(b)}(t) \tag{12.26}$$

as long as $n = a + b$ and where n, a, and b are integers, either positive or negative.

In particular, we have

$$y(t) = x^{(1)}(t) * h^{(-1)}(t) = x^{(1)}(t) * g(t) \tag{12.27}$$

Thus the response of an LTI system is also the convolution of the derivatives of its excitation and its step response.

---

* Here a superscript in parentheses denotes the order of derivative or integral, positive for derivative and negative for integral.

EXAMPLE 5 In the convolution problem of Example 2 of the previous section, we have

$$h'(t) = u_0(t) - u_0(t-1) \tag{12.28}$$

This function is depicted in Figure 12.12(a). At a particular instant t, $h'(t-\lambda)$ and $x(\lambda)$ as functions of λ are as shown in Figure 12.12(b). We can evaluate the convolution of these two functions by inspection because

$$\int_{-\infty}^{\infty} f(z)u_0(z_0 - z)\,dz = f(z_0) \tag{12.29}$$

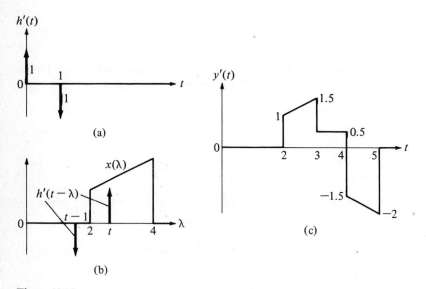

(a)

(b)

(c)

Figure 12.12

From (12.27) and with the aid of Figure 12.7(c) we can write

$$y^{(1)}(t) = 0, \qquad t < 2$$

$$y^{(1)}(t) = \frac{t}{2}, \qquad 2 < t < 3$$

$$y^{(1)}(t) = \frac{t}{2} - \frac{t-1}{2} = \tfrac{1}{2}, \qquad 3 < t < 4 \tag{12.30}$$

$$y^{(1)}(t) = -\frac{t-1}{2}, \qquad 4 < t < 5$$

$$y^{(1)}(t) = 0, \qquad 5 < t$$

This $y^{(1)}(t)$ is shown in Figure 12.12(c). This function is clearly the derivative of the $y(t)$ of Figure 12.8. Or, equivalently, we could have obtained the $y(t)$ of Figure 12.8 by integrating the $y^{(1)}(t)$ of Figure 12.12(c).

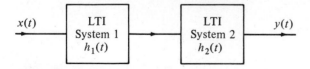

Figure 12.13   The cascade of two LTI systems.

When two networks are connected in cascade, as shown in Figure 12.13, the output of network 1 is the input of network 2. Hence the impulse response of the cascade connection is the convolution of the two impulse responses, or

$$h(t) = h_1(t) * h_2(t) \tag{12.31}$$

Convolution of a number of functions is associative, namely,

$$f_1(t) * [f_2(t) * f_3(t)] = [f_1(t) * f_2(t)] * f_3(t) \tag{12.32}$$

Convolution is distributive with respect to addition, namely,

$$f_1(t) * [f_2(t) + f_3(t)] = f_1(t) * f_2(t) + f_1(t) * f_3(t) \tag{12.33}$$

12.4   Remarks on the convolution integral

We approached the convolution integral from the point of view that it was a useful tool to determine the output of an LTI network with an arbitrary input when we knew the impulse or step response of the network. The problem was posed in this form primarily because it tied in well with the background you had acquired so far. Our justification for presenting the problem this way was quite valid. But the usefulness of the convolution integral is not limited to the evaluation of the time-domain response of an LTI network. Convolution integrals arise in many other areas quite independently of the network-response interpretation. They occur in the complex-frequency domain as well as the time domain. They appear in communication systems together with modulations, correlations, and many theorems with probabilistic propositions. The convolution integral is also a very useful tool in the analysis of nonlinear systems.

Thus it is important that you are able to perform the convolution of two functions, as well as knowing the steps that are sometimes taken to perform a convolution integral. Although you may not have too many occasions to actually evaluate convolution integrals (most of such evaluations are now done numerically by digital computers), an understanding of the process involved is essential because the derivations of advanced theories in many topics are based on it. The examples we used were largely arbitrarily concocted, for our convenience. This should not diminish their instructional value, which is of prime importance at this point.

12.5　The system concept

At the beginning of this volume, we made a brief reference to the three terms *circuit*, *network*, and *system*. As stated in Section 1.1 and as we have been doing thus far, these three words are used interchangeably. We have now reached an appropriate point for some clarification of the common usage of these three terms, in particular the broader usage of *system*.

The word "system" is used by the public at large to describe anything that is somewhat organized—the military system, the retail marketing system, the state university system, and so on.

In engineering, "system" is used to describe anything that is self-contained and has a cause–consequence relationship. Thus we have several systems in an automobile—fuel, coolant, brake (hydraulic), and electrical. A computer system could mean anything from a nationwide interconnection of many large-scale computers with many accessible points to a small minicomputer. Although the word "system" is grossly overused in every discipline, the phrase "systems approach to engineering" implies an overall study of many interconnected units of the same or of different types. The emphasis here is on the interaction and coordination of these units, rather than the internal details of each unit.

In electrical engineering, the systems approach is usually associated with the block-diagram formulation of a problem. A simple example is the block diagram of an AM superheterodyne receiver, shown in Figure 12.14, in which each block performs a very specific function. What is contained in each block is a separate matter. With the advent of integrated circuits, some of these blocks could very well represent separately encapsulated units

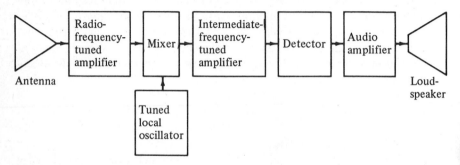

Figure 12.14　Block diagram of an AM superheterodyne receiver.

purchased from manufacturers. We may not know the arrangement or construction inside them. We may not need to know them. Or else, each block may be another system itself, such as the loudspeaker system.

For the purposes of this volume so far, any distinction between the term "system" and the terms "network" or "circuit" is largely moot. Since we are confining ourselves to reasonably simple electrical systems, every system is also a circuit or network, in that the internal detailed arrangement is known in every case. Hence whether we call a circuit a system or not is primarily a matter of choice. For example, in the circuit of Figure 12.2, $e_s(t)$ is the excitation. If we consider $i(t)$ as the response, then we would describe the circuit as a system in which the input and the output are related in the time domain through the differential equation:

$$\frac{1}{C}\int_0^t y\, dt + Ry + L\frac{dy}{dt} = x(t) \tag{12.34}$$

Or else we could describe the system as having an impulse response given by (12.1). The block diagram of Figure 12.1 is tacitly implied. From the systems point of view, the only thing that matters is (12.1) or (12.34). The identity of the circuit is immaterial.

Since we are approaching several aspects of electrical engineering by starting with simple problems and gradually adding complexity as we go, it is not necessary for us to distinguish the fuzzy lines that determine when one term is more appropriate than another. However, we should recognize that there are people in our profession who prefer an approach in the opposite direction. They would rather develop first a body of knowledge that's applicable to systems of any complexity. Then more specialized systems are subsets of these general systems. There is some merit to this approach and we should be aware of it.

The block-diagram scheme of describing a system has several advantages: (1) It enables us to divide a large problem into several small problems; (2) it enables us to visualize better the individual roles of each unit of a system; and (3) it enables us to assign idealized system components first and study the performance of the system with these idealized components. Once the system performance is deemed satisfactory, we can face the problem of constructing a component that will approximate the idealized performance. In Chapters 14 and 15, we shall be tackling some examples of this last problem.

Problems

12.1 Find the impulse responses of the networks shown in Figure P12.1. The functions y's are to be considered the responses.

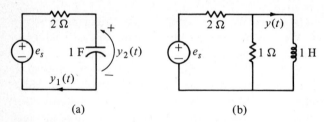

(a)   (b)

Figure P12.1

12.2 Find the step responses of the circuits in Figure P12.1.

12.3 For the circuits of Figure P12.1, find the responses, given that
$e_s(t) = \epsilon^{-t}u_{-1}(t)$

12.4 Find $f(t) * f(t)$ for the $f(t)$ given in Figure P12.4 for the interval $1 < t < 2$.

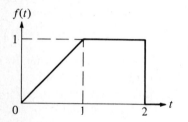

Figure P12.4

12.5 Find the convolution integral for the two functions $g(t) = \epsilon^{-3t}u_{-1}(t)$ and $h(t) = \epsilon^{-5t}u_{-1}(t)$.

12.6 Convolve the two functions $f_1(t) = \epsilon^{-t}u_{-1}(t-1)$ and $f_2(t) = u_{-1}(t-2)$. Give your answer in analytical form, using u_{-1} functions to indicate the range in which the expression is valid.

12.7 Find $f(t) = f_1(t) * f_2(t)$ for the functions given in Figure P12.7 for all values of t.

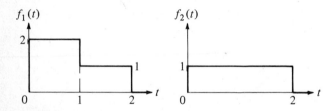

Figure P12.7

12.8 Find $f(t) = f_1(t) * f_2(t)$ for the functions given in Figure P12.8 for all values of t.

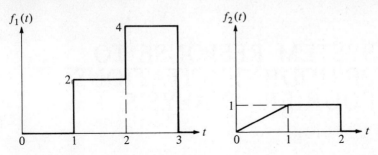

Figure P12.8

12.9 Find $f_1(t) * f_2(t)$ for the functions given in Figure P12.9.

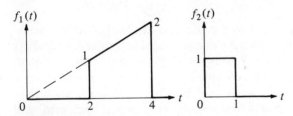

Figure P12.9

12.10 Find $f_1(t) * f_2(t)$ for the functions given in Figure P12.10. Give your answer in both analytical and graphical forms.

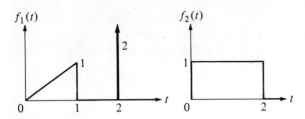

Figure P12.10

13 | SYSTEM RESPONSE TO PERIODIC EXCITATIONS: FOURIER ANALYSIS

Systems are frequently subjected to periodic excitations that are not sinusoidal. In this chapter we shall discuss a mathematical technique for handling such situations—*Fourier analysis*. This technique is not only important practically, but it has important conceptual implications that will serve as the springboard for further development of numerous other concepts such as the frequency spectrum, modulation techniques, Fourier transform, and filtering.

13.1 The Fourier series

A function is said to be *periodic* if it repeats its mode of variation at regular intervals. Each interval in which the variation of the function is complete is a *period*, denoted by T. If T is the period of a function, then nT may also be considered as its period.

For the sake of simplicity we shall first study only functions whose period is 2π. Later on we shall apply the method to functions of periods other than 2π. Any function of period 2π is defined completely if it is specified within an interval of 2π, since throughout the rest of the axis there will be only repetitions of this same variation. Thus only one complete period of a periodic function needs to be specified or shown graphically. It is usually convenient to choose the basic interval of a function $y = f(x)$ between $x = 0$ and $x = 2\pi$, or between $x = -\pi$ and $x = \pi$.

Always remember that, when we say that a function is specified throughout a region, we do not necessarily mean that it is specified by one single analytical expression. For example, the function shown in Figure 13.1

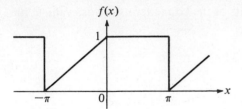

Figure 13.1

may be specified as:

$$f(x) = 1 + \frac{x}{\pi}, \qquad -\pi < x < 0$$

$$f(x) = 1, \qquad 0 < x < \pi$$

It can be shown that, if a periodic function $y = f(x)$ has only a finite number of discontinuities and a finite number of maxima and minima in the interval between $x = -\pi$ and $x = \pi$, and if the integral

$$\int_{-\pi}^{\pi} |f(x)| \, dx \tag{13.1}$$

is finite, then the function may be expressed as an infinite series.

$$f(x) = A_0 + a_1 \cos x + a_2 \cos 2x + a_3 \cos 3x + \cdots$$
$$+ b_1 \sin x + b_2 \sin 2x + b_3 \sin 3x + \cdots \tag{13.2}$$

in which A_0, the a's, and the b's are all unique. This is known as the *Fourier series* of the function $f(x)$.

Expression (13.2) may alternatively be written as

$$f(x) = A_0 + A_1 \cos(x + \phi_1) + A_2 \cos(2x + \phi_2) + A_3 \cos(3x + \phi_3) + \cdots \tag{13.3}$$

The term A_0 is invariant with respect to x and is known as the *constant term* of the series. It is also known as the dc term to electrical engineers, especially when the function represents a voltage or a current. The a_1, b_1, and A_1 terms are known as the *fundamental* terms. All others are *harmonic* terms. These harmonic terms may be designated to be of different orders according to the coefficient that appears with the variable x. For example, the A_3 term is called the third harmonic term of the series.

If the function $f(x)$ has a discontinuity at x_1, then the Fourier series converges to the average of the values of this function on the two sides of this point. For instance, the function of Figure 13.1 has a discontinuity at $x = \pi$. Thus the function $f(x)$, when expressed as a Fourier series, will have a value of $f(x) = \frac{1}{2}$ at $x = \pi$.

In order to obtain the coefficients of the cosine terms, let us evaluate the following integral:

$$\int_{-\pi}^{\pi} f(x) \cos nx \, dx \qquad (13.4)$$

Substituting the expression for $f(x)$ of (13.2) into (13.4), we have

$$\int_{-\pi}^{\pi} f(x) \cos nx \, dx = \int_{-\pi}^{\pi} A_0 \cos nx \, dx + \int_{-\pi}^{\pi} a_1 \cos x \cos nx \, dx + \cdots$$

$$+ \int_{-\pi}^{\pi} a_n \cos^2 nx \, dx + \cdots + \int_{-\pi}^{\pi} b_1 \sin x \cos nx \, dx + \cdots$$

$$+ \int_{-\pi}^{\pi} b_n \sin nx \cos nx \, dx + \cdots \qquad (13.5)$$

All the terms on the right-hand side of the expression, except the term whose integrand is $a_n \cos^2 nx$, are zero. And since

$$\int_{-\pi}^{\pi} \cos^2 nx \, dx = \pi \qquad (13.6)$$

we have

$$a_n = \frac{1}{\pi} \int_{-\pi}^{\pi} f(x) \cos nx \, dx \qquad (13.7)$$

For the special case in which $n = 0$, (13.7) gives

$$a_0 = \frac{1}{\pi} \int_{-\pi}^{\pi} f(x) \, dx \qquad (13.8)$$

Since

$$A_0 = \frac{1}{2\pi} \int_{-\pi}^{\pi} f(x) \, dx = \text{average value of } f(x) \qquad (13.9)$$

therefore

$$A_0 = \frac{a_0}{2} \qquad (13.10)$$

For reasons of consistency and convenience in later developments, we shall write the constant term of a Fourier series as $a_0/2$ instead of A_0.

In a similar manner, in order to obtain the coefficients of the sine terms, we evaluate the integral

$$\int_{-\pi}^{\pi} f(x) \sin nx \, dx = \int_{-\pi}^{\pi} A_0 \sin nx \, dx + \int_{-\pi}^{\pi} a_1 \cos x \sin nx \, dx + \cdots$$

$$+ \int_{-\pi}^{\pi} a_n \cos nx \sin nx \, dx + \cdots$$

$$+ \int_{-\pi}^{\pi} b_1 \sin x \sin nx \, dx + \cdots$$

$$+ \int_{-\pi}^{\pi} b_n \sin^2 nx \, dx + \cdots \tag{13.11}$$

All the terms on the right-hand side of (13.11), except the term whose integrand is $b_n \sin^2 nx$, are zero. And since

$$\int_{-\pi}^{\pi} \sin^2 nx \, dx = \pi \tag{13.12}$$

we have

$$b_n = \frac{1}{\pi} \int_{-\pi}^{\pi} f(x) \sin nx \, dx \tag{13.13}$$

When $n = 0$, $b_0 = 0$. Therefore Equations (13.7) and (13.13) are valid for all values of n that are nonnegative integers.

It is well to understand what is taking place in (13.7) or (13.13). In many cases an investigation of the integrand leads to some obvious conclusions. In both equations, the integrand is the product of the original function and a trigonometric function. Then this product is integrated over a complete period. Finally the integral is divided by π, which is one-half of the period.

In many instances the function given is not of any regular shape or cannot be expressed analytically. Equations (13.7) and (13.13) are, however, still the correct relationships to use for getting the coefficients. Only then the integrals must be evaluated segment by segment, or by some numerical techniques.

EXAMPLE 1   For the rectangular periodic function given in Figure 13.2, we have

$$a_n = \frac{1}{\pi} \int_{-\pi}^{0} (-\cos nx) \, dx + \frac{1}{\pi} \int_{0}^{\pi} \cos nx \, dx = 0 \qquad \text{for all } n$$

$$b_n = \frac{1}{\pi} \int_{-\pi}^{0} (-\sin nx) \, dx + \frac{1}{\pi} \int_{0}^{\pi} \sin nx \, dx$$

$$= \frac{1}{n\pi} \cos nx \Big|_{x=-\pi}^{x=0} - \frac{1}{n\pi} \cos nx \Big|_{x=0}^{x=\pi}$$

$$= \frac{1}{n\pi} \pm \frac{1}{n\pi} \pm \frac{1}{n\pi} + \frac{1}{n\pi}$$

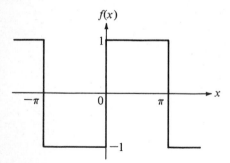

Figure 13.2

where the upper signs apply to odd n and the lower signs apply to even n.
Hence we get

$$b_n = 0, \qquad \text{for even } n$$

$$b_n = \frac{4}{n\pi}, \qquad \text{for odd } n$$

and the Fourier series of the rectangular wave is

$$f(x) = \frac{4}{\pi} \sin x + \frac{4}{3\pi} \sin 3x + \frac{4}{5\pi} \sin 5x + \cdots$$

$$= \sum_{n=1}^{\infty} \frac{4}{(2n-1)\pi} \sin(2n-1)x$$

If this series is truncated after the Nth term, we have an approximation of
$f(x)$ of Figure 13.2. Let this approximating function be denoted by

$$f_N(x) = \sum_{n=1}^{N} \frac{4}{(2n-1)\pi} \sin(2n-1)x$$

Figure 13.3 shows several plots of the truncated Fourier series of this function
over one-half of its period. (The other half is the negative of this half.) We
see that, as N is increased, $f_N(x)$ becomes a better approximation of $f(x)$.

However, on the two sides of a discontinuity there is an overshoot,
followed by a damped oscillation. The amount of the overshoot remains
essentially the same for all N. Increasing N only reduces the region over
which this overshoot takes place. As $N \to \infty$, the overshoot lasts only
infinitesimally long, as shown in the last graph of Figure 13.3. But it is
still approximately 9% of the discontinuity, or 18% of the discontinuity about
the average of the functional values on the two sides of the discontinuity.
This is known as the *Gibbs phenomenon*.

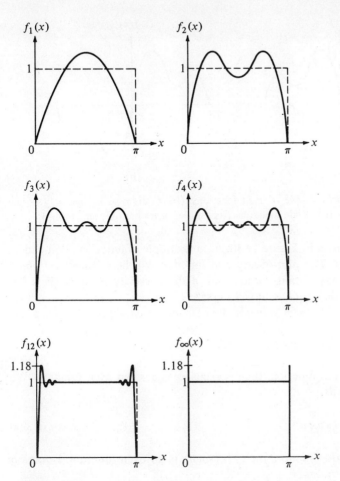

Figure 13.3 Truncated Fourier series representation of a rectangular wave—the Gibbs phenomenon.

13.2 Some special cases

Even and odd functions   The function $f(x)$ is said to be *even* if

$$f(x) = f(-x) \qquad\qquad (13.14)$$

Figure 13.4(a) shows an example of a function that satisfies this requirement. The plot of any even function will be symmetrical *about the y axis*. The left half of the curve is the image of the right half, if a mirror is placed along the y axis perpendicular to the xy plane.

The function $f(x)$ is said to be *odd* if

$$f(x) = -f(-x) \qquad\qquad (13.15)$$

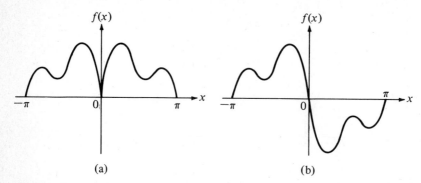

Figure 13.4 (a) An example of even functions. (Its Fourier series has only cosine terms.) (b) An example of odd functions. (Its Fourier series has only sine terms.)

The function shown in Figure 13.4(b) is an example of functions that satisfy this requirement. The plot of any odd function will be symmetrical *about the origin*. We may obtain the left half of the curve by rotating the right half 180° about the origin, and vice versa.

A function is even, if and only if its Fourier series contains only cosine terms ($b_n = 0$). The constant term may be considered as a cosine term.

A function is odd, if and only if its Fourier series contains only sine terms ($a_n = 0$).

If $f(x)$ is an even function, then $f(x) \cos nx$ is also an even function. We may write (13.7) as

$$a_n = \frac{2}{\pi} \int_0^\pi f(x) \cos nx \, dx \qquad (13.16)$$

If $f(x)$ is an odd function, then $f(x) \sin nx$ is an even function. Equation (13.13) may be written as

$$b_n = \frac{2}{\pi} \int_0^\pi f(x) \sin nx \, dx \qquad (13.17)$$

Separation of even and odd parts   Suppose we assume that

$$f(x) = f_e(x) + f_o(x) \qquad (13.18)$$

in which

$$f_e(x) = f_e(-x) \qquad (13.19)$$

and

$$f_o(x) = -f_o(-x) \qquad (13.20)$$

In other words, $f_e(x)$ is an even function and $f_o(x)$ is an odd function. Since

$$f(x) + f(-x) = f_e(x) + f_e(-x) + f_o(x) + f_o(-x) = 2f_e(x) \qquad (13.21)$$

we have

$$f_e(x) = \frac{f(x)+f(-x)}{2} \tag{13.22}$$

and since

$$f(x) - f(-x) = f_e(x) - f_e(-x) + f_o(x) - f_o(-x) = 2f_o(x) \tag{13.23}$$

we have

$$f_o(x) = \frac{f(x)-f(-x)}{2} \tag{13.24}$$

Equations (13.22) and (13.24) may therefore be used to obtain the even part, $f_e(x)$, and the odd part, $f_o(x)$, of any function $f(x)$.

The operations implied by (13.22) and (13.24) can be described verbally. Equation (13.22) states in effect that the even part of any function is the average of the function itself and the line image of the function about the y axis. Equation (13.24) states in effect that the odd part of any function is the average of the function itself and the point image of the function about the origin. Figure 13.5 shows how the even part and the odd part of the function of Figure 13.1 are obtained by these operations.

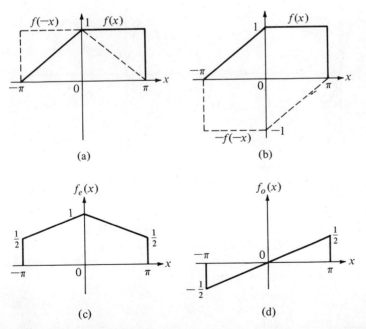

Figure 13.5 Example showing how a function is separated into an even-function part and an odd-function part.

Since the cosine terms of the Fourier series of $f(x)$ are its even part, it is clear that

$$f_e(x) = \frac{a_0}{2} + \sum_{n=1}^{\infty} a_n \cos nx \qquad (13.25)$$

Likewise, the sine terms may be identified with the odd part, or

$$f_o(x) = \sum_{n=1}^{\infty} b_n \sin nx \qquad (13.26)$$

Functions containing only odd or only even terms The Fourier expansion of a function $f(x)$ contains only odd terms (all even terms have zero co-efficients), if and only if

$$f(x + \pi) = -f(x) \qquad (13.27)$$

This is evidenced by the fact that

$$\cos n(x + \pi) = -\cos nx, \qquad \text{and} \qquad \sin n(x + \pi) = -\sin nx$$

if and only if n is odd. Figure 13.6(a) shows an example of functions that satisfy this requirement. The curve of any function that satisfies such a

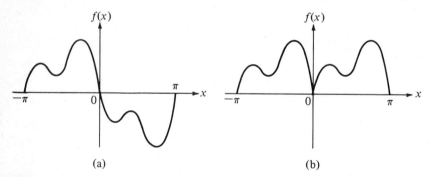

(a)   (b)

Figure 13.6 (a) An example of functions with half-wave symmetry. (Fourier series has only odd harmonics.) (b) An example of functions with double-frequency symmetry. (Fourier series has only even harmonics.)

requirement is said to possess *half-wave symmetry*. We can obtain the second half of the curve of such a function by inverting the first half.

The Fourier expansion of a function $f(x)$ contains only even terms (all odd terms have zero coefficients), if and only if

$$f(x + \pi) = f(x) \qquad (13.28)$$

This is evidenced by the fact that

$$\cos n(x + \pi) = \cos nx, \qquad \text{and} \qquad \sin n(x + \pi) = \sin nx$$

if and only if n is even. Figure 13.6(b) shows a function that satisfies this requirement. The curve of any function that satisfies such a requirement is said to possess *double-frequency symmetry*. The second half of the curve is identical to the first half.

Shift of origin It is sometimes desirable to shift the position of the origin with respect to the curve. The shift of the origin may introduce some symmetry that did not exist originally. In other instances, the Fourier series of a function may be obtained from a function whose Fourier expansion is already known.

If the curve of the function $f(x)$ is shifted to the right by an amount a, the shifted curve is represented by $f(x-a)$. Two curves that differ from each other only by a shift of the origin by an amount a are shown in Figure 13.7,

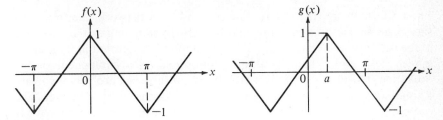

Figure 13.7 The shifting of the origin.

in which

$$f(x) = g(x+a) \tag{13.29}$$

$$g(x) = f(x-a) \tag{13.30}$$

These figures illustrate how a shift of the origin may sometimes save some analytical work. If we desire to find the Fourier expansion of $g(x)$, it is easier to find the expansion of $f(x)$ (which has only odd cosine terms) first and then to replace every x in the expansion of $f(x)$ by $(x-a)$ to obtain the expansion of $g(x)$.

Change of scale The basic period used so far has been 2π. This was chosen mainly because of the consequent simplicity in the mathematical expressions. If the actual period of a periodic function is T, the Fourier expansion of this function may be obtained from the Fourier expansion of a similar function of period 2π by replacing its independent variable x by

$$x = \frac{2\pi}{T}t \tag{13.31}$$

where t is the independent variable of the function with period T. The quantity $2\pi/T$ is often written as $2\pi f_0$ or ω_0.

The formulas for evaluating the coefficients of the Fourier series of the function $f(t)$ become

$$A_0 = \frac{1}{T} \int_{-T/2}^{T/2} f(t)\, dt$$

$$a_n = \frac{2}{T} \int_{-T/2}^{T/2} f(t) \cos n\omega_0 t\, dt = \frac{\omega_0}{\pi} \int_{-\pi/\omega_0}^{\pi/\omega_0} f(t) \cos n\omega_0 t\, dt$$

$$b_n = \frac{2}{T} \int_{-T/2}^{T/2} f(t) \sin n\omega_0 t\, dt = \frac{\omega_0}{\pi} \int_{-\pi/\omega_0}^{\pi/\omega_0} f(t) \sin n\omega_0 t\, dt$$

13.3 Application to circuit problems

In an LTI network, the steady-state response of a network due to a non-sinusoidal but periodic excitation may be found by summing up the responses of the network to all harmonics. If the excitation is expressed in its Fourier series, each term, which by itself is sinusoidal, is a component of the excitation. The response of the network to each term is a problem involving a sinusoidal excitation and may be dealt with in the regular manner. The response to the composite excitation—the nonsinusoidal excitation—is obtained by summing up the responses to all the components.

For example, suppose that, in the circuit of Figure 13.8(a), $e_s(t)$ is as given in Figure 13.8(b). Fourier analysis will give

$$e_s(t) = \frac{8}{\pi^2} \left(\cos t + \frac{1}{3^2} \cos 3t + \frac{1}{5^2} \cos 5t + \cdots \right)$$

$$= 0.811 \cos t + 0.090 \cos 3t + 0.032 \cos 5t + 0.016 \cos 7t + \cdots \quad (13.32)$$

The impedance seen by the source is

$$Z(j\omega) = 1 + j0.5\omega$$

We may now find the components of $i(t)$ one by one, as follows.

$$I_1 = \frac{0.811}{Z(j1)} = \frac{0.811}{1 + j0.5} = 0.725 \, \underline{/-26.6°}$$

$$I_3 = \frac{0.090}{Z(j3)} = \frac{0.090}{1 + j1.5} = 0.050 \, \underline{/-56.3°}$$

$$I_5 = \frac{0.032}{Z(j5)} = \frac{0.032}{1 + j2.5} = 0.012 \, \underline{/-68.2°}$$

$$I_7 = \frac{0.016}{Z(j7)} = \frac{0.016}{1 + j3.5} = 0.004 \, \underline{/-74.1°}$$

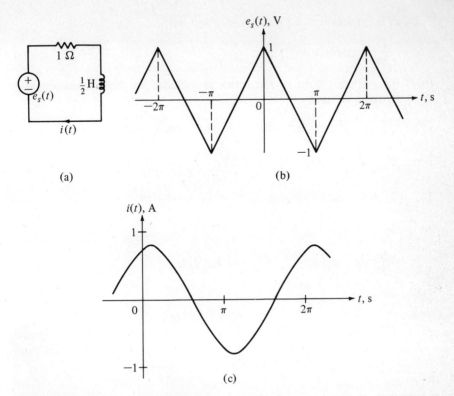

Figure 13.8 Fourier-series analysis of a circuit whose excitation is periodic and nonsinusoidal.

Thus we get

$$i(t) = 0.725 \cos(t - 26.6°) + 0.050 \cos(3t - 56.3°)$$

$$+ 0.012 \cos(5t - 68.2°) + 0.004 \cos(7t - 74.1°) + \cdots \qquad (13.33)$$

This current waveform, which is not a pure sinusoid, is shown in Figure 13.8(c).

13.4 Effective value of a periodic quantity

As we explained in Section 5.4 [Equation (5.62)], the effective value of a periodic function $f(t)$ is given by the equation

$$f_{\text{eff}} = \sqrt{\frac{1}{T} \int_{-T/2}^{T/2} [f(t)]^2 \, dt} \qquad (13.34)$$

If $f(t)$ is expressed as a Fourier series and written in the form

$$f(t) = \sum_{n=0}^{\infty} A_n \cos(n\omega t + \phi_n) \tag{13.35}$$

(here the constant term of the series is included in the summation and $\phi_0 = 0$), then we have

$$[f(t)]^2 = \sum_{n=0}^{\infty} A_n^2 \cos^2(n\omega t + \phi_n) + \sum_{\substack{n=0 \\ m=0 \\ m \neq n}}^{\infty} A_n A_m \cos(n\omega t + \phi_n) \cos(m\omega t + \phi_m)$$

But $\tag{13.36}$

$$\int_{-T/2}^{T/2} \cos(n\omega t + \phi_n) \cos(m\omega t + \phi_m) \, dt = 0, \qquad m \neq n$$

and

$$\int_{-T/2}^{T/2} \cos^2(n\omega t + \phi_n) \, dt = \frac{T}{2}, \qquad n = 1, 2, 3, 4, \ldots$$

Therefore we get

$$\int_{-T/2}^{T/2} [f(t)]^2 \, dt = A_0^2 T + A_1^2 \frac{T}{2} + A_2^2 \frac{T}{2} + A_3^2 \frac{T}{2} + \cdots + A_n^2 \frac{T}{2} + \cdots \tag{13.37}$$

Substituting (13.37) into (13.34) gives

$$f_{\text{eff}} = \sqrt{A_0^2 + \sum_{n=1}^{\infty} \frac{A_n^2}{2}} = \sqrt{A_0^2 + \frac{A_1^2}{2} + \frac{A_2^2}{2} + \frac{A_3^2}{2} + \cdots} \tag{13.38}$$

Each term under the radical is the square of either the dc value or the effective value of a harmonic, since

Effective value of $[A_n \cos(n\omega t + \phi_n)] = A_n / \sqrt{2}$ $\tag{13.39}$

Thus the effective value of a periodic function is the square root of the sum of the squares of the effective values of all its harmonics.

13.5 Average power in a circuit with periodic excitations

In the one-port of Figure 13.9, if $i(t)$ and $e(t)$ are periodic and expressed in Fourier series, we have in general

$$i(t) = \sum_{n=0}^{\infty} I_n \cos(n\omega t + \phi_n), \qquad \text{where } \phi_0 = 0 \tag{13.40}$$

and

$$e(t) = \sum_{n=0}^{\infty} E_n \cos(n\omega t + \psi_n), \qquad \text{where } \psi_0 = 0 \tag{13.41}$$

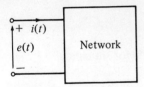

Figure 13.9 Convention used to derive the relationship between the power delivered to a one-port and its voltage and current, both of which are periodic and nonsinusoidal.

Then we have

$$i(t)e(t) = \sum_{n=0}^{\infty} I_n E_n \cos(n\omega t + \phi_n) \cos(n\omega t + \psi_n)$$

$$+ \sum_{\substack{n=0 \\ m=0 \\ m \neq n}}^{\infty} I_m E_n \cos(m\omega t + \phi_m) \cos(n\omega t + \psi_n) \tag{13.42}$$

But

$$\int_{-T/2}^{T/2} \cos(m\omega t + \phi_m) \cos(n\omega t + \psi_n)\, dt = 0, \qquad m \neq n \tag{13.43}$$

and

$$\int_{-T/2}^{T/2} \cos(n\omega t + \phi_n) \cos(n\omega t + \psi_n)\, dt = \frac{T}{2}\cos(\phi_n - \psi_n) \tag{13.44}$$

Therefore the average power delivered to the one-port is

$$P = \frac{1}{T}\int_{-T/2}^{T/2} i(t)e(t)\, dt$$

$$= \frac{1}{T}\left[I_0 E_0 T + I_1 E_1 \frac{T}{2}\cos(\phi_1 - \psi_1) + I_2 E_2 \frac{T}{2}\cos(\phi_2 - \psi_2) + \cdots\right.$$

$$\left. + I_n E_n \frac{T}{2}\cos(\phi_n - \psi_n) + \cdots\right]$$

$$= I_0 E_0 + \sum_{n=1}^{\infty} \frac{I_n E_n}{2}\cos(\phi_n - \psi_n) \tag{13.45}$$

Each term in (13.45) is the average power of a particular harmonic. One may say, therefore, that as far as the average power is concerned all harmonics act independently from one another. This phenomenon is a consequence of the fact that different harmonics are "orthogonal" [(13.43)] to each other.

The apparent power and power factor may be defined for a nonsinusoidal voltage and a nonsinusoidal current as

Apparent power $= I_{\text{eff}}\, E_{\text{eff}} \tag{13.46}$

$$\text{Power factor} = \frac{\text{average power}}{\text{apparent power}} \tag{13.47}$$

These definitions are logical extensions of those made for sinusoids.

13.6 Fourier series in complex form

The nth harmonic of a periodic function has been written in one of the two forms

$$a_n \cos nx + b_n \sin nx$$

or

$$A_n \cos(nx + \phi_n)$$

Another way of representing the nth harmonic is to use the exponential functions. Since

$$\cos nx = \frac{\epsilon^{jnx} + \epsilon^{-jnx}}{2}, \qquad \sin nx = \frac{\epsilon^{jnx} - \epsilon^{-jnx}}{2j}$$

we have

$$a_n \cos nx + b_n \sin nx = \frac{\epsilon^{jnx} + \epsilon^{-jnx}}{2} a_n + \frac{\epsilon^{jnx} - \epsilon^{-jnx}}{2j} b_n$$

$$= \frac{a_n - jb_n}{2} \epsilon^{jnx} + \frac{a_n + jb_n}{2} \epsilon^{-jnx} \tag{13.48}$$

If we let

$$\alpha_n = \frac{a_n - jb_n}{2}, \qquad \alpha_{-n} = \frac{a_n + jb_n}{2} \tag{13.49}$$

then

$$a_n \cos nx + b_n \sin nx = \alpha_n \epsilon^{jnx} + \alpha_{-n} \epsilon^{-jnx} \tag{13.50}$$

It is clear that

$$\alpha_n = \alpha^*_{-n} \tag{13.51}$$

For $n = 0$, either one of the two equations in (13.49) may be used, and both give $\alpha_0 = a_0/2$.

Thus the Fourier series of a periodic function $f(x)$ may be written as

$$f(x) = \cdots + \alpha_{-n} \epsilon^{-jnx} + \cdots + \alpha_{-2} \epsilon^{-j2x} + \alpha_{-1} \epsilon^{-jx} + \alpha_0 + \alpha_1 \epsilon^{jx}$$

$$+ \alpha_2 \epsilon^{j2x} + \cdots + \alpha_n \epsilon^{jnx} + \cdots$$

or

$$f(x) = \sum_{n=-\infty}^{\infty} \alpha_n \, \epsilon^{jnx} \tag{13.52}$$

We can obtain the coefficient α's by properly combining the a's and b's according to (13.49), especially if a's and b's are already available. They can also be evaluated directly from $f(x)$. From (13.49) we have

$$\alpha_n = \tfrac{1}{2}(a_n - jb_n) = \frac{1}{2}\left[\frac{1}{\pi}\int_{-\pi}^{\pi} f(x) \cos nx \, dx - j\frac{1}{\pi}\int_{-\pi}^{\pi} f(x) \sin nx \, dx\right]$$

$$= \frac{1}{2\pi}\int_{-\pi}^{\pi} f(x)(\cos nx - j \sin nx)\, dx$$

$$= \frac{1}{2\pi}\int_{-\pi}^{\pi} f(x)\epsilon^{-jnx}\, dx \tag{13.53}$$

Since $\alpha_n = \alpha^*_{-n}$ and $f(x)$ is real, we have

$$\alpha_{-n} = \frac{1}{2\pi}\int_{-\pi}^{\pi} f(x)\epsilon^{jnx}\, dx \tag{13.54}$$

We see that (13.54) is the same as (13.53). Actually, (13.53) is sufficient if we allow n to assume negative, positive, and zero values. This is one of the reasons why we prefer to use the exponential series—only one equation is needed for Fourier analysis.

We may draw the following conclusions about the coefficients.

1 If $f(x)$ is an even function, then all α's are real and $\alpha_n = \alpha_{-n}$.

2 If $f(x)$ is an odd function, then all α's are imaginary and $\alpha_n = -\alpha_{-n}$.

3 If $f(x)$ has half-wave symmetry, then all α's with even subscripts are zero.

For the function $e_s(t)$ of Figure 13.8, we have

$$e_s(t) = \frac{4}{\pi^2}\left[\cdots + \frac{1}{7^2}\epsilon^{-j7t} + \frac{1}{5^2}\epsilon^{-j5t} + \frac{1}{3^2}\epsilon^{-j3t} + \epsilon^{-jt} + \epsilon^{jt}\right.$$

$$\left. + \frac{1}{3^2}\epsilon^{j3t} + \frac{1}{5^2}\epsilon^{j5t} + \frac{1}{7^2}\epsilon^{j7t} + \cdots\right]$$

Each term of $e_s(t)$ is now in the form of $E\epsilon^{st}$. When this $e_s(t)$ is applied to the circuit in Figure 13.8, we can find the current $i(t)$ term by term as before. We have

$$I_{-5} = \frac{4/\pi^2 5^2}{Z(-j5)} = \frac{0.016}{1 - j2.5} = 0.006 \, \underline{/68.2°}$$

$$I_{-3} = \frac{4/\pi^2 3^2}{Z(-j3)} = \frac{0.045}{1 - j1.5} = 0.025 \, \underline{/56.3°}$$

$$I_{-1} = \frac{4/\pi^2}{Z(-j)} = \frac{0.406}{1-j0.5} = 0.363 \underline{/26.6^\circ}$$

$$I_1 = \frac{4/\pi^2}{Z(j)} = \frac{0.406}{1+j0.5} = 0.363 \underline{/-26.6^\circ}$$

$$I_3 = \frac{4/\pi^2 3^2}{Z(j3)} = \frac{0.045}{1+j1.5} = 0.025 \underline{/-56.3^\circ}$$

$$I_5 = \frac{4/\pi^2 5^2}{Z(j5)} = \frac{0.016}{1+j2.5} = 0.006 \underline{/-68.2^\circ}$$

and

$$i(t) = \cdots + 0.006\epsilon^{j68.2^\circ}\epsilon^{-j5t} + 0.025\epsilon^{j56.3^\circ}\epsilon^{-j3t} + 0.363\epsilon^{j26.6^\circ}\epsilon^{-jt}$$
$$+ 0.363\epsilon^{-j26.6^\circ}\epsilon^{jt} + 0.025\epsilon^{-j56.3^\circ}\epsilon^{j3t} + 0.006\epsilon^{-j68.2^\circ}\epsilon^{j5t} + \cdots \qquad (13.55)$$

This current is, of course, identical to the one given in (13.33).

13.7 Frequency spectrum and the concept of transform

In this section we shall use the periodic function to illustrate two fundamental concepts: the *transform* between the time domain and the frequency domain, and the *frequency spectrum.*

First we shall point out that any function of time (t) is also a function of the frequency (ω). We shall delineate this relationship using the periodic function. Suppose that we have a periodic voltage with a period T specified in the *time* domain. This is to say that we know the voltage function $e(t)$. We can find the coefficients of its Fourier series

$$\alpha_n = \frac{\omega_0}{2\pi} \int_{-\pi/\omega_0}^{\pi/\omega_0} e(t)\epsilon^{-jn\omega_0 t} dt \qquad (13.56)$$

where $\omega_0 = 2\pi/T$. Now α_n may be regarded as a discrete function of ω. Let $\alpha_n = \alpha(n\omega_0)$. It is a function that assumes a specific value at discrete points ($\omega = n\omega_0$, n integer) along the real angular frequency ($j\omega$) axis. For every given $e(t)$, its corresponding $\alpha(n\omega_0)$ is unique. The function $\alpha(n\omega_0)$ is the time function $e(t)$ described in the frequency domain. It tells us quantitatively how much of each frequency is contained in e, just as the function $e(t)$ tells us how much e is at each instant.

Conversely, if we know the Fourier series coefficients of a quantity, we also know its value at any instant t because

$$e(t) = \sum_{n=-\infty}^{\infty} \alpha_n \epsilon^{jn\omega_0 t} dt \qquad (13.57)$$

Hence (13.56) and (13.57) are a pair of *transforms* that take us back and forth between the frequency domain and the time domain. If we know a quantity in either domain, we can find its expression in the other domain through this pair of transforms.

In the example problem of the previous section, the voltage $e(t)$ was given in the time domain, and we wanted to find the answer $i(t)$ also in the time domain. But we found it expedient to solve the problem in the frequency domain. So we transformed the voltage $e(t)$ into the frequency domain, where we could use the techniques of ac analysis and superposition. After finding the current i in the frequency domain, we obtained $i(t)$ by applying the inverse transform to take it back to the time domain.

We are quite accustomed to the representation of a function specified in the time domain in a graph, which gives the value of the function at different instants. This graphical representation is often done in the frequency domain as well. The graph then gives the value of the function α at different frequencies and is known as the *frequency spectrum* of the function. Since n can assume only integer values, the frequency spectrum of a function is a discontinuous one and it has significance only at discrete points. Therefore, these spectra are groups of equally spaced vertical lines—*line spectra*.

Since the function α is, in general, complex, two plots are necessary to represent a given function. These may be plots of the real part and the imaginary part, but usually the plots of the magnitude and the phase angle are more convenient to use. The following statements are true:

1 The magnitude of α is an even function.
2 The phase angle of α is an odd function.
3 The real part of α is an even function.
4 The imaginary part of α is an odd function.

For these reasons usually only the positive half of a spectrum is actually drawn. The other half is either the mirror image or the point image of the positive half.

EXAMPLE 2   The periodic function $e(t)$ is shown in Figure 13.10. It is,

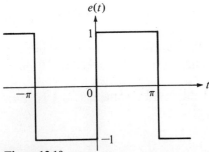

Figure 13.10

analytically,

$$e(t) = -1, \qquad -\pi < t < 0$$

$$e(t) = 1, \qquad 0 < t < \pi$$

From (13.53) and since $\omega_0 = 1$, we have

$$\alpha_n = \frac{1}{2\pi} \int_{-\pi}^{\pi} f(t) \epsilon^{-jnt}\, dt$$

$$= -\frac{1}{2\pi} \int_{-\pi}^{0} \epsilon^{-jnt}\, dt + \frac{1}{2\pi} \int_{0}^{\pi} \epsilon^{-jnt}\, dt$$

$$= \frac{1}{2\pi jn}(1 - \epsilon^{jn\pi} - \epsilon^{-jn\pi} + 1)$$

$$= \frac{1}{jn\pi}(1 - \cos n\pi) \qquad\qquad (13.58)$$

Thus we get

$$\alpha = \frac{2}{jn\pi} \qquad \text{for odd } n \qquad \text{and} \qquad \alpha = 0 \qquad \text{for even } n$$

The frequency spectra of $e(t)$ are shown in Figure 13.11(a) and (b). The dashed curve in Figure 13.11(a) is a regular hyperbola. It is drawn in to facilitate the construction of the spectral lines.

Suppose that this voltage $e(t)$ is applied across an RC branch. The admittance of the branch is

$$Y(\omega) = \frac{1}{R - j(1/\omega C)}$$

The frequency-domain representation of the current would be

$$\alpha'(n\omega_0) = \alpha(n\omega_0) Y(\omega) = \frac{1 - \cos n\pi}{jn\pi[R - j(1/\omega C)]}$$

The problem is then solved, at least in the frequency domain. The current in the time domain is the inverse transform of α'.

The remaining parts of Figure 13.11 also illustrate how we can obtain the frequency spectrum of the current by combining the frequency spectrum of the voltage and the frequency characteristics of the network function (the admittance). In general, the frequency characteristic of the network is given in the form of

$$A(\omega)\, \epsilon^{j\beta(\omega)}$$

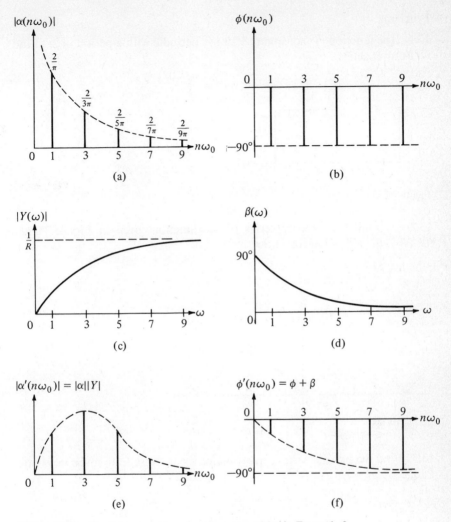

Figure 13.11 Frequency spectra of various quantities in Example 2.

The magnitude spectrum and the phase spectrum of the response are given by

$$|\alpha'(n\omega_0)| = A(\omega)|\alpha(n\omega_0)| \tag{13.59}$$

and

$$\phi'(n\omega_0) = \phi(n\omega_0) + \beta(n\omega_0) \tag{13.60}$$

respectively.

Problems

13.1 The function $f(x)$ of Figure P13.1 is periodic with a period of 2π. Find its Fourier series.

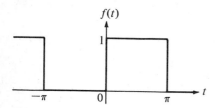

Figure P13.1

13.2 (a) Find the Fourier series of the function given in Figure P13.2. (b) With the aid of part (a) show that

$$1 + \frac{1}{3^2} + \frac{1}{5^2} + \frac{1}{7^2} + \cdots = \frac{\pi^2}{8}$$

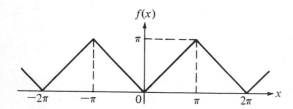

Figure P13.2

13.3 Find the Fourier series expansion for the impulse train given in Figure P13.3.

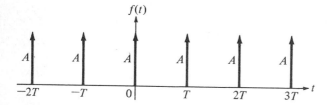

Figure P13.3

13.4 Obtain the Fourier series for the function $f(x) = x^2 \ (-\pi < x < \pi)$ and from it deduce the relations

$$\frac{\pi^2}{6} = 1 + \frac{1}{2^2} + \frac{1}{3^2} + \frac{1}{4^2} + \cdots, \qquad \text{and} \qquad \frac{\pi^2}{12} = 1 - \frac{1}{2^2} + \frac{1}{3^2} - \frac{1}{4^2} + \cdots$$

13.5 An even function, $e(x) = \sin x \ (0 < x < \pi)$, has a period of 2π. Find its Fourier series.

13.6 Suppose that $f(x) = 0 \ (-\pi < x < 0)$ and $f(x) = x \ (0 < x < \pi)$. (a) Find the Fourier expansion of this function. (b) Use the result of (a) to check the result of Problem 13.2.

13.7 From the result of Problem 13.1, obtain the Fourier series of the function of Figure P13.7.

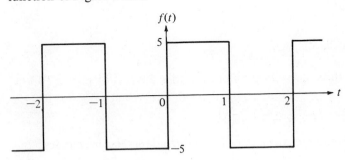

Figure P13.7

13.8 Suppose that $f(x) = 0 \ (-\pi < x < 0)$ and $f(x) = \sin x \ (0 < x < \pi)$. (a) Find a_0. (b) Sketch the even part of this function. (c) Sketch the odd part of this function. (d) Obtain the Fourier series of this function.

13.9 Show that, except for the constant term and a constant multiplier, the result of Problem 13.1 may be obtained by differentiating the result of Problem 13.2(a).

13.10 The Fourier series for the function $f(x)$ shown in Figure P13.10 is found to be

$$f(x) = \sin x - \frac{1}{3^2} \sin 3x + \frac{1}{5^2} \sin 5x - \cdots$$

Write the equation for the function $g(t)$.

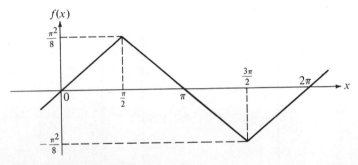

Figure P13.10 (continued on page 428)

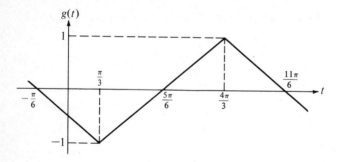

Figure P13.10 (continued)

13.11 The first three terms in the Fourier series for $f(x)$ of Figure P13.11 are given by

$$f(x) = 0.5 + 0.637 \sin x + 0.212 \sin 3x + \cdots$$

Determine the Fourier expansion for $g(t)$ to include similar harmonics.

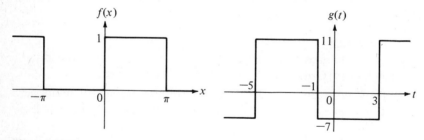

Figure P13.11

13.12 Given that the Fourier series for $f(x)$ of Figure P13.12 is

$$f(x) = \frac{4}{\pi}(\cos x - \tfrac{1}{3}\cos 3x + \tfrac{1}{5}\cos 5x - \cdots)$$

find the Fourier series for $g(t)$.

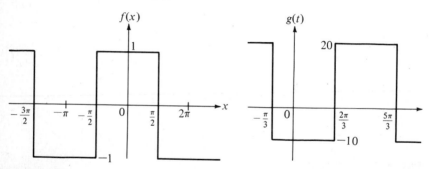

Figure P13.12

13.13 Find the Fourier expansion in exponential form for the saw-toothed wave of Figure P13.13.

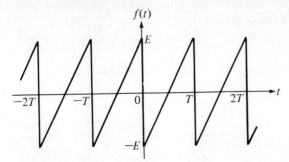

Figure P13.13

13.14 Show graphically that the function $e(t)$ of Figure P13.14 may be obtained by adding two saw-toothed waves, one as given in Figure P13.13 and the other the negative of that function with the origin shifted by $T/2$ in either direction. In this manner, obtain the Fourier expansion in exponential form for the function of Figure P13.14.

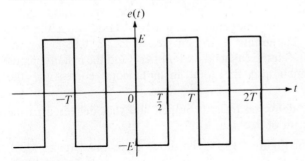

Figure P13.14

13.15 Find the complex Fourier series for the sequence of impulses shown in Figure P13.15.

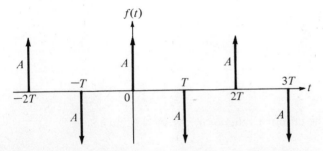

Figure P13.15

13.16 For $f(t)$ of Figure P13.16, $\alpha_n = (1/jn\pi)(1-\cos n\pi)$. Find the Fourier series in exponential form for $g(t)$, which is a periodic function with a period of 2. [*Hint:* $g(t)$ is the sum of a constant, a rectangular wave of period 2, and another rectangular wave of period 1.]

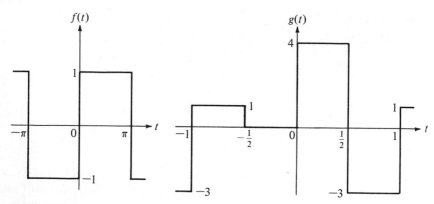

Figure P13.16

13.17 The voltage $e(t) = 1540 \sin 377t + 310 \sin(3 \times 377t) - 280 \sin(5 \times 377t)$ is applied to the parallel combination of two branches, one containing a 10-ohm resistance, a 0.1-henry inductance, and a 10^{-4}-farad capacitance in series, and the other containing a 15-ohm resistance, a 0.05-henry inductance, and a 50×10^{-6}-farad capacitance in series. Find the instantaneous currents in each branch and the total instantaneous current of the combination.

13.18 Find the power delivered to each branch and that delivered to the combination of the circuit of Problem 13.17.

13.19 In the circuit of Figure P13.19, the diode is assumed to be ideal. The source voltage $e_s(t)$ is ac, 110 volt, 60 Hz, or $e_s(t) = 110\sqrt{2}\sin 377t$. Find the dc, fundamental, and the second harmonic of the output voltage $e_o(t)$.

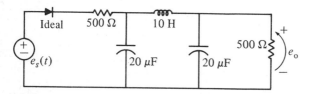

Figure P13.19

13.20 Show that the effective value of $a_n \cos n\omega t + b_n \sin n\omega t$ is $\sqrt{a_n^2/2 + b_n^2/2}$.

14 | FOURIER TRANSFORM AND APPLICATIONS

In the previous chapter we established, through the Fourier series, the relationship between the representation of a periodic signal in the time domain and its corresponding frequency-domain representation. We shall now extend that concept to the similar interrelationship for nonperiodic signals.

14.1 The Fourier integral

In the discussion of Fourier series representation of a time function, we assumed that the function was periodic. We then introduced the concept of the frequency spectrum. Since a nonperiodic function may be thought of as a periodic function with a period that is infinitely long, it would appear that the Fourier series concept is directly applicable to nonperiodic functions. However, a few details need be worked out with some care. Let us take the formula

$$\alpha(n\omega_0) = \frac{\omega_0}{2\pi} \int_{-T/2}^{T/2} f(t)\epsilon^{-jn\omega_0 t}\, dt \tag{14.1}$$

In addition, let us define a new frequency-domain function

$$g(n\omega_0) = \frac{\alpha(n\omega_0)}{\omega_0} = \frac{1}{2\pi} \int_{-T/2}^{T/2} f(t)\epsilon^{-jn\omega_0 t}\, dt \tag{14.2}$$

The only difference between these two functions is a multiplicative constant.
Let us see what happens to a periodic function when its period is made

successively larger. Take the periodic function $f_1(t)$ of Figure 14.1. Straight-forward Fourier analysis yields

$$\alpha_1(n\omega_1) = \frac{L}{T} \frac{\sin(n\omega_1 L/2)}{n\omega_1 L/2} \tag{14.3}$$

where $\omega_1 = 2\pi/T$, and

$$g_1(n\omega_1) = \frac{\alpha_1(n\omega_1)}{\omega_1} = \frac{L}{2\pi} \frac{\sin(n\omega_1 L/2)}{n\omega_1 L/2} \tag{14.4}$$

These two spectra are shown in Figure 14.1 (for $T = 2L$). (Since α and g of this function are always real, only one graph is needed for each spectrum.)

Now we change $f_1(t)$ to $f_2(t)$ by deleting every other pulse, as shown

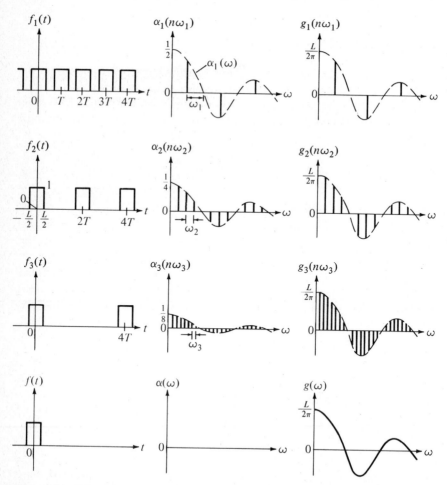

Figure 14.1 Effect of the period on the frequency spectrum of a periodic function.

in Figure 14.1. (Or, equivalently, we increase the period from T to $2T$.) The new frequency spectra are now given by

$$\alpha_2(n\omega_2) = \frac{L}{2T} \frac{\sin(n\omega_2 L/2)}{n\omega_2 L/2} \tag{14.5}$$

and

$$g_2(n\omega_2) = \frac{L}{2\pi} \frac{\sin(n\omega_2 L/2)}{n\omega_2 L/2} \tag{14.6}$$

in which $\omega_2 = \omega_1/2$.

Let us continue this doubling of the period one more and make the new period $4T$, shown as $f_3(t)$ in Figure 14.1. The new frequency spectra are given by

$$\alpha_3(n\omega_3) = \frac{L}{4T} \frac{\sin(n\omega_3 L/2)}{n\omega_3 L/2} \tag{14.7}$$

and

$$g_3(n\omega_3) = \frac{L}{2\pi} \frac{\sin(n\omega_3 L/2)}{n\omega_3 L/2} \tag{14.8}$$

in which $\omega_3 = \omega_2/2$. The functions $f_2(t)$ and $f_3(t)$, as well as the spectra of (14.5), (14.6), (14.7), and (14.8), are all given in Figure 14.1.

From these spectra, we observe that, every time the period is doubled, the spectral lines of both α and g are twice as close as before. The heights of the spectral lines of α are halved, but the heights of the spectral lines of g are unchanged wherever they occur. As a group of functions, all g's are bound by the same envelope.

If we continue this process indefinitely, in the limit, as $T \to \infty$, we have the following situations:

1 The spacing of the spectral lines (which is also the angular frequency of the fundamental) approaches zero ($\omega_0 = 2\pi/T = d\omega \to 0$).

2 The variable $n\omega_0$ may assume any value. In other words, $n\omega_0$ is a continuous variable ($n\omega_0 \to \omega$).

3 The frequency spectra become continuous [$(\alpha(n\omega_0) \to \alpha(\omega)$].

4 The function $\alpha(n\omega_0) \to \alpha(\omega)$ approaches zero and the spectrum is no longer visible.

5 The spectrum of the function $g(n\omega_0) \to g(\omega)$ becomes a continuous curve.

These facts are illustrated by the function $f(t)$ (Figure 14.1), which has only a single pulse. Its $\alpha(\omega)$ is zero, and its $g(\omega)$ is a continuous curve that, when placed on top of g_1, g_2, or g_3, coincides with the tips of their spectral lines. Analytically, $g(\omega)$ is given by

$$g(\omega) = \frac{L}{2\pi}\frac{\sin(\omega L/2)}{\omega L/2} \tag{14.9}$$

In a way we may think of $g_i(\omega)$ as the enlarged version of $\alpha_i(\omega)$. In the limit, as $T \to \infty$, $\alpha(\omega)$ is so minute that the naked eye cannot discern how it varies. So we multiply it by a very large number, $1/\omega_0$. This multiplication may be likened to seeing $\alpha(\omega)$ through a microscope of tremendous magnification. The result is $g(\omega)$. Although $\alpha(\omega)$ is extremely small, its relative frequency distribution is still relevant.

Since the only difference between $\alpha(\omega)$ and $g(\omega)$ is a constant multiplier, the properties of $g(\omega)$ are similar to those of $\alpha(\omega)$. This is important because it leads us to the conclusion that we may treat g in the frequency domain in the same way as α and all the advantages of dealing with α also exist when we deal with g.

In the limit, $g(\omega)$ is given by

$$g(\omega) = \lim_{\omega_0 \to 0} g(n\omega_0) = \lim_{\omega_0 \to 0} \frac{\alpha(n\omega_0)}{\omega_0}$$

$$= \frac{1}{2\pi}\int_{-\infty}^{\infty} f(t)\epsilon^{-j\omega t}\,dt \tag{14.10}$$

Conversely, if we want to find the time-domain description of a quantity whose frequency-domain description we know, we go to (13.57), which reads

$$f(t) = \sum_{n=-\infty}^{\infty} \alpha(n\omega_0)\epsilon^{jn\omega_0 t} = \sum_{n=-\infty}^{\infty} \omega_0 g(n\omega_0)\epsilon^{jn\omega_0 t} \tag{14.11}$$

Now as $T \to \infty$, $n\omega_0 \to \omega$, and $\omega_0 \to d\omega$, (14.11) approaches an integral, namely,

$$f(t) = \int_{-\infty}^{\infty} g(\omega)\epsilon^{j\omega t}\,d\omega \tag{14.12}$$

By choice and for consistency of notation with the Laplace transform in the next chapter, we prefer an alternative definition to (14.10) and (14.12), namely,

$$G(\omega) = 2\pi g(\omega) = \int_{-\infty}^{\infty} f(t)\epsilon^{-j\omega t}\,dt \tag{14.13}$$

and

$$f(t) = \frac{1}{2\pi}\int_{-\infty}^{\infty} G(\omega)\epsilon^{j\omega t}\,d\omega \tag{14.14}$$

Of course, the only difference between $g(\omega)$ and $G(\omega)$ is the multiplier 2π. The function $G(\omega)$ as defined by (14.13) is known as the *Fourier integral* or the *Fourier transform* of $f(t)$. Equation (14.13) gives the frequency-domain description of the time-domain function $f(t)$. To return to the time domain, we use (14.14). This latter operation is the *inverse Fourier transform*.

The operations implied by (14.13) and (14.14) are frequently represented symbolically by

$$G(\omega) = \mathscr{F}[f(t)] \tag{14.15}$$

and

$$f(t) = \mathscr{F}^{-1}[G(\omega)] \tag{14.16}$$

respectively.

The graphical representation of $G(\omega)$ will generally require two graphs, one for the magnitude and one for the phase. As in the case of $\alpha(n\omega_0)$, the magnitude of $G(\omega)$ is an even function while its phase is an odd function.

From (14.13) we may conclude that the Fourier transform of $f(t)$ exists if the integral

$$\int_{-\infty}^{\infty} f(t)\epsilon^{-j\omega t}\,dt$$

exists. Since $|\epsilon^{-j\omega t}| = 1$, we may say that

$$\left|\int_{-\infty}^{\infty} f(t)\epsilon^{-j\omega t}\,dt\right| \leq \int_{-\infty}^{\infty} |f(t)|\,dt \tag{14.17}$$

Hence the Fourier transform of $f(t)$ exists if $f(t)$ is absolutely integrable or if

$$\int_{-\infty}^{\infty} |f(t)|\,dt < \infty \tag{14.18}$$

Note that (14.18) does not rule out $f(t) = u_0(t)$. It does rule out the sinusoids ($\sin \beta t$ or $\cos \beta t$), the step function $u_{-1}(t)$, the ramp function $u_{-2}(t)$, any function that increases exponentially with time, such as $\epsilon^{at}u_{-1}(t)$, $\epsilon^{\alpha t}\cos \beta t\, u_{-1}(t)(\alpha \geq 0)$, and so on.

EXAMPLE 1   Suppose that we have

$$f(t) = 0, \qquad t < 0$$
$$f(t) = \epsilon^{-at}, \qquad t > 0 \tag{14.19}$$

Applying (14.13), we have

$$G(\omega) = \int_0^{\infty} \epsilon^{-at}\epsilon^{-j\omega t}\,dt$$

$$= \int_0^{\infty} \epsilon^{(-a-j\omega)t}\,dt$$

$$= -\frac{1}{a+j\omega}\epsilon^{(-a-j\omega)t}\bigg]_0^{\infty} = \frac{1}{a+j\omega} \tag{14.20}$$

At this point it is tempting to let $a \to 0$, in order to obtain the Fourier transform of a unit step. But remember! Since a unit step is not absolutely integrable, $\mathscr{F}\,[u_{-1}(t)]$ obtained in this way may not be correct.

EXAMPLE 2   We may state the properties of the impulse function as

$$u_0(t) = 0, \qquad t \neq 0$$

$$\int_{-\infty}^{\infty} u_0(t)\,dt = 1 \qquad\qquad (14.21)$$

From (14.13) and applying (12.29), we have

$$G(\omega) = \int_{-\infty}^{\infty} u_0(t)\epsilon^{-j\omega t}\,dt = 1 \qquad\qquad (14.22)$$

Hence an impulse function contains an equal amount of all frequencies.

EXAMPLE 3   The pulse function of Figure 14.2 and $f(t)$ of Figure 14.1 differ only in their heights. The height of $f(t)$ of Figure 14.1 is unity, whereas that of the pulse function of Figure 14.2 is $1/L$. From (14.9), we see that the

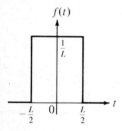

Figure 14.2   A rectangular pulse function.

Fourier transform of $f(t)$ of Figure 14.2 is

$$G(\omega) = \frac{\sin(\omega L/2)}{\omega L/2} \qquad\qquad (14.23)$$

Now, if we let $L \to 0$, $1/L \to \infty$ in such a way that the area under the rectangular pulse remains unity, then in the limit, the pulse approaches a unit impulse and $G(\omega)$ of (14.23) approaches unity.

14.2   Properties of the Fourier transform

Most of the following properties are fairly obvious. A few require brief proofs, which are given.

1 *Multiplication by a scalar*   If $G(\omega)$ is the Fourier transform of $f(t)$, then $aG(\omega)$ is the Fourier transform of $af(t)$.

2 *Additivity* If $G_1(\omega)$ and $G_2(\omega)$ are the Fourier transforms of $f_1(t)$ and $f_2(t)$, then the Fourier transform of $[f_1(t) + f_2(t)]$ is $[G_1(\omega) + G_2(\omega)]$.

3 *Mirror image in the time domain* If $G(\omega)$ is the Fourier transform of $f(t)$, then $G(-\omega)$ is the Fourier transform of $f(-t)$.

PROOF

$$\mathscr{F}[f(-t)] = \int_{-\infty}^{\infty} f(-t) \epsilon^{-j\omega t} \, dt$$

Setting $x = -t$, we get

$$\mathscr{F}[f(-t)] = \int_{-\infty}^{\infty} f(x) \epsilon^{j\omega x} \, dx = G(-\omega) \qquad (14.24)$$

4 *Time and frequency scaling* If $G(\omega)$ is the Fourier transform of $f(t)$, then the Fourier transform of $f(at)$ is $(1/a) G(\omega/a)$.

PROOF

$$\mathscr{F}[f(at)] = \int_{-\infty}^{\infty} f(at) \epsilon^{-j\omega t} \, dt$$

Setting $x = at$, we obtain

$$\mathscr{F}[f(at)] = \frac{1}{a} \int_{-\infty}^{\infty} f(x) \epsilon^{-j(\omega/a)x} \, dx = \frac{1}{a} G\left(\frac{\omega}{a}\right) \qquad (14.25)$$

5 *Delay* If $G(\omega)$ is the Fourier transform of $f(t)$, then the Fourier transform of $f(t - t_0)$ is $G(\omega) \epsilon^{-j\omega t_0}$.

PROOF

$$\mathscr{F}[f(t - t_0)] = \int_{-\infty}^{\infty} f(t - t_0) \epsilon^{-j\omega t} \, dt$$

Setting $x = t - t_0$, we get

$$\mathscr{F}[f(t - t_0)] = \int_{-\infty}^{\infty} f(x) \epsilon^{-j\omega x} \epsilon^{-j\omega t_0} \, dx = G(\omega) \epsilon^{-j\omega t_0} \qquad (14.26)$$

6 *Frequency (complex) translations* If $G(\omega)$ is the Fourier transform of $f(t)$, then $G(\omega + \omega_0)$ is the Fourier transform of $f(t) \epsilon^{-j\omega_0 t}$.

7 *Time differentiation* If $G(\omega)$ is the Fourier transform of $f(t)$ and if $\mathscr{F}[f^{(n)}(t)]$ exists, the latter is given by $(j\omega)^n G(\omega)$.

8 *Time integral* If $G(\omega)$ is the Fourier transform of $f(t)$, then the Fourier transform of $f^{(-1)}(t) = \int_{-\infty}^{t} f(t) \, dt$ is $(1/j\omega) G(\omega)$, provided the division of $G(\omega)$ by $j\omega$ does not produce a pole at $\omega = 0$.

9 *Frequency differentiation* If $G(\omega)$ is the Fourier transform of $f(t)$, then $G^{(n)}(\omega)$ is the transform of $(-jt)^{(n)}f(t)$.

10 *Time-frequency symmetry* If $G(\omega)$ is the Fourier transform of $f(t)$, then $2\pi f(\pm\omega)$ is the transform of $G(\mp t)$. In other words,

$$\mathscr{F}[f(t)] = G(\omega)$$

implies that

$$\mathscr{F}[G(t)] = 2\pi f(-\omega) \tag{14.27}$$

and

$$\mathscr{F}[G(-t)] = 2\pi f(\omega) \tag{14.28}$$

PROOF Interchanging ω and t in (14.14), we get

$$2\pi f(\omega) = \int_{-\infty}^{\infty} G(t)\,e^{j\omega t}\,dt$$

Hence we obtain

$$2\pi f(-\omega) = \int_{-\infty}^{\infty} G(t)\,\epsilon^{-j\omega t}\,dt = \mathscr{F}[G(t)] \tag{14.29}$$

EXAMPLE 4 From (14.22) we have

$$\mathscr{F}[u_0(t)] = 1$$

By property 5, we have

$$\mathscr{F}\left[u_0\left(t - \frac{L}{2}\right)\right] = \epsilon^{-j(\omega L/2)}$$

Likewise

$$\mathscr{F}\left[u_0\left(t + \frac{L}{2}\right)\right] = \epsilon^{j(\omega L/2)}$$

By properties 1 and 2, we have

$$\mathscr{F}\left[\frac{1}{L}u_0\left(t + \frac{1}{2}\right) - \frac{1}{L}u_0\left(t - \frac{L}{2}\right)\right] = \frac{\epsilon^{j(\omega L/2)} - \epsilon^{-j(\omega L/2)}}{L} = \frac{2j}{L}\sin\frac{\omega L}{2} \tag{14.30}$$

The function to be transformed is shown in Figure 14.3, which is also the derivative of $f(t)$ of Figure 14.2. By property 8, we should have

$$\mathscr{F}[f(t)] = \frac{2j\sin(\omega L/2)}{j\omega L} \tag{14.31}$$

which agrees with (14.23). [The function $G(\omega)$ of (14.31) does not become unbounded as ω tends to zero.]

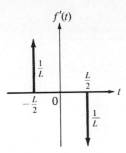

Figure 14.3 Derivative of the function depicted in Figure 14.2.

EXAMPLE 5   Referring to Figure 14.4, in order to find the Fourier transform of $f(t)$, we can again start with $f''(t)$ and work step by step, as follows.

$$\mathscr{F}[f''(t)] = \frac{A}{b}\epsilon^{j\omega b} - \frac{2A}{b} + \frac{A}{b}\epsilon^{-j\omega b} = -\frac{4A}{b}\sin^2\left(\frac{\omega b}{2}\right)$$

$$\mathscr{F}[f'(t)] = -\frac{4A}{j\omega b}\sin^2\left(\frac{\omega b}{2}\right)$$

$$\mathscr{F}[f(t)] = \frac{4A}{\omega^2 b}\sin^2\left(\frac{\omega b}{2}\right) = Ab\left[\frac{\sin(\omega b/2)}{\omega b/2}\right]^2$$

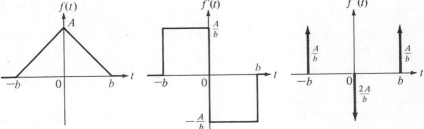

Figure 14.4

14.3   Relationship between impulse response and network function

The Fourier transform also provides us with a link between the time-domain analysis (Chapter 12) and the frequency-domain analysis (Chapter 11) of an LTI system.

The block diagram of Figure 14.5(a) indicates a standard description of an LTI system in the time domain. We excite the system with a unit impulse. The response we get is the impulse response. Figure 14.5(b) indicates the response of an LTI system to an arbitrary excitation in the time domain. If the excitation applied to the LTI system is $x(t)$, the response $y(t)$ is found

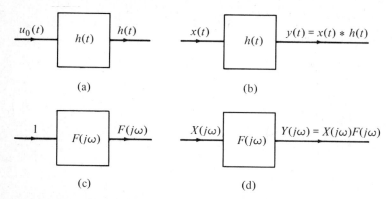

Figure 14.5 Time-domain and frequency-domain descriptions of an LTI system.

by convolving $x(t)$ and $h(t)$, or

$$y(t) = x(t) * h(t) \tag{14.32}$$

In the frequency domain, the standard description is the network function. A network function F is defined as the ratio of the response Y (for example, E_2 or I_2) to the excitation X (for example, E_1 or I_1) as a function of s or $j\omega$. At present we are concerned with

$$F(j\omega) = \frac{Y(j\omega)}{X(j\omega)} \tag{14.33}$$

This relationship is shown in Figure 14.5(d). Equation (14.33) may alternatively be expressed as

$$F(j\omega) = Y(j\omega)|_{X=1} \tag{14.34}$$

This relationship is indicated in Figure 14.5(c).

A comparison of Figure 14.5(a) and (c) clearly tells us that they are the same occurrence described in the time and frequency domains, respectively. Since

$$\mathscr{F}[u_0(t)] = 1 \tag{14.35}$$

it follows that

$$\mathscr{F}[h(t)] = F(j\omega) \tag{14.36}$$

In other words, *the Fourier transform of the impulse response is the network function as a function of* $j\omega$.

Similarly a comparison of Figure 14.5(b) and (d) reveals that they describe the same situation from two points of view. If $X(j\omega)$ is the Fourier transform of $x(t)$, then $Y(j\omega)$ should be the transform of $y(t)$. But since

$$Y(j\omega) = X(j\omega)F(j\omega) \tag{14.37}$$

we may conclude that

$$\mathcal{F}[x(t) * h(t)] = \mathcal{F}[x(t)] \mathcal{F}[h(t)] \tag{14.38}$$

Although we have arrived at (14.38) through network considerations, this relationship need not be tied to networks. In other words, $x(t)$, $h(t)$, and $y(t)$ need not have the physical identifications we have just given them. In general, we may say that *the Fourier transform of the convolution of two functions is the product of their individual Fourier transforms*. This is another reason why we frequently prefer to perform a network-analysis problem in the frequency domain.

Although the above reasoning is straightforward, it does not constitute a formal proof of (14.38). We shall give such a developement presently. Starting with (12.12),

$$y(t) = \int_{-\infty}^{\infty} x(\lambda) h(t-\lambda) \, d\lambda \tag{14.39}$$

we have

$$\mathcal{F}[y(t)] = \int_{-\infty}^{\infty} \left[\int_{-\infty}^{\infty} x(\lambda) h(t-\lambda) \, d\lambda \right] \epsilon^{-j\omega t} \, dt$$

$$= \int_{\lambda=-\infty}^{\lambda=\infty} x(\lambda) \int_{t=-\infty}^{t=\infty} h(t-\lambda) \epsilon^{-j\omega t} \, dt \, d\lambda \tag{14.40}$$

In the inner integral, if we let $\tau = t - \lambda$, (14.40) becomes

$$\mathcal{F}[y(t)] = \int_{\lambda=-\infty}^{\lambda=\infty} x(\lambda) \int_{\tau=-\infty-\lambda}^{\tau=\infty-\lambda} h(\tau) \epsilon^{-j\omega(\tau+\lambda)} \, d\tau \, d\lambda$$

$$= \int_{\lambda=-\infty}^{\lambda=\infty} x(\lambda) \epsilon^{-j\omega\lambda} \, d\lambda \int_{\tau=-\infty}^{\tau=\infty} h(\tau) \epsilon^{-j\omega\tau} \, d\tau$$

$$= \mathcal{F}[x(t)] \mathcal{F}[h(t)] \tag{14.41}$$

This confirms (14.38).

EXAMPLE 6 For the circuit of Figure 14.6, the impulse response was given (see Figure 4.10) as

$$h(t) = \frac{1}{L} \epsilon^{-(R/L)t} u_{-1}(t) \tag{14.42}$$

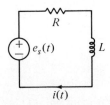

Figure 14.6

The network function in question is the admittance seen by the source, or

$$Y(j\omega) = \frac{I}{E_s} = \frac{1}{R+j\omega L} \tag{14.43}$$

If we take the Fourier transform of $h(t)$ of (14.42), we get

$$\mathscr{F}[h(t)] = \frac{1}{L}\int_0^\infty \epsilon^{-(R/L)t}\epsilon^{-j\omega t}\,dt$$

$$= \frac{1}{L}\times\frac{\epsilon^{[-(R/L)-j\omega]t}}{-(R/L)-j\omega}\bigg|_{t=0}^{t=\infty} = \frac{1}{R+j\omega L} \tag{14.44}$$

which checks with (14.43).

EXAMPLE 7   The Fourier transform of the function $f(t)$ of Figure 14.7(a) can be found to be

$$\mathscr{F}[f(t)] = \frac{B(1-\epsilon^{j\omega a})}{j\omega} \tag{14.45}$$

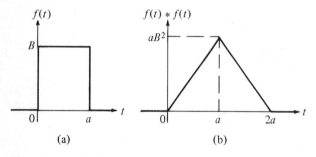

Figure 14.7

If we wish to find the Fourier transform of $f(t)*f(t)$, we know from (14.38) that

$$\mathscr{F}[f(t)*f(t)] = -\frac{B^2(1-\epsilon^{j\omega a})^2}{\omega^2} \tag{14.46}$$

The function $f(t)*f(t)$ is shown in Figure 14.7(b). We can also find the Fourier transform of this function directly, as in Example 5 of Section 14.2, whence we find that

$$\mathscr{F}[f(t)*f(t)] = B^2a^2\left[\frac{\sin(\omega a/2)}{\omega a/2}\right]^2\epsilon^{-j\omega a} \tag{14.47}$$

The expressions in (14.46) and (14.47) can be shown to be identical. (This is left as an exercise in Problem 14.19.)

In a manner similar to that by which we derived (14.38), we can show that

$$\mathcal{F}[f_1(t)f_2(t)] = \frac{1}{2\pi}\int_{-\infty}^{\infty} G_1(u)\,G_2(\omega-u)\,du$$

$$= \frac{1}{2\pi}[G_1(\omega) * G_2(\omega)] \qquad (14.48)$$

14.4 Circuit analysis using the Fourier transform

When a network is subjected to an excitation that is nonperiodic, its response can also be found in the frequency domain, just as when the excitation is periodic. We first find the Fourier transform of the excitation. Then we multiply this transform by the network function to obtain the Fourier transform of the response. Finally we find the response in the time domain by applying the inverse Fourier transform. This procedure is best illustrated by an example.

In the circuit of Figure 14.6, let

$$e_s(t) = \epsilon^{-at}u_{-1}(t)$$

From (14.20) we have

$$\mathcal{F}[e_s(t)] = \frac{1}{a+j\omega} \qquad (14.49)$$

The network function is

$$Y(j\omega) = \frac{1}{R+j\omega L} \qquad (14.50)$$

Hence the current $i(t)$ in the frequency domain is given by

$$\mathcal{F}[i(t)] = \frac{1}{(a+j\omega)(R+j\omega L)}$$

$$= \frac{1}{R-aL}\left[\frac{1}{a+j\omega} - \frac{1}{R/L+j\omega}\right] \qquad (14.51)$$

Comparing each term in (14.51) with the transform pair (14.19) and (14.20), we may conclude that

$$i(t) = \frac{1}{R-aL}[\epsilon^{-at} - \epsilon^{-(R/L)t}]u_{-1}(t) \qquad (14.52)$$

Although, in theory, most circuit problems can be analyzed this way, the Fourier-transform method is generally not the most convenient method of circuit analysis. Some quantities, such as the step function, do not have Fourier transforms. The variable $j\omega$ used in the transform is restricted to the j axis of the s plane. As we shall see later in Chapter 15, when we remove this restriction, we remove many limitations imposed on the Fourier transform. The resulting technique, known as the Laplace transform, is a much more suitable tool for circuit analysis.

The Fourier transform is nevertheless an extremely important concept that is indispensable in electrical engineering as well as in many other branches of engineering and science. In many applications this is the transform to use, especially when we must deal with a problem in terms of the real frequency (or, equivalently, the j axis of the s plane). The following sections provide some examples.

14.5 Ideal low-pass filters

From property 5 of the Fourier transform, we may conclude that, if a network function is

$$F(j\omega) = K\epsilon^{-j\omega T_d} \tag{14.53}$$

the spectra of this network would be as shown in Figure 14.8. Such a network

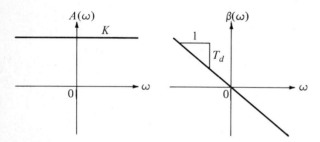

Figure 14.8 Characteristics of a distortionless network.

has a *constant gain*, since $|F(j\omega)| \equiv K$ and the signal of any frequency is amplified by the same factor, K, as it goes through the network. (The factor K may be greater or smaller than unity. If $K = 1$, the constant-gain feature is termed "all-pass.") Since $\arg[F(j\omega)] = -\omega T_d$, the phase lag of the network is proportional to ω. This property is known as *linear phase* and is depicted in Figure 14.8. The linear-phase property means that signals of all frequencies are delayed by the same amount of time—T_d. The combination of these two properties—constant gain and linear phase—results in the fact that, when any signal $x(t)$ is applied to such a network, the response is $x(t)$

amplified by K and delayed by T_d without any distortion, or

$$y(t) = Kx(t-T_d) \tag{14.54}$$

The proof of this is left as an exercise (Problem 14.20). We can realize such a transfer function by cascading a lossless transmission line to provide the delay and an amplifier of infinite bandwidth to provide the gain.

In the real world, of course, nothing is ever infinite. If we are interested in the effect of an amplifier that has only a finite bandwidth, we might pose the following problem: If it were possible to construct a network with the transfer voltage-ratio characteristics given in Figure 14.9, what would be the output voltage waveshape when the input voltage was a rectangular pulse, as shown in Figure 14.10?

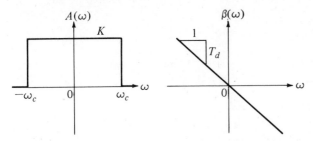

Figure 14.9 Idealized low-pass linear-phase characteristics.

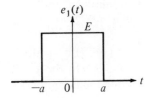

Figure 14.10 A rectangular pulse function.

The Fourier transform of the input voltage is

$$E_1 = \mathscr{F}[e_1(t)] = \frac{2E \sin a\omega}{\omega} \tag{14.55}$$

The Fourier transform of the output voltage is

$$E_2(j\omega) = 0, \qquad \omega < -\omega_c \qquad \text{and} \qquad \omega_c < \omega$$

$$E_2(j\omega) = \frac{2KE \sin a\omega}{\omega}\epsilon^{-jT_d\omega}, \qquad -\omega_c < \omega < \omega_c$$

The output is then

$$e_2(t) = \frac{K}{2\pi} \int_{-\omega_c}^{\omega_c} \frac{2E \sin a\omega}{\omega} \epsilon^{-jT_d\omega} \epsilon^{j\omega t} \, d\omega$$

$$= \frac{KE}{\pi} \int_{-\omega_c}^{\omega_c} \frac{\sin a\omega \, \epsilon^{j(t-T_d)\omega}}{\omega} \, d\omega$$

$$= \frac{KE}{\pi} \int_{-\omega_c}^{\omega_c} \frac{\sin a\omega \, \cos(t-T_d)\omega}{\omega} \, d\omega + j \frac{KE}{\pi} \int_{-\omega_c}^{\omega_c} \frac{\sin a\omega \, \sin(t-T_d)\omega}{\omega} \, d\omega$$

$$\tag{14.56}$$

The integrand in the first integral is an even function. Therefore the first integral may be evaluated between 0 and ω_c and then doubled. The second integral vanishes, since its integrand is an odd function. Hence we get

$$e_2(t) = \frac{2KE}{\pi} \int_0^{\omega_c} \frac{\sin a\omega \, \cos(t-T_d)\omega}{\omega} \, d\omega$$

$$= \frac{KE}{\pi} \int_0^{\omega_c} \frac{\sin(t-T_d+a)\omega}{\omega} \, d\omega - \frac{KE}{\pi} \int_0^{\omega_c} \frac{\sin(t-T_d-a)\omega}{\omega} d\omega$$

$$= \frac{KE}{\pi} \int_0^{(t-T_d+a)\omega_c} \frac{\sin u}{u} \, du - \frac{KE}{\pi} \int_0^{(t-T_d-a)\omega_c} \frac{\sin v}{v} \, dv$$

$$= \frac{KE}{\pi} \, \text{Si} \left[(t-T_d+a)\omega_c \right] - \frac{KE}{\pi} \, \text{Si} \left[(t-T_d-a)\omega_c \right] \tag{14.57}$$

The function $\text{Si}(x)$ is known as the *sine integral*, and is tabulated in Table 14.1. It is an odd function, with ripples about $\pi/2$ and $-\pi/2$, as shown in Figure 14.11.

We can obtain the plots of the two terms of $e_2(t)$ in (14.57) by shifting and modifying the scales of the plot of Figure 14.11. To locate the point at which the curves cross the horizontal axis, we set the individual arguments

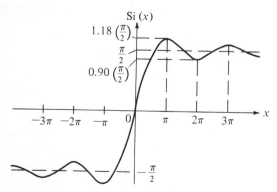

Figure 14.11 The sine-integral function.

Table **14.1**   Values of Si$(x) = \int_0^x \sin u/u \, du$

x	Si(x)	x	Si(x)
0	0	14.5	1.591
0.5	0.493	15.0	1.618
1.0	0.946	15.5	1.633
1.5	1.325	16.0	1.631
2.0	1.605	16.5	1.616
2.5	1.778	17.0	1.590
3.0	1.849	17.5	1.561
π	1.852	18.0	1.537
3.5	1.833	18.5	1.521
4.0	1.758	19.0	1.519
4.5	1.654	19.5	1.529
5.0	1.550	20.0	1.548
5.5	1.469	21.0	1.595
6.0	1.425	22.0	1.616
2π	1.418	23.0	1.595
6.5	1.422	24.0	1.555
7.0	1.455	25.0	1.531
7.5	1.511	26.0	1.545
8.0	1.574	27.0	1.580
8.5	1.630	28.0	1.605
9.0	1.665	29.0	1.597
3π	1.675	30.0	1.567
9.5	1.674	31.0	1.542
10.0	1.658	32.0	1.544
10.5	1.628	33.0	1.570
11.0	1.578	34.0	1.595
11.5	1.536	35.0	1.597
12.0	1.505	36.0	1.575
12.5	1.492	37.0	1.551
13.0	1.499	38.0	1.546
13.5	1.523	39.0	1.563
14.0	1.556	40.0	1.587

to zero. The plots of these two terms are shown in Figure 14.12, (a) and (b), and their sum is shown in Figure 14.12(c). The maximum overshoot is approximately 9% of the pulse. The similarity between $e_2(t)$ and $Ke_1(t - T_d)$, which is what $e_2(t)$ would be if ω_c were infinitely large, is indicated by the superposition of the two functions in Figure 14.12(c).

Figure 14.13 displays a series of plots showing the effects of $f_c = \omega_c/2\pi$ on the waveshape of $e_2(t)$. One might say, as a rule of thumb, that $f_c = 2/2a$

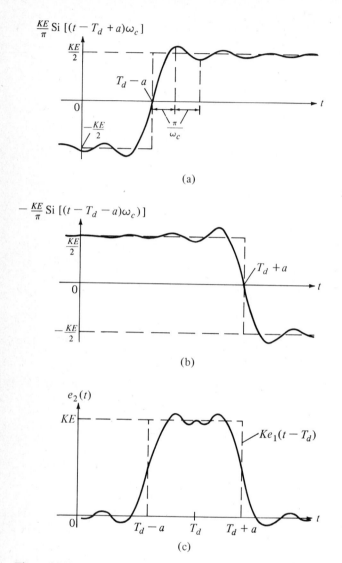

(a)

(b)

(c)

Figure 14.12 Values of the individual terms and the functional value of $e_2(t)$ given by (14.57).

is a dividing point. If f_c is well below this value, the output will cease to resemble the input. On the other hand, if f_c is well above this value, the output will be a good replica of the input. The exact dividing point, of course, will depend largely on the particular application requirement at hand.

The graphs of Figure 14.13 also reveal another phenomenon. As f_c is increased, the ripples that occur near the pulse edges are pushed closer together. The amount of ripple is, however, unchanged. The maximum over-

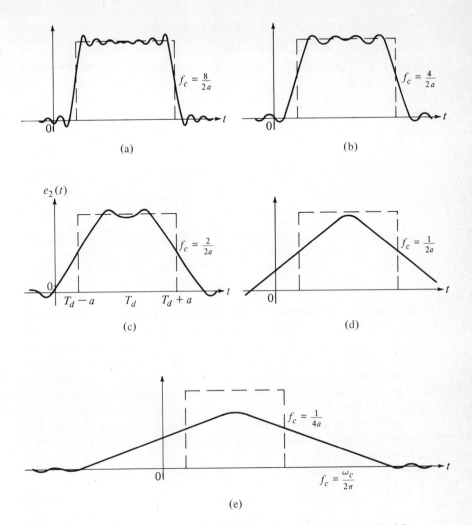

Figure 14.13 Effects of filter cutoff frequency on the output of an idealized low-pass linear-phase network with a rectangular pulse input.

shoot remains at approximately 9% of the pulse height. This is similar to the Gibbs phenomenon in the truncation of the Fourier series at a point of discontinuity. The slopes of the main rising and declining portions of $e_2(t)$ are directly proportional to the value of f_c.

Another phenomenon in this analysis is the fact that $e_2(t)$ may be nonzero for $t < -a$. This defies all physical reasoning. How could an output occur before an input is applied? Such a system is noncausal. We must have done something wrong. The fallacy is in the assumed frequency characteristics of Figure 14.10. Such a system cannot be realized with real-world components.

14.6 Modulation theorem and amplitude modulation

Another property of the Fourier transform is known as the *modulation theorem*: If the Fourier transform of $f(t)$ is $G(\omega)$, then the Fourier transform of $f(t) \cos \omega_0 t$ is

$$\tfrac{1}{2}G(\omega - \omega_0) + \tfrac{1}{2}G(\omega + \omega_0)$$

PROOF

$$\mathscr{F}\left[f(t) \cos \omega_0 t\right] = \int_{-\infty}^{\infty} f(t) \cos \omega_0 t \, \epsilon^{-j\omega t} \, dt$$

$$= \frac{1}{2} \int_{-\infty}^{\infty} f(t) \epsilon^{j\omega_0 t} \epsilon^{-j\omega t} \, dt + \frac{1}{2} \int_{-\infty}^{\infty} f(t) \epsilon^{-j\omega_0 t} \epsilon^{-j\omega t} \, dt$$

$$= \frac{1}{2} \int_{-\infty}^{\infty} f(t) \epsilon^{-j(\omega - \omega_0)t} \, dt + \frac{1}{2} \int_{-\infty}^{\infty} f(t) \epsilon^{-j(\omega + \omega_0)t} \, dt$$

$$= \tfrac{1}{2}G(\omega - \omega_0) + \tfrac{1}{2}G(\omega + \omega_0) \tag{14.58}$$

The phenomenon described by the modulation theorem is illustrated in Figure 14.14. We shall assume that $f(t)$ is band-limited. That is to say, its Fourier transform $G(\omega)$ is zero for $|\omega| > \omega_c$, as shown in Figure 14.14(a). We shall also assume that $\omega_0 > \omega_c$. The modulation theorem states that the modulation process, in effect, separates $G(\omega)$ into two halves and relocates one of them ω_0 above and the other ω_0 below the origin. This is illustrated in Figure 14.14(b). If the carrier frequency is doubled, the two halves of the frequency spectrum are separated further apart, as shown in Figure 14.14(c). Figure 14.14(d) shows what happens when $\omega_0 < \omega_c$—the two halves begin to interfere with each other.

As one of the applications of this phenomenon, consider

$$f(t) = 1 + ms(t) \tag{14.59}$$

Here $s(t)$ is a normalized signal with a maximum value of unity in either direction, as shown in Figure 14.15(a). The factor m is known as the *modulation index*. Figure 14.15(b) shows a modulation index of 0.5, and Figure 14.15(c) a modulation index of unity.

This modulation scheme is known as amplitude modulation—specifically, *ordinary amplitude modulation*. One application of the scheme is to transmit voice signals [for which the typical frequency of $s(t)$ is 2 kHz] at radio frequencies (whose f_0 may range from 500 kHz to 50 MHz). It is most revealing to view this practice through the Fourier transform. The modulation process converts the low-frequency signal, which is not suitable for long-range transmission, into a frequency range suitable for transmission. This is seen in Figure 14.14(b) and (c). The frequencies to be transmitted are mostly in the neighborhood of the carrier frequency. At the receiving end,

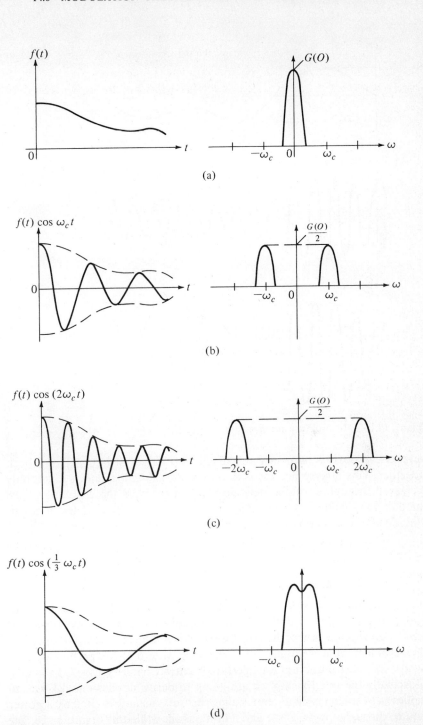

Figure 14.14 The amplitude modulation and its spectra in the frequency domain.

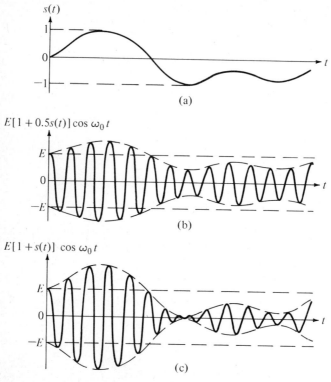

Figure 14.15 The ordinary amplitude modulation.

a reverse process is necessary to put the two halves of the spectrum back together. This reverse process is known as *demodulation*, and is commonly achieved through envelope detection, which recovers the envelope of the modulation signal $s(t)$. One simple method is to use the peak-detector circuit described in Chapter 6 (see Figure 6.24).

14.7 Far-field pattern of an aperture antenna

So far, we have limited our applications of the Fourier transform to the link between the time domain and the frequency domain. We shall now describe an application of the transform that is not tied to these two domains. The problem is the calculation of the far-field pattern of an aperture antenna whose field distribution at the aperture is known.

Actually the relationship we are going to derive applies equally well to optics as to antennas. In antennas, the aperture is usually excited by a power source through a wave-guide and a horn, as illustrated in Figure 14.16. We know the distribution of $E(x')$ [or $H(x')$] at the aperture, and we can usually

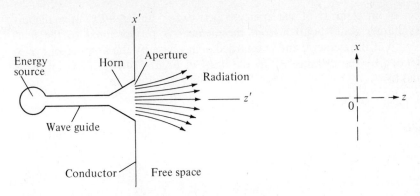

Figure 14.16 Far-field pattern of an aperture antenna.

assume that this distribution is the same as it would be if the horn continued on indefinitely. We want to know the radiation pattern $E(x)$ along an axis perpendicular to the axis of the horn at a distance from the aperture.

The analogous problem in optics is depicted in Figure 14.17. A laser (monochromatic) light source illuminates a screen in which there is an opening. We want to know the illumination pattern on another screen at a distance from the opening.

In both problems, we assume that there is no variation along the direction perpendicular to the paper—the y direction. The problem is a one-dimensional one. It is also assumed that the opening is at least several wavelengths across, so that the radiation pattern is highly directive.

We first assume that the electric field at the aperture is given by

$$E(x') = f(x')e^{j\phi(x')} \tag{14.60}$$

which is the complex amplitude of the quantity

$$E(x',t) = f(x')\cos[\omega t + \phi(x')] = \text{Re}[E(x')e^{j\omega t}] \tag{14.61}$$

where ω is the angular frequency of the source. By Huygens' principle, the

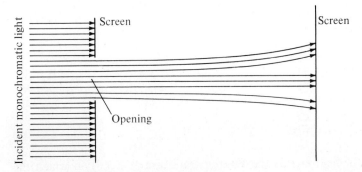

Figure 14.17 Optical analog of the aperture antenna.

effect of an element of the aperture between x' and $x'+dx'$ at a distant (Fraunhofer zone) point r from the element is proportional to the field strength at the element, and is retarded ω in phase by the number of cycles extended by the distance r. On the basis of Figure 14.18, this quantity is equal to

$$E(x')\,dx'\epsilon^{-j(2\pi r/\lambda)} = E(x')\,dx'\epsilon^{-j\beta r}$$

where $\lambda = c/f = 2\pi c/\omega$ is the wavelength, c is the speed of light, and $\beta = 2\pi/\lambda$ is the phase constant.

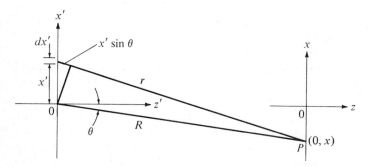

Figure 14.18 Coordinate system used to derive the far field of an aperture antenna.

At a distant point P from $x' = 0$, $z' = 0$, and for small θ, we may make the following approximation.

$$r = R + x' \sin \theta$$

The distance from points on the x axis to points at the aperture may be regarded as constant. In other words, as x' and x (and therefore $\sin \theta$) vary, we may assume that R is constant. The field at any point along the x axis is given by

$$E_x(\beta \sin \theta) = \int_{-\infty}^{\infty} f(x')\,\epsilon^{j\phi(x')}\epsilon^{-j\beta R}\epsilon^{-j(\beta \sin \theta)x'}\,dx' \tag{14.62}$$

Redefining, we get

$$E_1(x') = f(x')\,\epsilon^{j[\phi(x') - \beta R]} \tag{14.63}$$

and (14.62) becomes

$$E_x(\beta \sin \theta) = \int_{-\infty}^{\infty} E_1(x')\,\epsilon^{-j(\beta \sin \theta)x'}\,dx' \tag{14.64}$$

We see that the field at P is the Fourier transform of $E_1(x')$, in which the variable in the transformed domain is $\beta \sin \theta$.

The analogy between the time-frequency analysis and the antenna radiation pattern is now apparent, if we compare the following quantities:

Time (t) — Aperture distance (x')
Angular frequency (ω) — Angular variable $(\beta \sin \theta)$
Time-domain function $[f(t)]$ — Modified aperture field distribution $[E_1(x')]$
Frequency spectrum $[G(\omega)]$ — Angular radiation pattern $[E_x(\beta \sin \theta)]$

The Fourier transform problems worked out earlier in this chapter can readily be interpreted to apply to certain antenna problems. Figure 14.19 shows three examples. Figure 14.19(a) gives the far-field radiation pattern of an aperture that is uniformly illuminated. This is analogous to the $f(t)$-$G(\omega)$ pair of Figure 14.1.

Since the Fourier transform of an impulse function is unity, we can expect a uniform radiation pattern from a very small aperture. This is illustrated in Figure 14.19(b).

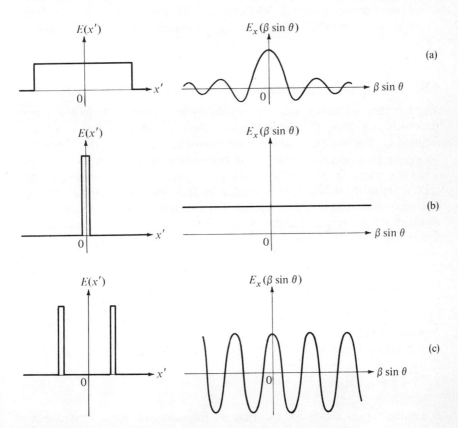

Figure 14.19 Expected far-field patterns of three aperture antennas.

The Fourier transform of a pair of impulses is

$$\mathscr{F}\left[u_0(t-t_0)+u_0(t+t_0)\right] = \epsilon^{j\omega t_0} + \epsilon^{-j\omega t_0}$$

$$= 2\cos\omega t_0 \qquad (14.65)$$

Hence we can expect the radiation pattern from two small apertures to be sinusoidal, as illustrated in Figure 14.19(c).

If we carry this analogy to the inverse Fourier transform, the latter enables us to obtain the illumination pattern at the aperture for a given radiation pattern desired in a distant region. The necessary field pattern at the aperture can then be approximately produced by transmission lines feeding an array of dipoles. This technique is known as *aperture synthesis*.

In our exposition of the one-dimensional aperture problem, the aperture was assumed to be infinitely long and the field was assumed to be invariant in the y direction. Most practical aperture antennas have finite dimensions in both the x and y directions. A generalization of the Fourier transform to two dimensions is necessary. For a large aperture, it is no longer adequate to assume that we know the field over the plane of the aperture. In these situations, we generally obtain the radiation pattern by other techniques.

14.8 The limiting cases of some Fourier transforms

The fact that a function must be absolutely integrable to have a Fourier transform is a rather disappointing restriction on the transform as a technique. For the sake of argument, one may make a case for the transform by saying that no practical signal is ever infinite in strength or duration. Thus one might say that all physical signals are absolutely integrable. But this is arguable at best. As a matter of fact, the usual formulation of analysis problems is just the opposite. For example, when we talk about the ac steady-state analysis of a circuit, we consider the sinusoidal excitation to last indefinitely—from $t = -\infty$ to $t = \infty$. Thus we neglect the transient, if any.

From the practical standpoint, then, there should be little difference between a signal that lasts "long enough" and a signal that lasts "from here to eternity". Common sense tells us that the two signals should behave just like each other. Why then should mathematics make such a fine distinction between them?

The answer is that it doesn't. The condition in (14.18) which states that

$$\int_{-\infty}^{\infty} |f(t)|\,dt < \infty \qquad (14.66)$$

is a *sufficient* condition for the Fourier transform to exist. That doesn't mean that a Fourier transform is automatically ruled out for a function that is not absolutely integrable. Recall that the Fourier transform of $f(t)$ exists if

$$\int_{-\infty}^{\infty} f(t)\epsilon^{-j\omega t}\, dt \tag{14.67}$$

exists. When $|f(t)|$ is not absolutely integrable, the integral of (14.67) becomes an improper integral. Such an integral may or may not converge. When it does, the Fourier transform of $f(t)$ still exists. In general, improper integrals should be handled with more care. Let us now look at several examples that are of engineering significance.

1 *The Fourier transform of a constant*   Starting with the Fourier transform of the unit impulse, we have

$$\mathscr{F}\,[u_0(t)] = 1 \tag{14.68}$$

It would seem appropriate to say that the inverse Fourier transform of $G(\omega) = 1$ is a unit impulse, or

$$\mathscr{F}^{-1}[1] = \frac{1}{2\pi}\int_{-\infty}^{\infty} \epsilon^{j\omega t}\, d\omega \triangleq u_0(t) \tag{14.69}$$

We cannot evaluate this integral in the usual manner. The equal sign is "forced" upon the two quantities on each side of the $\triangleq$ sign because they are one and the same. Admittedly this type of practice can be dangerous, but there are so many examples tending to enforce this equality that it is difficult not to believe it. For our purposes, the $\triangleq$ sign in (14.69) should be interpreted as "defined to equal."

Interchanging t and ω in (14.69), we get

$$u_0(\omega) = \frac{1}{2\pi}\int_{-\infty}^{\infty} \epsilon^{j\omega t}\, dt \tag{14.70}$$

Replacing ω with $-\omega$, we have

$$u_0(-\omega) = \frac{1}{2\pi}\int_{-\infty}^{\infty} \epsilon^{-j\omega t}\, dt \tag{14.71}$$

But $u_0(\omega) = u_0(-\omega)$. Hence we get

$$\mathscr{F}\,[1] = \int_{-\infty}^{\infty} 1\epsilon^{-j\omega t}\, dt = 2\pi u_0(\omega) \tag{14.72}$$

Thus the Fourier transform of $f(t) = 1$ is an impulse function of strength 2π located at $\omega = 0$. This result makes sense. The function $f(t) = 1$ is a dc quantity. Its frequency spectrum $\alpha(n\omega_0)$ will have just one line at $\omega = 0$. When we define $G(n\omega_0) = 2\pi\alpha(n\omega_0)/\omega_0$ and as $\omega_0 \to 0$, $G(\omega)$ becomes infinite at $\omega = 0$, but is still zero elsewhere.

2 *The Fourier transform of a unit step* A unit step can be separated into an even and an odd part, as shown in Figure 14.20.

$$f_1(t) = \tfrac{1}{2}, \qquad f_2(t) = \tfrac{1}{2}u_{-1}(t) - \tfrac{1}{2}u_{-1}(-t) \tag{14.73}$$

From (14.72) we have

$$\mathscr{F}[f_1(t)] = \pi u_0(t) \tag{14.74}$$

We shall now show that the Fourier transform of $f_2(t)$ is $1/j\omega$.

$$\mathscr{F}^{-1}\left[\frac{1}{j\omega}\right] = \frac{1}{2\pi}\int_{-\infty}^{\infty}\frac{1}{j\omega}e^{j\omega t}\,d\omega = \frac{1}{2\pi}\int_{-\infty}^{\infty}\frac{\cos\omega t + j\sin\omega t}{j\omega}\,d\omega$$

$$= \frac{1}{2\pi}\int_{-\infty}^{\infty}\frac{\sin\omega t}{\omega}\,d\omega$$

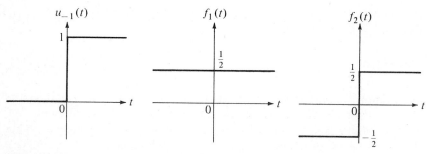

Figure 14.20 Even and odd parts of a unit step function.

The last integral is the complete sine integral with a parameter t. When t is positive, the integral is equal to π. When t is negative, the integral is equal to $-\pi$. Hence

$$\mathscr{F}^{-1}\left[\frac{1}{j\omega}\right] = f_2(t)$$

Thus

$$\mathscr{F}[u_{-1}(t)] = \pi u_0(\omega) + \frac{1}{j\omega} \tag{14.75}$$

Earlier in this chapter we mentioned that

$$u_{-1}(t) = \lim_{a\to 0}[\epsilon^{-at}u_{-1}(t)] \tag{14.76}$$

Since

$$\mathscr{F}[\epsilon^{-at}u_{-1}(t)] = \frac{1}{a+j\omega} \tag{14.77}$$

it would seem that

$$\mathscr{F}[u_{-1}(t)] = \lim_{a \to 0}\{\mathscr{F}[\epsilon^{-at}u_{-1}(t)]\} = \lim_{a \to 0}\left(\frac{1}{a+j\omega}\right) = \frac{1}{j\omega} \tag{14.78}$$

We now see why this is incorrect.

Actually this incorrectness is not in the notion related to (14.76). Rather, it stems from the last step in passing the limit in (14.78). Rationalizing, we get

$$\frac{1}{a+j\omega} = \frac{a}{a^2+\omega^2} - \frac{j\omega}{a^2+\omega^2} \tag{14.79}$$

The two terms are the real and imaginary parts of $1/(a+j\omega)$. The real part has the property that, whatever a is, the area under it is a constant, or

$$\int_{-\infty}^{\infty} \frac{a}{a^2+\omega^2}\, d\omega = \tan^{-1}\frac{\omega}{a}\Big|_{-\infty}^{\infty} = \pi \tag{14.80}$$

Figure 14.21 shows the plots of this function for several values of a. From this trend, we see that as a becomes smaller, the peak becomes taller and narrower. In the limit, we have

$$\lim_{a \to 0}\left[\frac{a}{a^2+\omega^2}\right] = \pi u_0(\omega) \tag{14.81}$$

Thus the last step in (14.78) should read

$$\lim_{a \to 0}\left[\frac{a}{a-j\omega}\right] = \pi u_0(\omega) + \frac{1}{j\omega} \tag{14.82}$$

which checks with (14.75).

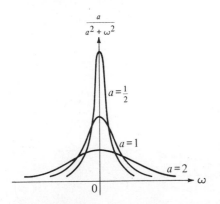

Figure 14.21 The function $a/(a^2+\omega^2)$.

3 *The Fourier transform of a sinusoid*

$$\mathscr{F}[\cos \omega_0 t] = \int_{-\infty}^{\infty} \cos \omega_0 t \, \epsilon^{-j\omega t} \, dt$$

$$= \frac{1}{2} \int_{-\infty}^{\infty} \epsilon^{-j(\omega - \omega_0)t} \, dt + \frac{1}{2} \int_{-\infty}^{\infty} \epsilon^{-j(\omega + \omega_0)t} \, dt$$

$$= \pi [u_0(\omega - \omega_0) + u_0(\omega + \omega_0)] \qquad (14.83)$$

This transform pair is shown in Figure 14.22.

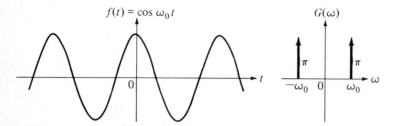

Figure 14.22 The Fourier transform of a sinusoid.

4 *The Fourier transform of a general periodic function* For a general periodic function with its Fourier series in complex form, namely,

$$f(t) = \sum_{n=-\infty}^{\infty} \alpha_n \, \epsilon^{jn\omega_0 t}$$

its transform is

$$\mathscr{F}[f(t)] = \sum_{n=-\infty}^{\infty} 2\pi \alpha_n \, u_0(\omega - n\omega_0) \qquad (14.84)$$

which is an infinite train of impulses.

Problems

14.1 Find the Fourier transforms of the time functions in Figure P14.1.

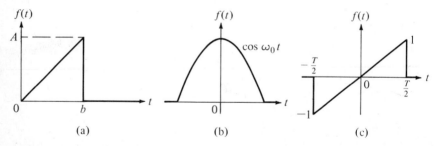

(a)　　　　　　(b)　　　　　　(c)

Figure P14.1 (continued on page 461)

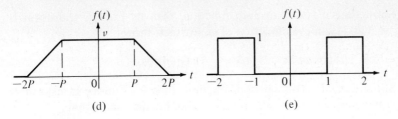

(d)   (e)

Figure P14.1 (continued)

14.2 Find the Fourier transforms of: (a) $\epsilon^{-a|t|}$; (b) $te^{-at}u_{-1}(t)$; (c) $\epsilon^{-at}u_{-1}(t)-\epsilon^{at}u_{-1}(-t)$; (d) $1/(a^2+t^2)$. (In each case, a is real and positive.)

14.3 The function

$$G(\omega) = \left[\frac{1-\epsilon^{-j\omega}}{j\omega}\right]^3$$

is the Fourier transform of the pulse $f(t)$ of Figure P14.3(a). Find the Fourier series coefficients a_1 and b_1 of the periodic function $f_p(t)$ of Figure P14.3(b).

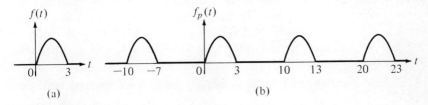

(a)   (b)

Figure P14.3

14.4 Given that $G_1(\omega)$ and $G_2(\omega)$ are the Fourier transforms of $f_1(t)$ and $f_2(t)$ and $G_1(\omega)$ and $G_2(\omega)$ are both real, prove that

$$\mathscr{F}\,[f_1(t)f_2(t)] = \frac{1}{2\pi}\int_{-\infty}^{\infty} G_1(\lambda)\,G_2(\omega-\lambda)\,d\lambda$$

14.5 Suppose that the voltage $e_s(t)$ of Figure P14.5 assumes the time variation of $e_1(t)$ in Figure 14.10. Find the current $i(t)$ from its Fourier transform.

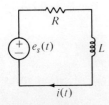

Figure P14.5

14.6 Show that, if $f(t)$ is an even function, then its Fourier transform is purely real and is an even function of ω. Further, show that

$$G(\omega) = 2 \int_0^\infty f(t) \cos \omega t \, dt, \qquad f(t) = \frac{1}{\pi} \int_0^\infty G(\omega) \cos \omega t \, d\omega$$

14.7 Show that, if $f(t)$ is an odd function, then its Fourier transform is purely imaginary and is an odd function of ω. Further, show that

$$G(\omega) = -2j \int_0^\infty f(t) \sin \omega t \, dt, \qquad f(t) = -\frac{1}{j\pi} \int_0^\infty G(\omega) \sin \omega t \, d\omega$$

14.8 Given that $|G(\omega)| = \epsilon^{-|\omega/2\pi|}$, find $f(t)$, (a) if $f(t)$ is an even function, and (b) if $f(t)$ is an odd function.

14.9 For the LTI network of Figure 14.5(b), show that

$$\int_{-\infty}^\infty y(t) \, dt = \int_{-\infty}^\infty x(t) \, dt \int_{-\infty}^\infty h(t) \, dt.$$

14.10 For the LTI system of Figure 14.5(b), show that, if

$$\int_{-\infty}^\infty x(t) \, dt = 0, \qquad \text{then} \qquad \int_{-\infty}^\infty y(t) \, dt = 0.$$

14.11 A unit rectangular voltage pulse with a duration of 50 microseconds (μs) is applied to an amplifier with flat response up to f_c Hz (all frequencies above f_c are cut off entirely) and a constant time delay of 30 μs. Suppose that the amplification $A(\omega)$ inside the pass band is 1, and $f_c = 100$ kHz. Plot the output voltage.

14.12 Find the Fourier transform of $i_1(t)$ for $e(t) = \epsilon^{-at} u_{-1}(t)$ in Figure P14.12.

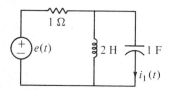

Figure P14.12

14.13 Find the network function as a function of ω of a system whose impulse response is $h(t) = |t|^{-1/2} u_{-1}(t)$.

14.14 If the Fourier transform of $f(t)$ is $G(\omega)$, what is the transform of $f(t) \sin \omega_c t$?

14.15 Let $f(t)$ be a single cycle of sinusoid, or

$$f(t) = \cos 2\pi t \left[u_{-1}(t + \tfrac{1}{2}) - u_{-1}(t - \tfrac{1}{2}) \right]$$

Sketch the frequency spectrum of (a) $f_1(t) = f(t) \cos 40\pi t$; (b) $f_2(t) = [1 + f(t)] \cos 40\pi t$; (c) $f_3(t) = [1 + \tfrac{1}{2} f(t)] \cos 40\pi t$.

14.16 The voltage signal $e(t) = (1+m \cos t) \cos 100t$ is applied to a series RLC circuit, which is tuned to the carrier $(LC = 10^{-4})$ and has a Q of 100. Calculate the steady-state voltage across R. What is the modulation index of this voltage?

14.17 In the circuit of Figure P14.17,

$$e(t) = [1+s(t)] \cos \omega_0 t, \qquad |s(t)| < 1$$

Assuming the diode to be ideal, show that $v_R(t)$ has a component that is proportional to $s(t)$ and evaluate this component.

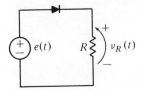

Figure P14.17

14.18 Find the Fourier transform of: (a) $f(t) = \sin \omega_0 t$; (b) $f(t) = \cos \omega_0 t u_{-1}(t)$; (c) $f(t) = \sin \omega_0 t u_{-1}(t)$; (d) $f(t) = \epsilon^{-t^2/2\sigma^2}$; (e) $f(t) = \cos \omega_1 t \cos \omega_2 t$; (f) $f(t) = \cos \omega_1 t \cos \omega_2 t u_{-1}(t)$.

14.19 Show that (14.46) and (14.47) are identical.

14.20 Show that, if $x(t)$ is applied to a network whose transfer function is given by (14.53), the output of the network is given by (14.54).

15 | LAPLACE TRANSFORM AND APPLICATIONS

In this chapter, we shall further generalize the Fourier transform in order to develop the concept of the two-sided Laplace transform. Once this concept has been established, we shall specialize it to the one-sided Laplace transform. System analysis using these two transforms will be devloped as appropriate.

One major shortcoming of the Fourier-transform technique of system analysis is the fact that some time functions do not have Fourier transforms. Functions such as t, t^2, and ϵ^{at} $(a \neq 0)$ are not Fourier-transformable. Even the functions discussed in Section 14.8 are only marginally transformable. Their transforms must be represented by impulse functions, so that in the frequency domain these quantities are theoretical rather than physical.

Part of the reason why some functions are not Fourier-transformable is the fact that the frequency variable used in the Fourier transform is restricted to the j axis of the s plane. When this restriction is removed, more functions become transformable. If we extend the Fourier transform by considering the behavior of a function on a contour away from the j axis, this leads us to the *Laplace transform*.

15.1 The two-sided Laplace transform

Suppose that we multiply a given function $f(t)$ by another function $\epsilon^{-\sigma t}$, in which σ is real and constant, and which is chosen to ensure that

$$f(t)\epsilon^{-\sigma t} \tag{15.1}$$

is Fourier-transformable. In other words,

$$\int_{-\infty}^{\infty} f(t)\,\epsilon^{-\sigma t}\epsilon^{-j\omega t}\,dt = F(\sigma+j\omega) \tag{15.2}$$

exists. Integral (15.2) is the Fourier transform of $f(t)\epsilon^{-\sigma t}$. It can also be considered as another transform of $f(t)$. This new transform is the *two-sided (or bilateral) Laplace transform* of $f(t)$. It differs from the Fourier transform only in the additional part, σ, wherever the variable $j\omega$ appears.

These two transforms are identical in form, but the parameters used in them are slightly different. In the Fourier transform, the parameter is $j\omega$. In the Laplace transform, the parameter is $s = \sigma + j\omega$. Hence we can regard the Laplace transform as an extension of the Fourier transform. Instead of limiting the variable s to purely imaginary values, we now allow it to be complex, but *with a fixed real part*. Conversely, we may regard the Fourier transform as a restricted case of the Laplace transform: $\sigma = 0$.

Just like the Fourier transform, which tells us the relative frequency content of a function along the j axis, the two-sided Laplace transform gives us the relative frequency content of the function along a line parallel to the j axis and σ away from it, as shown in Figure 15.1. The notion of the time–frequency relationship remains valid. In principle, the various schemes of analysis of system problems in the frequency domain are also usable in this new transform.

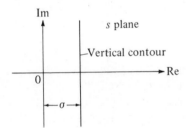

Figure 15.1 The complex frequency plane and the vertical contour of the Laplace transform.

To go back from the frequency domain to the time domain, we observe that, since

$$\mathscr{F}^{-1}[F(\sigma+j\omega)] = \frac{1}{2\pi} \int_{-\infty}^{\infty} F(\sigma+j\omega)\epsilon^{j\omega t}\, d\omega$$

$$= \frac{\epsilon^{-\sigma t}}{2\pi} \int_{-\infty}^{\infty} F(\sigma+j\omega)\epsilon^{\sigma t}\epsilon^{j\omega t}\, d\omega$$

$$= f(t)\epsilon^{-\sigma t} \tag{15.3}$$

we have

$$f(t) = \frac{1}{2\pi} \int_{-\infty}^{\infty} F(\sigma+j\omega)\epsilon^{(\sigma+j\omega)t}\, d\omega$$

$$= \frac{1}{2\pi j} \int_{\sigma-j\infty}^{\sigma+j\infty} F(s)\epsilon^{st}\, ds \tag{15.4}$$

Integral (15.4) is a contour integral whose contour is a vertical path, as shown in Figure 15.1. (Such a contour is known as the Bromwich contour.) This transform is called the *inverse Laplace transform.*

The value of σ that gives us the two-sided Laplace transform of a function depends on the function. The term $\epsilon^{-\sigma t}$ itself is unbounded at one of the two ends of the t axis. Hence it is quite clear that, unless the effect of this unboundedness of $\epsilon^{-\sigma t}$ is counteracted by $f(t)$ itself, integral (15.2) will not exist. Generally, it is extremely important to specify the range of values of σ. The region in which the vertical contour may lie is known as the *region of convergence* of the transform. This can best be illustrated by a few examples.

EXAMPLE 1   For the function of Figure 15.2(a),

$$f(t) = \epsilon^{-at}u_{-1}(t) \tag{15.5}$$

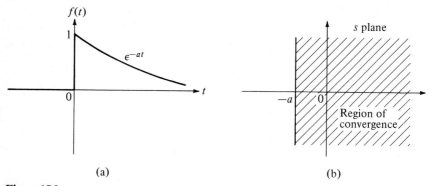

(a)   (b)

Figure 15.2

Its two-sided Laplace transform is

$$F(\sigma+j\omega) = \int_0^\infty \epsilon^{-at}\epsilon^{-\sigma t}\epsilon^{-j\omega t}\,dt = \int_0^\infty \epsilon^{(-a-\sigma-j\omega)t}\,dt$$

$$= -\frac{\epsilon^{(-a-\sigma-j\omega)t}}{a+\sigma+j\omega}\bigg|_{t=0}^{t=\infty} \tag{15.6}$$

When $t = \infty$ is substituted into the integrated function, the latter is only defined (equal to zero) if $-a-\sigma < 0$. If we let $\sigma+j\omega = s$, (15.6) becomes

$$F(\sigma+j\omega) = \frac{1}{a+s}, \qquad \text{if } \sigma > -a \tag{15.7}$$

The function in (15.7) gives us the frequency content of $f(t) = \epsilon^{-at}u_{-1}(t)$ along any vertical path to the right of $s = -a$.

Conversely, if we take the inverse Laplace transform of (15.7), we have

$$\frac{1}{2\pi j}\int_{\sigma-j\infty}^{\sigma+j\infty} \frac{1}{a+s}\epsilon^{st}\,ds = \epsilon^{-at}u_{-1}(t), \qquad \sigma > -a \tag{15.8}$$

The integral in (15.8) may be evaluated along any vertical path, but it must lie to the right of $s = -a$. We indicate this fact by stating that the region of convergence of this transform is the shaded area of Figure 15.2(b).

EXAMPLE 2   For the function of Figure 15.3(a),

$$f(t) = -\epsilon^{-at} u_{-1}(-t) \tag{15.9}$$

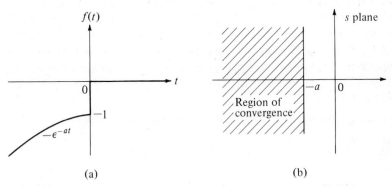

(a)   (b)

Figure 15.3

Its two-sided Laplace transform is

$$F(\sigma+j\omega) = -\int_{-\infty}^{\infty} \epsilon^{-at}\epsilon^{-\sigma t}\epsilon^{-j\omega t}\, dt$$

$$= \frac{\epsilon^{-(a+\sigma+j\omega)t}}{a+\sigma+j\omega}\bigg|_{-\infty}^{0} \tag{15.10}$$

The integrated function is not defined for $t = -\infty$ unless $a+\sigma < 0$. If $a+\sigma < 0$, then the integrated function vanishes at $t = -\infty$. Hence

$$F(\sigma+j\omega) = \frac{1}{a+s}, \qquad \text{if } \sigma < -a \tag{15.11}$$

Now we have

$$\frac{1}{2\pi j}\int_{\sigma-j\infty}^{\sigma+j\infty} \frac{1}{a+s}\epsilon^{st}\, ds = -\epsilon^{-at}u_{-1}(-t) \tag{15.12}$$

Equation (15.12) stands if $\sigma < -a$. The region of convergence for this transform pair is to the left of $s = -a$, as shown in Figure 15.3(b).

The preceding examples point out a few things about the Laplace transform. First we see that the value of σ depends on the function. For example, in the transform of $\epsilon^{-at}u_{-1}(t)$, σ may be negative, say $\sigma = -a/2$. The term $\epsilon^{-\sigma t} = \epsilon^{at/2}$ becomes unbounded as $t \to \infty$. But $f(t)$ itself tends to zero faster than $\epsilon^{-\sigma t}$. The integral of (15.6) is still defined.

On the other hand, $-\epsilon^{-at}u_{-1}(-t)$ is unbounded as $t \to -\infty$. So we must choose a value for σ larger than a, so that $\epsilon^{-\sigma t}$ will tend to zero faster than ϵ^{-at}, to be sure that (15.10) is defined.

Second, the transforms of $\epsilon^{-at}u_{-1}(t)$ and $-\epsilon^{-at}u_{-1}(-t)$ have the same form, but their regions of convergence are different. This becomes clear if we look at their inverse transforms. The integrals of (15.8) and (15.12) are identical in form. But their corresponding contours (values of σ) are different. When we choose a contour to the right of $s = -a$, the integral gives us $\epsilon^{-at}u_{-1}(t)$. When we choose a contour to the left of $s = -a$, the integral gives us $-\epsilon^{-at}u_{-1}(-t)$. This fact illustrates how essential it is to associate each transform with a valid σ. When we go outside the region of convergence, either the transform does not exist or the inverse transform gives us a different (wrong) time function.

EXAMPLE 3 We may write the function of Figure 15.4(a) as

$$f(t) = \epsilon^{-a|t|}, \qquad a > 0 \tag{15.13}$$

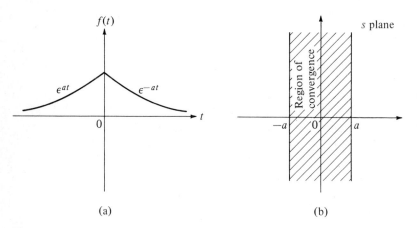

(a)   (b)

Figure 15.4

Its two-sided Laplace transform is

$$F(s) = \int_{-\infty}^{0} \epsilon^{at}\epsilon^{-st}\,dt + \int_{0}^{\infty} \epsilon^{-at}\epsilon^{-st}\,dt$$

$$= -\frac{\epsilon^{-(s-a)t}}{s-a}\Big|_{-\infty}^{0} - \frac{\epsilon^{-(s+a)t}}{a+s}\Big|_{0}^{\infty}$$

$$= -\frac{\epsilon^{-(\sigma-a)t}\epsilon^{j\omega t}}{s-a}\Big|_{-\infty}^{0} - \frac{\epsilon^{-(a+\sigma)t}\epsilon^{j\omega t}}{a+s}\Big|_{0}^{\infty} \tag{15.14}$$

The first integral exists only if $\sigma < a$. The second integral exists only if

$\sigma > -a$. If σ satisfies both inequalities, we have

$$F(s) = -\frac{1}{s-a} + \frac{1}{a+s} = \frac{2a}{a^2 - s^2} \qquad (15.15)$$

The region of convergence of (15.15) is

$$-a < \sigma < a \qquad (15.16)$$

which is illustrated in Figure 15.4(b).

EXAMPLE 4   The function

$$f(t) = -2(\sinh at)u_{-1}(t) \qquad (15.17)$$

is illustrated in Figure 15.5(a). Its transform may be written as

$$F(s) = \int_0^\infty (\epsilon^{-at} - \epsilon^{at}) \epsilon^{-st}\, dt$$

$$= \int_0^\infty \epsilon^{-at}\epsilon^{-st}\, dt - \int_0^\infty \epsilon^{at}\epsilon^{-st}\, dt$$

$$= \left[\frac{\epsilon^{-(a+\sigma)t}\epsilon^{-j\omega t}}{a+s} - \frac{\epsilon^{(a-\sigma)t}\epsilon^{-j\omega t}}{a-s} \right]_0^\infty \qquad (15.18)$$

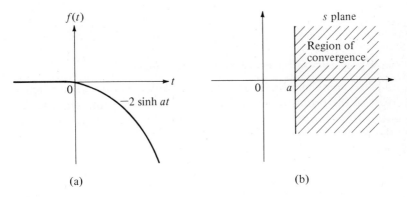

(a)   (b)

Figure 15.5

The first integral is defined if $\sigma > -a$. The second integral is defined if $\sigma > a$. Hence we get

$$F(s) = \frac{1}{a+s} + \frac{1}{a-s} = \frac{2a}{a^2 - s^2}, \qquad \sigma > a \qquad (15.19)$$

The region of convergence is shown in Figure 15.5(b). A comparison can again be made between (15.19) and (15.15): The two transforms have the same form, but their regions of convergence are different.

Another observation can also be made from the preceding examples. The factor $\epsilon^{-\sigma t}$ is a damping factor, which when multiplied with $f(t)$ makes the product absolutely integrable. Thus, if $f(t)$ becomes unbounded as $t \to \infty$ (as in Example 4), σ ought to be positive to offset this unboundedness. The larger σ is, the faster $\epsilon^{-\sigma t}f(t)$ approaches zero, and the "safer" the integration becomes. If $f(t)$ becomes unbounded as $t \to -\infty$ (as in Example 2), σ ought to be negative so that $\epsilon^{-\sigma t}f(t)$ will be held down, so to speak. The more negative σ becomes, the "safer" the integration will be. When $f(t)$ tends to zero at both ends of the axis (as in Example 3), σ can be either positive or negative as long as it does not become too large in magnitude ($|\sigma| < |a|$). Thus, heuristically, we may expect that, if $f(t)$ either decays exponentially (or faster) or vanishes identically as $t \to \infty$, the region of convergence will extend leftward. On the other hand, if $f(t)$ either decays exponentially (or faster) or vanishes identically as $t \to -\infty$, the region of convergence will extend rightward.

It is also quite clear that, if $f(t)$ becomes unbounded at both ends of the t axis ($f(t) = \epsilon^{a|t|}$, $a > 0$; $f(t) = t$), then no value of σ will make the product $\epsilon^{-\sigma t}f(t)$ integrable. It is also quite clear that the unboundedness of $f(t)$ at one end of the t axis should not approach infinity any faster than exponentially. (Functions that do have this property are termed *functions of exponential order*.) For example, $\epsilon^{t^2}u_{-1}(t)$ does not have a Laplace transform. The function $t^n u_{-1}(t)$ does.

15.2 Some properties of the two-sided Laplace transform

Table 15.1 lists some important properties of the two-sided Laplace transform. Most of the proofs of these properties follow the same sequence of steps as for similar properties of the Fourier transform. One major difference is that the region of convergence must be carefully stated in the Laplace transform. In Table 15.1, the time functions are denoted by the lower-case letters f, f_1, and f_2; their corresponding two-sided Laplace transforms are denoted by the capital letters F, F_1, and F_2, respectively; and their corresponding regions of convergence are denoted by $\sigma' < \sigma < \sigma''$, $\sigma'_1 < \sigma < \sigma''_1$, and $\sigma'_2 < \sigma < \sigma''_2$, respectively.

15.3 Application of two-sided Laplace transform to circuit problems

The application of the two-sided Laplace transform to circuit problems follows the same pattern as the Fourier transform. In addition to the steps parallel to the Fourier-transform approach, the region of convergence of each transform must be closely followed.

Table **15.1** Some properties of two-sided Laplace transforms

Time function	Two-sided Laplace transform	Region of convergence	Equation number
$af(t)$	$aF(s)$	$\sigma' < \sigma < \sigma''$	(15.20)
$f_1(t)+f_2(t)$	$F_1(s)+F_2(s)$	$\max(\sigma_1',\sigma_2') < \sigma < \min(\sigma_1'',\sigma_2'')$	(15.21)
$f(-t)$	$F(-s)$	$-\sigma'' < \sigma < -\sigma'$	(15.22)
$f(at), [a>0]$	$\dfrac{1}{a}F\left(\dfrac{s}{a}\right)$	$a\sigma' < \sigma < a\sigma''$	(15.23)
$f(t-t_0)$	$F(s)\epsilon^{-st_0}$	$\sigma' < \sigma < \sigma''$	(15.24)
$f(t)\epsilon^{s_0 t}$	$F(s-s_0)$	$\sigma'+\sigma_0 < \sigma < \sigma''+\sigma_0, \ \sigma_0 = \mathrm{Re}[s_0]$	(15.25)
$\dfrac{df(t)}{dt}$	$sF(s)$	$\sigma' < \sigma < \sigma''$	(15.26)
$f^{(-1)}(t) = \displaystyle\int_{-\infty}^{t} f(\lambda)\,d\lambda$	$\dfrac{F(s)}{s}$	$\max(0,\sigma') < \sigma < \sigma''$	(15.27)
$-tf(t)$	$\dfrac{dF(s)}{ds}$	$\sigma' < \sigma < \sigma''$	(15.28)
$f_1(t)*f_2(t)$	$F_1(s)F_2(s)$	$\max(\sigma_1',\sigma_2') < \sigma < \min(\sigma_1'',\sigma_2'')$	(15.29)
$f_1(t)f_2(t)$	$\dfrac{1}{2\pi j}[F_1(s)*F_2(s)] = \dfrac{1}{2\pi j}\displaystyle\int_{\sigma-j\infty}^{\sigma+j\infty} F_1(\lambda)F_2(s-\lambda)\,d\lambda$	$\max(\sigma_1',\sigma_2') < \sigma < \min(\sigma_1'',\sigma_2'')$	(15.30)

EXAMPLE 5 Let the voltage $e_s(t)$ in the circuit of Figure 15.6(a) be specified as shown in Figure 15.6(b). We wish to find the current $i(t)$. We first take the transform of $e_s(t)$.

$$E_s(s) = \int_{-\infty}^{0} \epsilon^{-st} \, dt + \int_{0}^{\infty} \epsilon^{-t}\epsilon^{-st} \, dt$$

$$= -\frac{\epsilon^{-(\sigma+j\omega)t}}{s} \bigg|_{-\infty}^{0} - \frac{\epsilon^{-(1+\sigma+j\omega)t}}{s+1} \bigg|_{0}^{\infty}$$

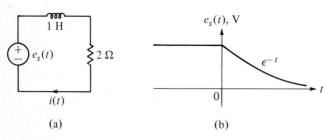

$e_s(t)$, V

ϵ^{-t}

1 H

$e_s(t)$

2 Ω

$i(t)$

(a)

(b)

Figure 15.6

The first integral is defined if $\sigma < 0$. The second integral is defined if $\sigma > -1$. Hence we get

$$E_s(s) = -\frac{1}{s} + \frac{1}{s+1} = -\frac{1}{s(s+1)}, \qquad -1 < \sigma < 0 \qquad (15.31)$$

The network function is the two-sided Laplace transform of the impulse response of the circuit

$$h(t) = \epsilon^{-2t}u_{-1}(t) \qquad (15.32)$$

From (15.7) we have

$$H(s) = \frac{1}{s+2}, \qquad \sigma > -2 \qquad (15.33)$$

This $H(s)$ is also the admittance of the RL branch. The transform of $i(t)$ is

$$I(s) = H(s)E_s(s) = -\frac{1}{s(s+1)(s+2)}, \qquad -1 < \sigma < 0 \qquad (15.34)$$

The region of convergence is the region that is common to both $E_s(s)$ and $H(s)$. We easily verify that

$$I(s) = -\frac{1}{2s} + \frac{1}{s+1} - \frac{1}{2(s+2)}, \qquad -1 < \sigma < 0 \qquad (15.35)$$

The first term of $I(s)$ fits (15.12) with $a = 0$. (Note that the region of convergence is to the left of $\sigma = 0$.) The second and third terms fit (15.8) with

$\sigma = -1$ and $\sigma = -2$, respectively. (Note that the regions of convergence are to the right of $\sigma = -1$ and $\sigma = -2$, respectively.) Hence

$$i(t) = \tfrac{1}{2}u_{-1}(-t) + \epsilon^{-t}u_{-1}(t) - \tfrac{1}{2}\epsilon^{-2t}u_{-1}(t) \qquad (15.36)$$

15.4   The one-sided Laplace transform

The two-sided Laplace transform is a logical extension of the Fourier transform in which we shift the contour away from the j axis. Conversely, then, the Fourier transform may be viewed as a special class of the two-sided Laplace transform. We present these two transforms in this order because the Fourier transform can be associated with the real-frequency spectrum, and thus, presumably, we can gain some understanding of its significance. In a larger sense, both the Fourier transform and the Laplace transform are special cases of the general theory of integral transforms, which is a well-established area in mathematics. We hope that this particular approach will enable us to associate physical interpretations with some of the steps in the derivation.

The two-sided Laplace transform is indispensable for solving some problems in electrical engineering. The significance of the region of convergence associated with each function is also best explained in the light of the two-sided transform. We could go on and develop all the details of the two-sided Laplace transform. However, it is more practical to concentrate on the one-sided Laplace transform.

The *one-sided* (*unilateral*) *Laplace transform* of a time function $f(t)$ is defined as

$$F(s) = \int_0^\infty f(t)\epsilon^{-st}\,dt \qquad (15.37)$$

There are several reasons why only the one-sided transform is treated in many texts. For one thing, a two-sided Laplace transform can always be written as the sum of two one-sided transforms, namely,

$$\int_{-\infty}^\infty f(t)\epsilon^{-st}\,dt = \int_{-\infty}^0 f(t)\epsilon^{-st}\,dt + \int_0^\infty f(t)\epsilon^{-st}\,dt$$

$$= \int_0^\infty f(-t)\epsilon^{st}\,dt + \int_0^\infty f(t)\epsilon^{-st}\,dt \qquad (15.38)$$

Both integrals are one-sided transforms. The reversal in the sign of s merely means that, in the first integral, the complex plane is the $-s$ plane instead of the s plane. Thus, if we get the information for only one side of the function at a time, we do eventually get the information for both sides of the function.

Another argument for using the one-sided Laplace transform is that the response of any causal system to an excitation must start at some definite time. No real-time physical system was ever turned on at $t = -\infty$ (mankind was not around then). For convenience, we designate this time reference as $t = 0$.

However, it is precisely the inability of the one-sided transform to take into account what went on before $t = 0$ that creates the limitations of this transform. We must have all the information on the condition of the system at $t = 0$—the initial condition—before we can proceed to analyze the system for $t > 0$. Once we have this information, the one-sided transform is adequate to handle the analysis of the system for $t > 0$.

Henceforth, unless otherwise stated, we shall use the term *Laplace transform* to denote the one-sided Laplace transform.

In a sense, we may view the one-sided Laplace transform as a special case of the two-sided one. We simply ignore the part of $f(t)$ for $t < 0$. Hence the one-sided Laplace transform may also be defined as

$$F(s) = \int_{-\infty}^{\infty} f(t) u_{-1}(t) \epsilon^{-st} \, dt \qquad (15.39)$$

We need to agree on another detail. When $f(t)$ includes an impulse function at $t = 0$, the integral of (15.37) becomes ambiguous. We shall assume that the lower limit of (15.37) is always the point just to the left of $t = 0$. Thus, if $f(t)$ should contain a $u_0(t)$ term, this impulse would be included in the integral. In other words, (15.37) implies that

$$F(s) = \int_{0^-}^{\infty} f(t) \epsilon^{-st} \, dt \qquad (15.40)$$

As we mentioned earlier, since the function to be integrated in (15.39) vanishes identically for $t < 0$, the region of convergence always extends to the right. As long as the function is of exponential order, we can always find a value of σ large enough that its transform exists. For the one-sided transform, we are generally concerned only about how small (in the algebraic sense) σ can be and still have a Laplace integral. The lower bound of all permissible σ values is known as the *abscissa of convergence*, shown as σ_a in Figure 15.7.

The one-sided inverse Laplace transform has the same form as (15.4).

$$f(t) = \frac{1}{2\pi j} \int_{\sigma - j\infty}^{\sigma + j\infty} F(s) \epsilon^{st} \, ds, \qquad [\sigma > \sigma_a], \qquad t > 0$$

$$f(t) = 0, \qquad t < 0 \qquad (15.41)$$

The operations implied by (15.40) and (15.41) are represented symbolically by

$$F(s) = \mathscr{L}[f(t)] \qquad (15.42)$$

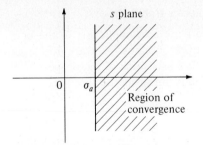

Figure 15.7 The region of convergence of the one-sided Laplace transform is to the right of its abscissa of convergence, σ_a.

and

$$f(t) = \mathscr{L}^{-1}[F(s)] \tag{15.43}$$

respectively.

EXAMPLE 6   From (15.7) we have

$$\mathscr{L}[\epsilon^{-at}] = \frac{1}{s+a}, \qquad \sigma > -a \tag{15.44}$$

This transform is equally valid for both positive and negative a.

EXAMPLE 7   Letting $a = 0$ in (15.44), we obtain

$$\mathscr{L}[u_{-1}(t)] = \frac{1}{s}, \qquad \sigma > 0 \tag{15.45}$$

EXAMPLE 8

$$\mathscr{L}[u_0(t)] = \int_{0^-}^{0^+} u_0(t)\,\epsilon^{-st}\,dt = 1, \qquad \sigma > -\infty \tag{15.46}$$

EXAMPLE 9

$$\mathscr{L}[\sin \omega_0 t] = \int_0^\infty \sin \omega_0 t\,\epsilon^{-st}\,dt = \int_0^\infty \frac{\epsilon^{j\omega_0 t} - \epsilon^{-j\omega_0 t}}{2j}\,\epsilon^{-st}\,dt$$

$$= \frac{1}{2j}\left[-\frac{\epsilon^{-(\sigma + j\omega - j\omega_0)t}}{s - j\omega_0} + \frac{\epsilon^{-(\sigma - j\omega - j\omega_0)t}}{s + j\omega_0} \right]_0^\infty$$

$$= \frac{1}{2j}\left(\frac{1}{s - j\omega_0} - \frac{1}{s + j\omega_0} \right) = \frac{\omega_0}{s^2 + \omega_0^2}, \qquad \sigma > 0 \tag{15.47}$$

EXAMPLE 10   Similarly, we have

$$\mathscr{L}[\cos \omega_0 t] = \frac{s}{s^2 + \omega_0^2}, \qquad \sigma > 0 \tag{15.48}$$

15.5 Some properties of the one-sided Laplace transform

Most of the properties listed in Table 15.1 are also applicable to the one-sided transforms. One difference is that upper bounds for σ are no longer necessary, since $f(t) = 0$ for $t < 0$. Table 15.2 lists some of the properties of the one-sided Laplace transforms. The following properties are peculiar to the one-sided Laplace transform.

Table 15.2 Some properties of the one-sided Laplace transforms

Time function	One-sided Laplace transform	Region of convergence	Equation
$f(t)$	$F(s)$	$\sigma_a < \sigma$	(15.49)
$af(t)$	$aF(s)$	$\sigma_a < \sigma$	(15.50)
$f_1(t) + f_2(t)$	$F_1(s) + F_2(s)$	$\max(\sigma_{a1}, \sigma_{a2}) < \sigma$	(15.51)
$f(at), [a > 0]$	$\dfrac{1}{a}F\left(\dfrac{s}{a}\right)$	$a\sigma_a < \sigma$	(15.52)
$f(t-t_0)u_{-1}(t-t_0)$	$F(s)\epsilon^{-st_0}$	$\sigma_a < \sigma$	(15.53)
$f(t)\epsilon^{s_0 t}$	$F(s-s_0)$	$\sigma_a + \sigma_0 < \sigma$, $[\sigma_0 = \mathrm{Re}(s_0)]$	(15.54)
$-tf(t)$	$\dfrac{dF(s)}{ds}$	$\sigma_a < \sigma$	(15.55)
$f_1(t) * f_2(t)$	$F_1(s)F_2(s)$	$\max(\sigma_{a1}, \sigma_{a2}) < \sigma$	(15.56)
$f_1(t)f_2(t)$	$\dfrac{1}{2\pi j}[F_1(s) * F_2(s)]$	$\max(\sigma_{a1}, \sigma_{a2}) < \sigma$	(15.57)

Time differentiation

$$\mathscr{L}\left[\frac{df(t)}{dt}\right] = \int_{0^-}^{\infty}\frac{df}{dt}\epsilon^{-st}\,dt = \int_{0^-}^{\infty}\epsilon^{-st}\,df = f(t)\epsilon^{-st}\Big|_{0^-}^{\infty}$$

$$+ s\int_{0^-}^{\infty}f(t)\epsilon^{-st}\,dt = sF(s) - f(0^-) \tag{15.58}$$

In the last step, we made use of the fact that, if σ is sufficiently large, $f(t)\epsilon^{-st}$ tends to zero as $t \to \infty$.

To generalize,

$$\mathscr{L}\left[\frac{f^n(t)}{dt^n}\right] = s^nF(s) - s^{n-1}f(0^-) - s^{n-2}f^{(1)}(0^-) - \cdots - sf^{(n-2)}(0^-)$$

$$- f^{(n-1)}(0^-)$$

EXAMPLE 11 Let

$$f(t) = \epsilon^{-at}u_{-1}(t)$$

Then

$$F(s) = \frac{1}{s+a}$$

Since

$$f^{(1)}(t) = u_0(t) - a\epsilon^{-at}u_{-1}(t)$$

it follows that

$$\mathscr{L}[f^{(1)}(t)] = 1 - \frac{a}{a+s} = \frac{s}{s+a} \qquad (15.59)$$

Alternatively, applying (15.58), we have*

$$\mathscr{L}[f^{(1)}(t)] = s\left(\frac{1}{s+a}\right) - f(0^-) = \frac{s}{s+a} \qquad (15.60)$$

which checks with the answer in (15.59).

Time integration Let

$$f^{(-1)}(t) = \int_{t_0}^{t} f(t)\,dt, \qquad t_0 < 0^-$$

$$\mathscr{L}[f^{(-1)}(t)] = \int_{0^-}^{\infty}\left[\int_{t_0}^{t} f(t)\,dt\right]\epsilon^{-st}\,dt = -\frac{1}{s}\int_{t=0^-}^{t=\infty}\left[\int_{t_0}^{t} f(t)\,dt\right]d(\epsilon^{-st})$$

$$= -\frac{\epsilon^{-st}}{s}\int_{t_0}^{t} f(t)\,dt\,\Big|_{0^-}^{\infty} + \int_{0^-}^{\infty}\frac{\epsilon^{-st}}{s}f(t)\,dt$$

It can be shown that, if $f(t)$ is of exponential order, then $f^{(-1)}(t)$ is also of exponential order. Hence

$$\mathscr{L}[f^{(-1)}(t)] = \frac{F(s)}{s} + \frac{f^{(-1)}(0^-)}{s} \qquad (15.61)$$

where

$$f^{(-1)}(0^-) = \int_{t_0}^{0^-} f(t)\,dt, \qquad t_0 < 0^-$$

Repeated applications of (15.61) give

$$\mathscr{L}[f^{(-n)}(t)] = \frac{F(s)}{s^n} + \sum_{i=1}^{n}\frac{f^{(-i)}(0^-)}{s^{n-i+1}} \qquad (15.62)$$

---

* You might wonder at this point why the $f(0^-)$ term is necessary if we define all our time functions to vanish for $t < 0$. This term plays an extremely important part in the analysis of linear systems in which initial energy is present. The meaning of this quantity will become clear later (Section 15.9).

EXAMPLE 12   For the $f(t)$ of Figure 15.8(a), we first find the transform of $f'(t)$ of Figure 15.8(b). Since

$$\mathscr{L}[f'(t)] = 1 - \epsilon^{-sT} \tag{15.63}$$

we have

$$\mathscr{L}[f(t)] = \frac{1 - \epsilon^{-sT}}{s} \tag{15.64}$$

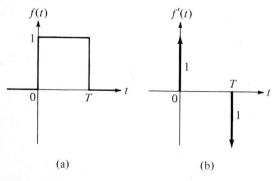

(a)   (b)

Figure 15.8

Division by time   Starting with

$$\int_s^\infty F(s)\, ds = \int_s^\infty \int_{0^-}^\infty f(t)\epsilon^{-st}\, dt\, ds$$

we reverse the order of integration to get

$$\int_0^\infty f(t) \int_s^\infty \epsilon^{-st}\, ds\, dt = \int_{0^-}^\infty \frac{-f(t)\epsilon^{-st}}{t}\bigg|_s^\infty\, dt = \int_s^\infty \frac{f(t)}{t}\epsilon^{-st}\, dt = \mathscr{L}\left[\frac{f(t)}{t}\right]$$

Hence we get

$$\mathscr{L}\left[\frac{f(t)}{t}\right] = \int_s^\infty F(s)\, ds \tag{15.65}$$

Generalizing, we would have

$$\mathscr{L}\left[\frac{f(t)}{t^n}\right] = \int_s^\infty ds \int_s^\infty ds \cdots \int_s^\infty F(s)\, ds \tag{15.66}$$

EXAMPLE 13

$$\mathscr{L}\left[\frac{\sin \omega_0 t}{t}\right] = \int_s^\infty \frac{\omega_0}{s^2 + \omega_0^2}\, ds = \tan^{-1}\frac{s}{\omega_0}\bigg|_s^\infty$$

$$= \frac{\pi}{2} - \tan^{-1}\left(\frac{s}{\omega_0}\right) = \cot^{-1}\left(\frac{s}{\omega_0}\right) \tag{15.67}$$

EXAMPLE 14   To find

$$\mathscr{L}^{-1}\left[\ln\left(\frac{s+a}{s+b}\right)\right]$$

we let

$$F(s) = \ln\left(\frac{s+a}{s+b}\right) = \ln(s+a) - \ln(s+b)$$

Then

$$\frac{dF}{ds} = \frac{1}{s+a} - \frac{1}{s+b}$$

and

$$\mathscr{L}^{-1}\left[\frac{dF}{ds}\right] = (\epsilon^{-at} - \epsilon^{-bt})u_{-1}(t)$$

Hence

$$\left(\frac{\epsilon^{-at} - \epsilon^{-bt}}{t}\right)u_{-1}(t) = \mathscr{L}^{-1}\left[\int_s^\infty \frac{dF}{ds}\,ds\right] = \mathscr{L}^{-1}[F(s)] = \mathscr{L}^{-1}\left[\ln\left(\frac{s+a}{s+b}\right)\right] \tag{15.68}$$

EXAMPLE 15   To find the transform of the triangular pulse of Figure 15.9(a), we first consider the function as the sum of the three ramp functions shown in Figure 15.9(b). Or

$$f(t) = \frac{t}{T}u_{-1}(t) - \frac{2(t-T)}{T}u_{-1}(t-T) + \frac{t-2T}{T}u_{-1}(t-2T)$$

From (15.55) we have

$$\mathscr{L}[tu_{-1}(t)] = -\frac{d}{ds}\left(\frac{1}{s}\right) = \frac{1}{s^2}$$

By virtue of (15.53), we have

$$\mathscr{L}[f(t)] = \frac{1}{Ts^2} - \frac{2\epsilon^{-sT}}{Ts^2} + \frac{\epsilon^{-2sT}}{Ts^2} = \frac{(1-\epsilon^{-sT})^2}{Ts^2} \tag{15.69}$$

Or else we take the first and second derivatives of $f(t)$, shown in Figure 15.9(c) and (d). Now we have

$$\mathscr{L}[f''(t)] = \frac{1}{T} - \frac{2}{T}\epsilon^{-st} + \frac{1}{T}\epsilon^{-2sT}$$

Applying (15.62), we have

$$\mathscr{L}[f(t)] = \frac{1}{s^2T}(1 - 2\epsilon^{-sT} + \epsilon^{-2sT}) = \frac{(1-\epsilon^{-sT})^2}{s^2T} \tag{15.70}$$

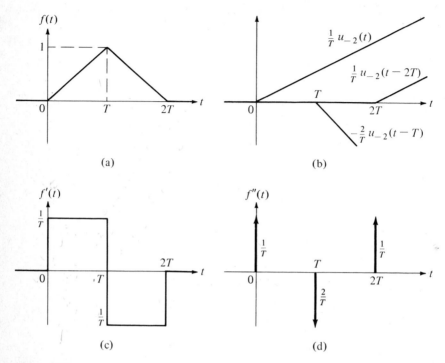

(a)

(b)

(c)

(d)

Figure 15.9

Causal periodic functions If we know the Laplace transform of the first cycle of a periodic function, we can find the transform of the whole perodic function by a simple procedure. Let the periodic function be denoted by $f_p(t)$ and its first cycle by $f(t)$, as shown in Figure 15.10. From (15.53), it is quite clear that

$$F_p(s) = F(s)(1 + \epsilon^{-sT} + \epsilon^{-2sT} + \epsilon^{-3sT} + \epsilon^{-4sT} + \cdots) \tag{15.71}$$

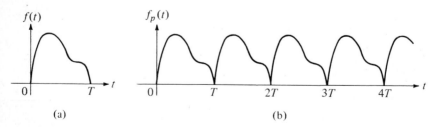

(a)

(b)

Figure 15.10 Relationship between a periodic function $f_p(t)$ and a nonperiodic function $f(t)$.

Multiplying both sides by $(1-\epsilon^{-sT})$, we get

$$(1-\epsilon^{-sT})F_p(s) = F(s) \tag{15.72}$$

Hence

$$F_p(s) = \frac{F(s)}{1-\epsilon^{-sT}} \tag{15.73}$$

EXAMPLE 16 From (15.69) and (15.73) it is quite clear that the transform of the periodic function of Figure 15.11 is

$$\mathscr{L}[f(t)] = \frac{(1-\epsilon^{-sT})^2}{Ts^2(1-\epsilon^{-2sT})} = \frac{1-\epsilon^{-sT}}{Ts^2(1+\epsilon^{-sT})} \tag{15.74}$$

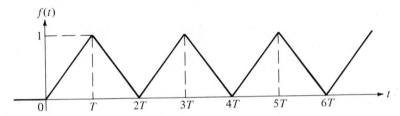

Figure 15.11

15.6 The inverse Laplace transform: Tables of Laplace transform

The process of going back from the complex-frequency domain to the real-time domain uses the inverse Laplace transform of (15.41) or

$$\mathscr{L}^{-1}[F(s)] = f(t) = \frac{1}{2\pi j}\int_{\sigma-j\infty}^{\sigma+j\infty} F(s)\,\epsilon^{st}\,ds \tag{15.75}$$

This is a contour integral whose contour of integration is a vertical line to the right of the abscissa of convergence. In theory, for a given $F(s)$, we can evaluate the integral of (15.75) by various techniques of contour integration. In practice, this integration is generally quite difficult to perform. Therefore this reverse step is usually done by breaking up $F(s)$ into a sum of simpler functions whose inverse transforms either are known or perhaps are easier to find. We can usually generate these transforms by starting with a few basic transform pairs and then applying the special properties given in Section 15.5. Table 15.3 lists a number of such transforms.

All the frequency-domain functions in Table 15.3 are rational functions. This is quite adequate for the analysis of lumped LTI systems. When the system is distributed—as is the case when transmission lines, wave-guides, or antennas are involved—irrational functions will result. Table 15.4 gives some Laplace transforms that are not rational.

Table 15.3 Laplace transforms of rational functions

Laplace transform, $F(s)$	Time Function, $f(t)\,(t \geq 0)$
1	$u_0(t)$ (unit impulse function)
$\dfrac{1}{s}$	$u_{-1}(t)$ (unit step function)
$\dfrac{1}{s^2}$	t (unit ramp function)
$\dfrac{1}{s^{n+1}}$	$\dfrac{1}{n!}t^n, \qquad n =$ positive integer
$\dfrac{1}{s+a}$	ϵ^{-at}
$\dfrac{1}{(s+a)^2}$	$t\epsilon^{-at}$
$\dfrac{s}{(s+a)^2}$	$(1-at)\epsilon^{-at}$
$\dfrac{1}{(s+a)(s+b)}$	$\dfrac{\epsilon^{-at}-\epsilon^{-bt}}{b-a}$
$\dfrac{1}{(s+a)^n}$	$\dfrac{1}{(n-1)!}t^{n-1}\epsilon^{-at}, \qquad n =$ positive integer
$\dfrac{1}{s(s+a)}$	$\dfrac{1}{a}(1-\epsilon^{-at})$
$\dfrac{1}{s^2(s+a)}$	$\dfrac{1}{a^2}(\epsilon^{-at}+at-1)$
$\dfrac{1}{s(s+a)(s+b)}$	$\dfrac{1}{ab}\left(1-\dfrac{b}{b-a}\epsilon^{-at}+\dfrac{a}{b-a}\epsilon^{-bt}\right), \qquad a \neq b$
$\dfrac{1}{(s+a)(s+b)(s+c)}$	$\dfrac{\epsilon^{-at}}{(b-a)(c-a)}+\dfrac{\epsilon^{-bt}}{(a-b)(c-b)}+\dfrac{\epsilon^{-ct}}{(a-c)(b-c)}$
$\dfrac{s}{(s+a)(s+b)(s+c)}$	$\dfrac{-a\epsilon^{-at}}{(b-a)(c-a)}-\dfrac{b\epsilon^{-bt}}{(a-b)(c-b)}-\dfrac{c\epsilon^{-ct}}{(a-c)(b-c)}$
$\dfrac{1}{s(s+a)^2}$	$\dfrac{1}{a^2}[1-(1+at)\epsilon^{-at}]$

Table **15.3**—*continued*

Laplace transform, $F(s)$	Time function, $f(t)$ $(t \geq 0)$
$\dfrac{\omega_0}{s^2+\omega_0^2}$	$\sin \omega_0 t$
$\dfrac{s}{s^2+\omega_0^2}$	$\cos \omega_0 t$
$\dfrac{1}{s^2-a^2}$	$\dfrac{1}{a} \sinh at$
$\dfrac{s}{s^2-a^2}$	$\cosh at$
$\dfrac{\omega_0^2}{s^2+2\zeta\omega_0 s+\omega_0^2}$	$\dfrac{\omega_0^2}{1-\zeta^2} \epsilon^{-\zeta\omega_0 t} \sin \omega_0 \sqrt{1-\zeta^2}\,t$
$\dfrac{\omega_0^2}{s(s^2+2\zeta\omega_0 s+\omega_0^2)}$	$1 + \dfrac{1}{\sqrt{1-\zeta^2}} \epsilon^{-\zeta\omega_0 t} \sin(\omega_0\sqrt{1-\zeta^2}\,t - \phi),$ where $\phi = \tan^{-1}\dfrac{\sqrt{1-\zeta^2}}{-\zeta}$
$\dfrac{1}{(s+a)^2+b^2}$	$\dfrac{1}{b}\epsilon^{-at}\sin bt$
$\dfrac{s+a}{(s+a)^2+b^2}$	$\epsilon^{-at}\cos bt$
$\dfrac{\omega_0^2}{s(s^2+\omega_0^2)}$	$1 - \cos \omega_0 t$
$\dfrac{s}{(s^2+\omega_0^2)^2}$	$\dfrac{1}{2\omega_0}t\sin \omega_0 t$

Table **15.4** Laplace transforms (irrational functions)

Laplace transform, $F(s)$	Time function,* $f(t)$ $(t > 0)$
$\dfrac{1}{\sqrt{s}}$	$\dfrac{1}{\sqrt{\pi t}}$
$\dfrac{1}{s\sqrt{s}}$	$2\sqrt{\dfrac{t}{\pi}}$

Table **15.4**—*continued*

Laplace transform, $F(s)$	Time function,* $f(t)$ $(t > 0)$
$\dfrac{1}{s^n}$ (n is not necessarily an integer)	$\dfrac{t^{n-1}}{\Gamma(n)}$
$\dfrac{1}{(s-a)\sqrt{s}}$	$\dfrac{1}{\sqrt{a}}\,\epsilon^{at}erf(\sqrt{at})$
$\dfrac{2}{a}\epsilon^{-a\sqrt{s}}, \quad a > 0$	$\dfrac{\epsilon^{-a^2/4t}}{\sqrt{\pi t^3}}$
$\dfrac{\epsilon^{-a\sqrt{s}}}{\sqrt{s}}, \quad a \geq 0$	$\dfrac{\epsilon^{-a^2/4t}}{\sqrt{\pi t}}$
$\dfrac{\epsilon^{-a\sqrt{s}}}{s}, \quad a \geq 0$	$1 - erf\dfrac{a}{a\sqrt{t}} = erfc\dfrac{a}{2\sqrt{t}}$
$\dfrac{\sqrt{a}}{s\sqrt{s+a}}$	$erf(\sqrt{at})$
$\dfrac{1}{\sqrt{s}+\sqrt{a}}$	$\dfrac{1}{\sqrt{\pi t}} - \sqrt{a}\,\epsilon^{at}erfc(\sqrt{at})$
$\dfrac{1}{\sqrt{s}(\sqrt{s}+\sqrt{a})}$	$\epsilon^{at}erfc(\sqrt{at})$
$\dfrac{1}{\sqrt{s^2+a^2}}$	$J_0(at)$
$\dfrac{1}{\sqrt{s^2-a^2}}$	$I_0(at)$
$\dfrac{1}{\sqrt{s}\sqrt{s+a}}$	$\epsilon^{-at/2}I_0\left(\dfrac{at}{2}\right)$
$\dfrac{1}{s+\sqrt{s^2+a^2}}$	$\dfrac{1}{at}J_1(at)$
$\dfrac{1}{(s+\sqrt{s^2+a^2})\sqrt{s^2+a^2}}$	$\dfrac{1}{a}J_1(at)$

* In this column $\Gamma(n)$ is the gamma function, erf(x) is the error function, also known as the probability integral, $erfc(x) = 1-erf(x)$ is the complementary error function, and J_0, I_0, and J_1 are Bessel functions. See, for example, B. O. Pierce, *A Short Table of Integrals*, Ginn and Company, Boston, 1956, and *CRC Standard Mathematical Tables*, CRC Press, Cleveland, Ohio, 1976.

15.7 Partial-fraction expansion of a rational function

In lumped LTI systems the network functions are rational functions of s. In many physical problems, the transforms of the excitations are also rational functions. These time functions include the impulse function, the step function, the ramp function, the exponential function, and the sinusoidal functions. Hence a large number of system-analysis problems involve the inverse transform of rational functions. This last step can be accomplished by first expanding the rational function into smaller functions and then making use of the Laplace transform table. The technique for accomplishing this expansion is known as the *partial-fraction expansion* of a rational function.

If a rational function

$$F(s) = \frac{N(s)}{D(s)} = \frac{a_n s^n + a_{n-1} s^{n-1} + \cdots + a_1 s + a_0}{b_m s^m + b_{m-1} s^{m-1} + \cdots + b_1 s + b_0} \tag{15.76}$$

is improper (that is, if $n > m$), a polynomial can always be removed from it, leaving a remainder that is a proper fraction. We can find this polynomial simply by long division. For example, suppose we have

$$F(s) = \frac{2s^4 + 7s^3 + 13s^2 + 13s + 4}{s^2 + 2s + 3}$$

Performing the long division

$$
\begin{array}{r}
2s^2 + 3s + 1 \\
s^2 + 2s + 3 \overline{) \; 2s^4 + 7s^3 + 13s^2 + 13s + 4} \\
\underline{2s^4 + 4s^3 + 6s^2} \\
3s^3 + 7s^2 + 13s \\
\underline{3s^3 + 6s^2 + 9s} \\
s^2 + 4s + 4 \\
\underline{s^2 + 2s + 3} \\
2s + 1
\end{array}
$$

we get

$$F(s) = 2s^2 + 3s + 1 + \frac{2s+1}{s^2 + 2s + 3} \tag{15.77}$$

We can now restrict our discussion to the case in which $F(s)$ is a proper fraction. We first need to find all the poles of $F(s)$. If $F(s)$ has a simple pole at $s = s_i$, real or complex, then we write

$$F(s) = \frac{N(s)}{D_1(s)(s - s_i)} \tag{15.78}$$

This pole can be extracted from $F(s)$, in which case, $F(s)$ is expressible as

$$F(s) = \frac{N_1(s)}{D_1(s)} + \frac{K_i}{s - s_i} \tag{15.79}$$

where N_1/D_1 is another proper fraction. (K_i is known as the residue in the pole at $s = s_i$.) To find K_i, we multiply both sides of (15.79) by $(s - s_i)$ and then set $s = s_i$. We get

$$K_i = \left[-\frac{(s - s_i) N_1(s)}{D_1(s)} + (s - s_i) F(s) \right]_{s = s_i}$$

$$= \left[(s - s_i) F(s) \right] \bigg|_{s = s_i} = \frac{N(s)}{D_1(s)} \bigg|_{s = s_i} \qquad (15.80)$$

EXAMPLE 17   Let

$$F(s) = \frac{s^3 + 5s^2 + 2s + 1}{(s^3 + s^2 + 5s + 6)(s + 2)}$$

This $F(s)$ must contain a term

$$\frac{K}{s + 2}$$

and

$$K = \frac{s^3 + 5s^2 + 2s + 1}{s^3 + s^2 + 5s + 6} \bigg|_{s = -2} = -\frac{9}{8}$$

Generally, we are not interested in finding $N_1(s)$. However, $N_1(s)/D_1(s)$ can always be found by straightforward subtraction.

$$\frac{N_1(s)}{D_1(s)} = F(s) + \frac{\frac{9}{8}}{s + 2} = \frac{s^3 + 5s^2 + 2s + 1 + \frac{9}{8}(s^3 + s^2 + 5s + 6)}{(s^3 + s^2 + 5s + 6)(s + 2)}$$

$$= \frac{17s^3 + 49s^2 + 61s + 62}{8(s^3 + s^2 + 5s + 6)(s + 2)}$$

$$= \frac{17s^2 + 15s + 31}{8(s^3 + s^2 + 5s + 6)} \qquad (15.81)$$

The last step involves the cancellation of the factor $(s + 2)$ between the numerator and the denominator. The fact that the numerator contains a factor $(s + 2)$ is, of course, no coincidence.

If $F(s)$ has a pole of rth order at $s = s_j$, then we can write

$$F(s) = \frac{N(s)}{D_2(s)(s - s_j)^r} \qquad (15.82)$$

This multiple pole can be extracted from $F(s)$, and the function $F(s)$ is expressible as

$$F(s) = \frac{N_2(s)}{D_2(s)} + \frac{K_{j1}}{s - s_j} + \frac{K_{j2}}{(s - s_j)^2} + \cdots + \frac{K_{jr}}{(s - s_j)^r} \qquad (15.83)$$

To find K_{jr}, we multiply through (15.83) by $(s-s_j)^r$ and then set $s = s_j$. Whence we obtain

$$K_{jr} = [F(s)(s-s_j)^r]_{s=s_j} = \frac{N(s)}{D_2(s)}\bigg|_{s=s_j} \tag{15.84}$$

To find $K_{j(r-1)}$, we first multiply (15.83) by $(s-s_j)^r$ and then differentiate both sides with respect to s. We have

$$\frac{d}{ds}[F(s)(s-s_j)^r] = \frac{d}{ds}\left[\frac{N_2(s)}{D_2(s)}(s-s_j)^r\right] + (r-1)K_{j1}(s-s_j)^{r-2}$$

$$+ (r-2)K_{j2}(s-s_j)^{r-3} + \cdots + 2K_{j(r-2)}(s-s_j) + K_{j(r-1)} \tag{15.85}$$

Letting $s = s_j$ in (15.85), we have

$$K_{j(r-1)} = \left\{\frac{d}{ds}\left[F(s)(s-s_j)^r\right]\right\}_{s=s_j} = \left\{\frac{d}{ds}\left[\frac{N(s)}{D_2(s)}\right]\right\}_{s=s_j} \tag{15.86}$$

If we kept differentiating (15.85) and after each differentiation set $s = s_i$, we would get in general

$$K_{j(r-k)} = \frac{1}{k!}\left\{\frac{d^k}{ds^k}\left[F(s)(s-s_j)^r\right]\right\}_{s=s_j} = \frac{1}{k!}\left\{\frac{d^k}{ds^k}\left[\frac{N(s)}{D_2(s)}\right]\right\}_{s=s_j} \tag{15.87}$$

When these rules have been applied to all the poles of $F(s)$, there will be nothing left. The collection of all the terms representing all the poles is the partial-fraction expansion of the function.

When $F(s)$ has complex poles, they must occur in conjugate pairs. In these cases, their coefficients must also be conjugate of each other. Hence it is necessary to evaluate only one of the two coefficients. Furthermore, conjugate pairs of terms are usually combined together.

EXAMPLE 18   We wish to expand

$$F(s) = \frac{2s^2 + 4s + 3}{(s+2)(s+1)^2} = \frac{K_1}{s+2} + \frac{K_2}{s+1} + \frac{K_3}{(s+1)^2} \tag{15.88}$$

From (15.84), we get for the pole at $s = -1$

$$K_3 = \frac{2s^2 + 4s + 3}{s+2}\bigg|_{s=-1} = 1$$

From (15.86), we have

$$K_2 = \left[\frac{d}{ds}\left(\frac{2s^2 + 4s + 3}{s+2}\right)\right]_{s=-1} = \frac{(s+2)(4s+4)-(2s^2+4s+3)}{(s+2)^2}\bigg|_{s=-1} = -1$$

For the pole at $s = -2$, we use (15.80) to get

$$K_1 = \frac{2s^2 + 4s + 3}{(s+1)^2}\bigg|_{s=-2} = 3$$

Thus

$$F(s) = \frac{2s^2+4s+3}{(s+2)(s+1)^2} = \frac{3}{s+2} - \frac{1}{s+1} + \frac{1}{(s+1)^2} \tag{15.89}$$

EXAMPLE 19

$$F(s) = \frac{s+15}{s^2(s^2+2s+5)} = \frac{s+15}{s^2(s+1-j2)(s+1+j2)}$$

$$= \frac{K_1}{s} + \frac{K_2}{s^2} + \frac{K_3}{s+1-j2} + \frac{K_3^*}{s+1+j2} \tag{15.90}$$

$$K_3 = \frac{s+15}{s^2(s+1+j2)}\Big|_{s=-1+j2} = \frac{14+j2}{(-1+j2)^2(j4)} = \frac{2-j14}{4(-3-j4)}$$

$$= \frac{(2-j14)(-3+j4)}{4(-3-j4)(-3+j4)} = \frac{50+j50}{100} = \frac{1}{2} + j\frac{1}{2}$$

$$K_2 = \frac{s+15}{s^2+2s+5}\Big|_{s=0} = 3$$

$$K_1 = \left[\frac{d}{ds}\left(\frac{s+15}{s^2+2s+5}\right)\right]\Big|_{s=0} = \frac{(s^2+2s+5)-(2s+2)(s+15)}{(s^2+2s+5)^2}\Big|_{s=0} = -1$$

Thus

$$F(s) = \frac{s+15}{s^2(s^2+2s+5)} = -\frac{1}{s} + \frac{3}{s^2} + \frac{\frac{1}{2}+j\frac{1}{2}}{s+1-j2} + \frac{\frac{1}{2}-j\frac{1}{2}}{s+1+j2}$$

$$= -\frac{1}{s} + \frac{3}{s^2} + \frac{s-1}{(s+1)^2+4} \tag{15.91}$$

15.8 Solution of differential equations by Laplace transform

One of the most important applications of the Laplace transform is the solution of linear differential equations with constant coefficients. A simple example will illustrate this application. Consider the equation

$$\frac{d^2y}{dt^2} + 3\frac{dy}{dt} + 2y = \cos 10t, \qquad t > 0 \tag{15.92}$$

with the condition that

$$y'(0^-) = \frac{dy}{dt}\Big|_{t=0^-} = 2, \qquad y(0^-) = -1 \tag{15.93}$$

Taking the Laplace transform of both sides of (15.92), we get

$$s^2 Y(s) - sy(0^-) - y'(0^-) + 3sY(s) - 3y(0^-) + 2Y(s) = \frac{s}{s^2+100} \tag{15.94}$$

Substituting the initial conditions in (15.93) into (15.94) and solving for $Y(s)$, we get

$$Y(s) = \frac{-s^3 - s^2 - 99s - 100}{(s+1)(s+2)(s^2+100)} \tag{15.95}$$

Applying the partial-fraction expansion technique, we obtain

$$Y(s) = -\frac{\frac{1}{101}}{s+1} - \frac{\frac{51}{52}}{s+2} - \frac{\frac{1}{5252}(49s-150)}{s^2+100}$$

The inverse transform of each term gives

$$y(t) = -\tfrac{1}{101}\epsilon^{-t} - \tfrac{51}{52}\epsilon^{-2t} - \tfrac{49}{5252}\cos 10t + \tfrac{15}{5252}\sin 10t \tag{15.96}$$

We can make the following observations about the Laplace-transform method of solving a differential equation in the preceding example.

1 Since the equation is of second order, two boundary (initial) conditions are needed for the complete solution. These are given in (15.93). Although these conditions are strictly mathematical in the context of our current problem, they can usually be identified with certain physical quantities and obtained from physical considerations in a real problem.

2 Equation (15.92) is valid for $t > 0$. The initial conditions are given for $t = 0^-$. When we use (15.93) in the solution of (15.92), we are tacitly assuming that these initial conditions continue into the beginning of the time period $t > 0$. This is not overconfident, because we have no reason to expect that $x(t)$ and $x'(t)$ would change suddenly at $t = 0$. In a physical problem, this is usually quite obvious because these functions do represent some physical quantities.

3 Although (15.92) is a differential equation, it is quite clear that integral terms can be accommodated in exactly the same manner as we handled the derivative terms in this particular example.

4 The Laplace transform converts an integral-differential equation in the time domain into an algebraic equation in the complex-frequency domain. The solution for an unknown function is much more easily done in the frequency domain, since we have to solve only algebraic equations. After finding the unknown in the frequency domain, we find the answer in the time domain by the use of the inverse Laplace transform.

5 In the Laplace-transform method of solving an integral-differential equation, we obtain the complete solution in one step. Instead of finding a general solution first and then forcing the arbitrary constants to satisfy the initial conditions, we insert the initial conditions into the problem at the outset. Thus we obtain the whole solution as a complete package. In the solution given in (15.96), the first two terms are the complementary function and the last two terms are the particular integral of the differential equation (15.92).

Thus, when we apply the Laplace-transform method to the solution of an LTI system, we find both the transient response and the steady-state response at the same time. We shall see how this is accomplished in the next section.

15.9   The complete solution of network problems

Since the Laplace-transform technique can be used to solve linear integral-differential equations, it is a powerful tool for analyzing systems that are describable by integral-differential equations with constant coefficients. We shall first illustrate the steps involved using a couple of examples. Then we will be in a position to state a few general rules for more general problems.

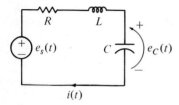

Figure 15.12

For example, in the RLC series circuit of Figure 15.12, KVL gives

$$Ri(t) + L\frac{di(t)}{dt} + \frac{1}{C}\int_{-\infty}^{t} i(t)\,dt = e_s(t), \qquad t > 0 \tag{15.97}$$

Taking the Laplace transform of (15.97), we get

$$RI(s) + sLI(s) - Li(0^-) + \frac{I(s)}{sC} + \frac{i^{(-1)}(0^-)}{sC} = E_s(s) \tag{15.98}$$

The initial-condition terms in (15.98) can now be identified with appropriate electric quantities in the circuit. The quantity $i(0^-)$ is the current that existed just prior to the moment when (15.97) came into effect ($t = 0$). The quantity

$$i^{(-1)}(0^-) = \int_{-\infty}^{0^-} i(t)\,dt = q(0^-) \tag{15.99}$$

is the net total accumulation of electric charge effected by the current that might have been flowing prior to $t = 0^-$. Since the capacitor is the only element that can store any electric charge, this quantity is readily interpreted as the charge stored in the capacitor just prior to $t = 0$. Alternatively, we may express

$$\frac{q(0^-)}{C} = e_C(0^-)$$

as the voltage that existed just prior to $t = 0$, or the initial voltage across the capacitor. Solving for $I(s)$ from (15.98), we get

$$I(s) = \frac{E_s(s) + Li(0^-) - [e_C(0^-)/s]}{R + sL + (1/sC)} \qquad (15.100)$$

The denominator of (15.100) is simply the impedance of the RLC branch. If $i(0^-)$ and $e_C(0^-)$ are both zero, (15.100) is identical to the steady-state solution of the circuit. When $i(0^-)$ and $e_C(0^-)$ are both nonzero, (15.100) gives the complete solution of $i(t)$ in the frequency domain.

As another example, to analyze the circuit of Figure 15.13, we shall use

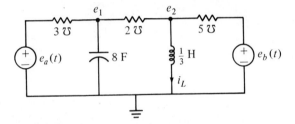

Figure 15.13

node analysis with e_1 and e_2 as the variables. In this circuit, KCL gives

$$3(e_1 - e_a) + 8\frac{de_1}{dt} + 2(e_1 - e_2) = 0$$

$$\qquad (15.101)$$

$$2(e_2 - e_1) + 3\int_{t_0}^{t} e_2(t)\,dt + 5(e_2 - e_b) = 0$$

Taking the transform, we arrive at

$$3E_1(s) - 3E_a(s) + 8sE_1(s) - 8e_1(0^-) + 2E_1(s) - 2E_2(s) = 0$$

$$\qquad (15.102)$$

$$2E_2(s) - 2E_1(s) + \frac{3E_2(s)}{s} + \frac{3e_2^{(-1)}(0^-)}{s} + 5E_2(s) - 5E_b(s) = 0$$

Here $e_1(0^-)$ is the initial voltage across the 8-F capacitor. The quantity $3e_2^{(-1)}(0^-)$ may be interpreted as

$$3\int_{-\infty}^{0^-} e_2(t)\,dt = \frac{1}{L}\int_{-\infty}^{0^-} e_2(t)\,dt = i_L(0^-)$$

which is the current through the inductance just prior to $t = 0$. Rearranging

(15.102), we get

$$(5+8s)E_1 - 2E_2 = 3E_a + 8e_1(0^-)$$

$$-2E_1 + \left(7 + \frac{3}{s}\right)E_2 = 5E_b - \frac{i_L(0^-)}{s}$$
(15.103)

Again, if $e_1(0^-)$ and $i_L(0^-)$ are zero, the expressions in (15.103) become the node equations for the steady-state analysis of the circuit of Figure 15.13, using the admittances of the various elements. Suppose now we have $e_1(0^-) = 2$ V and $i_L(0^-) = 10$ A, and, for $t > 0$,

$$e_a = 10 \text{ V}, \qquad e_b = 5 \text{ V}$$
(15.104)

Then (15.103) becomes

$$(5+8s)E_1 - 2E_2 = \frac{30}{s} + 16; \qquad -2E_1 + \left(7 + \frac{3}{s}\right)E_2 = \frac{25}{s} - \frac{10}{s}$$
(15.105)

Solving for E_1, we would get

$$E_1(s) = \frac{\begin{vmatrix} \dfrac{30}{s} + 16 & -2 \\[2mm] \dfrac{15}{s} & 7 + \dfrac{3}{s} \end{vmatrix}}{\begin{vmatrix} 5+8s & -2 \\[2mm] -2 & 7 + \dfrac{3}{s} \end{vmatrix}} = \frac{90 + 288s + 112s^2}{s(15 + 55s + 56s^2)}$$

$$= \frac{6}{s} - \frac{42 + 224s}{15 + 55s + 56s^2}$$

$$= \frac{6}{s} - \frac{4(s+0.491)}{(s+0.491)^2 + (0.163)^2} + \frac{1.214}{(s+0.491)^2 + (0.163)^2}$$

The inverse Laplace transform of $E_1(s)$ would give

$$e_1(t) = 6 - 4\epsilon^{-0.491t} \sin 0.163t + 7.430\epsilon^{-0.491t} \cos 0.163t \text{ V}$$

15.10 Network elements with initial energy

From the foregoing examples, we see that, when a capacitor or an inductor contains a certain amount of energy at $t = 0^-$, an extra term will appear in the Laplace transform of its voltage or current. We shall now examine what we must do to take this extra term into account. Take a capacitor with an initial voltage $e(0^-)$. The voltage across such a capacitor is [see Figure

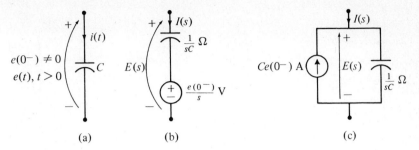

Figure 15.14 Laplace transform of a capacitor with initially stored energy.

15.14(a)]

$$e(t) = \frac{1}{C} \int_{0^-}^{t} i(t)\, dt \qquad (15.106)$$

The Laplace transform of (15.106) is

$$E(s) = \frac{I(s)}{sC} + \frac{i^{(-1)}(0^-)}{sC}$$

$$= \frac{I(s)}{sC} + \frac{e_C(0^-)}{s} \qquad (15.107)$$

Equation (15.107) states that the voltage $E(s)$ is the current $I(s)$ times the impedance of the capacitance plus the Laplace transform of $e(0^-)u_{-1}(t)$. Hence, in the frequency domain, a capacitor with an initial voltage $e(0^-)$ may be replaced by an initially uncharged capacitor in series with a source whose voltage is $e(0^-)/s$, as shown in Figure 15.14(b).

Also the current through the capacitor is given by

$$i(t) = C\frac{de(t)}{dt} \qquad (15.108)$$

The Laplace transform of (15.108) is

$$I(s) = sCE(s) - Ce(0^-) \qquad (15.109)$$

This current is seen to be the difference between the product of $E(s)$ and the admittance of a capacitor and a constant current equal to the Laplace transform of the impulse function $Ce(0^-)u_0(t)$. Hence, in the frequency domain, a capacitor with an initial voltage of $e(0^-)$ volts may be replaced by an initially uncharged capacitor and a current source in parallel, as shown in Figure 15.14(c).

In a dual fashion, an inductance L with the voltage–current relationship (see Figure 15.15(a)]

$$e(t) = L\frac{di(t)}{dt} \qquad (15.110)$$

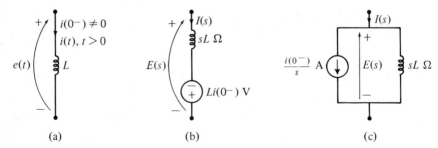

Figure 15.15 Laplace transform of an inductor with initially stored energy.

will have a Laplace transform

$$E(s) = sLI(s) - Li(0^-) \tag{15.111}$$

Equation (15.111) gives the equivalent circuit in the frequency domain, as shown in Figure 15.15(b). Or alternatively the transform of

$$i(t) = \frac{1}{L} \int_{0^-}^{t} e(t) \, dt \tag{15.112}$$

is

$$I(s) = \frac{E(s)}{sL} + \frac{e^{(-1)}(0^-)}{sL}$$

$$= \frac{E(s)}{sL} + \frac{i(0^-)}{s} \tag{15.113}$$

which gives the equivalent circuit of Figure 15.15(c).

One can readily observe that the equivalent circuit of Figures 15.14 and 15.15 are simply the frequency-domain equivalents of the equivalent circuits of similar elements in Figure 4.15.

EXAMPLE 20   The circuit of Figure 15.13, with the initial conditions and sources specified in (15.104), has the frequency-domain equivalent shown in Figure 15.16. Application of node analysis will give

$$3\left(E_1 - \frac{10}{s}\right) + 8s\left(E_1 - \frac{2}{s}\right) + 2(E_1 - E_2) = 0$$

$$\tag{15.114}$$

$$2(E_2 - E_1) + \frac{10}{s} + \frac{3}{s}E_2 + 5\left(E_2 - \frac{5}{s}\right) = 0$$

We easily see that these equations are identical to (15.105).

EXAMPLE 21   The circuit of Figure 15.17(a) is initially idle. At $t = 0$, switch S is closed. Find the current $i_2(t)$.

SOLUTION   Transforming the circuit to the frequency domain, we get the circuit of Figure 15.17(b). Since there is no energy in the circuit at $t = 0$,

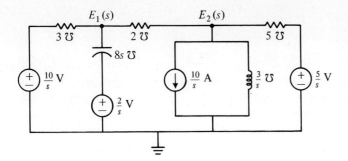

Figure 15.16 Laplace transform of the circuit of Figure 15.13.

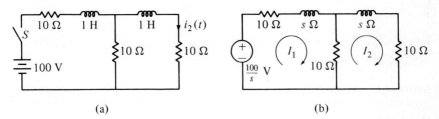

(a)   (b)

Figure 15.17 (a) A dc voltage applied to an initially idle circuit. (b) Laplace transform for the circuit of (a) for $t > 0$.

the only source present is the transform of the constant 100-V source. Now we can use mesh analysis.

$$(s+20)I_1 - 10I_2 = \frac{100}{s}; \qquad -10I_1 + (s+20)I_2 = 0 \qquad (15.115)$$

Solving for I_2, we get

$$I_2 = \frac{\begin{vmatrix} s+20 & 100/s \\ -10 & 0 \end{vmatrix}}{\begin{vmatrix} s+20 & -10 \\ -10 & s+20 \end{vmatrix}} = \frac{1000}{s(s^2+40s+300)}$$

$$= \frac{3.333}{s} - \frac{5}{s+10} + \frac{1.667}{s+30} \qquad (15.116)$$

Taking the inverse transform of I_2, we get

$$i_2(t) = 3.333 - 5\epsilon^{-10t} + 1.667\epsilon^{-30t} \text{ A} \qquad (15.117)$$

EXAMPLE 22 Suppose the switch of the circuit of Figure 15.17(a) is opened 0.1 s after it has been closed. What would be the current $i_2(t)$ after $t = 0.1$?

SOLUTION   Based on the result of the previous example, we can find i_2 at $t = 0.1$.

$$i_2(0.1) = 3.333 - 5\epsilon^{-1} + 1.667\epsilon^{-3} = 1.577 \text{ A} \qquad (15.118)$$

The situation after $t = 0.1$ is shown in Figure 15.18(a), with $i_2(0.1^-) = 1.557$ A. We can think of $t = 0.1$ as a new time reference. In other words, let $t_1 = t - 0.1$. The inductor of Figure 15.18(a) has an initial current $i_2(t_1 = 0^-)$ of 1.577 A. The frequency-domain equivalent is shown in Figure

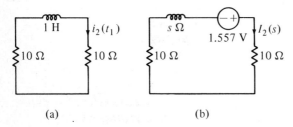

(a)   (b)

Figure 15.18   Equivalent circuits for the circuit of Figure 15.17(a), with S closed at $t = 0$ and then opened at $t = 0.1$. (a) Circuit for $t > 0.1$. (b) Laplace transform of the circuit in (a).

15.18(b). From this we readily get

$$I_2(s) = \frac{1.577}{s + 20}$$

Hence we have

$$i_2(t_1) = 1.577\epsilon^{-20t_1}, \qquad t_1 > 0$$

or

$$i_2 = 1.577\epsilon^{-20(t-0.1)}, \qquad t > 0.1 \qquad (15.119)$$

EXAMPLE 23   The circuit of Figure 15.6 may be analyzed in two separate steps. First, for $t < 0$, it is easy to see that a dc voltage is applied across the RL combination and a dc current of 0.5 A is flowing. For $t > 0$, we have

$$e_s(t) = \epsilon^{-t}; \qquad E_s(t) = \frac{1}{s+1} \qquad (15.120)$$

The inductance has an initial current of 0.5 A. Hence the frequency-domain equivalent circuit for $t > 0$ is as shown in Figure 15.19. We then have

$$I(s) = \frac{0.5 + 1/(s+1)}{s+2} = \frac{0.5s + 1.5}{(s+1)(s+2)}$$

$$= \frac{1}{s+1} - \frac{1}{2(s+2)} \qquad (15.121)$$

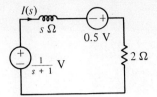

Figure 15.19 Circuit of Figure 15.6 analyzed by using dc analysis and one-sided Laplace transform.

$$i(t) = \epsilon^{-t} - 0.5\epsilon^{-2t} \text{ A}, \qquad t > 0 \tag{15.122}$$

which checks with (15.36) for the time interval $t > 0$.

EXAMPLE 24   The voltage source in the circuit of Figure 15.20 is a 110-V 60-Hz ac supply, or

$$e_s(t) = 110 \times \sqrt{2} \sin 377t \text{ V} \tag{15.123}$$

Assume that switch S has been in position a long enough for the steady state to have been reached. Also assume that, at $t = 0$, switch S is moved to position b. Find $e_2(t)$ for $t > 0$.

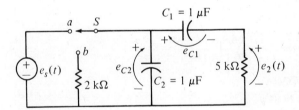

Figure 15.20

SOLUTION   For the condition of the circuit before $t = 0$, we perform an ac analysis. The circuit is shown in Figure 15.21(a). (The 2-kΩ resistor does not affect this part of the circuit.)

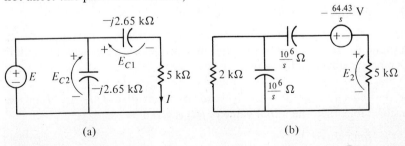

(a)   (b)

Figure 15.21   (a) The circuit of Figure 15.20 for $t < 0$. (b) Laplace transform of the circuit of Figure 15.20 for $t > 0$.

$$E = 110 \underline{/0°}$$

$$I = \frac{110}{(5-j2.65)\,k} = \frac{110}{5.66\,k\,\underline{/-27.95°}} = 19.44 \times 10^{-3}\,\underline{/27.95°}$$

$$E_{C1} = E - I \times 5\,k = 110 - 97.20\,\underline{/27.95°} = 24.14 - j45.56$$

$$= 51.56\,\underline{/-62.08°}$$

$$E_{C2} = E = 110\,\underline{/0°}$$

$$e_{c1}(t) = \sqrt{2} \times 51.56 \sin(377t - 62.08°)$$

$$e_{c1}(0) = \sqrt{2} \times 51.56 \sin(-62.08°) = -64.43$$

$$e_{c2}(0) = 0$$

For $t > 0$, we use the Laplace-transform technique. The equivalent circuit with the initial conditions taken into account is shown in Figure 15.21(b). A simple application of the voltage-division rule gives

$$E_2 = \frac{5\,k \times (64.43/s)}{5\,k + 10^6/s + \dfrac{2\,k \times 10^6/s}{2\,k + 10^6/s}}$$

$$= \frac{64.43(s+500)}{s^2 + 900s + 100{,}000} = \frac{64.43(s+500)}{(s+770.156)(s+129.844)}$$

$$= \frac{27.19}{s+770.156} + \frac{37.24}{s+129.844} \tag{15.124}$$

Thus we have

$$e_2(t) = 27.19\epsilon^{-770.156t} + 37.24\epsilon^{-129.844t}\ \text{V}, \qquad t > 0 \tag{15.125}$$

15.11 The initial-value and final-value theorems

If the Laplace transform of a time function is known, it is possible to determine its time-domain initial and final values without actually finding the complete time function itself.

The initial-value theorem If $f(t)$ and its derivative $f'(t)$ are Laplace-transformable, then the initial value of $f(t)$ is given by

$$f(0^+) = \lim_{s \to \infty} [sF(s)] \tag{15.126}$$

PROOF Consider the transform of the derivative of $f(t)$. From (15.57), we have

$$sF(s) - f(0^-) = \int_{0^-}^{\infty} \frac{df}{dt} \epsilon^{-st} \, dt$$

$$= \int_{0^-}^{0^+} \frac{df}{dt} \epsilon^{-st} \, dt + \int_{0^+}^{\infty} \frac{df}{dt} \epsilon^{-st} \, dt$$

If there is a discontinuity at $t = 0$, then $f(0^-) \neq f(0^+)$. In this case, we have

$$\int_{0^-}^{0^+} \frac{df}{dt} \epsilon^{-st} \, dt = \int_{0^-}^{0^+} [f(0^+) - f(0^-)] u_0(t) \, dt = f(0^+) - f(0^-)$$

Hence

$$sF(s) = f(0^+) + \int_{0^+}^{\infty} \frac{df}{dt} \epsilon^{-st} \, dt \qquad (15.127)$$

Since df/dt is finite, the last integral vanishes as $s \to \infty$. Passing the limit for $s \to \infty$ in (15.126), we obtain

$$f(0^+) = \lim_{s \to \infty} [sF(s)]$$

For example, for the circuit of Figure 15.17, from (15.116) we have

$$I_2(s) = \frac{1000}{s(s^2 + 40s + 300)}$$

Using (15.126), we may say that

$$i_2(0^+) = \lim_{s \to \infty} [sI_2(s)] = 0$$

which checks with $i_2(0^+)$ of (15.117).

As another example, for the current of Figure 15.19, from (15.121) we have

$$I(s) = \frac{0.5s + 1.5}{(s+1)(s+2)}$$

Applying (15.126), we have

$$i(0^+) = \lim_{s \to \infty} \frac{(0.5s + 1.5) s}{(s+1)(s+2)} = 0.5$$

which checks with the $i(0^+)$ given by (15.122).

Final-value theorem If $f(t)$ and its first derivative are Laplace-transformable, then its final value is given by

$$f(\infty) = \lim_{s \to 0} [sF(s)] \qquad (15.128)$$

PROOF   Again starting with (15.57), we get

$$sF(s) = f(0^-) + \int_{0^-}^{\infty} \frac{df}{dt} \epsilon^{-st}\, dt$$

Now we pass the limit for $s \to 0$ to obtain

$$\lim_{s \to 0} sF(s) = f(0^-) + \int_{0^-}^{\infty} \frac{df}{dt}\, dt = f(0^-) + f(t)\bigg|_{0^-}^{\infty} = f(\infty)$$

Take the same examples used for the initial-value theorem. From (15.116), we get

$$I_2(s) = \frac{1000}{s(s^2+40s+300)}$$

The final-value theorem gives

$$i_2(\infty) = \lim_{s \to 0} \frac{1000}{s^2+40s+300} = \frac{10}{3}$$

which checks with what we would have obtained from (15.117).

Again, for the current of Figure 15.19, and from (15.121) we get

$$I(s) = \frac{0.5s+1.5}{(s+1)(s+2)}$$

The final-value theorem gives

$$i(\infty) = \lim_{s \to 0} \frac{(0.5s+1.5)\, s}{(s+1)(s+2)} = 0$$

which again agrees with what we would have obtained from (15.122).

In both of these theorems, we have assumed that $f(0^+)$ or $f(\infty)$ exists in the limit. It is possible that the limit of the time function does not exist, while the limit of $sF(s)$ does. In that case, the theorems are no longer valid. For example, if we have

$$\mathcal{L}[\cos \omega_0 t] = \frac{s}{s^2+\omega_0^2} = F(s)$$

the limit will be

$$\lim_{s \to 0} [sF(s)] = \lim_{s \to 0} \frac{s^2}{s^2+\omega_0^2} = 0$$

But

$$\lim_{t \to \infty} (\cos \omega_0 t)$$

does not exist.

Generally speaking, the theorem is no longer applicable if $F(s)$ has j-axis or right-half-plane poles.

15.12   Calculation of impulse response by Laplace transform

In Chapter 12, we described the procedure to analyze a circuit problem in the time domain. The circuit is characterized by its impulse response. The actual response is the convolution of the particular excitation and the impulse response.

In Chapter 14 (specifically Section 14.3), a parallelism was pointed out between the time-domain analysis and the analysis on the j axis of the frequency domain. The following terms were cited as counterparts in the two domains:

Time domain		Frequency domain
$x(t)$	[Excitation]	$X(j\omega)$
$y(t)$	[Response]	$Y(j\omega)$
$h(t)$		$F(j\omega)$

Impulse response	Network function
$y(t) = h(t) * x(t)$	$Y(j\omega) = F(j\omega) X(j\omega)$
$x(t) = u_0(t)$	$X(j\omega) = 1$

This idea of a time–frequency domain relationship is also applicable to the Laplace transform. The only new point is that now we are no longer restricted to the j axis of the s plane. More time functions are transformable. The notation is more compact (s in place of $j\omega$). For the one-sided transform, we require no knowledge of what went on before $t = 0$. As long as we know the conditions for $t = 0^-$, we can apply the Laplace transform to the complete solution of circuit problems, as illustrated in Section 15.9.

Back in Chapter 12, we mentioned that the solution of the impulse response of a network is seldom done in the time domain. It should be obvious to you now why it is so much easier to find the impulse response in the frequency domain. In finding the impulse response, we are really solving a very special class of network problem. We let the excitation be 1 volt or 1 ampere. All the initial conditions are zero. We get the response in the s domain. Then we perform the inverse transform. That's it!

As an example, take the circuit of Figure 12.3, for which we set up the integral-differential equation (12.6). We did not carry out the analysis after that. To find the impulse response now, we first get its s-domain circuit, as shown in Figure 15.22. Using node analysis and considering the branch with the capacitor as a single branch, we have

$$\frac{E_1 - 1}{1} + \frac{E_1}{1+s} + \frac{E_1}{1+1/s} = 0 \tag{15.129}$$

Solving for E_1, we get

$$E_1 = \tfrac{1}{2}$$

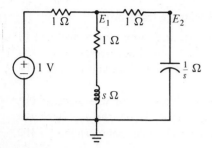

Figure 15.22 Equivalent circuit used to find the impulse response of the circuit of Figure 12.3

Thus

$$E_2 = \frac{1/s}{1+1/s} E_1 = \frac{1}{1+s} E_1 = \frac{\frac{1}{2}}{1+s}$$ (15.130)

Hence the impulse response is

$$h(t) = e_2(t)|_{e_s(t)=u_0(t)} = 0.5\epsilon^{-t}$$ (15.131)

In the solution of E_1 from (15.129), we cancelled the factor $(s+1)$. That is the reason why the answer for E_1 happens to be so simple. This fact is not at all apparent from (12.6).

15.13 Finding the two-sided Laplace transform from the one-sided Laplace transforms

In Section 15.4 we mentioned that one of the reasons why the two-sided transform is not as widely studied as the one-sided transform is the fact that the former can be found from the latter. We shall now explain briefly how to accomplish this. It is also important to understand this relationship because most published tables are for the one-sided transform.

Given an $f(t)$ from $t=-\infty$ to $t=\infty$, we can always split it up into two functions, of which one is equal to zero for $t<0$ and the other for $t>0$. In other words, we define

$$f_1(t) = f(t)u_{-1}(t)$$ (15.132)

and

$$f_2(t) = f(t)u_{-1}(-t)$$ (15.133)

The two-sided Laplace transform of $f(t)$ is

$$\int_{-\infty}^{\infty} f(t)\epsilon^{-st}\,dt = \int_{-\infty}^{0} f_2(t)\epsilon^{-st}\,dt + \int_{0}^{\infty} f_1(t)\epsilon^{-st}\,dt$$

Changing the sign of t in the first integral, we get

$$\int_{-\infty}^{\infty} f(t)\epsilon^{-st}\,dt = \int_{0}^{\infty} f_2(-t)\epsilon^{st}\,dt + \int_{0}^{\infty} f_1(t)\epsilon^{-st}\,dt$$

$$= F_2(-s) + F_1(s) \tag{15.134}$$

where

$$F_1(s) = \mathscr{L}[f_1(t)] \tag{15.135}$$

and

$$F_2(s) = \mathscr{L}[f_2(-t)] \tag{15.136}$$

The first term on the right-hand side of (15.134), $F_2(-s)$, is the one-sided Laplace transform of the mirror image of $f_2(t)$, with every s replaced by $-s$. The region of convergence of $[F_1(s)+F_2(-s)]$ is the region of convergence common to both $F_1(s)$ and $F_2(-s)$. Since both $F_1(s)$ and $F_2(s)$ are one-sided transforms, their regions of convergence extend to the right. If we denote their abscissas of convergence as σ_{a1} and σ_{a2}, respectively, then their regions of convergence are $\sigma > \sigma_{a1}$ and $\sigma > \sigma_{a2}$, respectively. Hence the region of convergence for $F_2(-s)$ is $\sigma < -\sigma_{a2}$ and the region of convergence for the two-sided transform $[F_1(s)+F_2(-s)]$ is $\sigma_{a1} < \sigma < -\sigma_{a2}$. This is illustrated in Figure 15.23. If these two regions fail to overlap, then the two-sided Laplace transform of $f(t)$ does not exist.

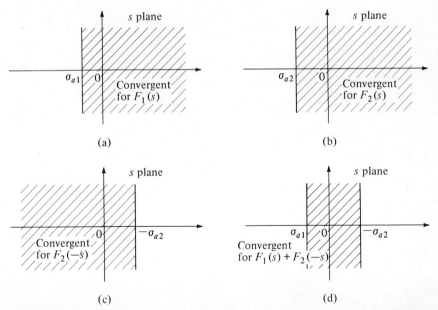

Figure 15.23 Region of convergence of the two-sided Laplace transform of a function as related to the abscissas of convergence of the one-sided transforms of the same function.

EXAMPLE 25   For the $f(t)$ of Figure 15.24, we have

$$f_1(t) = \epsilon^{-at}u_{-1}(t), \qquad a > 0$$

$$f_2(t) = \epsilon^{bt}u_{-1}(-t), \qquad b > 0$$

$$f_2(-t) = \epsilon^{-bt}u_{-1}(t)$$

$$F_1(s) = [f_1(t)] = \frac{1}{s+a}, \qquad \sigma > -a$$

$$F_2(s) = [f_2(-t)] = \frac{1}{s+b}, \qquad \sigma > -b$$

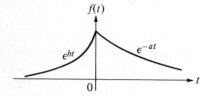

Figure 15.24

Hence we get

$$\int_{-\infty}^{\infty} f(t)\epsilon^{-st}\,dt = F_1(s) + F_2(-s) = \frac{1}{s+a} + \frac{1}{b-s}, \qquad -a < \sigma < b$$

$$(15.137)$$

EXAMPLE 26   For the function

$$f(t) = t, \qquad -\infty < t < \infty$$

we have

$$f_1(t) = tu_{-1}(t)$$

$$f_2(-t) = -tu_{-1}(t)$$

$$F_1(s) = \frac{1}{s^2}, \qquad \sigma > 0$$

$$F_2(s) = -\frac{1}{s^2}, \qquad \sigma > 0$$

$$F_2(-s) = -\frac{1}{s^2}, \qquad \sigma < 0$$

The regions of convergence of $F_1(s)$ and $F_2(-s)$ fail to overlap each other. Hence the two-sided Laplace transform of $f(t) = t$ does not exist.

Problems

15.1 Find the two-sided Laplace transform of each of the functions in Figure P15.1. Give their regions of convergence.

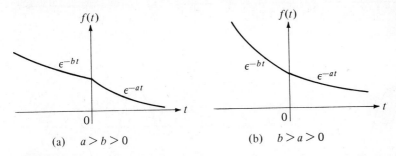

(a) $a > b > 0$ (b) $b > a > 0$

Figure P15.1

15.2 Find the inverse Laplace transforms of the following functions:

(a) $F(s) = \dfrac{s}{(s+1)(s+2)}, \qquad \sigma < -2$

(b) $F(s) = \dfrac{s}{(s+1)(s+2)}, \qquad -2 < \sigma < -1$

(c) $F(s) = \dfrac{s}{(s+1)(s+2)}, \qquad -1 < \sigma$

15.3 Find the regions of convergence of the two-sided Laplace transforms of the following functions: (a) $\epsilon^{tu_{-1}(t)}$;   (b) $\epsilon^{-tu_{-1}(t)}$.

15.4 Find the one-sided Laplace transforms of the following functions: (a) $t^2 \epsilon^{-t}$;   (b) $t \sin \beta t$.

15.5 Find the Laplace transforms of each of the functions in Figure P15.5.

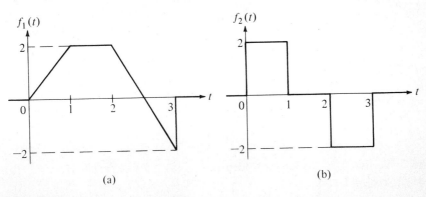

(a)   (b)

Figure P15.5 (continued on page 506)

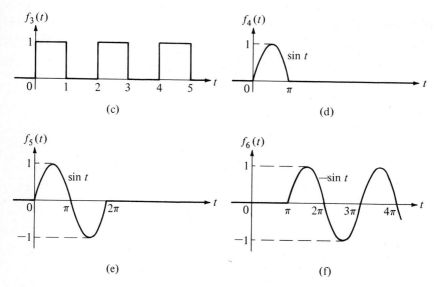

Figure P15.5 (continued)

15.6 Find the Laplace transform of the functions in Figure P15.6.

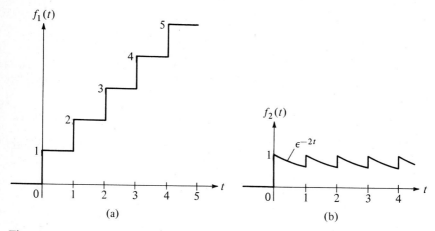

Figure P15.6

15.7 Verify the following identities: (a) $\mathcal{L}\left[1/\sqrt{\pi t}\right] = 1/\sqrt{s}$; (b) $\mathcal{L}\left[2\sqrt{t/\pi}\right] = 1/s\sqrt{s}$.

15.8 Find the inverse Laplace transforms (one-sided) of the following functions:

(a) $\dfrac{s^2-s+1}{s^2(s+1)}$

(b) $\dfrac{8s^2+8s+1}{4s^2+6s+2}$

(c) $\dfrac{s(s+2)}{s^2+2s+2}$

(d) $\dfrac{s+2}{s^3(s^2+1)}$

(e) $\dfrac{1}{s(s^2-2s+5)}$

(f) $\dfrac{1}{s^3(s^2-1)}$

(g) $\dfrac{1}{s\cosh s}$

(h) $\dfrac{1}{s\sinh s}$

(i) $\dfrac{n!}{s(s+1)(s+2)\cdots(s+n)}$

15.9 Solve the following differential equations by the Laplace-transform method for the part of the x axis where $x > 0$.

(a) $\dfrac{d^2y}{dx^2}+4\dfrac{dy}{dx}+3y=0,\qquad y(0)=1,\qquad \dfrac{dy}{dt}(0)=-1$

(b) $\dfrac{d^2y}{dx^2}+4\dfrac{dy}{dx}+3y=3,\qquad y(0)=1,\qquad \dfrac{dy}{dx}(0)=3$

(c) $\dfrac{d^2y}{dx^2}+\dfrac{dy}{dx}=x^2+2x,\qquad y(0)=4,\qquad \dfrac{dy}{dx}(0)=-2$

15.10 Find $i(t)$ for $t > 0$ for the circuit of Figure P15.10. The battery remains in place from $t = -\infty$ to $t = \infty$, and $e_s = 4u_{-1}(t)$ V.

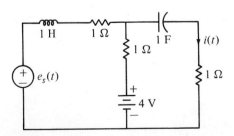

Figure P15.10

15.11 Find $e_o(t)$ for $t > 0$ for the circuit of Figure P15.11. Assume that $e_s(t) = 4 - \epsilon^{-t}u_{-1}(t)$ V.

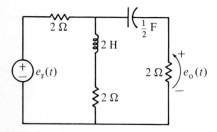

Figure P15.11

15.12 Find $i_L(t)$ for $t > 0$ for the circuit of Figure P15.12. Assume that $i_L(0^-) = 1$ A and $e_s = 2u_{-1}(t)$ V.

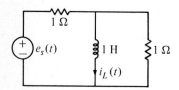

Figure P15.12

15.13 In the circuit of Figure P15.13, the battery has been in place since $t = -\infty$. Switch S is closed at $t = 0$. Find $i_2(t)$ for $t > 0$.

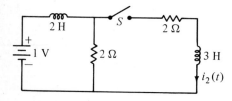

Figure P15.13

15.14 The circuit of Figure P15.14 is initially idle. At $t = 0$, switch S is closed. Find $i_1(t)$ for $t > 0$.

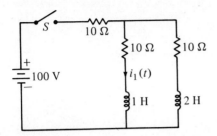

Figure P15.14

15.15 With switch S in position a, the circuit of Figure P15.15 has attained steady state. At $t = 0$, S is moved to position b. Find $e_2(t)$ for $t > 0$.

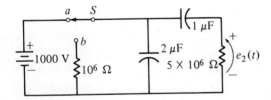

Figure P15.15

15.16 In the circuit of Figure P15.16, switch S is open and the circuit has reached a steady state. Switch S is closed at $t = 0$. Find $i_2(t)$ for $t > 0$.

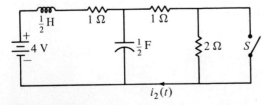

Figure P15.16

15.17 In the circuit of Figure P15.17 the steady state has been attained and switch S is opened at $t = 0$. Find $i_1(t)$ for $t > 0$.

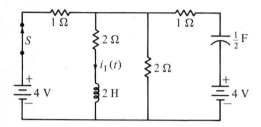

Figure P15.17

15.18 In the circuit of Figure P15.18, $e_s(t) = 2 \cos 3t$ V. After the steady state has been reached, switch S is opened at $t = 0$. Find $e_2(t)$ for $t > 0$.

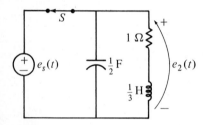

Figure P15.18

15.19 Find the initial and final values of the time functions that correspond to the following frequency-domain functions:

(a) $\dfrac{7s-2}{s^2+2s+3}$

(b) $\dfrac{s^2+3}{s(s+2)(s+4)}$

(c) $\dfrac{1}{s^2+s+1}$

(d) $\dfrac{s^2+1}{s(s^2+s+1)}$

15.20 Find the two-sided Laplace transform of the function $f(t) = \epsilon^{-tu} - 1(t)$ through the one-sided transforms.

15.21 Which of the inverse Laplace transforms found in Problem 15.2 can be found by using a table of one-sided transforms? For those that can, find their corresponding time functions.

16 | STATE-VARIABLE METHOD OF SYSTEM ANALYSIS

In Chapter 2, we presented several systematic methods of writing out a set of equations to solve for a set of independent unknowns in a network or system. These methods readily give the answers in linear networks either when the network is memoryless or when only the steady-state ac solution is of interest. When the network is not memoryless and we seek the complete solution—both transient and steady-state—we must use integral-differential equations. Solution of these equations is then best carried out in the complex-frequency (s) domain through the Laplace transform.

Earlier we also mentioned that there are many techniques other than the loop, cutset, mesh, and node-analysis methods that are just as general and just as systematic. Furthermore, some of these can be even more powerful under certain special circumstances. This chapter deals with one such method—the *state-variable method*.

Unlike the classical method of solving a memory system by first reducing the equations to a single equation that involves only one unknown, the state-variable method leads to a set of first-order differential equations. The properties of such a group of equations and their solution have been thoroughly studied. Thus it is possible to gain insight into a system through this set of equations. The state-variable method is also a convenient means of implementing the analysis of a system by analog or digital computers.

When we are looking for the solution of a time-varying or nonlinear network, the state-variable method is the most convenient to use. In fact, it is almost an indispensable tool. In this chapter, however, we shall limit our examples to LTI networks. Unfortunately, the powerfulness of this method is not obvious when applied to simple LTI networks. Hence the material in this chapter is not designed to confirm the effectiveness of the state-variable method as compared with others. Rather, it simply demonstrates how the implementation of this method differs from that of other methods and the details that are involved in the LTI case.

16.1   The concept of the state of a network and its state equation

Let us take a simple circuit whose behavior is already well known to us to illustrate the concept of the *state* of a network. The process of charging a capacitor through a resistor is illustrated in Figure 16.1(a). From Figure 4.10, we have

$$e_C(t) = E(1 - \epsilon^{-(1/RC)t}) \tag{16.1}$$

This voltage is illustrated in Figure 16.1(c).

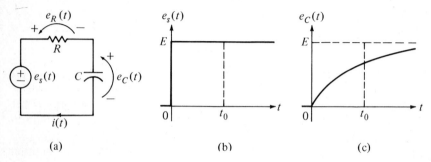

(a)   (b)   (c)

Figure 16.1   The charging of a capacitor.

We can make a couple of observations about this problem. First, our knowledge of $e_C(t)$, along with the information about $e_s(t)$, gives us complete information on the behavior of the circuit. This is to say, if we know $e_s(t)$ and $e_C(t)$, we know almost everything there is to know about the circuit. There are only two other quantities in the circuit—$e_R(t)$ and $i(t)$. Both can be found readily.

$$e_R(t) = e_s(t) - e_C(t) \tag{16.2}$$

$$i(t) = C\frac{de_C(t)}{dt} = \frac{e_s(t) - e_C(t)}{R} \tag{16.3}$$

The other observation is that, if we know $e_C(t)$ at any $t = t_0$ and $e_s(t)$ for $t > t_0$, the behavior of the network for $t > t_0$ is completely determined [this is equivalent to saying that $e_C(t)$ is completely determined for $t > t_0$]. In other words, it does not matter how $e_C(t)$ attained its value at $t = t_0$ and it does not matter how $e_s(t)$ varied before $t = t_0$. The situation indicated in Figure 16.1 is merely one of the many ways $e_C(t)$ could have arrived at $e_C(t_0)$. For example, in Figure 16.2, exactly the same value for $e_C(t_0)$ is reached in a

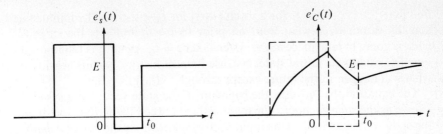

Figure 16.2 A different sequence of events leading to the identical occurrence for $t > t_0$ as in Figure 16.1.

different manner. But since $e'_s(t) = E$ for $t > t_0$, we must have $e_C(t) = e'_C(t)$ for $t > t_0$. If we covered up the parts of the graphs to the left of $t = t_0$ in both Figures 16.1 and 16.2, we could not tell the difference between the two sets of voltages. In other words, $e_C(t_0)$ describes the *state* of the circuit at $t = t_0$ that completely describes the behavior of the circuit for all $t \geq t_0$ for a given $e_s(t)$.

Following the pattern of this very simple example, we see that, in general, we can select a set of variables in a system (either currents or voltages, or both) to describe the situation of the system at any particular time. These are called *state variables*. The values of these variables at any instant describe the *state* of the system at that time. The analysis of a system by the state-variable method amounts to finding the state of the system in any desired time interval. Once we have done this, we can express any desired quantities in terms of the state variables.

The state-variable method is schematically represented by the block diagram of Figure 16.3. There are n state variables—$x_1, x_2, ..., x_n$. The vector $[x]$ whose elements are the state variables is known as the *state vector*. There are m inputs and p outputs—$u_1, u_2, ..., u_m$ and $y_1, y_2, ..., y_p$, respectively. In a particular problem, the state vector at t_0, $[x(t_0)]$, is known as the *initial state* for the state vector in the time interval $t_0 < t < t_1$. The problem is to

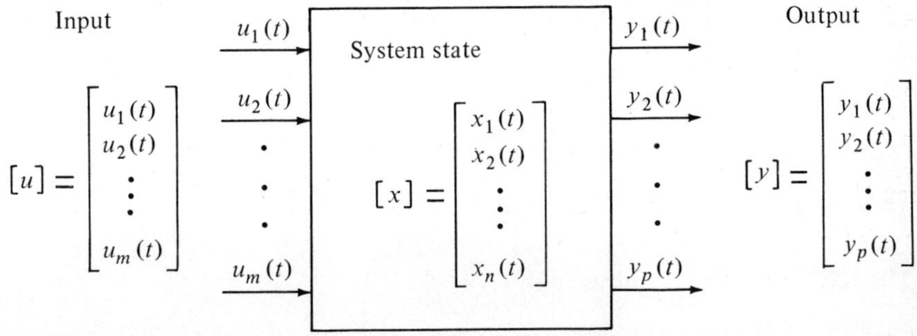

Input $u_1(t)$ System state $y_1(t)$ Output

$$[u] = \begin{bmatrix} u_1(t) \\ u_2(t) \\ \vdots \\ u_m(t) \end{bmatrix} \qquad \begin{matrix} u_1(t) \\ u_2(t) \\ \cdot \\ \cdot \\ u_m(t) \end{matrix} \qquad [x] = \begin{bmatrix} x_1(t) \\ x_2(t) \\ \vdots \\ x_n(t) \end{bmatrix} \qquad \begin{matrix} y_1(t) \\ y_2(t) \\ \cdot \\ \cdot \\ y_p(t) \end{matrix} \qquad [y] = \begin{bmatrix} y_1(t) \\ y_2(t) \\ \vdots \\ y_p(t) \end{bmatrix}$$

Figure 16.3 State-variable representation of a system or network.

find $[x(t)]$ for $t_0 < t < t_1$ for a given $[u(t)]$ for $t_0 < t < t_1$. The initial state actually summarizes what went on prior to $t = t_0$ and sets the stage for what is going to take place in the system after $t = t_0$. Again it is unimportant how $[x]$ attains its initial state, because its past history has no bearing on what will happen in the future except through $[x(t_0)]$.

The equation that governs the behavior of the state vector of a system is known as the *state equation*. The relationship between the output vector and the state vector, as well as the input vector, is known as the *output equation*.

In the simple system of Figure 16.1 every vector is one-dimensional. Nevertheless, the concept of the state-variable method still applies. Specifically, the input vector is

$$[u(t)] = e_s(t) = u_{-1}(t) \tag{16.4}$$

and the state vector is

$$[x(t)] = e_C(t) \tag{16.5}$$

The state equation is

$$e_s(t) = RC\frac{de_C}{dt} + e_C \tag{16.6}$$

If $i(t)$ is designated as the output (or response), then

$$[y(t)] = i(t) = -\frac{1}{R}e_C(t) + \frac{1}{R}e_s(t) = -\frac{1}{R}[x(t)] + \frac{1}{R}[u(t)] \tag{16.7}$$

would be the output equation.

Let us now look at a slightly more complex system. Suppose we have the circuit of Figure 16.4. We choose $e_C(t)$ and $i_L(t)$ as our state variables, or

$$[x] = \begin{bmatrix} e_C \\ i_L \end{bmatrix} \tag{16.8}$$

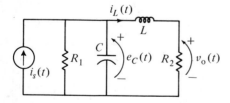

Figure 16.4

The KCL equation requires that

$$C\frac{de_C}{dt} = -\frac{1}{R_1}e_C + i_s - i_L \tag{16.9}$$

The KVL equation requires that

$$L\frac{di_L}{dt} = e_C - R_2 i_L \tag{16.10}$$

We may write (16.9) and (16.10) in matrix form.

$$\begin{bmatrix} \dfrac{de_C}{dt} \\[2mm] \dfrac{di_L}{dt} \end{bmatrix} = \begin{bmatrix} -\dfrac{1}{R_1 C} & -\dfrac{1}{C} \\[2mm] \dfrac{1}{L} & -\dfrac{R_2}{L} \end{bmatrix} \begin{bmatrix} e_C \\[2mm] i_L \end{bmatrix} + \begin{bmatrix} \dfrac{1}{C} \\[2mm] 0 \end{bmatrix} i_s \tag{16.11}$$

This is the state equation. If we designate the voltage across R_2 as the output, then the output equation will read

$$v_o = \begin{bmatrix} 0 & R_2 \end{bmatrix} \begin{bmatrix} e_C \\[1mm] i_L \end{bmatrix} + [0] i_s \tag{16.12}$$

The state equation and the output equation of a system have the general form

$$\frac{d}{dt}[x] = [\dot{x}] = [A][x] + [B][u] \tag{16.13}$$

$$[y] = [C][x] + [D][u] \tag{16.14}$$

This format is known as the *normal* or *standard* form.

16.2 The proper network and its state equation

The examples we used in the last section were both very simple and we obtained their state equations by simple manipulation of the terms in the KVL and KCL equations into the normal form. For more complicated networks, some systematic methods that will enable us to arrive at the state equations straightforwardly are highly desirable. One such scheme is described here first for a special class of networks and then, by way of examples, for any general network.

In Chapter 2, we used the concept of the tree and cotree to ensure that the number of unknowns used and the number of independent equations obtained were just right for the analysis of a network. An extension of that idea is used here for the state-variable method.

First of all, when we use the state-variable method, it is most convenient to treat each element as an individual branch. There is no question that we *can* do this. Indeed, it will soon become clear that, if we combined several elements in one branch, we might obscure the roles of the individual elements. This is contrary to the purpose of the state-variable method.

If we are to obtain a convenient set of state equations in normal form, our choice of state variables is important. We want only the first derivatives (no integrals or higher derivatives) of the variables to appear in the state equation without further manipulation. For this purpose, we define a network as *proper* if it has a tree that includes all the capacitive branches and no inductive branches, and if, at the same time, the cotree includes all the inductive branches and no capacitive branches. Such a tree is called a *proper tree*. In constructing a proper tree of a network, we may have to include some resistive branches in both the tree and the cotree. As before, all voltage sources (controlled and independent) should be included in the tree and all current sources should be included in the cotree.

Of course, not every network has a proper tree. Each of the networks of Figure 16.5(a) and (b) has a proper tree, as indicated by the heavy lines.

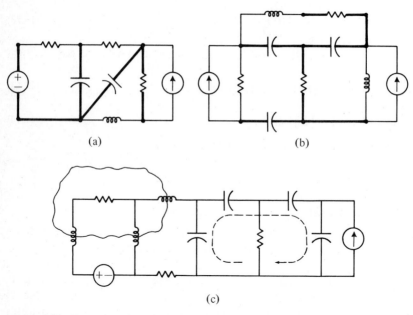

(a) (b)

(c)

Figure 16.5 Examples of proper and improper networks.

But, in the network of Figure 16.5(c), there is no way to include all four capacitors in any tree and all three inductors in its cotree. This occurs when we have closed loops made up of only capacitors and voltage sources, and when we have cutsets that include only inductors and current sources. Methods for handling a network that is not proper will be discussed later.

We distinguish a proper network from an improper one because the number of state variables necessary and sufficient to describe a proper network is exactly the total number of inductors and capacitors. This is evident from the following two considerations:

1 Once all the capacitor voltages and the inductor currents are known, the voltages and the currents in the remainder of the network are completely defined, inasmuch as the remainder of the network is memoryless. Hence the capacitor voltages and the inductor currents are sufficient to define the state of the network.

2 If a number of capacitors form a closed loop, their voltages, both initial and subsequent, are not independent. Hence not all of these voltages need to be included as the state variables. A similar statement can be made about a number of inductive currents that are intersected by a closed ambit.

We shall now formulate a set of procedures by which to obtain the state equation of a proper network.

1 Choose a proper tree, and thereby its associated cotree, for the network.

2 Assign a voltage variable to each capacitor and a current variable to each inductor. These are the state variables.

3 Assign a voltage variable to each resistor in the tree and a current variable to each resistor in the cotree.

4 Write each capacitor current in terms of its voltage $[i_C = C(de_C/dt)]$ and express it in terms of the link currents by the KCL equation for the ambit that intersects only the tree branch with this capacitor and some links.

5 Write each inductor voltage in terms of its current $[e_L = L(di_L/dt)]$ and express it in terms of the tree voltages by the KVL equation for the loop that traces only the link with this inductor and some tree branches.

6 For each tree resistor, write its current in terms of its voltage $(i = e/R)$ and then express it in terms of the link currents.

7 For each link resistor, write its voltage in terms of its current $(e = iR)$ and then express it in terms of the tree-branch voltages.

8 From the equations obtained in steps 6 and 7, solve for the tree resistor voltages and link resistor currents in terms of the state variables.

9 Substitute the solutions obtained in step 8 into those obtained in steps 4 and 5. Rearrange them in matrix form to arrive at the state equation in normal form.

EXAMPLE 1   For the network shown in Figure 16.6 we choose the tree as shown. Step 4 reads

$$\frac{de_1}{dt} = i_2 + i_5 + i_s \tag{16.15}$$

Step 5 gives

$$\frac{di_2}{dt} = -e_3 - e_1 \tag{16.16}$$

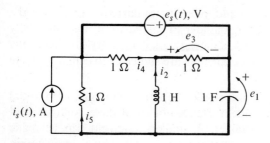

Figure 16.6

Step 6 gives

$$e_3 = i_2 + i_4 \qquad (16.17)$$

Step 7 yields

$$i_4 = -e_3 - e_s \qquad (16.18)$$

$$i_5 = e_s - e_1 \qquad (16.19)$$

Writing (16.17) through (16.19) into a set of simultaneous equations, we get

$$e_3 - i_4 = i_2; \qquad e_3 + i_4 = -e_s; \qquad i_5 = -e_1 + e_s$$

Generally, we need to solve these three equations simultaneously. However, in this case the solution is much simpler because several of the coefficients on the left-hand side happen to be zero. Whence we get

$$e_3 = \tfrac{1}{2}(i_2 - e_s); \qquad i_4 = \tfrac{1}{2}(-i_2 - e_s); \qquad i_5 = -e_1 + e_s \qquad (16.20)$$

This is step 8. As step 9, we substitute (16.20) into (16.15) and (16.16) to get

$$\frac{de_1}{dt} = i_2 - e_1 + e_s + i_s; \qquad \frac{di_2}{dt} = -\tfrac{1}{2}(i_2 - e_s) - e_1$$

Rearranging, we get

$$\begin{bmatrix} \dfrac{de_1}{dt} \\[2mm] \dfrac{di_2}{dt} \end{bmatrix} = \begin{bmatrix} -1 & 1 \\ -1 & -\tfrac{1}{2} \end{bmatrix} \begin{bmatrix} e_1 \\ i_2 \end{bmatrix} + \begin{bmatrix} 1 & 1 \\ \tfrac{1}{2} & 0 \end{bmatrix} \begin{bmatrix} e_s \\ i_s \end{bmatrix} \qquad (16.21)$$

which is in normal form.

EXAMPLE 2   For the network of Figure 16.7, we have for steps 4 and 5

$$C_1 \frac{de_1}{dt} = -i_3 + i_5$$

$$C_2 \frac{de_2}{dt} = i_3 - i_6 + i_s \qquad (16.22)$$

$$L_3 \frac{di_3}{dt} = -e_2 + e_1$$

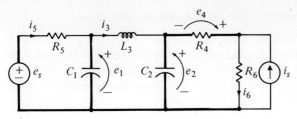

Figure 16.7

For steps 6 and 7, we have

$$\frac{e_4}{R_4} = -i_6 + i_s; \qquad i_5 R_5 = -e_1 + e_s; \qquad i_6 R_6 = e_2 + e_4 \qquad (16.23)$$

or

$$\begin{bmatrix} \dfrac{1}{R_4} & 0 & 1 \\[2mm] 0 & R_5 & 0 \\[2mm] -1 & 0 & R_6 \end{bmatrix} \begin{bmatrix} e_4 \\[2mm] i_5 \\[2mm] i_6 \end{bmatrix} = \begin{bmatrix} i_s \\[2mm] -e_1 + e_s \\[2mm] e_2 \end{bmatrix} \qquad (16.24)$$

which gives

$$e_4 = -\frac{R_4}{R_4 + R_6} e_2 + \frac{R_4 R_6}{R_4 + R_6} i_s$$

$$i_5 = -\frac{e_1}{R_5} + \frac{e_s}{R_5} \qquad (16.25)$$

$$i_6 = \frac{e_2}{R_4 + R_6} + \frac{R_4}{R_4 + R_6} i_s$$

Substitution gives

$$\begin{bmatrix} \dfrac{de_1}{dt} \\[3mm] \dfrac{de_2}{dt} \\[3mm] \dfrac{di_3}{dt} \end{bmatrix} = \begin{bmatrix} -\dfrac{1}{C_1 R_5} & 0 & -\dfrac{1}{C_1} \\[3mm] 0 & -\dfrac{1}{C_2(R_4 + R_6)} & \dfrac{1}{C_2} \\[3mm] \dfrac{1}{L_3} & -\dfrac{1}{L_3} & 0 \end{bmatrix} \begin{bmatrix} e_1 \\[3mm] e_2 \\[3mm] i_3 \end{bmatrix}$$

$$+ \begin{bmatrix} \dfrac{1}{C_1 R_5} & 0 \\[3mm] 0 & \dfrac{R_6}{C_2(R_4 + R_6)} \\[3mm] 0 & 0 \end{bmatrix} \begin{bmatrix} e_s \\[3mm] i_s \end{bmatrix} \qquad (16.26)$$

16.3 Networks with controlled sources and mutual inductances

When controlled sources are present in a network, the procedure is exactly the same as when the network has only independent sources. We first treat the controlled sources as if they were independent ones. An additional step is then required after step 8, in which we express the strengths of all the controlled sources in terms of the state variables.

EXAMPLE 3   For the network of Figure 16.8, we have

$$C_1 \frac{de_1}{dt} = i_2 + i_4; \qquad L_2 \frac{di_2}{dt} = -e_1 + e_s + e_{cs} + e_3 \tag{16.27}$$

and

$$\frac{e_3}{R_3} = i_{cs} - i_2; \qquad i_4 R_4 = -e_1 + e_s \tag{16.28}$$

Substitution of the expressions for e_3 and i_4 from (16.28) into (16.27) accomplishes step 8. Thus we get

$$C_1 \frac{de_1}{dt} = i_2 - \frac{e_1}{R_4} + \frac{e_s}{R_4}$$

$$L_2 \frac{di_2}{dt} = -e_1 + e_s + r_m\left(-\frac{e_1}{R_4} + \frac{e_s}{R_4}\right) + R_3\left(\alpha C_1 \frac{de_1}{dt} - i_2\right) \tag{16.29}$$

Writing (16.29) in matrix form we get

$$
\begin{bmatrix} C_1 & 0 \\ -\alpha C_1 R_3 & L_2 \end{bmatrix}
\begin{bmatrix} \dfrac{de_1}{dt} \\ \dfrac{di_2}{dt} \end{bmatrix}
=
\begin{bmatrix} -\dfrac{1}{R_4} & 1 \\ -1 - \dfrac{r_m}{R_4} & -R_3 \end{bmatrix}
\begin{bmatrix} e_1 \\ i_2 \end{bmatrix}
$$
$$
+ \begin{bmatrix} \dfrac{1}{R_4} \\ 1 + \dfrac{r_m}{R_4} \end{bmatrix} e_s \tag{16.30}
$$

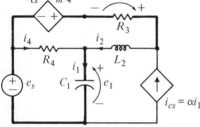

Figure 16.8

Multiplying both sides from the left by

$$
\begin{bmatrix} C_1 & 0 \\ -\alpha C_1 R_3 & L_2 \end{bmatrix}^{-1} = \begin{bmatrix} \dfrac{1}{C_1} & 0 \\ \dfrac{\alpha R_3}{L_2} & \dfrac{1}{L_2} \end{bmatrix}
$$

gives

$$
\begin{bmatrix} \dfrac{de_1}{dt} \\ \dfrac{di_2}{dt} \end{bmatrix} = \begin{bmatrix} -\dfrac{1}{C_1 R_4} & \dfrac{1}{C_1} \\ -\dfrac{\alpha R_3 + R_4 + r_m}{L_2 R_4} & \dfrac{(\alpha-1)R_3}{L_2} \end{bmatrix} \begin{bmatrix} e_1 \\ i_2 \end{bmatrix}
$$

$$
+ \begin{bmatrix} \dfrac{1}{C_1 R_4} \\ \dfrac{\alpha R_3 + R_4 + r_m}{L_2 R_4} \end{bmatrix} e_s \tag{16.31}
$$

Since mutual inductances can be replaced by controlled sources, we can treat mutual inductances in a network in exactly the same way as controlled sources.

16.4 State equation of an improper network

When a network does not have a proper tree or cotree, we simply choose as many capacitors as permissible to complete a tree and as many inductors as permissible to complete a cotree. Then we use only tree capacitor voltages and link inductor currents as the state variables and proceed as before. The effects of link capacitor currents and tree inductor voltages are somewhat similar to those of controlled sources. This is best illustrated by an example.

EXAMPLE 4   Take the network of Figure 16.9. We cannot include all three capacitors in a tree. So we leave C_3 in the cotree. We now have

$$
C_1 \frac{de_1}{dt} = i_4 - i_3 - i_5; \qquad C_2 \frac{de_2}{dt} = -i_3 - i_5 \tag{16.32}
$$

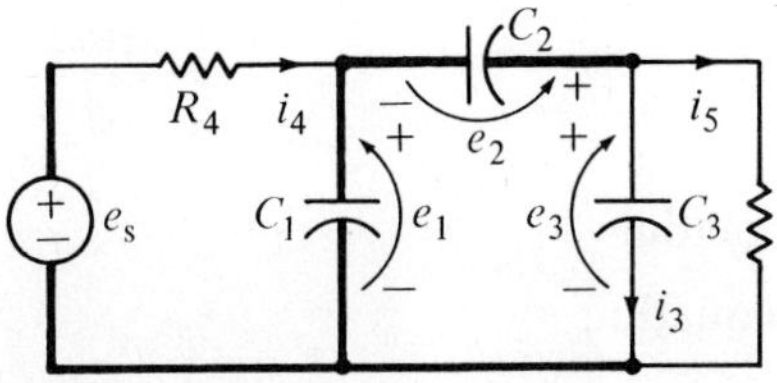

Figure 16.9 Example of steps used to obtain the state equation of an improper network.

and

$$R_4 i_4 = -e_1 + e_s; \qquad R_5 i_5 = e_1 + e_2; \qquad e_3 = e_1 + e_2 \qquad (16.33)$$

The last equation in (16.33) is now replaced by

$$i_3 = C_3 \frac{de_3}{dt} = C_3 \frac{de_1}{dt} + C_3 \frac{de_2}{dt}$$

Substitution gives

$$C_1 \frac{de_1}{dt} = -\frac{e_1}{R_4} + \frac{e_s}{R_4} - C_3 \frac{de_1}{dt} - C_3 \frac{de_2}{dt} - \frac{e_1}{R_5} - \frac{e_2}{R_5}$$

$$C_2 \frac{de_2}{dt} = -C_3 \frac{de_1}{dt} - C_3 \frac{de_2}{dt} - \frac{e_1}{R_5} - \frac{e_2}{R_5}$$

or

$$\begin{bmatrix} C_1 + C_3 & C_3 \\ C_3 & C_2 + C_3 \end{bmatrix} \begin{bmatrix} \dfrac{de_1}{dt} \\ \dfrac{de_2}{dt} \end{bmatrix} = \begin{bmatrix} -\dfrac{1}{R_4} - \dfrac{1}{R_5} & -\dfrac{1}{R_5} \\ -\dfrac{1}{R_5} & -\dfrac{1}{R_5} \end{bmatrix} \begin{bmatrix} e_1 \\ e_2 \end{bmatrix}$$

$$+ \begin{bmatrix} \dfrac{1}{R_4} \\ 0 \end{bmatrix} e_s$$

Multiplying both sides from the left by

$$\begin{bmatrix} C_1 + C_3 & C_3 \\ C_3 & C_2 + C_3 \end{bmatrix}^{-1} = \frac{1}{\Delta} \begin{bmatrix} C_2 + C_3 & -C_3 \\ -C_3 & C_1 + C_3 \end{bmatrix}$$

where $\Delta = C_1 C_2 + C_2 C_3 + C_3 C_1$, gives

$$\begin{bmatrix} \dfrac{de_1}{dt} \\ \dfrac{de_2}{dt} \end{bmatrix} = \frac{1}{\Delta} \begin{bmatrix} -\dfrac{C_2}{R_4} - \dfrac{C_2}{R_5} - \dfrac{C_3}{R_4} & -\dfrac{C_2}{R_5} \\ \dfrac{C_3}{R_4} - \dfrac{C_1}{R_5} & -\dfrac{C_1}{R_5} \end{bmatrix} \begin{bmatrix} e_1 \\ e_2 \end{bmatrix} + \frac{1}{\Delta} \begin{bmatrix} \dfrac{C_2 + C_3}{R_4} \\ -\dfrac{C_3}{R_4} \end{bmatrix} e_s$$

$$(16.34)$$

16.5 Time-domain solution of the state equation

We shall now discuss the solution of the equation

$$[\dot{x}] = \begin{bmatrix} \dfrac{dx}{dt} \end{bmatrix} = [A][x] + [B][u] \qquad (16.35)$$

in the time domain. That is to say, with $[A]$, $[B]$, and $[x(t_0)]$ known and $[u(t)]$ given for $t > t_0$, we wish to find $[x(t)]$ for $t > t_0$. First, we shall look at the situation in which $[x]$ is a scalar. In that case, (16.35) reduces to a single differential equation of the first order.

$$\dot{x}(t) = ax(t) + bu(t) \tag{16.36}$$

Multiplying the equation through by ϵ^{-at}, we get

$$\epsilon^{-at}\dot{x} - a\epsilon^{-at}x = \frac{d}{dt}(x\epsilon^{-at}) = \epsilon^{-at}bu(t)$$

Integrating from t_0 to t gives

$$\int_{t_0}^{t} \frac{d}{d\tau}[x(\tau)\epsilon^{-a\tau}]\,d\tau = x(t)\epsilon^{-at} - x(t_0)\epsilon^{-at_0} = \int_{t_0}^{t} \epsilon^{-a\tau}bu(\tau)\,d\tau$$

and

$$x(t) = \epsilon^{a(t-t_0)}x(t_0) + \int_{t_0}^{t} \epsilon^{a(t-\tau)}bu(\tau)\,d\tau \tag{16.37}$$

The two terms in (16.37) are readily identified as the complementary function and the particular integral of the differential equation (16.36). We shall call the particular integral term

$$x_a(t) = \int_{t_0}^{t} \epsilon^{a(t-\tau)}bu(\tau)\,d\tau \tag{16.38}$$

and the complementary function

$$x_b(t) = \epsilon^{a(t-t_0)}x(t_0) \tag{16.39}$$

This completes the formal solution of the scalar differential equation (16.36).

We shall now develop a parallel solution for the case in which $[x]$ is a vector. First, as we did for the complementary function, we let the solution to the homogeneous equation

$$[\dot{x}_b] = [A][x_b] \tag{16.40}$$

be

$$[x_b(t)] = \epsilon^{[A](t-t_0)}[x_b(t_0)] \tag{16.41}$$

The term $\epsilon^{[A](t-t_0)}$ is the exponential function of a matrix that has not been defined. As in the scalar case, we define

$$\epsilon^{[A](t-t_0)} = [I] + [A](t-t_0) + \frac{[A]^2}{2!}(t-t_0)^2 + \frac{[A]^3}{3!}(t-t_0)^3 + \cdots \tag{16.42}$$

where $[I]$ is the identity matrix. The fact that (16.41), with the definition of (16.42), satisfies (16.40) is easily verified by substitution. We can show that the matrix series of (16.42) converges for any $[A]$ for all t. The solution for $[x_b(t)]$ as required by (16.41) is also the solution for $[x(t)]$ of (16.35), if $[u(t)] = [0]$. The expression $[x_b(t)]$ is known as the *zero-input state response*. Equation (16.41) relates the state vector at any time t to the vector at t_0 through matrix $\epsilon^{[A](t-t_0)}$. The latter is known as the *state transition matrix* and is usually denoted by

$$[\phi(t - t_0)] = \epsilon^{[A](t-t_0)} \tag{16.43}$$

EXAMPLE 5   Find the state transition matrix for the matrix

$$[A] = \begin{bmatrix} -3 & 1 \\ -2 & 0 \end{bmatrix}$$

SOLUTION   Assuming that $t_0 = 0$, by (16.42) we have

$$[\phi(t)] = \begin{bmatrix} 1 & 0 \\ 0 & 1 \end{bmatrix} + \begin{bmatrix} -3 & 1 \\ -2 & 0 \end{bmatrix} t + \frac{1}{2} \begin{bmatrix} -3 & 1 \\ -2 & 0 \end{bmatrix}^2 t^2$$

$$+ \frac{1}{6} \begin{bmatrix} -3 & 1 \\ -2 & 0 \end{bmatrix}^3 t^3 + \cdots$$

$$= \begin{bmatrix} 1 - 3t + \frac{7}{2}t^2 - \frac{5}{2}t^3 + \cdots & t - \frac{3}{2}t^2 + \frac{7}{6}t^3 + \cdots \\ -2t + 3t^2 - \frac{7}{3}t^3 + \cdots & 1 - t^2 + t^3 + \cdots \end{bmatrix} \tag{16.44}$$

It is not easy to write these elements in closed form. Usually closed-form solutions are obtained by other means. It is easy to verify that

$$[\phi(t)] = \begin{bmatrix} -\epsilon^{-t} + 2\epsilon^{-2t} & \epsilon^{-t} - \epsilon^{-2t} \\ -2\epsilon^{-t} + 2\epsilon^{-2t} & 2\epsilon^{-t} - \epsilon^{-2t} \end{bmatrix} \tag{16.45}$$

agrees with the matrix of (16.44).

Let us now return to the problem of the complete solution of (16.35). Having obtained $[\phi(t - t_0)]$ for a given $[A]$, we find that the complete solution is

$$[x(t - t_0)] = [\phi(t - t_0)][x(t_0)] + \int_{t_0}^{t} [\phi(t - \tau)][B][u(\tau)] \, d\tau \tag{16.46}$$

The last term, which corresponds to the particular integral in the scalar case, would have been the state response if the initial state $[x(t_0)]$ had been zero. This term is known as the *zero-state response*. Since $[\phi(t - t_0)]$, $[B]$, and $[u(t)]$ are all known, we can find the zero-state response by integration.

EXAMPLE 6   For the transition matrix of Example 5, find the zero-state response for

$$[B] = \begin{bmatrix} 1 \\ 0 \end{bmatrix}; \quad u(t) = u_{-1}(t); \quad t_0 = 0$$

SOLUTION

$$[x_a(t)] = \int_0^t \begin{bmatrix} -\epsilon^{-(t-\tau)}+2\epsilon^{-2(t-\tau)} & \epsilon^{-(t-\tau)}-\epsilon^{-2(t-\tau)} \\ -2\epsilon^{-(t-\tau)}+2\epsilon^{-2(t-\tau)} & 2\epsilon^{-(t-\tau)}-\epsilon^{-2(t-\tau)} \end{bmatrix} \begin{bmatrix} 1 \\ 0 \end{bmatrix} u_{-1}(\tau)\, d\tau$$

$$= \int_0^t \begin{bmatrix} -\epsilon^{-(t-\tau)}+2\epsilon^{-2(t-\tau)} \\ -2\epsilon^{-(t-\tau)}+2\epsilon^{-2(t-\tau)} \end{bmatrix} d\tau = \begin{bmatrix} \epsilon^{-t}-\epsilon^{-2t} \\ -1+2\epsilon^{-t}-\epsilon^{-2t} \end{bmatrix}$$

Hence for a system whose state equation is

$$\begin{bmatrix} \dot{x}_1 \\ \dot{x}_2 \end{bmatrix} = \begin{bmatrix} -3 & 1 \\ -2 & 0 \end{bmatrix} \begin{bmatrix} x_1 \\ x_2 \end{bmatrix} + \begin{bmatrix} 1 \\ 0 \end{bmatrix} u_{-1}(t)$$

the complete solution is

$$\begin{bmatrix} x_1(t) \\ x_2(t) \end{bmatrix} = \begin{bmatrix} -\epsilon^{-t}+2\epsilon^{-2t} & \epsilon^{-t}-\epsilon^{-2t} \\ -2\epsilon^{-t}+2\epsilon^{-2t} & 2\epsilon^{-t}-\epsilon^{-2t} \end{bmatrix} \begin{bmatrix} x_1(0) \\ x_2(0) \end{bmatrix}$$

$$+ \begin{bmatrix} \epsilon^{-t}-\epsilon^{-2t} \\ -1+2\epsilon^{-t}-\epsilon^{-2t} \end{bmatrix}$$

16.6 Laplace-transform solution of the state equation

The classical time-domain solution of the state equation described in the last section does not usually lead to solutions in closed form. However, we should note that the time-domain method is still a basic one and can be very useful in situations in which a closed-form solution is not essential or is unobtainable. For example, in some problems we are more interested in the numerical answer. Methods are available to obtain the trajectory (or locus) of the state vector by computational techniques. When a system is either nonlinear or time-variant, or both, the time-domain method may be the only practical way to get a solution for the system.

If the system is linear and time-invariant, then the one-sided Laplace transform offers a compact solution to its state equation in closed form. Taking the one-sided Laplace transform of (16.35), with $t_0 = 0$, we have*

$$s[X(s)] = [A][X(s)] + [B][U(s)] + [x(0)] \tag{16.47}$$

Here $[x(0)]$ is the initial state. Solving for $[X(s)]$, we get

$$X(s) = (s[I] - [A])^{-1}[x(0)] + (s[I] - [A])^{-1}[B][U(s)] \tag{16.48}$$

where $[I]$ is the identity matrix. This is the solution of the state equation in the s domain. To get the solution in the time domain, we merely take the

---

* The Laplace transform of a matrix is a matrix whose elements are the Laplace transforms of the elements of the matrix.

inverse Laplace transform of the right-hand side of (16.48). This is usually easier than obtaining the solution directly in the time domain, since extensive tables of Laplace transforms are available.

EXAMPLE 7   By the Laplace-transform method solve the state equation

$$\begin{bmatrix} \dot{x}_1 \\ \dot{x}_2 \end{bmatrix} = \begin{bmatrix} -2 & 1 \\ -2 & -5 \end{bmatrix}\begin{bmatrix} x_1 \\ x_2 \end{bmatrix} + \begin{bmatrix} 1 \\ 0 \end{bmatrix}u_{-1}(t)$$

SOLUTION

$$s[I] - [A] = \begin{bmatrix} s+2 & -1 \\ 2 & s+5 \end{bmatrix}$$

$$|s[I] - [A]| = s^2 + 7s + 12$$

$$(s[I] - [A])^{-1} = \frac{1}{s^2 + 7s + 12}\begin{bmatrix} s+5 & 1 \\ -2 & s+2 \end{bmatrix}$$

$$\mathscr{L}^{-1}\{(s[I] - [A])^{-1}\} = \mathscr{L}^{-1}\begin{bmatrix} \dfrac{s+5}{s^2+7s+12} & \dfrac{1}{s^2+7s+12} \\[3ex] \dfrac{-2}{s^2+7s+12} & \dfrac{s+2}{s^2+7s+12} \end{bmatrix}$$

$$= \mathscr{L}^{-1}\begin{bmatrix} \dfrac{2}{s+3} - \dfrac{1}{s+4} & \dfrac{1}{s+3} - \dfrac{1}{s+4} \\[3ex] -\dfrac{2}{s+3} + \dfrac{2}{s+4} & -\dfrac{1}{s+3} + \dfrac{2}{s+4} \end{bmatrix}$$

$$= \begin{bmatrix} 2\epsilon^{-3t} - \epsilon^{-4t} & \epsilon^{-3t} - \epsilon^{-4t} \\ -2\epsilon^{-3t} + 2\epsilon^{-4t} & -\epsilon^{-3t} + 2\epsilon^{-4t} \end{bmatrix}$$

$$(s[I] - [A])^{-1}[B][U(s)] = \frac{1}{s^2+7s+12}\begin{bmatrix} s+5 & 1 \\ -2 & s+2 \end{bmatrix}\begin{bmatrix} 1 \\ 0 \end{bmatrix} \times \frac{1}{s}$$

$$= \begin{bmatrix} \dfrac{s+5}{s(s+3)(s+4)} \\[3ex] \dfrac{-2}{s(s+3)(s+4)} \end{bmatrix}$$

$$= \begin{bmatrix} \dfrac{5}{12s} - \dfrac{2}{3(s+3)} + \dfrac{1}{4(s+4)} \\[3ex] -\dfrac{1}{6s} + \dfrac{2}{3(s+3)} - \dfrac{1}{2(s+4)} \end{bmatrix}$$

$$= \mathscr{L}\begin{bmatrix} \frac{5}{12} - \frac{2}{3}\epsilon^{-3t} + \frac{1}{4}\epsilon^{-4t} \\[2ex] -\frac{1}{6} + \frac{2}{3}\epsilon^{-3t} - \frac{1}{2}\epsilon^{-4t} \end{bmatrix}$$

Thus we get

$$[x(t)] = \mathscr{L}^{-1}[X(s)] = \begin{bmatrix} 2\epsilon^{-3t} - \epsilon^{-4t} & \epsilon^{-3t} - \epsilon^{-4t} \\ -2\epsilon^{-3t} + 2\epsilon^{-4t} & -\epsilon^{-3t} + 2\epsilon^{-4t} \end{bmatrix} \begin{bmatrix} x_1(0) \\ x_2(0) \end{bmatrix}$$

$$+ \begin{bmatrix} \frac{5}{12} - \frac{2}{3}\epsilon^{-3t} + \frac{1}{4}\epsilon^{-4t} \\ -\frac{1}{6} + \frac{2}{3}\epsilon^{-3t} - \frac{1}{2}\epsilon^{-4t} \end{bmatrix} \qquad (16.49)$$

If we compare (16.48) with (16.46), it is apparent that the two parts of their right-hand sides correspond to each other. As a matter of fact, this can be shown formally. We first take the Laplace transform of the identity

$$[\phi(t)] = [I] + [A]t + \frac{[A]^2}{2!}t^2 + \frac{[A]^3}{3!}t^3 + \cdots \qquad (16.50)$$

to get

$$[\Phi(s)] = \frac{[I]}{s} + \frac{[A]}{s^2} + \frac{[A]^2}{s^3} + \frac{[A]^3}{s^4} + \cdots$$

Multiplying both sides from the left by $(s[I] - [A])$, we get

$$(s[I] - [A])\mathscr{L}[\phi(t)] = [I] \qquad (16.51)$$

Hence

$$(s[I] - [A])^{-1} = \mathscr{L}[\phi(t)]$$

or

$$[\phi(t)] = \mathscr{L}^{-1}\{(s[I] - [A])^{-1}\} \qquad (16.52)$$

From (16.52), we deduce that

$$\mathscr{L}^{-1}\{(s[I] - [A])^{-1}[B][U(s)]\} = \int_0^t [\phi(t - \tau)][B][u(\tau)]\, d\tau \qquad (16.53)$$

which states that multiplication in the s domain corresponds to convolution in the time domain in matrix form. If the state equation is scalar, (16.53) is a consequence of (15.56).

16.7 Concluding remarks

In this chapter we have really given only some representative features of the state-variable technique of system analysis, mainly through examples. The importance of this technique is not limited to problems similar to the examples given. The state-variable method is a very useful tool in many areas of *system theory* and *control engineering*, as well as other areas of engineering and computer science, for several reasons.

First of all, the state-variable method may be regarded as a method of solving an nth-order differential equation by expressing it as a set of n first-order differential equations. The state variables are merely the auxiliary or intermediate variables. The actual solution desired is either one of these variables or a simple function of some of these variables and the inputs. There are some computational advantages in preferring a set of n first-order differential equations to one nth-order equation. These intermediate variables may or may not correspond to certain physical counterparts, although, in all the examples we have seen, every state variable is either a current or a voltage.

In a system that includes nonlinear and time-variant elements, the time-domain solution is seldom expressible in closed form. The transition matrix enables us to start with a known initial state and numerically obtain states subsequent to the initial one.

The state-variable method is also a very attractive technique for dealing with large-scale systems—systems involving several hundred components, say. Here a systematic approach like this is absolutely essential.

When a system is laid out in block-diagram form, it is usually quite simple to write out its state equation, because the process really amounts to getting the information down piece by piece. On the other hand, to arrange the input–output relationship into a single equation or a set of simultaneous equations can be quite a laborious task in itself.

Another advantage of using the state-variable approach is that it is usually quite easy to construct a block diagram or flow graph for a system whose state equation and output equation are known. This is not the case with the classical approach.

Again, although we are presenting the state-variable method primarily by means of examples of LTI networks, this is only a means to an end. The state-variable method has much wider applications than we have covered in this presentation. It is a basic and useful tool in several other areas in engineering.

Problems

16.1 Obtain the state equation for each of the networks in Figure P16.1, using the variables shown as the state variables.

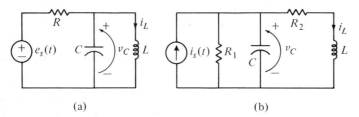

(a)   (b)

Figure P16.1 (continued on page 529)

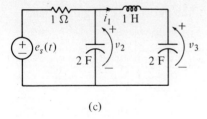

(c)

Figure P16.1 (continued)

16.2 Write the state equations in normal form for the networks in Figure P16.2, using the variables given as the state variables.

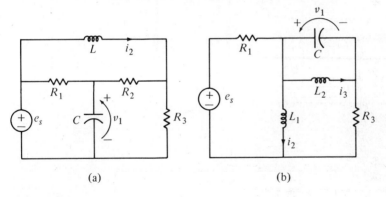

(a)　　　　　　　　　　　　(b)

Figure P16.2

16.3 Using v_1, v_2, and i_3 as the state variables, write the state equation for the network of Figure P16.3 in normal form.

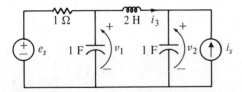

Figure P16.3

16.4 Obtain the state equation for each of the networks in Figure P16.4.

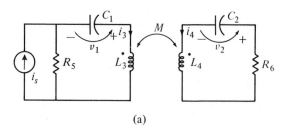

(a)

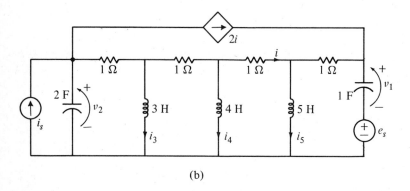

(b)

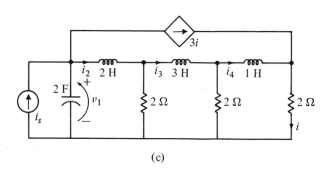

(c)

Figure P16.4

16.5 Find the state transition matrix for the following matrices:

(a) $[A] = \begin{bmatrix} -2 & -3 \\ -1 & -2 \end{bmatrix}$ (b) $[A] = \begin{bmatrix} 0 & 1 & 0 \\ 0 & 0 & 1 \\ -6 & -11 & -6 \end{bmatrix}$

16.6 Find the state transition matrix for each of the networks shown in Figure P16.6.

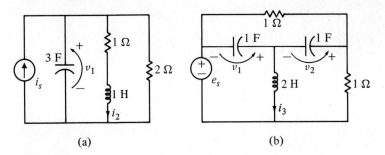

(a)   (b)

Figure P16.6

16.7 Using the state variables shown, obtain the state equation for the improper networks shown in Figure P16.7.

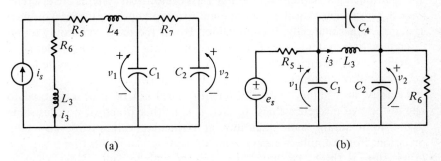

(a)   (b)

Figure P16.7

16.8 Prove that $[\phi(t_0 - t_0)] = [I]$.

16.9 Prove that $[\phi(t_2 - t_1)][\phi(t_1 - t_0)] = [\phi(t_2 - t_0)]$.

16.10 Prove that $[\phi(t_1 - t_0)] = [\phi(t_0 - t_1)]^{-1}$.

17 | LOGIC CIRCUITS

We mentioned in Chapter 1 that a large class of electrical systems are discrete-valued. This means that the electric quantities (voltages or currents) in these systems can assume only discrete values. By far the most commonly found discrete-valued systems are *binary* ones, for example, computers, telephone switching circuits, digital communication systems. In a binary system, the voltages and/or currents can assume only one of two values.

Actually, in a binary system, a quantity need not be precisely equal to one of the two discrete values. In fact, it is neither practical nor desirable to try to maintain such quantities at particular values with any high precision. For example, we may want to ascertain only whether a voltage in a system is "high" or "low." The voltage will be called "high" if it is, say, between 9 and 11 V and "low" if it is, say, between −1 and 1 V. Of course, the circuit should be designed so that the voltages fall within just one of these two ranges. (A voltage of 5 V would be ambiguous.)

Assuming that a voltage in a system can have only either a "high" or a "low" value, we can say that the voltage is a binary variable, whether this voltage is in the "high" range or the "low" range. We can describe it alternatively by saying that it is in either the 1 or 0 state.

If we choose to call a more-positive quantity 1 and a less-positive one 0, the convention is said to be *positive* logic. If the reverse is true, it is called *negative* logic. For simplicity, we shall use positive logic exclusively here. The principles are, of course, equally applicable to negative logic.

A *binary circuit* is one in which there may be one or several input variables, each of which may be 1 or 0, and one or several output variables, each of which may be 1 or 0. Recall the two simple binary circuits that were given in Figures 6.26 and 6.27. The analysis of a binary circuit is a study of how these binary variables are related. The synthesis of a binary circuit involves finding a circuit that will produce an interrelationship among these binary variables. Because of the close similarity between the behavior of binary circuits and *propositional logic*, which is a well-developed area in philosophy and mathematics, a binary circuit is frequently called a *logic circuit*.

A field closely allied to both logic circuits and propositional logic is *switching theory*. The similarities among these three areas are illustrated by the AND and OR circuits of Figures 6.26 and 6.27. The behavior of the OR circuit of Figure 6.26 can be described by the sentence: e_o is 1, if e_A is 1, *or* if e_B is 1, *or* if e_C is 1. This is analogous to connecting a lamp to the power source through three switches in parallel. The lamp is ON if any one or more of the three switches are on. An analogous statement in propositional logic might be: It is true that you are sick, (1) if you have a high temperature, *or* (2) if you have severe pain, *or* (3) if you are bleeding profusely.

The behavior of the AND circuit of Figure 6.27 can be described by the sentence: e_o is 1, only if e_A is 1, *and* if e_B is 1, *and* if e_C is 1. This is analogous to connecting a lamp to the power source through three switches in series. The lamp is on only if all three switches are on. An analogous statement in propositional logic might be: You will pass this course only if (1) you do your homework, *and* (2) you attend all the classes, *and* (3) you pass all the quizzes. (You have an unreasonable instructor, no doubt.)

In this chapter we shall start with the definitions of some basic building blocks for logic circuits in terms of the different operations they perform. Then we shall describe the binary arithmetic that is used to analyze more complicated functions of binary variables. Then we shall look at some fairly simple digital functional blocks constructed from these basic building blocks.

17.1 The logic operations

In a logic circuit, it is assumed that each variable can only assume either the value 1 or the value 0. The following are some basic operations defined for these variables.

1 *The NOT operation* The NOT operation (or the *complementation* operation) on a variable causes it to assume the other value. It is denoted by an overbar ($\overline{A}$). A device that performs this operation is called a NOT gate, also known as an *inverter*. The symbol for a NOT gate is shown in Figure 17.1, and the functional relationship between the input and output variables is shown in the table. (A table of the type shown in Figure 17.1 is known as a *truth table*.)

2 *The OR operation* The OR operation of two or more variables is 0 if all variables are 0, and 1 if any of the variables is 1. This function is denoted by the + sign $(A + B)$. A device that performs this operation is known as an OR gate. Figure 17.2 shows the symbol for an OR gate and its function. An OR gate can have more than two inputs.

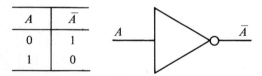

A	$\bar{A}$
0	1
1	0

Figure 17.1 Definition of the NOT operation and symbol for the NOT gate.

A	B	$A + B$
0	0	0
0	1	1
1	0	1
1	1	1

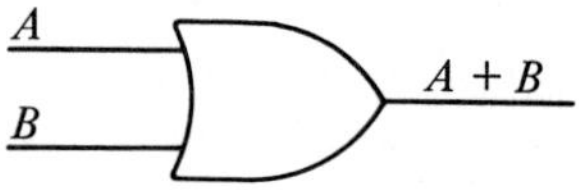

Figure 17.2 Definition of the OR operation and symbol for the OR gate.

3 *The AND operation* The AND operation of several variables is 0 if any of the variables is 0, and 1 if all the variables are 1. We can denote this function by a centered dot $(A \cdot B)$ or simply by placing the variables side by side (AB). A device that performs this operation is known as an AND gate. Figure 17.3 shows the symbol for an AND gate and its function. An AND gate can also have several inputs.

A	B	AB
0	0	0
0	1	0
1	0	0
1	1	1

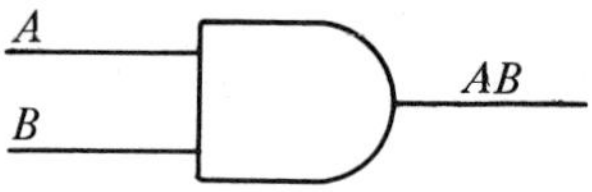

Figure 17.3 Definition of the AND operation and symbol for the AND gate.

EXAMPLE 1   Construct the truth table for the circuit of Figure 17.4.

SOLUTION   We can easily see in Figure 17.4 that

$$F = A + B \cdot \bar{C} \tag{17.1}$$

By performing these operations successively, we get the results shown in Table 17.1.

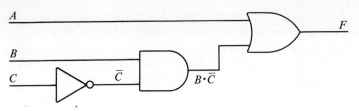

Figure 17.4

Table **17.1**

C	$\bar{C}$	B	$B \cdot \bar{C}$	A	F
1	0	1	0	0	0
1	0	1	0	1	1
1	0	0	0	0	0
1	0	0	0	1	1
0	1	1	1	0	1
0	1	1	1	1	1
0	1	0	0	0	0
0	1	0	0	1	1

4 *The NOR operation* The NOR operation is the complement of the OR operation and is written as $\overline{A+B}$. It is clear that we can effect a NOR operation by performing an OR operation and a NOT operation in succession. Hence we can realize a NOR gate by cascading an OR gate and a NOT gate. The symbol for a NOR gate and its function are shown in Figure 17.5. (Note that $\overline{A+B} \neq \bar{A}+\bar{B}$.) Its realization using an OR gate and a NOT gate is also shown in Figure 17.5.

A	B	$\overline{A+B}$
0	0	1
0	1	0
1	0	0
1	1	0

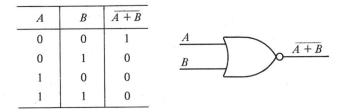

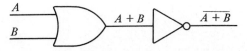

Figure 17.5 Definition of the NOR operation, symbol for the NOR gate, and realization of the NOR gate by an OR gate and a NOT gate.

5 *The NAND operation* The NAND operation is the complement of the AND operation and is written as $\overline{AB}$. It is clear that we can effect a NAND operation by performing an AND operation and a NOT operation in succession. Hence we can realize a NAND gate by cascading an AND gate and a NOT gate. The symbol for a NAND gate and its function are shown in Figure 17.6. (Note that $\overline{AB} \neq \overline{A}\,\overline{B}$.) Figure 17.6 also shows its realization using an AND gate and a NOT gate.

A	B	$\overline{AB}$
0	0	1
0	1	1
1	0	1
1	1	0

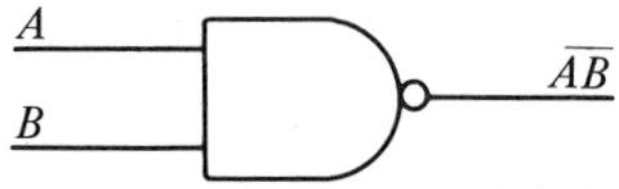

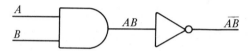

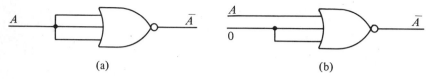

Figure 17.6 Definition of the NAND operation, symbol for the NAND gate, and realization of the NAND gate by an AND gate and a NOT gate.

EXAMPLE 2 To employ the NOR gate as a NOT gate, we can use the arrangements of Figure 17.7. In Figure 17.7(a) we have, in effect,

$$\overline{A + A + A} = \overline{A} \tag{17.2}$$

while in Figure 17.7(b) we have

$$\overline{A + 0 + 0} = \overline{A} \tag{17.3}$$

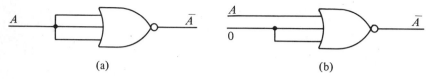

(a)   (b)

Figure 17.7 The NOR gate used as a NOT gate.

EXAMPLE 3 To employ the NAND gate as a NOT gate, we can use the arrangements of Figure 17.8. In Figure 17.8(a) we have

$$\overline{A \cdot A \cdot A} = \overline{A} \tag{17.4}$$

while in Figure 17.8(b) we have

$$\overline{A \cdot 1 \cdot 1} = \overline{A} \tag{17.5}$$

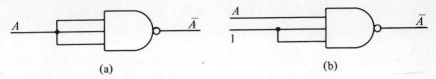

(a)   (b)

Figure 17.8 The NAND gate used as a NOT gate.

The following operations are not elementary, in that we can obtain them by interconnecting basic operations listed earlier. However, for convenience, these are often considered as individual operations.

6 *The EXCLUSIVE-OR operation* The normal OR operation gives 1 when either A or B is 1 and also when A and B are both 1. This operation is sometimes referred to as the INCLUSIVE-OR. The EXCLUSIVE-OR does not give 1 when both A and B are 1. It is denoted by the $\oplus$ sign. Hence $A \oplus B$ is 0 if A and B are of the same value, and is 1 if A and B are different. The symbol for an EXCLUSIVE-OR gate and its truth table are shown in Figure 17.9. It is easy to verify that

$$A \oplus B = \bar{A} \cdot B + A \cdot \bar{B} \tag{17.6}$$

A	B	$A \oplus B$
0	0	0
0	1	1
1	0	1
1	1	0

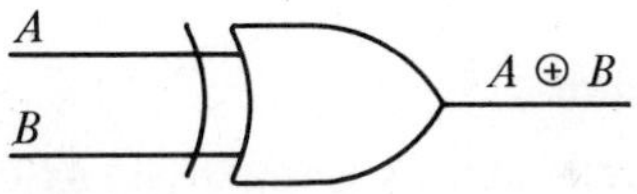

Figure 17.9 Definition of the EXCLUSIVE-OR operation and symbol for the EXCLUSIVE-OR gate.

Thus we can realize an EXCLUSIVE-OR gate by the arrangement of Figure 17.10.

An EXCLUSIVE-OR gate can have more than two inputs. The output

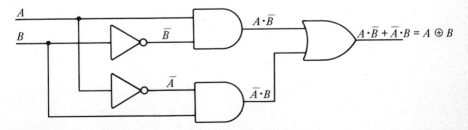

Figure 17.10 A realization of the EXCLUSIVE-OR gate.

of a multiple-input EXCLUSIVE-OR gate is 1 if an odd number of inputs are 1, and is 0 if an even number of inputs are 1.

7 *The EQUIVALENCE operation* A direct extension of the preceding operations is the complement of the EXCLUSIVE-OR operations, known as the EQUIVALENCE, or COINCIDENCE, operation. This function is 1 if A and B are of the same value, and is 0 if A and B are different. The operation is denoted by a $\odot$ sign. The symbol for the EQUIVALENCE gate and its truth table are shown in Figure 17.11. We can easily verify that

$$A \odot B = \bar{A} \cdot \bar{B} + A \cdot B = \overline{(A \oplus B)} \tag{17.7}$$

A	B	$A \odot B$
0	0	1
0	1	0
1	0	0
1	1	1

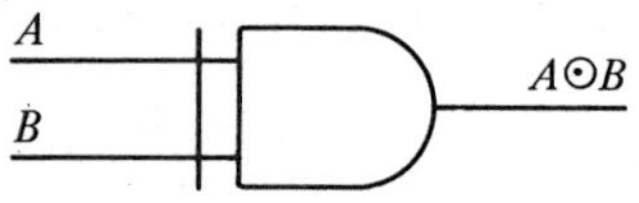

Figure 17.11 Definition of the EQUIVALENCE operation and symbol for the EQUIVALENCE gate.

17.2 Boolean algebra

It should be apparent at this point that, as digital circuits become more and more complex, we begin to use longer expressions of binary variables. A systematic set of rules for handling and simplifying these expressions is highly desirable. Fortunately such a set of rules already exists, which is known as *Boolean algebra*. Boolean algebra can be derived on the basis of set theory. Or we can start with a set of postulates and basic laws and derive the set of rules from them. We shall use the latter approach.

We can regard some of the basic operations defined in Section 17.1 as the postulates of Boolean algebra. These operations are as follows.

$$\left. \begin{array}{l} \bar{1} = 0 \\ \bar{0} = 1 \end{array} \right\} \quad \text{(The NOT operation)}$$

$$\begin{array}{l} 0 + 0 = 0 \\ 0 + 1 = 1 \\ 1 + 0 = 1 \\ 1 + 1 = 1 \end{array} \quad \text{(The OR operation)}$$

$$\begin{array}{l} 0 \cdot 0 = 0 \\ 1 \cdot 0 = 0 \\ 0 \cdot 1 = 0 \\ 1 \cdot 1 = 1 \end{array} \quad \text{(The AND operation)}$$

From these postulates alone, we can verify that the following relationships are valid. This is easily done, since each variable can only be either 1 or 0 and the possible combinations of variable values are limited.

$$A + 1 = 1 \tag{17.8}$$

$$A + 0 = A \tag{17.9}$$

$$A \cdot 0 = 0 \tag{17.10}$$

$$A \cdot 1 = A \tag{17.11}$$

$$A + \bar{A} = 1 \tag{17.12}$$

$$A \cdot \bar{A} = 0 \tag{17.13}$$

$$A + B = B + A \quad \text{(The OR operation is commutative.)} \tag{17.14}$$

$$A \cdot B = B \cdot A \quad \text{(The AND operation is commutative.)} \tag{17.15}$$

$$(A + B) + C = A + (B + C) \quad \text{(OR operations are associative.)} \tag{17.16}$$

$$(A \cdot B) \cdot C = A \cdot (B \cdot C) \quad \text{(AND operations are associative.)} \tag{17.17}$$

$$\bar{\bar{A}} = A \quad \text{(The complement of } \bar{A} \text{ is } A.) \tag{17.18}$$

$$A + A = A \quad \text{(Absorption of the OR operation)} \tag{17.19}$$

$$A \cdot A = A \quad \text{(Absorption of the AND operation)} \tag{17.20}$$

$$A \cdot (B + C) = (A \cdot B) + (A \cdot C) \quad \text{(The AND operation is distributive over OR operations.)} \tag{17.21}$$

$$A + (B \cdot C) = (A + B) \cdot (A + C) \quad \text{(The OR operation is distributive over AND operations.)} \tag{17.22}$$

$$\left. \begin{array}{l} \overline{(AB)} = \bar{A} + \bar{B} \\ \overline{(A+B)} = \bar{A} \cdot \bar{B} \end{array} \right\} \text{(de Morgan's theorem)} \quad \begin{array}{l} (17.23) \\ (17.24) \end{array}$$

Some examples of the application of these relationships follow.

EXAMPLE 4   Show that (17.22) is correct by using only relationships given prior to that relationship.

SOLUTION

$$
\begin{aligned}
(A + B)(A + C) &= (A + B)A + (A + B)C && \text{by (17.21)} \\
&= AA + AC + BA + BC && \text{by (17.15) and (17.21)} \\
&= A + AB + AC + BC && \text{by (17.14), (17.15), and (17.20)} \\
&= A(1 + B) + AC + BC && \text{by (17.11) and (17.21)} \\
&= A + AC + BC && \text{by (17.8) and (17.11)} \\
&= A(1 + C) + BC && \text{by (17.11) and (17.21)} \\
&= A + BC && \text{by (17.8) and (17.11)}
\end{aligned}
$$

We can also verify this identity by constructing a truth table (Table 17.2) that includes all the possible combinations of values of all the variables on both sides of the equation. We see from Table 17.2 that the two columns under $A + BC$ and $(A + B)(A + C)$ are identical.

Table **17.2**

A	B	C	BC	$A+BC$	$A+B$	$A+C$	$(A+B)(A+C)$
0	0	0	0	0	0	0	0
0	0	1	0	0	0	1	0
0	1	0	0	0	1	0	0
0	1	1	1	1	1	1	1
1	0	0	0	1	1	1	1
1	0	1	0	1	1	1	1
1	1	0	0	1	1	1	1
1	1	1	1	1	1	1	1

EXAMPLE 5 Show that

$$A(A + B) = A$$

SOLUTION

$$
\begin{aligned}
A(A + B) &= (A + 0) \cdot (A + B) &&\text{by (17.9)} \\
&= A + (0 \cdot B) &&\text{by (17.22)} \\
&= A + 0 &&\text{by (17.10)} \\
&= A &&\text{by (17.9)}
\end{aligned}
$$

EXAMPLE 6 To simplify $A + \bar{A}B$, we follow the steps

$$
\begin{aligned}
A + \bar{A}B &= (A + \bar{A})(A + B) &&\text{by (17.22)} \\
&= 1 \cdot (A + B) &&\text{by (17.12)} \\
&= A + B &&\text{by (17.11)}
\end{aligned}
$$

EXAMPLE 7 To simplify $AB + \bar{A}C + BC$, we have

$$
\begin{aligned}
AB + \bar{A}C + BC &= AB + \bar{A}C + (A + \bar{A})BC &&\text{by (17.12) and (17.11)} \\
&= AB + \bar{A}C + ABC + \bar{A}BC &&\text{by (17.21)} \\
&= AB(1 + C) + \bar{A}C(1 + B) &&\text{by (17.14) and (17.21)} \\
&= AB + \bar{A}C &&\text{by (17.8) and (17.11)}
\end{aligned}
$$

17.3 Boolean expressions for a binary function

For many digital-circuit applications the requirement is given in the form of a truth table. In order to devise a digital circuit that will perform the function prescribed by this table, it is convenient to obtain an explicit expression in terms of the variables and basic operations defined in Section 17.1. We shall next describe two techniques for accomplishing this step and illustrate the techniques with examples.

The first method is known as the *sum-of-products method*. Suppose we want to obtain an expression for $F = f(A, B, C)$ that will give the functional relationship described in the first four columns of Table 17.3. One method is to form as many subfunctions as there are 1 values in the F column. These are shown as f_1 and f_2 in columns 5 and 6. Then we express each of these subfunctions as the product of the variables or their complements, according to their values in the row in which the 1 appears in the subfunction. Thus f_1 is 1 only if $\bar{A}$ and B and $\bar{C}$ are all 1. And f_2 is 1 only if A and B and C are all 1. Or, $f_1 = \bar{A}B\bar{C}$ and $f_2 = ABC$. Then we sum all subfunctions, or

$$F = f(A, B, C) = \bar{A}B\bar{C} + ABC \tag{17.25}$$

Table **17.3**

1	2	3	4	5	6	7	8
A	B	C	$F = f(A, B, C)$	f_1	f_2	g_1	g_2
0	0	1	0	0	0	0	1
0	1	0	1	1	0	1	1
0	1	1	0	0	0	1	0
1	1	1	1	0	1	1	1

The other method, called the *product-of-sums method*, is the complement of the sum-of-products one. We form as many subfunctions as there are 0 values under column 4. These are shown as g_1 and g_2 in columns 7 and 8 of Table 17.3. Then we make g_1 equal to 0 only if A and B and $\bar{C}$ are all equal to 0, by letting $g_1 = A + B + \bar{C}$. Likewise, we make g_2 equal to 0 only if A and $\bar{B}$ and $\bar{C}$ are all equal to 0, by letting $g_2 = A + \bar{B} + \bar{C}$. Then we let F be the product of all subfunctions, or

$$F = f(A, B, C) = (A + B + \bar{C})(A + \bar{B} + \bar{C}) \tag{17.26}$$

Incidentally, we can expect the expressions in (17.25) and (17.26) to be equal to each other only for the four sets of values of A, B, and C given in Table 17.3. For other combinations of A, B, and C, they may or may not be equal. (Of course, if all possible combinations of these variable values and their corresponding functional values have been specified in a problem, then we can always show that the expressions obtained by these two methods are identical to each other.)

The function described by (17.25) can be implemented by the circuit of Figure 17.12, and the function described by (17.26) can be implemented by

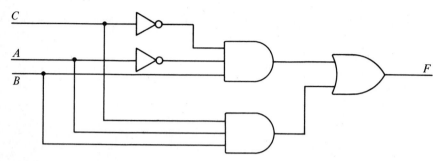

Figure 17.12   Circuit performing the function of (17.25).

the circuit of Figure 17.13. Both circuits give the same functional relationship required by Table 17.3.

Obviously, for any given function, there are many realizations possible. From the point of view of economy in engineering, some realizations will be preferable to others. For example, the realizations we just achieved for the function f of Table 17.3 require five gates each. Actually, this function can

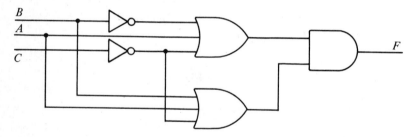

Figure 17.13   Circuit performing the function of (17.26).

also be performed by three gates, as shown in Figure 17.14, which satisfies the truth table given by Table 17.4. The variable F as a function of A, B, and C prescribed in Table 17.3 is also required in Table 17.4. Hence the realization of Figure 17.14 also gives what Table 17.3 requires. There are methods for minimizing the realization of functions using various building blocks but we shall not discuss them here.

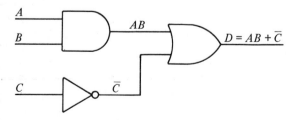

Figure 17.14   Circuit performing the function required in Table 17.4, which also satisfies the function required in Table 17.3.

Table **17.4**

A	B	C	F
0	0	0	1
0	0	1	0
0	1	0	1
0	1	1	0
1	0	0	1
1	0	1	0
1	1	0	1
1	1	1	1

17.4 Circuits of logic gates

We shall now describe a few simple circuits that implement some of the gates defined in Section 17.1. These gates are known by various names, depending on the devices used.

1 *Diode logic (DL)* The OR and AND gates using resistors and diodes were discussed earlier, in Section 6.6 (see Figures 6.26 and 6.27).

2 *A transistor NOT gate* A basic transistor NOT-gate circuit is shown in Figure 17.15(a). The transistor is *n-p-n* for positive logic. As we mentioned

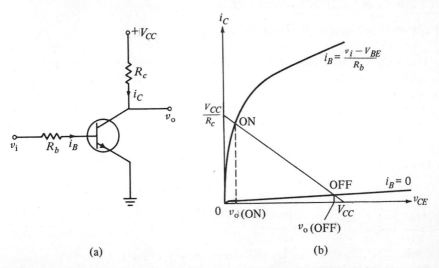

(a)   (b)

Figure 17.15 A basic transistor NOT-gate circuit and its operation.

in Chapter 9, as long as v_i is substantially higher than the cut-in voltage of the emitter junction, the emitter-to-base voltage is approximately constant and is approximately equal to the cut-in voltage (V_γ) of the junction. Hence the operating point will be at the point marked ON in Figure 17.15(b). This denotes the state in which a large i_C is flowing. The value of v_o is $v_{o(ON)}$, which is very small. When v_i is very small, $i_B \cong 0$ and the operating point is at the point marked OFF. This denotes the state in which i_C is practically zero. The value of v_o is $v_{o(OFF)}$, which is very nearly equal to V_{CC}. We can see that this circuit acts as a NOT gate.

3 *Resistor-transistor logic (RTL)*   Figure 17.16 shows an RTL NOR-gate circuit, in which, if $v_A = v_B = v_C = 0$, the base voltage is negative and the emitter junction is reverse-biased. The transistor is OFF and $v_{o(OFF)} \cong V_{CC}$. If a signal of sufficient strength appears in any one or more of the input terminals, the base voltage is made positive, so as to turn ON the transistor and to make v_o very small. Thus the circuit performs the NOR operation.

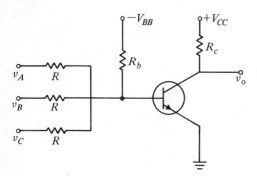

Figure 17.16   An RTL NOR-gate circuit.

4 *Diode-transistor logic (DTL)*   A DTL NAND circuit is shown in Figure 17.17. This arrangement is essentially a cascade of a DL AND gate and a

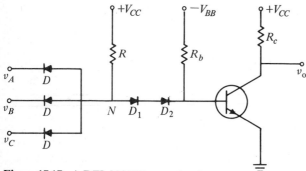

Figure 17.17   A DTL NAND-gate circuit.

transistor NOT gate. As long as one (or more) of the input voltages is small, node N will be approximately V_γ volts above ground. This is not enough to turn on the transistor; hence the transistor remains OFF and $v_o \cong V_{CC}$. If v_A, v_B, and v_C are all positive, node N will have a voltage that is equal to, say, $v_A + V_\gamma$, which is considerably higher than $2V_\gamma$ (the total voltage across D_1 and D_2). Thus the transistor will be turned ON and v_o is very small.

5 *Transistor-transistor logic (TTL)* Figure 17.18(a) shows a TTL NAND-gate circuit, which is very similar to the DTL circuit of Figure 17.17. The three diodes (D's) are now replaced by the emitter junctions of the input transistors. The offset diodes D_1 and D_2 are replaced by the collector

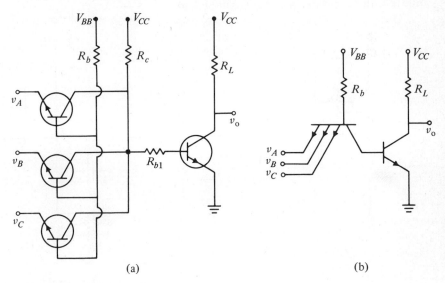

(a)   (b)

Figure 17.18 A TTL NAND-gate circuit.

junctions of the input transistors. If any of the input voltages is small, that particular emitter junction will be forward-biased. This reduces the base and collector voltages of these transistors to the extent that the output transistor is turned OFF, resulting in a large value for v_o.

If all the input voltages are high, the emitter junctions of the input transistors are reverse-biased and their collector junctions are forward-biased. The base currents flow into the base of the output transistor and turn the latter ON. This results in a small value for v_o.

In integrated-circuit technology, the input resistors are replaced by a multi-emitter transistor, as shown in Figure 17.18(b). The principle of operation is similar in both circuits. But the combining of several transistors into one greatly reduces the area required by these devices on the wafer.

6 *MOSFET gates* MOSFET gates consist entirely of MOSFETs and no other devices such as resistors, diodes, or transistors. They are typically slower in response than TTL gates. The chief advantages of MOSFET gates are their low power consumption and the small chip area required per gate.

Figure 17.19(a) shows a MOSFET NOT gate. Both Q_1 and Q_2 are n-channel. The gate and drain of Q_1 are tied together, Q_1 actually acts as a load resistor, and Q_2 is the driver. When v_A is positive and sufficiently high, the drain current in Q_2 is large and v_o is low. When v_A is zero, the drain current in Q_2 is also low, resulting in a high v_o.

Figure 17.19(b) shows a two-input NOR gate. This is essentially the same circuit as Figure 17.19(a) except that the driver is replaced by two MOSFETs in parallel. Thus, when either v_A or v_B, or both, is high (positive), v_o will be low. If both v_A and v_B are zero, v_o will be high.

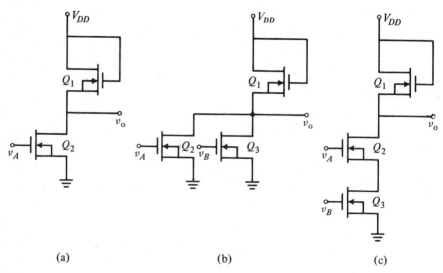

(a)	(b)	(c)

Figure 17.19 MOSFET gates. (a) A NOT gate. (b) A NOR gate. (c) A NAND gate.

In Figure 17.19(c), the driver of Figure 17.19(a) is replaced by two MOSFETs in series. The value of v_o will be low when, and only when, the values of both v_A and v_B are high. Thus it is a NAND gate.

7 *Complementary MOS (CMOS) gates* Modern IC technology can produce both n-channel and p-channel MOSFETs on the same chip. The use of both types of MOSFET can reduce greatly the quiescent power required per gate and thus enable us to increase the density of gates per unit area.

An example of a CMOS gate is the NOT gate circuit shown in Figure 17.20, in which Q_1 is p-channel and Q_2 is n-channel. If $v_A = 0$, Q_2 is cut off. But v_{GS} of Q_1 is nearly $-V_{DD}$ and its resistance from the drain to its source

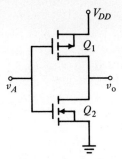

Figure 17.20 A CMOS NOT gate.

is low. Hence v_o is very nearly equal to V_{DD}. On the other hand, when v_A is positive and high, Q_1 is cut off and Q_2 offers very low resistance from the output terminal to ground, making the value of v_o very low.

The foregoing are merely a few examples of the principles of some simple logic gates. A thorough study of the various logic building blocks would involve a comparison of their loading effects, speeds of switching, power consumption, immunity to noise, cost, temperature stability, and so on, and is another specialized subject.

17.5 The binary number system

The most important applications of digital circuits are in computers. One of the major functions of a computer is to perform arithmetic operations— addition, subtraction, multiplication, and division. Many computers perform arithmetic operations in binary form internally.

Each digit of a number in a decimal system represents the multiplier of a power of the number 10. For example,*

$$(876)_{10} = 8 \times 10^2 + 7 \times 10^1 + 6 \times 10^0$$

Similarly each digit of a binary number (known as a *bit*) represents the multiplier of a power of the number 2. Hence*

$$(11001)_2 = 1 \times 2^4 + 1 \times 2^3 + 0 \times 2^2 + 0 \times 2^1 + 1 \times 2^0 = (25)_{10}$$

A number with fractions has the same meaning. For example,

$$(27.49)_{10} = 2 \times 10^1 + 7 \times 10^0 + 4 \times 10^{-1} + 9 \times 10^{-2}$$

and

$$(10.101)_2 = 1 \times 2^1 + 0 \times 2^0 + 1 \times 2^{-1} + 0 \times 2^{-2} + 1 \times 2^{-3} = (2.625)_{10}$$

* Here the subscript represents the base of the numbering system.

Table **17.5**   The 8421 code of decimal digits

Decimal digit	Binary code
0	0000
1	0001
2	0010
3	0011
4	0100
5	0101
6	0110
7	0111
8	1000
9	1001

We can perform the addition, subtraction, multiplication, and division of binary numbers much as we do for decimal numbers. Several simple examples will be described in Sections 17.10, 17.11, 17.12, 17.13, and 17.14.

The binary numbering system is not always satisfactory in representing real-world numbers. For example, to represent the number $(0.90)_{10}$ accurately in binary form would require an infinitely long number. The two 12-bit numbers that come closest to the exact number are:

$$(0.111,001,100,110)_2 = (0.899,902,343,75)_{10}$$

$$(0.111,001,100,111)_2 = (0.900,146,484,375)_{10}$$

This is one of the reasons why some computing schemes employ the binary-coded-decimal (BCD) system, in which each decimal digit is represented by a binary code, and the arithmetic is performed in the decimal domain. It requires four bits to represent, or *code*, each decimal digit. Since there are 16 permutations for each four-bit binary word, there are many possible ways to code each decimal digit. One of the commonly used codes is the weighted, or "8421," code, in which each decimal digit is simply represented by its binary integer representation, as shown in Table 17.5.

17.6   Combinational and sequential circuits

In the logic circuits described so far, the value of the output variable at time t is dependent only on the values of the input variables at time t. Thus either these circuits are time-independent, or their responses are so fast or the input signals vary so slowly that the delay is negligible. Also there is no feedback from the output to the input, so that the response of the circuit does not depend on what took place beforehand. These are called *combinational* circuits.

Most useful digital systems also require memory elements. These elements "remember" the values of variables at a particular time and make these values available to be applied at a later time. Digital circuits using memory elements are known as *sequential* circuits. Generally these circuits involve the feedback of an earlier output to a later input.

We shall now look at some memory digital building blocks and some circuits realizing them.

17.7 The flip-flop (FF)

The flip-flop is a binary storage or memory device. Its function is to store a binary signal indefinitely until certain required signals appear at its inputs.

The simplest FF is the T type (trigger or toggle input). Figure 17.21 shows the symbol and definition of this type of FF. It has one input and

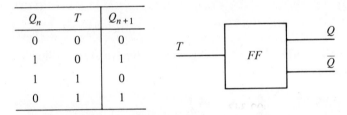

Q_n	T	Q_{n+1}
0	0	0
1	0	1
1	1	0
0	1	1

Figure 17.21 Definition and symbol of a T-type FF.

two outputs, which are complements of each other. In the truth table, Q_n stands for the binary value of Q before signal T is applied and Q_{n+1} stands for the binary value of Q after signal T is applied. Thus Q will remain unchanged as long as the voltage applied at T is zero. When a positive voltage pulse of appropriate strength and duration is applied at T, and after a small delay, the values of Q and $\bar{Q}$ are interchanged. Thus a pulse acts as a trigger to cause this switching action.

The SR type of FF has two inputs and two outputs, whose values are complements of each other. The symbol and definition of this type of FF are shown in Figure 17.22. When a positive pulse is applied at the S input, Q is "set" to 1, regardless of its original value. When a positive pulse is applied at the R input, Q is "reset" to 0. Note that $R = 1$ and $S = 1$ do not occur simultaneously. The output for such a pair of inputs is undefined. In practice, we do not allow R and S to be 1 at the same time.

The arrangement of NOR gates in Figure 17.23 realizes an SR-type FF. A delay of δ seconds is explicitly indicated because the rest of the circuit is combinational. We can consider this as the representation of the inherent delay (no matter how short) that is always present in a circuit. It is also

Q_n	R	S	Q_{n+1}
0	0	0	0
0	0	1	1
0	1	0	0
1	0	0	1
1	0	1	1
1	1	0	0

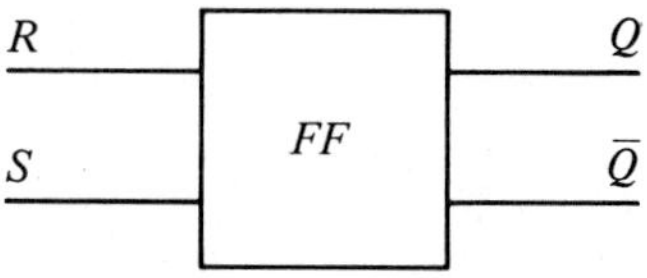

Figure 17.22 Definition and symbol of an SR-type FF.

necessary to avoid the mathematical ambiguity that would arise if the circuit were completely combinational. The Boolean relationships that the circuit must satisfy after switching delays are

$$Q = \overline{R + Q'} \tag{17.27}$$

$$Q' = \overline{S + Q} \tag{17.28}$$

To see the implications of (17.27) and (17.28), we shall investigate the following four input conditions.

1 Under the conditions $R = 0,\ S = 1$, we have

$$Q' = \overline{1 + Q} = 0, \qquad Q = \overline{0 + Q'} = \overline{Q'} = 1$$

2 Under the conditions $R = 1,\ S = 0$, we have

$$Q = \overline{1 + Q'} = 0, \qquad Q' = \overline{0 + Q} = \overline{Q} = 1$$

3 Under the conditions $R = 1,\ S = 1$, we have

$$Q' = \overline{1 + Q} = 0, \qquad Q = \overline{1 + Q'} = 0$$

4 Under the conditions $R = 0,\ S = 0$, either of the following two sets of conditions will satisfy (17.27) and (17.28):

$$Q' = 1 \quad \text{and} \quad Q = 0 \qquad \text{or} \qquad Q' = 0 \quad \text{and} \quad Q = 1$$

From these analyses, we see that, as long as we exclude the condition $R = S = 1$, we have $Q' = \overline{Q}$. Also, if we maintain $S = 1$ for long enough, Q will eventually be made 1, regardless of its original value. Hence a positive pulse at S sets Q to 1. On the other hand, if we maintain $R = 1$ for long enough, Q' will eventually be made 1, regardless of its original value. This makes $Q = 0$. Hence a positive pulse at R resets Q to 0. If $R = S = 0$, no change will take place in Q and Q' values.

Although the preceding analysis does show that the truth table of Figure 17.22 is satisfied, the delay in the circuit is vital for it to work as an FF. To understand the role of the delay, let us assume that initially $Q = 0$ and

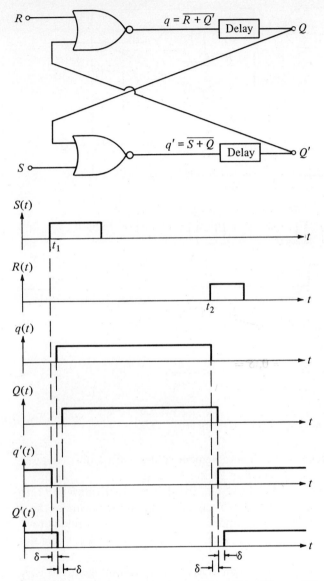

Figure 17.23 A NOR-gate implementation of the SR-type FF.

$Q' = 1$. We also have $q = 0$ and $q' = 1$. At $t = t_1$ a step occurs at S, as shown in Figure 17.24. This causes q' to go to 0 immediately. After δ seconds, Q' is forced to 0 also. This causes q to go to 1. After δ seconds, Q becomes 1 also. The circuit has now changed to the state of $Q = 1$ and $Q' = 0$. No further change is needed in the circuit after $t = t_1 + 2\delta$. Suppose that, after $t = t_1 + 2\delta$, S is returned to 0. This will cause no further change, since $Q = 1$ and this is sufficient to maintain $q' = 0$, regardless of the value of S.

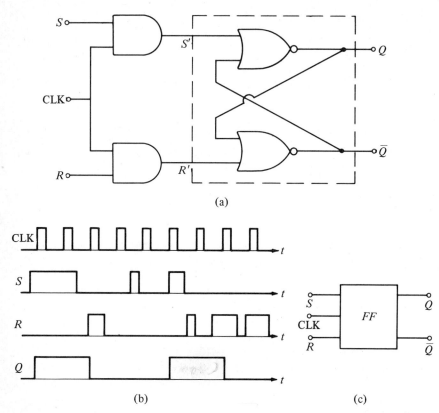

Figure 17.24 (a) A clocked SR-type FF circuit. (b) Example of input–output waveforms in (a). (c) Symbol for a clocked SR-type FF.

The same process is repeated with complement values when a positive pulse is introduced at R. This is depicted in Figure 17.23 at $t = t_2$.

In the preceding description of the FF, the device is activated *any time* a positive signal appears at the input. When a positive pulse appears at the T input, it triggers the FF. When one appears at the S terminal, it sets Q to 1. When one appears at the R terminal, it resets Q to 0. These devices are not clocked; they are operating *asynchronously*.

In many digital systems, particularly large ones, it is advantageous to have all the devices activated at the same time in a *synchronous* operation. The system is *clocked* by a train of pulses that are connected to all the elements. These elements are activated only if the clock pulse is present at its *clock* (CLK) terminal.

Figure 17.24(a) shows a clocked SR-type FF. The arrangement inside the dashed box is an unclocked SR FF (the delays are not shown but are implied). But the input is combined with the clock pulse through two NAND gates. Thus a positive signal will appear at S' (or R') only if a pulse is present at both the CLK terminal and the S (or R) terminal. The trains of pulses in Figure 17.24(b) illustrate how the pulses at S and R set or reset the FF only when a clock pulse is present. Pulses at R or S that occur between clock pulses will be ignored by the device. The symbol for a clocked SR FF has an additional terminal labeled CLK, as shown in Figure 17.24(c).

The JK-type FF is similar to the SR type except for the ambiguity of the output when $S = R = 1$ is removed. The truth table and symbol of such an FF are shown in Figure 17.25. The truth table has two more rows than that of the SR FF. When $S = R = 1$, the value of Q_{n+1} is equal to $\bar{Q}_n$.

Q_n	J	K	Q_{n+1}
0	0	0	0
0	0	1	0
0	1	0	1
0	1	1	1
1	0	0	1
1	0	1	0
1	1	0	1
1	1	1	0

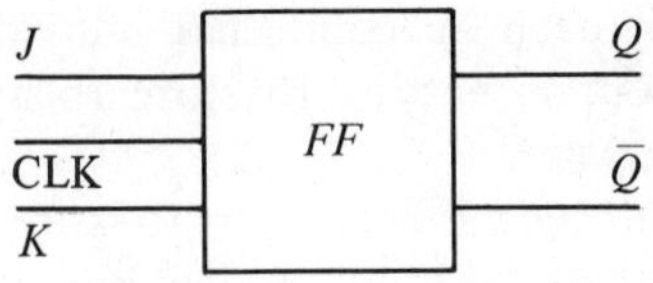

Figure 17.25 Definition and symbol of a JK-type FF.

D_n	Q_{n+1}
1	1
0	0

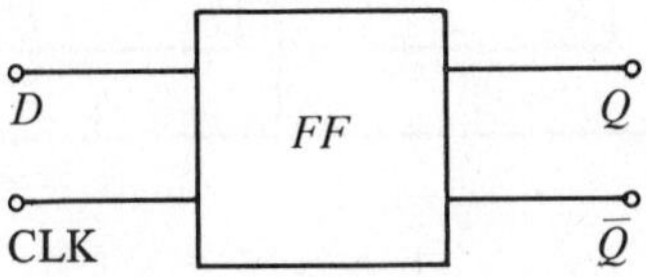

Figure 17.26 Definition and symbol of a D-type FF.

Q_n	R	S	T	Q_{n+1}
0	0	0	0	0
0	0	1	0	1
0	1	0	0	0
0	0	0	1	1
1	0	0	0	1
1	0	1	0	1
1	1	0	0	0
1	0	0	1	0

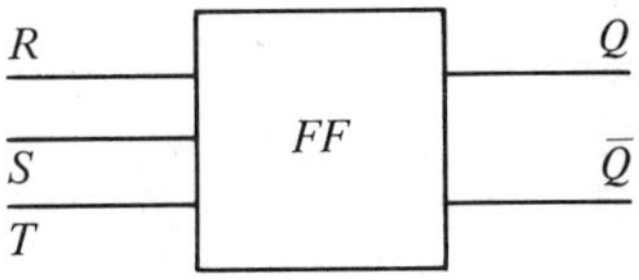

Figure 17.27 Definition and symbol of an RST-type FF.

The D (delay)-type FF is used to provide a delay whenever this is needed. Its input at one clock pulse is transferred to its output at the next clock pulse. Figure 17.26 shows its symbol and truth table. The RST-type FF combines the features of the T-type and the SR-type FF. Its truth table and symbol are given in Figure 17.27.

In the succeeding sections we shall look at some important applications of the FF.

17.8   Shift registers

An FF is a one-bit memory device. A bank of n FFs can be used to store an n-bit word. Such an arrangement is known as a *register*. If the n bits of signal can each be connected individually to a separate FF, no special arrangement is needed to store them. Such an arrangement is called a *parallel register*.

The *shift register* enables us to store a fixed number of serial bits. As new bits appear at the input, earlier bits are pushed away and are lost. Figure 17.28 shows the arrangement of a four-bit shift register. With each clock

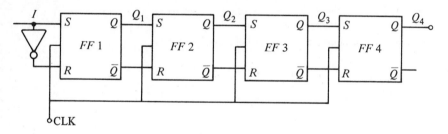

Figure 17.28   A shift register.

pulse, each Q_n is shifted to Q_{n+1}. Table 17.6 shows how the string of binary values 1,0,0,1,1,1,0 would be shifted successively from register to register when it was applied to I. The value of Q_4 is lost after each shift.

Table **17.6**

Time	t_1	t_2	t_3	t_4	t_5	t_6	t_7
I	1	0	0	1	1	1	0
Q_1		1	0	0	1	1	1
Q_2		0	1	0	0	1	1
Q_3		0	0	1	0	0	1
Q_4		0	0	0	1	0	0

17.9 The counter

The basic building block of the counter is the *binary counter*. A counter circuit is shown in Figure 17.29. From the circuit arrangement we have

$$S_1 = I\bar{Q}_2 \tag{17.29}$$

$$R_1 = IQ_2 \tag{17.30}$$

$$S_2 = \bar{I}Q_1 \tag{17.31}$$

$$R_2 = \bar{I}\bar{Q}_1 \tag{17.32}$$

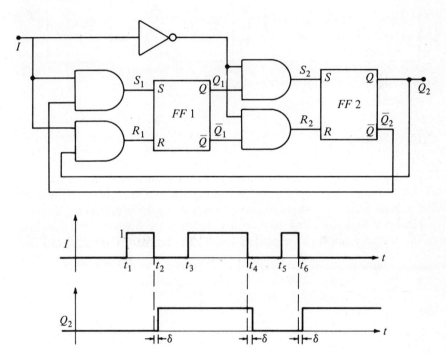

Figure 17.29 A binary counter.

In Figure 17.29, suppose that before $t = t_1$ every quantity is 0. At $t = t_1$, $I = 1$. From (17.29) to (17.32), we have $S_1 = 1$, $R_1 = 0$, $Q_1 = 1$, $S_2 = 0$, and $R_2 = 0$, which requires that $Q_2 = 0$. There is no contradiction. After $t = t_2$, $I = 0$, $S_1 = 0$, $R_1 = 0$, $Q_1 = 1$, $S_2 = 1$, $R_2 = 0$, and $Q_2 = 1$. After $t = t_3$, $I = 1$, $S_1 = 0$, $R_1 = 1$, $Q_1 = 0$, $S_2 = 0$, $R_2 = 0$, and $Q_2 = 1$. After $t = t_4$, $I = 0$, $S_1 = 0$, $R_1 = 0$, $Q_1 = 0$, $S_2 = 0$, $R_2 = 1$, and $Q_2 = 0$. At $t = t_5$, what took place at $t = t_1$ is repeated. The result is that Q_2 changes its value once for every two changes of I, as shown in Figure 17.29. Alternatively, every two complete positive pulses in I produce one complete positive pulse in Q_2. If two such binary counters are connected in cascade, then every four pulses at the input will cause one pulse to appear at the output of the last counter. Thus, if we have a number of binary counters connected in cascade, as shown in Figure 17.30, the number of pulses that have appeared at I would be equal to

$$Q_N \times 2^N + Q_{N-1} \times 2^{N-1} + \cdots + Q_2 \times 2^2 + Q_1 \times 2^1 + Q_0 \times 2^0$$

Hence the number of pulses is equal to the binary number whose digits are $Q_N Q_{N-1} \cdots Q_2 Q_1 Q_0$.

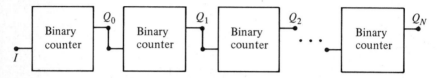

Figure 17.30 A counter for binary numbers.

17.10 The adder

A binary adder is a device with two sets of input terminals. The series of bits that correspond to the two binary numbers to be added appear at these terminals simultaneously. The output terminals give the bits of the sum of the two numbers. This mode of addition is called *parallel addition*.

The basic building block of a binary adder is the *half-adder*. It has two inputs, x and y, and two outputs, S and C, as shown in Figure 17.31. The

x	y	S	C
0	0	0	0
0	1	1	0
1	0	1	0
1	1	0	1

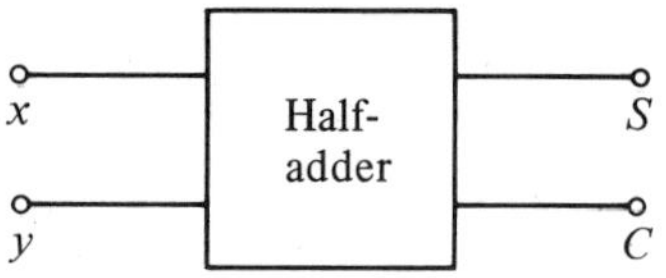

Figure 17.31 The truth table and symbol of a half-adder.

truth table of a half-adder is also shown in Figure 17.31. The S output of a half-adder gives the sum of each digit and output C gives the carry of that digit. Analytically, we have in a half-adder

$$S = x \oplus y = x\bar{y} + \bar{x}y \tag{17.33}$$

$$C = xy \tag{17.34}$$

Figure 17.32 is a realization of the half-adder.

A *full adder* is similar to a half-adder except for an additional input, which

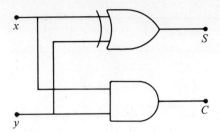

Figure 17.32 A half-adder.

is used to receive the carry from the lower significant digit. Figure 17.33 shows the block diagram and truth table of a full adder. Figure 17.34 is a realization of the full adder, using two half-adders and one OR gate. In the circuit, C_n represents the carry from the $(n-1)$th digit, x_n and y_n are the binary values of the nth digit of the augend and addend, respectively, and S_n is the sum and C_{n+1} the carry of the nth digit.

Figure 17.35 shows the arrangement of a parallel adder. The device adds two binary numbers whose digits are $x_n x_{n-1} \dots x_2 x_1 x_0$ and $y_n y_{n-1} \dots y_2 y_1 y_0$. The sum will have the digits $C_{n+1} S_n S_{n-1} \dots S_2 S_1 S_0$.

It should be noted that a parallel adder is a combinational device. It might be useful, for instance, when we want to monitor the sum of two voltages continuously.

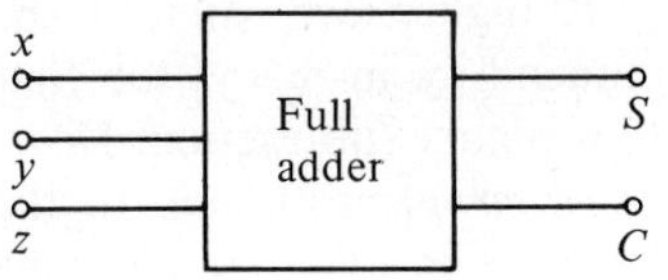

x	y	z	S	C
0	0	0	0	0
0	0	1	1	0
0	1	0	1	0
1	0	0	1	0
0	1	1	0	1
1	0	1	0	1
1	1	0	0	1
1	1	1	1	1

(block diagram: x, y, z → Full adder → S, C)

Figure 17.33 Definition and symbol of a full adder.

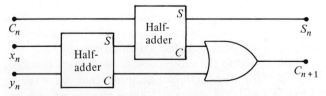

Figure 17.34 A full-adder circuit.

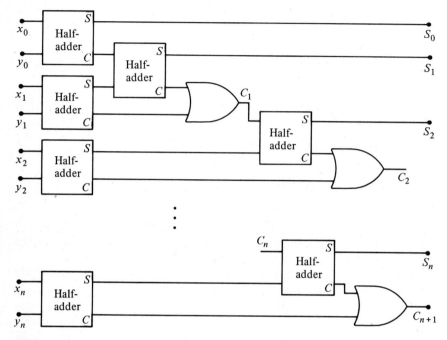

Figure 17.35 A parallel binary adder.

17.11 The subtractor

The usual method of subtracting one decimal number from another decimal number calls for borrowing a 1 from the next higher-level digit if the subtrahend (y in $x - y$) is larger than the minuend (x in $x - y$) for that digit. A similar operation can be implemented for binary subtraction. However, an easier method is to use the technique of *complementation*. In the subtraction of two decimal numbers this technique is illustrated by the following example.

$$8264 - 3547 = 8264 + (10{,}000 - 3547) - 10{,}000$$

$$= 8264 + 6453 - 10{,}000 = 14{,}717 - 10{,}000$$

$$= 4717$$

The number 6453 is the complement of the number 3547. We accomplish the last step by reducing the most significant digit by 1. This technique replaces a subtraction problem by one essentially of addition.

Analogously, the steps involved in the subtraction of two binary numbers may be illustrated by the following example. Suppose that we wish to subtract 0101 from 1100. We add and subtract 10000 to the operation.*

* Here the $+$ sign is the arithmetical "plus," not the logic "OR."

$$1100 - 0101 = 1100 + (10000 - 0101) - 10000$$

But

$$10000 - 0101 = 1111 + 1 - 0101$$
$$= 1010 + 1$$

Here we observe that 1010 is another number that is the digit-by-digit complement of 0101. Thus we have

$$1100 - 0101 = 1100 + 1010 + 1 - 10000 = 0111$$

In general, this operation is expressed as

$$x_n x_{n-1} \dots x_2 x_1 x_0 - y_n y_{n-1} \dots y_2 y_1 y_0 = x_n x_{n-1} \dots x_2 x_1 x_0$$
$$+ \bar{y}_n \bar{y}_{n-1} \dots \bar{y}_2 \bar{y}_1 \bar{y}_0 + 1 - 100 \dots 000$$

We can accomplish the last subtraction by simply dropping the leading digit of the sum of the first three terms. Figure 17.36 shows a circuit implementing this subtraction, which is a modified adder. The complementation of y's is accomplished by a number of NOT gates. An external 1 is artificially introduced. And the subtraction of $100 \dots 000$ is achieved by leaving out C_{n+1}. The difference is given by the binary number whose digits are $S_n S_{n-1} \dots S_2 S_1 S_0$.

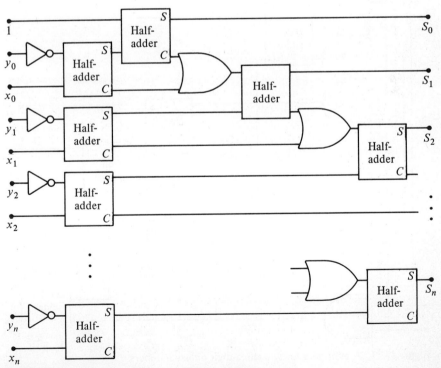

Figure 17.36 A subtractor for two binary numbers.

17.12   The multiplier

Multiplication of binary numbers is simpler than multiplication of decimal numbers because the one-digit multiplication table reduces to

$$0 \times 0 = 0, \qquad 0 \times 1 = 0, \qquad 1 \times 1 = 1$$

Hence there is no carrying of numbers from one digit to the other. It does involve some shifting or scaling of products before we take the sum. For example,

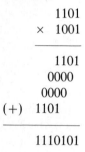

```
          1101
      ×   1001

          1101
          0000
          0000
(+)      1101

       1110101
```

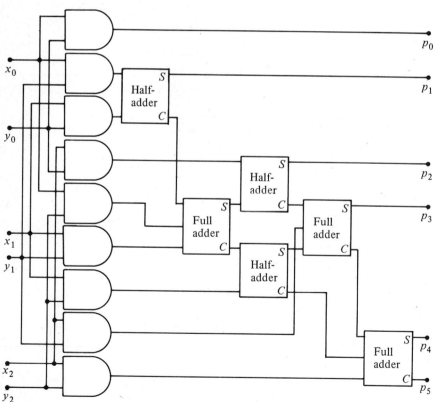

Figure 17.37   A multiplier for two three-digit binary numbers.

As an example of a very simple approach to implementing the multiplication of two three-digit binary numbers, let

$$x_2 x_1 x_0 \times y_2 y_1 y_0 = p_5 p_4 p_3 p_2 p_1 p_0$$

Let us perform the multiplication as usual.

		x_2	x_1	x_0
$(\times)$		y_2	y_1	y_0

			$x_2 y_2$	$x_1 y_0$	$x_0 y_0$
		$x_2 y_1$	$x_1 y_1$	$x_0 y_1$	
$(+)$	$x_2 y_2$	$x_1 y_2$	$x_0 y_2$		

We see in the first digit that

$$p_0 = x_0 y_0$$

In the second digit, we have

$$p_1 = (x_1 y_0) + (x_0 y_1)$$

This is the S output of a half-adder with $x_1 y_0$ and $x_0 y_1$ as its input. The C output of this adder must be carried to the next digit. The digit p_2 is the sum of $x_2 y_0$, $x_1 y_1$, $x_0 y_2$, and the carry-over from the last digit. And so on. A circuit to implement this multiplication is given in Figure 17.37.

17.13 The serial adder

The function of a binary serial adder is to add two binary numbers, each being represented by a sequence of pulses. The sum of these binary numbers is represented by another sequence of pulses. For instance, if $A = 10011$ and $B = 10111$, then the addition that we want to take place is

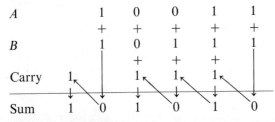

To perform this addition serially, we feed into an adder the series of pulses representing the successive bits of A and B (from the right to the left) and get an output that is another series of pulses representing the bits of the sum of A and B.

What we need is a circuit that will give the sum of the corresponding bits of A and B and the carry in such a fashion that

0 plus 0 (plus 0) equals 0
0 plus 1 (plus 0) equals 1
1 plus 1 (plus 0) equals 0 *and carries 1*
1 plus 1 plus 1 equals 1 *and carries 1*

These operations are all combinational except the CARRY operation, which is sequential. It takes the carry bit generated during one pulse period and reintroduces it at the input during the next pulse period.

The combinational part of the adder can be accomplished by the *full adder* of Figure 17.33. The S output gives the last digit of the sum of x, y, and z. The C output gives the carry generated by the same sum.

One way to accomplish the sequential part of the operation is to connect a delay device, as shown in Figure 17.38. The amount of delay is equal to the time between successive pulses of A and B.

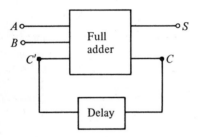

Figure 17.38 A binary serial adder.

An alternative implementation of the adder is shown in Figure 17.39(a). The full adder is buffered by three AND gates, and one of the terminals of each gate is connected to a clock signal, which is shown in Figure 17.39(b). The series of pulses corresponding to the binary bits of A and B arrive at the AND gates in synchronism with the clock pulses, as shown in Figure 17.39(c) and (d). The delay device is replaced by a D-type FF. Thus, for the series of pulses at C shown in Figure 17.39(f), the output at C' will be as shown in Figure 17.39(g). The key feature here is the delay between the input and the output. Also note that the output value C' is unchanged until it becomes unequal to the input value C. When this occurs, the value C' at t_{n+1} becomes that of C at t_n.

The output of AND gate 3, which is combinational, is 1 only if both $CLK(t)$ and $C'(t)$ are 1. Hence C'' is identical to C, except that the former is delayed by the time interval between clock pulses, t_d.

The operation of the addition of the binary numbers $A = 10011$ and $B = 10111$ is given in the pulse series of Figure 17.39. At $t = t_0$, $A = 1$, $B = 1$, $C'' = 0$; we have $S = 0$ and $C(t_0) = 1$. At $t = t_1$, $A = 1$, $B = 1$, $C'' = C(t_0) = 1$; we have $S = 1$ and $C(t_1) = 1$. At $t = t_2$, $A = 0$, $B = 1$, $C'' = C(t_1) = 1$; we have $S = 0$ and $C(t_2) = 1$. And so on.

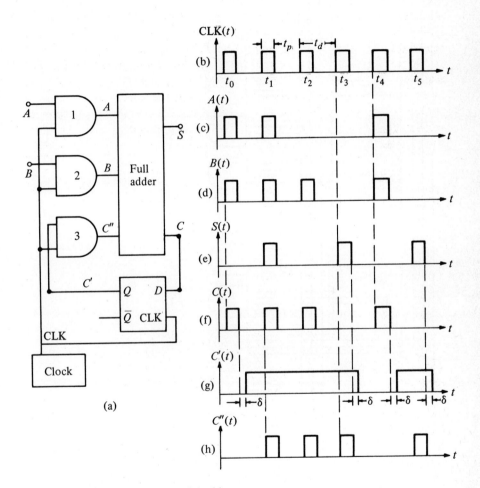

Figure 17.39 A synchronous serial adder.

17.14 A BCD-to-decimal decoder

In a digital system that uses the BCD numbering system described in Section 17.5, the answer will be in coded binary form. It is then necessary

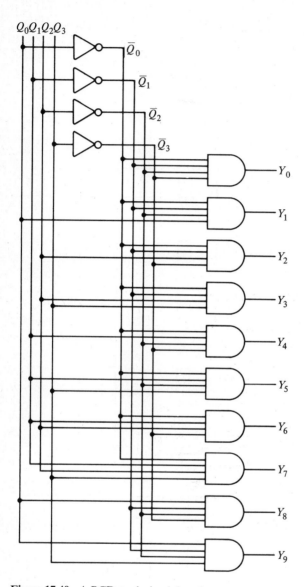

$Q_0 Q_1 Q_2 Q_3$

$\bar{Q}_0$

$\bar{Q}_1$

$\bar{Q}_2$

$\bar{Q}_3$

Y_0

Y_1

Y_2

Y_3

Y_4

Y_5

Y_6

Y_7

Y_8

Y_9

Figure 17.40 A BCD-to-decimal decoder.

to translate these codes back into decimal form. A device that accomplishes this is known as a BCD-to-decimal or a 4-to-10 line decoder.

Figure 17.40 shows an arrangement that converts a four-digit binary number $Q = Q_3 Q_2 Q_1 Q_0$ $(= Q_3 \times 2^3 + Q_2 \times 2^2 + Q_1 \times 2^1 + Q_0 \times 2^0)$ to a one-digit decimal number Y_n according to Table 17.5. In Figure 17.40, we have the following.

$$Y_0 = \bar{Q}_0 \bar{Q}_1 \bar{Q}_2 \bar{Q}_3 \qquad Y_5 = \bar{Q}_0 Q_1 \bar{Q}_2 Q_3$$
$$Y_1 = \bar{Q}_0 \bar{Q}_1 \bar{Q}_2 Q_3 \qquad Y_6 = \bar{Q}_0 Q_1 Q_2 \bar{Q}_3$$
$$Y_2 = \bar{Q}_0 \bar{Q}_1 Q_2 \bar{Q}_3 \qquad Y_7 = \bar{Q}_0 Q_1 Q_2 Q_3 \qquad\qquad (17.35)$$
$$Y_3 = \bar{Q}_0 \bar{Q}_1 Q_2 Q_3 \qquad Y_8 = Q_0 \bar{Q}_1 \bar{Q}_2 \bar{Q}_3$$
$$Y_4 = \bar{Q}_0 Q_1 \bar{Q}_2 \bar{Q}_3 \qquad Y_9 = Q_0 \bar{Q}_1 \bar{Q}_2 Q_3$$

Hence each binary number in Table 17.5 will cause one, and only one, of the 10 outputs to be 1. This output can then be used to turn on a decimal number, perhaps by making a certain number of light-emitting diodes light up, thus displaying the coded decimal number.

17.15 Concluding remarks

In this chapter, we tried to lay down some basic rules and techniques for dealing with digital circuits. We did not go into many finer points of the areas of digital systems and computers. Although we gave examples of certain functional blocks and specialty circuits, these were only meant to serve as examples. Given a digital function, to find a realization that uses the minimum number of devices is a special topic in itself. We have not gone into other details such as speed, cost, power consumption, or realizability. The techniques of producing the various functional blocks is another important field. Then there is the problem of storage of digital signals and how to retrieve them.

Digital devices are simple and cheap because they don't have to be extremely precise. However, in many situations, we need a large number of them. In IC technology, thousands of gates, FFs, registers, and so on, are fabricated on a single chip. Many digital circuits much more elaborate than the ones introduced in this chapter are being manufactured as MSI or LSI units and are available as off-the-shelf items. Modern applications of digital technology typically deal with functional modules much larger than simple gates, FFs, or registers. However, an understanding of these simple circuits is still fundamental to any work on digital systems and computer hardware.

Problems

17.1 Draw a logic circuit for each of the following relationships using only AND, OR, and NOT gates:

(a) $(A+B)(\bar{A}+C)(B+C)$;   (b) $AB + AB\bar{C} + (\overline{B+C+\bar{A}})$;

(c) $(A+B+C)(A+D)B$.

17.2 Express F in terms of A, B, and C for each of the circuits in Figure P17.2. Construct a truth table for this function. Simplify this expression by using the formulas in Section 17.2.

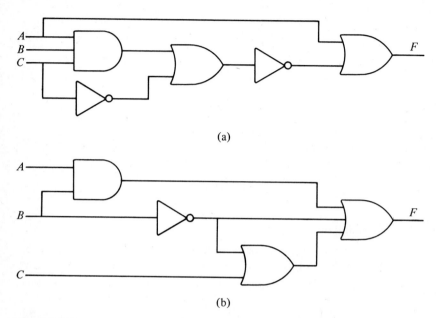

(a)

(b)

Figure P17.2

17.3 Construct a truth table for each of the following functions:

(a) $F = A + AB + BCD + AC + B$;   (b) $F = A\bar{B} + B\bar{C} + C\bar{A}$.

17.4 Simplify the expressions given in Problem 17.1.

17.5 Devise a circuit to implement the function defined in Table 17.7.

Table **17.7**

A	B	C	$F = f(A, B, C)$
0	0	0	0
0	1	0	1
0	0	1	1
1	1	0	0

17.6 Add $(15.25)_{10}$ and $(1.375)_{10}$ in binary form.

17.7 Subtract $(110011)_2$ from $(1001001)_2$.

17.8 Multiply $(111)_2$ and $(1011)_2$.

17.9 Verify the following identities:

(a) $A \oplus (A + B) = \bar{A}B$;   (b) $A \oplus (\bar{A}B) = A + B$;
(c) $A \oplus (\bar{A} + B) = \overline{(AB)}$;   (d) $A \odot (\bar{A}B) = \bar{A}B$;
(e) $A \odot (\bar{A} + B) = AB$;   (f) $A \odot (A + B) = A + \bar{B}$.

17.10 Show that:
(a) $(A \oplus B) \oplus C = A \oplus (B \oplus C)$;   (b) $AB + A\bar{B} + \bar{A}B = A + B$.

17.11 What operation does each of the circuits in Figure P17.11 perform?

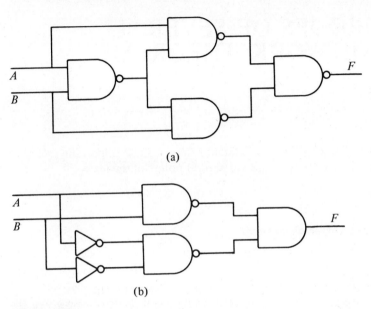

(a)

(b)

Figure P17.11

17.12 Show that the truth table of the JK-type FF is expressible as
$Q_{n+1} = J\bar{Q}_n + \bar{K}Q_n$

17.13 Find a half-adder circuit using only NOT and OR gates.

A | PROOFS OF SEVERAL NETWORK THEOREMS

In this appendix, we shall give detailed proofs of four important theorems in network theory that were used at several points of the text.

A.1 Proof of Thévenin's theorem

Thévenin's theorem gives a relationship at the terminals between the current and the voltage of a two-terminal LTI network with independent sources, provided that there is no mutual coupling between the network and whatever is connected to the terminal pair. This proviso rules out the validity of the theorem if there is an inductive coupling between any part of the network and what is connected to the terminal pair, or if any of the controlled sources in the network are controlled by electric quantities outside the network or vice versa.

To simplify the proof, we shall assume that the network in question is excited by an independent current source at its terminal pair (terminals a and b in Figure A.1). Furthermore we shall assume that the network contains $N-1$ independent current sources, M independent voltage sources, and a number of LTI network elements, including LTI controlled sources.

Since the network is LTI, the superposition property prevails. That is to say, V_{ab} is a linear combination of all the strengths of the independent sources. This fact can be expressed analytically as

$$V_{ab} = \sum_{j=1}^{N-1} Z_{Nj} I_{sj} + \sum_{k=1}^{M} H_{Nk} E_{sk} + Z_{NN} I_{sN} \tag{A.1}$$

where $Z_{Nj} I_{sj}$ is the contribution to V_{ab} from the jth independent current source and $H_{Nk} E_{sk}$ is the contribution from the kth independent voltage source. Each of these terms (including $Z_{NN} I_{sN}$) may be either calculated or measured by setting the strengths of all other sources to zero. (All controlled sources remain in operation.)

We may identify the first two summations on the right-hand side of

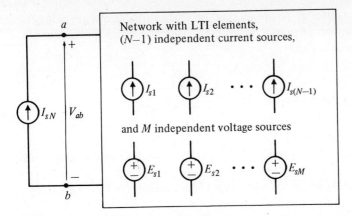

Figure A.1 An LTI network with independent sources excited by a current source.

(A.1) as

$$V_{oc} = \sum_{j=1}^{N-1} Z_{Nj} I_{sj} + \sum_{k=1}^{M} H_{Nk} E_{sk} \tag{A.2}$$

which is the value of V_{ab} if I_{sN} is set to zero. The coefficient in the last term of (A.1) can be either calculated or measured by the relationship

$$Z_{NN} = \frac{V_{ab}}{I_{sN}}\bigg|_{\text{All } E_s\text{'s and all } I_s\text{'s except } I_{sN} \text{ set to zero}} \tag{A.3}$$

Hence (A.1) reduces to

$$V_{ab} = V_{oc} + I_{sN} Z_{NN} \tag{A.4}$$

The circuit of Figure A.2 has exactly the relationship described by (A.4). The current source I_{sN} cannot tell the difference between the solid box in Figure A.1 and the dashed box in Figure A.2. Hence these two boxes are equivalent electrically.

Although we have specialized our proof to using a current source as the excitation at a terminal pair of a network, we have proved the equivalency between the two boxed networks. Clearly the voltage-current relationship

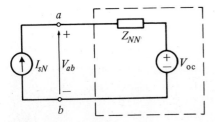

Figure A.2 Thévenin's equivalent of the network of Figure A.1.

that must be satisfied at terminal pair *ab* does not depend on what is connected to the terminal pair. This completes the proof of Thévenin's theorem.

A.2 Proof of Norton's theorem

We can demonstrate the validity of Norton's theorem in a similar fashion to the proof of Thévenin's theorem. However, it's easier to show that Norton's equivalent circuit can be obtained through Thévenin's equivalent circuit.

Starting with (A.4), we divide the equation throughout by Z_{NN}. This gives

$$I_{sN} = -\frac{V_{oc}}{Z_{NN}} + \frac{V_{ab}}{Z_{NN}} \tag{A.5}$$

If we now call

$$I_{sc} = \frac{V_{oc}}{Z_{NN}} \tag{A.6}$$

equation (A.5) is clearly satisfied by the circuit of Figure A.3. Since I_{sc} would flow in the short circuit if the circuit in the dashed box of Figure A.2 was short-circuited across terminals *a* and *b*, and since this circuit is equivalent to the network in the box of Figure A.1, the circuit in the dashed box of Figure A.3 is also equivalent to the network of Figure A.1. Thus we have proved Norton's theorem.

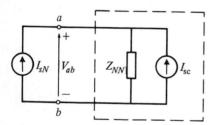

Figure A.3 Norton's equivalent of the network of Figure A.1.

A.3 Proof of Tellegen's theorem

Imagine a general network with n branches. One such network is shown in Figure A.4. We wish to show that

$$\sum_{i=1}^{n} e_i i_i = 0 \tag{A.7}$$

is always true.

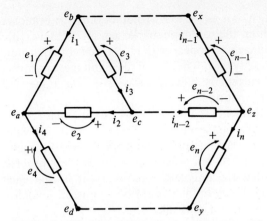

Figure A.4 A general network for the proof of Tellegen's theorem.

Suppose that we designate each node voltage as $e_a, e_b, ..., e_z$ with respect to some arbitrary reference, say the earth. Then we have

$$e_1 = e_b - e_a$$

$$e_2 = e_c - e_a$$

$$e_3 = e_b - e_c$$

$$\vdots$$

$$e_n = e_z - e_y$$

(A.8)

The individual terms in (A.7) become

$$e_1 i_1 = i_1(e_b - e_a)$$

$$e_2 i_2 = i_2(e_c - e_a)$$

$$e_3 i_3 = i_3(e_b - e_c)$$

$$\vdots$$

$$e_n i_n = i_n(e_z - e_y)$$

(A.9)

If we now sum up these equations and regroup the terms on the right-hand side according to their common voltage factors, we obtain the equation

$$\sum_{i=1}^{n} e_i i_i = e_a(-i_1 - i_2 + i_4) + e_b(i_1 + i_3 + \cdots) + e_c(i_2 - i_3 + \cdots) + \cdots$$

$$+ e_z(i_n - i_{n-1} - i_{n-2} - \cdots) = 0$$

(A.10)

Each quantity in the parentheses is readily identified as the total current leaving the node whose absolute voltage appears with the quantity. Hence each term on the right-hand side of (A.10) is zero because of KCL. Hence (A.7) must be true in general.

We should point out that (A.7) is equal to (A.10) only if *all* the branches in a network are included in the summation. When all branches are accounted for, each node voltage will appear with all the currents that flow either from or to that node exactly once. The sign of these voltages appearing in (A.9) are positive if the current is flowing away from the node and negative if it is flowing toward that node.

We should also point out that (A.8) is another way of stating that KVL is satisfied by the branch voltages of the network. Equation (A.10) is valid because KCL is satisfied by the currents of the network. Hence Tellegen's theorem is true for any type of network, *linear or nonlinear.* Our proof is formulated in such a way that the only other requirement is that each branch be a two-terminal one. Each branch could be a resistor, inductor, capacitor, an independent source, or a controlled source.

In this proof, we have assumed that the voltages and currents are all from the same network, for convenience. It should be clear that the argument still holds if the voltages (or the currents) are replaced by the voltages (or the currents) of another network, as long as the number of nodes and branches of these networks have the same topology.

A.4 Proof of reciprocity theorem

We shall now use Tellegen's theorem to prove the reciprocity theorem for a network that contains LTI resistors only.

Let us take a network with n branches, $n-2$ of which are resistive, as shown in Figure A.5(a). Two branches of this network, branches 1 and 2, are separated from the rest so as to leave the latter as a two-terminal pair network. Consider the two sets of voltage and current distributions shown in Figure A.5(a). Tellegen's theorem assures that

$$e_1' i_1 + e_2' i_2 + \sum_{k=3}^{n} e_k' i_k = 0$$

$$e_1 i_1' + e_2 i_2' + \sum_{k=3}^{n} e_k i_k' = 0 \tag{A.11}$$

But

$$e_k = i_k R_k$$

$$e_k' = i_k' R_k \tag{A.12}$$

Hence we get

$$\sum_{k=3}^{n} e_k' i_k = \sum_{k=3}^{n} i_k' R_k i_k = \sum_{k=3}^{n} i_k' e_k \tag{A.13}$$

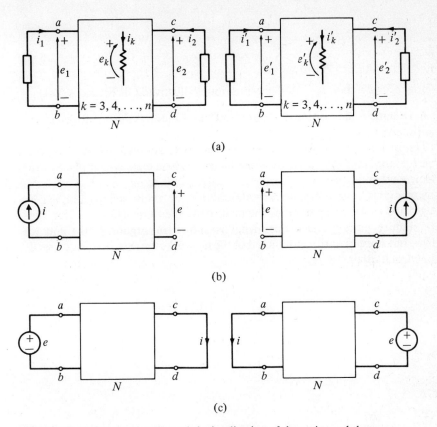

Figure A.5   Resistive networks and the implication of the reciprocal theorem.

Thus

$$e_1' i_1 + e_2' i_2 = e_1 i_1' + e_2 i_2'$$ (A.14)

From this relationship, we may arrive at the following two situations.

1   If $i_1' = 0$ and $i_2 = 0$, we have

$$e_1' i_1 = e_2 i_2'$$ (A.15)

or

$$\frac{e_1'}{i_2'} = \frac{e_2}{i_1}$$ (A.16)

If now $i_1 = i_2'$, then $e_1' = e_2$. This is illustrated in Figure A.5(b).

2   If $e_1' = 0$ and $e_2 = 0$, we have

$$e_2' i_2 = e_1 i_1'$$ (A.17)

or

$$\frac{i_2}{e_1} = \frac{i'_1}{e'_2} \tag{A.18}$$

If now $e_1 = e'_2$, then $i_2 = i'_1$. This situation is illustrated in Figure A.5(c).

A statement describing the situations in Figure A.5(b) and (c) is the reciprocity theorem.

This proof is obviously also valid for networks that include LTI capacitors and LTI inductors, if we use the impedances of these elements in place of the elements themselves.

Sometimes a verbal statement describing the relationships implied by (A.16) and (A.18) is regarded as the reciprocity theorem. These relationships are slightly more general than what is shown in Figure A.5(b) and (c). However, since linearity is assumed of the network, these two versions really imply each other.

B | MATRIX ALGEBRA

B.1 Definitions

A *matrix* is a rectangular array of elements. Each element is denoted by two subscripts. The first indicates the row and the second indicates the column in which the element appears. Thus matrix $[A]$ represents

$$[A] = \begin{bmatrix} a_{11} & a_{12} & a_{13} & \cdots & a_{1n} \\ a_{21} & a_{22} & a_{23} & \cdots & a_{2n} \\ \cdots\cdots\cdots\cdots\cdots\cdots\cdots \\ a_{m1} & a_{m2} & a_{m3} & \cdots & a_{mn} \end{bmatrix} = [a_{ij}] \tag{B.1}$$

The matrix in (B.1) is said to have a dimension of $m \times n$.

A *row matrix* (also called a row vector) has a dimension of $1 \times n$. Thus

$$[\alpha] = [\alpha_{11} \ \alpha_{12} \ \alpha_{13} \ \cdots \ \alpha_{1n}] \tag{B.2}$$

is a row matrix.

A *column matrix* (also called a column vector) has a dimension of $m \times 1$. Thus

$$[\beta] = \begin{bmatrix} \beta_{11} \\ \beta_{21} \\ \beta_{31} \\ \vdots \\ \beta_{m1} \end{bmatrix} \tag{B.3}$$

is a column matrix.

Two matrices are said to be *equal* if all their corresponding elements are equal. Thus, if

$$a_{ik} = b_{ik}, \qquad \text{for all } i \text{ and } k$$

then

$$[A] = [B]$$

If a matrix has only a single element, then it becomes a *scalar*.

The *determinant* of a square matrix is the determinant formed with the elements of the matrix. In other words, the determinant of $[A]$ is

$$|A| = \begin{vmatrix} a_{11} & a_{12} & \cdots & a_{1n} \\ a_{21} & a_{22} & \cdots & a_{2n} \\ \cdots & \cdots & \cdots & \cdot \\ a_{n1} & a_{n2} & \cdots & a_{nn} \end{vmatrix} \tag{B.4}$$

The *minor* of the *ij* element is the determinant formed from the original determinant by deleting the *i*th row and the *j*th column. Thus, for the determinant

$$|A| = \begin{vmatrix} a_{11} & a_{12} & a_{13} & a_{14} \\ a_{21} & a_{22} & a_{23} & a_{24} \\ a_{31} & a_{32} & a_{33} & a_{34} \\ a_{41} & a_{42} & a_{43} & a_{44} \end{vmatrix} \tag{B.5}$$

its 11, 23, and 41 minors are

$$M_{11} = \begin{vmatrix} a_{22} & a_{23} & a_{24} \\ a_{32} & a_{33} & a_{34} \\ a_{42} & a_{43} & a_{44} \end{vmatrix} \tag{B.6}$$

$$M_{23} = \begin{vmatrix} a_{11} & a_{12} & a_{14} \\ a_{31} & a_{32} & a_{34} \\ a_{41} & a_{42} & a_{44} \end{vmatrix} \tag{B.7}$$

$$M_{41} = \begin{vmatrix} a_{12} & a_{13} & a_{14} \\ a_{22} & a_{23} & a_{24} \\ a_{32} & a_{33} & a_{34} \end{vmatrix} \tag{B.8}$$

respectively.

The cofactor of the *ij* element of a determinant is denoted by A_{ij} and

$$A_{ij} = (-1)^{i+j} M_{ij} \tag{B.9}$$

We may obtain the value of a determinant by summing up the products of its elements and their cofactors along any row or any column. Hence we get

$$|A| = \sum_{i=1}^{n} a_{ij} A_{ij} = \sum_{j=1}^{n} a_{ij} A_{ij} \tag{B.10}$$

B.2 Algebraic rules of matrices

The addition of matrices follows the usual rule of addition *element by element*. Hence the sum of two matrices is a matrix whose elements are the sums of the corresponding elements of the addends. Thus, if

$$[A] + [B] = [C]$$

we have

$$c_{ik} = a_{ik} + b_{ik} \tag{B.11}$$

The subtraction of two matrices is performed similarly. If

$$[A] - [B] = [C]$$

then

$$c_{ij} = a_{ij} - b_{ij} \tag{B.12}$$

The multiplication of a matrix by a scalar is obtained by multiplying each element of the matrix by the scalar. Thus if

$$[B] = \alpha[A]$$

then

$$b_{ij} = \alpha a_{ij}, \qquad \text{for all } i \text{ and } j \tag{B.13}$$

If $[A]$ is $k \times m$ and $[B]$ is $m \times n$, then $[A]$ and $[B]$ are *conformable* in that order and the multiplication of $[A]$ and $[B]$ is defined. We obtain the ij element of the product $[A][B]$ by summing up the products of the elements from the ith row of $[A]$ and the elements from the jth column of $[B]$. That is to say, if

$$[C] = [A][B]$$

then

$$C_{ij} = a_{i1}b_{1j} + a_{i2}b_{2j} + a_{i3}b_{3j} + \cdots + a_{im}b_{mj} = \sum_{k=1}^{m} a_{ik}b_{kj} \tag{B.14}$$

For example,

$$
\begin{bmatrix} a_{11} & a_{12} & a_{13} \\ a_{21} & a_{22} & a_{23} \\ a_{31} & a_{32} & a_{33} \end{bmatrix}
\begin{bmatrix} x_{11} & x_{12} \\ x_{21} & x_{22} \\ x_{31} & x_{32} \end{bmatrix}
$$

$$
= \begin{bmatrix} a_{11}x_{11} + a_{12}x_{21} + a_{13}x_{31} & a_{11}x_{12} + a_{12}x_{22} + a_{13}x_{32} \\ a_{21}x_{11} + a_{22}x_{21} + a_{23}x_{31} & a_{21}x_{12} + a_{22}x_{22} + a_{23}x_{32} \\ a_{31}x_{11} + a_{32}x_{21} + a_{33}x_{31} & a_{31}x_{12} + a_{32}x_{22} + a_{33}x_{32} \end{bmatrix} \tag{B.15}
$$

Multiplication is generally not commutative, so that generally we have

$$[A][B] \neq [B][A] \tag{B.16}$$

Indeed, even if $[A]$ and $[B]$ are conformable, they may not be conformable in the reversed order.

B.3   Special matrices

1 *Unit matrix or identity matrix, $[U]$*

$$[U] = \begin{bmatrix} 1 & 0 & 0 & \cdots & 0 \\ 0 & 1 & 0 & \cdots & 0 \\ & & \cdots & & \\ 0 & 0 & 0 & \cdots & 1 \end{bmatrix} \tag{B.17}$$

2 *Scalar matrix, $[K]$*

$$[K] = k[U] = \begin{bmatrix} k & 0 & 0 & 0 & \cdots & 0 \\ 0 & k & 0 & 0 & \cdots & 0 \\ 0 & 0 & k & 0 & \cdots & 0 \\ & & & \cdots & & \\ 0 & 0 & 0 & 0 & \cdots & k \end{bmatrix} \tag{B.18}$$

3 *Diagonal matrix, $[D]$*

$$[D] = \begin{bmatrix} d_{11} & 0 & 0 & 0 & \cdots & 0 \\ 0 & d_{22} & 0 & 0 & \cdots & 0 \\ 0 & 0 & d_{33} & 0 & \cdots & 0 \\ & & & \cdots & & \\ 0 & 0 & 0 & 0 & \cdots & d_{nn} \end{bmatrix} \tag{B.19}$$

A diagonal matrix is frequently written as

$$[D] = \text{diag}[d_{11} \; d_{22} \; d_{33} \; \cdots \; d_{nn}]$$

to save space.

4 A matrix is *symmetric* if

$$a_{ij} = a_{ji}, \qquad \text{for all } i \text{ and } j$$

5 A matrix is *skew-symmetric* if

$$a_{ij} = -a_{ji}, \qquad \text{for all } i \text{ and } j$$

This definition requires that all diagonal elements a_{ii} be identically zero.

6 The *transpose* of a matrix is the matrix with its rows and columns interchanged. If we denote the transpose of $[A]$ by $[A]_t$ and if

$$[B] = [A]_t$$

then

$$b_{ij} = a_{ji} \tag{B.20}$$

For example,

$$\begin{bmatrix} 1 & 3 & -2 \\ x & 5 & 0 \end{bmatrix}_t = \begin{bmatrix} 1 & x \\ 3 & 5 \\ -2 & 0 \end{bmatrix}$$

A column matrix is frequently written as the transpose of a row matrix to save space. For example,

$$\begin{bmatrix} \beta_1 \\ \beta_2 \\ \vdots \\ \beta_m \end{bmatrix} = [\beta_1 \ \beta_2 \ \cdots \ \beta_m]_t$$

7 The *adjoint* of a square matrix $[A]$ is a new matrix formed by placing the cofactor of the ij element of $[A]$ in the ji position. Denoting the adjoint of $[A]$ by $\mathrm{adj}[A]$ and letting

$$[B] = \mathrm{adj}[A]$$

we get

$$b_{ij} = A_{ji} \tag{B.21}$$

For example, if we have

$$[A] = \begin{bmatrix} a_{11} & a_{12} & a_{13} \\ a_{21} & a_{22} & a_{23} \\ a_{31} & a_{32} & a_{33} \end{bmatrix}$$

then we get

$$\mathrm{adj}[A] = \begin{bmatrix} \begin{vmatrix} a_{22} & a_{23} \\ a_{32} & a_{33} \end{vmatrix} & -\begin{vmatrix} a_{12} & a_{13} \\ a_{32} & a_{33} \end{vmatrix} & \begin{vmatrix} a_{12} & a_{13} \\ a_{22} & a_{23} \end{vmatrix} \\ -\begin{vmatrix} a_{21} & a_{23} \\ a_{31} & a_{33} \end{vmatrix} & \begin{vmatrix} a_{11} & a_{13} \\ a_{31} & a_{33} \end{vmatrix} & -\begin{vmatrix} a_{11} & a_{13} \\ a_{21} & a_{23} \end{vmatrix} \\ \begin{vmatrix} a_{21} & a_{22} \\ a_{31} & a_{32} \end{vmatrix} & -\begin{vmatrix} a_{11} & a_{12} \\ a_{31} & a_{32} \end{vmatrix} & \begin{vmatrix} a_{11} & a_{12} \\ a_{21} & a_{22} \end{vmatrix} \end{bmatrix} \tag{B.22}$$

8 A square matrix is *singular* if its determinant is zero. Otherwise it is *nonsingular*.

9 The *inverse* of a nonsingular matrix $[A]$ is another matrix whose product with $[A]$ (in either order) is an identity matrix. The inverse of $[A]$ is denoted by $[A]^{-1}$.

The inverse of a matrix is unique, and is equal to its adjoint multiplied by a scalar equal to the reciprocal of its determinant.

$$[A]^{-1} = \frac{\text{adj}[A]}{|A|} \tag{B.23}$$

This can be shown to be true as we look at the product

$$[A](\text{adj}[A]) = [B] \tag{B.24}$$

The element b_{ii} is the sum of the products of the elements of the ith row of $[A]$ and the elements of the ith column of adj$[A]$. But the latter are the cofactors of the elements in the ith row of $[A]$. Hence $b_{ii} = |A|$. On the other hand, the element b_{ij} ($i \neq j$) is the sum of the products of the elements of the ith row of $[A]$ and the elements of the jth column of adj$[A]$. But the latter are the cofactors of the elements of the jth row of $[A]$. Hence this sum is none other than the value of the determinant whose ith row and jth row are identical. The value of such a determinant is, of course, zero. Hence

$$[A](\text{adj}[A]) = \text{diag}[|A||A| \cdots |A|]$$

Therefore

$$[A]\left(\frac{\text{adj}[A]}{|A|}\right) = [U]$$

and

$$[A]^{-1} = \frac{\text{adj}[A]}{|A|}$$

As an example, we have

$$\begin{bmatrix} 5 & 3 \\ 2 & -1 \end{bmatrix}^{-1} = \frac{1}{-11}\begin{bmatrix} -1 & -3 \\ -2 & 5 \end{bmatrix} = \begin{bmatrix} \frac{1}{11} & \frac{3}{11} \\ \frac{2}{11} & -\frac{5}{11} \end{bmatrix}$$

As another example, if

$$[A] = \begin{bmatrix} 4 & 6 & 0 \\ 8 & -1 & -5 \\ -2 & 3 & 2 \end{bmatrix}$$

then

$$|A| = -8 + 60 - 96 + 60 = 16$$

and we obtain

$$\text{adj}[A] = \begin{bmatrix} \begin{vmatrix} -1 & -5 \\ 3 & 2 \end{vmatrix} & -\begin{vmatrix} 6 & 0 \\ 3 & 2 \end{vmatrix} & \begin{vmatrix} 6 & 0 \\ -1 & -5 \end{vmatrix} \\[12pt] -\begin{vmatrix} 8 & -5 \\ -2 & 2 \end{vmatrix} & \begin{vmatrix} 4 & 0 \\ -2 & 2 \end{vmatrix} & -\begin{vmatrix} 4 & 0 \\ 8 & -5 \end{vmatrix} \\[12pt] \begin{vmatrix} 8 & -1 \\ -2 & 3 \end{vmatrix} & -\begin{vmatrix} 4 & 6 \\ -2 & 3 \end{vmatrix} & \begin{vmatrix} 4 & 6 \\ 8 & -1 \end{vmatrix} \end{bmatrix}$$

$$= \begin{bmatrix} 13 & -12 & -30 \\ -6 & 8 & 20 \\ 22 & -24 & -52 \end{bmatrix}$$

Hence

$$[A]^{-1} = \begin{bmatrix} \frac{13}{16} & -\frac{3}{4} & -\frac{15}{8} \\[6pt] -\frac{3}{8} & \frac{1}{2} & \frac{5}{4} \\[6pt] \frac{11}{8} & -\frac{3}{2} & -\frac{13}{4} \end{bmatrix}$$

B.4 Some useful theorems

1 Matrix multiplications are associative, or

$$([A][B])[C] = [A]([B][C]) \tag{B.25}$$

2 Matrix multiplications are distributive with respect to addition or subtraction, or

$$[A]([B] + [C]) = [A][B] + [A][C] \tag{B.26}$$

3

$$([A][B])_t = [B]_t[A]_t \tag{B.27}$$

4

$$([A][B])^{-1} = [B]^{-1}[A]^{-1} \tag{B.28}$$

5 The determinant of the product of two square matrices is equal to the product of their determinants, or

$$|[A][B]| = |[A]||[B]| \tag{B.29}$$

6 The determinant of an $n \times n$ matrix $[A]$ multiplied by a scalar α is $\alpha^n|A|$, or

$$|\alpha[A]| = \alpha^n|A| \tag{B.30}$$

7 The effect of multiplying a matrix by a diagonal matrix from the left is that every element in the ith row is multiplied by the ith element of the diagonal matrix. For example,

$$\begin{bmatrix} d_1 & 0 & 0 \\ 0 & d_2 & 0 \\ 0 & 0 & d_3 \end{bmatrix} \begin{bmatrix} x_{11} & x_{12} \\ x_{21} & x_{22} \\ x_{31} & x_{32} \end{bmatrix} = \begin{bmatrix} d_1 x_{11} & d_1 x_{12} \\ d_2 x_{21} & d_2 x_{22} \\ d_3 x_{31} & d_3 x_{32} \end{bmatrix} \tag{B.31}$$

8 The effect of multiplying a matrix by a diagonal matrix from the right is that every element in the ith column is multiplied by the ith element of the diagonal matrix. For example,

$$\begin{bmatrix} x_{11} & x_{12} \\ x_{21} & x_{22} \\ x_{31} & x_{32} \end{bmatrix} \begin{bmatrix} d_1 & 0 \\ 0 & d_2 \end{bmatrix} = \begin{bmatrix} d_1 x_{11} & d_2 x_{12} \\ d_1 x_{21} & d_2 x_{22} \\ d_1 x_{31} & d_2 x_{32} \end{bmatrix} \tag{B.32}$$

9 If $[A]$ is square and $[D]$ is diagonal, as given by (B.19), then

$$|[D][A]| = d_1 d_2 \cdots d_n |A| \tag{B.33}$$

B.5 Matrix notation in a set of linear simultaneous equations

The set of equations

$$a_{11} x_1 + a_{12} x_2 + \cdots + a_{1n} x_n = y_1$$
$$a_{21} x_1 + a_{22} x_2 + \cdots + a_{2n} x_n = y_2$$
$$\cdots\cdots\cdots\cdots\cdots\cdots\cdots \tag{B.34}$$
$$a_{m1} x_1 + a_{m2} x_2 + \cdots + a_{mn} x_n = y_m$$

may be written in matrix form as

$$\begin{bmatrix} a_{11} & a_{12} & \cdots & a_{1n} \\ a_{21} & a_{22} & \cdots & a_{2n} \\ \cdots & \cdots & \cdots & \cdots \\ a_{m1} & a_{m2} & \cdots & a_{mn} \end{bmatrix} \begin{bmatrix} x_1 \\ x_2 \\ \vdots \\ x_n \end{bmatrix} = \begin{bmatrix} y_1 \\ y_2 \\ \vdots \\ y_m \end{bmatrix} \tag{B.35}$$

or as

$$[A][X] = [Y] \tag{B.36}$$

If $m = n$ and $|A| \neq 0$, then a solution exists for x's in terms of y's. This solution is equivalent to the evaluation of the inverse of $[A]$, because

$$[X] = [A]^{-1}[Y] \tag{B.37}$$

B.6 Partitioning of matrices

We may sometimes perform certain operations involving matrices by subdividing or partitioning the matrices into smaller components called *submatrices*. Each submatrix then behaves like a single element for these operations. Specifically, let us take

$$[A] = \begin{bmatrix} a_{11} & a_{12} & \cdots & a_{1n} \\ a_{21} & a_{22} & \cdots & a_{2n} \\ \cdots & \cdots & \cdots & \cdots \\ a_{n1} & a_{n2} & \cdots & a_{nn} \end{bmatrix} \tag{B.38}$$

We indicate the partitioning of this matrix by dashed lines, as follows.

$$[A] = \begin{bmatrix} a_{11} \cdots a_{1r} & a_{1(r+1)} \cdots a_{1n} \\ \cdots & \cdots \\ a_{s1} \cdots a_{sr} & a_{s(r+1)} \cdots a_{sn} \\ a_{(s+1)1} \cdots a_{(s+1)r} & a_{(s+1)(r+1)} \cdots a_{(s+1)n} \\ \cdots & \cdots \\ a_{n1} \cdots a_{nr} & a_{n(r+1)} \cdots a_{nn} \end{bmatrix}$$

$$= \begin{bmatrix} \alpha_{11} & \alpha_{12} \\ \alpha_{21} & \alpha_{22} \end{bmatrix} \tag{B.39}$$

where

$$\alpha_{11} = \begin{bmatrix} a_{11} & \cdots & a_{1r} \\ \cdots & & \cdots \\ a_{s1} & \cdots & a_{sr} \end{bmatrix} \qquad \alpha_{12} = \begin{bmatrix} a_{1(r+1)} & \cdots & a_{1n} \\ \cdots & & \cdots \\ a_{s(r+1)} & \cdots & a_{sn} \end{bmatrix}$$

$$\alpha_{21} = \begin{bmatrix} a_{(s+1)1} & \cdots & a_{(s+1)r} \\ \cdots & & \cdots \\ a_{n1} & \cdots & a_{nr} \end{bmatrix} \qquad \alpha_{22} = \begin{bmatrix} a_{(s+1)(r+1)} & \cdots & a_{(s+1)n} \\ \cdots & & \cdots \\ a_{n(r+1)} & \cdots & a_{nn} \end{bmatrix}$$

If a second matrix $[B]$ is partitioned along its rows in the same way that $[A]$ is partitioned along its columns, then $[A]$ and $[B]$ are partitioned conformally with respect to the product $[A][B]$. We may evaluate the product by regarding the submatrices as matrix elements. For example, let

$$[A][B] = \begin{bmatrix} a_{11} & a_{12} & a_{13} \\ a_{21} & a_{22} & a_{23} \\ \hline a_{31} & a_{32} & a_{33} \\ a_{41} & a_{42} & a_{43} \end{bmatrix} \begin{bmatrix} b_{11} & b_{12} & b_{13} \\ b_{21} & b_{22} & b_{23} \\ \hline b_{31} & b_{32} & b_{33} \end{bmatrix} \qquad (B.40)$$

This yields

$$\alpha_{11} = \begin{bmatrix} a_{11} & a_{12} \\ a_{21} & a_{22} \end{bmatrix} \qquad \alpha_{12} = \begin{bmatrix} a_{13} \\ a_{23} \end{bmatrix}$$

$$\alpha_{21} = \begin{bmatrix} a_{31} & a_{32} \\ a_{41} & a_{42} \end{bmatrix} \qquad \alpha_{22} = \begin{bmatrix} a_{33} \\ a_{43} \end{bmatrix}$$

and

$$\beta_{11} = \begin{bmatrix} b_{11} \\ b_{21} \end{bmatrix} \qquad \beta_{12} = \begin{bmatrix} b_{12} & b_{13} \\ b_{22} & b_{23} \end{bmatrix}$$

$$\beta_{21} = [b_{31}] \qquad \beta_{22} = [b_{32} \ b_{33}]$$

Hence

$$[A][B] = \begin{bmatrix} \alpha_{11} & \alpha_{12} \\ \alpha_{21} & \alpha_{22} \end{bmatrix} \begin{bmatrix} \beta_{11} & \beta_{12} \\ \beta_{21} & \beta_{22} \end{bmatrix}$$

or

$$[A][B] = \begin{bmatrix} \alpha_{11}\beta_{11} + \alpha_{12}\beta_{21} & \alpha_{11}\beta_{12} + \alpha_{12}\beta_{22} \\ \alpha_{21}\beta_{11} + \alpha_{22}\beta_{21} & \alpha_{21}\beta_{12} + \alpha_{22}\beta_{22} \end{bmatrix} \qquad (B.41)$$

Each of the products among the α and β matrices is found to be conformable. Notice that the order among the submatrices is important. Observe also that conformability requires that rows of $[B]$ be grouped in the same way as the columns of $[A]$, but the subdivisions of the columns of $[B]$ need not be related to the subdivisions of the rows of $[A]$.

As an application of this principle, consider the following linear relationship:

$$[A][X] = [Y] \qquad (B.42)$$

where $[A]$ is a square matrix. We let

$$[A] = \begin{bmatrix} \alpha_{11} & \alpha_{12} \\ \alpha_{21} & \alpha_{22} \end{bmatrix} \qquad [X] = \begin{bmatrix} \xi_1 \\ \xi_2 \end{bmatrix} \qquad [Y] = \begin{bmatrix} \eta_1 \\ \eta_2 \end{bmatrix} \qquad (B.43)$$

Here the number of columns of α_{11} must be the same as the number of rows of ξ_1 and η_1. Then we have

$$\alpha_{11}\xi_1 + \alpha_{12}\xi_2 = \eta_1 \tag{B.44}$$

$$\alpha_{21}\xi_1 + \alpha_{22}\xi_2 = \eta_2 \tag{B.45}$$

If α_{11} and α_{22} are both square and if α_{22}^{-1} exists, then we could multiply (B.45) from the left by α_{22}^{-1} to obtain

$$\xi_2 = \alpha_{22}^{-1}\eta_2 - \alpha_{22}^{-1}\alpha_{21}\xi_1 \tag{B.46}$$

Substituting this result into (B.44), we obtain

$$(\alpha_{11} - \alpha_{12}\alpha_{22}^{-1}\alpha_{21})\xi_1 = \eta_1 - \alpha_{12}\alpha_{22}^{-1}\eta_2$$

Solving for ξ_1, we have

$$\xi_1 = (\alpha_{11} - \alpha_{12}\alpha_{22}^{-1}\alpha_{21})^{-1}(\eta_1 - \alpha_{12}\alpha_{22}^{-1}\eta_2) \tag{B.47}$$

Similarly, we have

$$\xi_2 = (\alpha_{22} - \alpha_{21}\alpha_{11}^{-1}\alpha_{12})^{-1}(\eta_2 - \alpha_{21}\alpha_{11}^{-1}\eta_1) \tag{B.48}$$

A special case of interest is when $\eta_2 = 0$. Then (B.47) becomes

$$\xi_1 = (\alpha_{11} - \alpha_{12}\alpha_{22}^{-1}\alpha_{21})^{-1}\eta_1 \tag{B.49}$$

This gives a relationship of the first group of variables in $[X]$ in terms of the first group of variables in $[Y]$.

EXAMPLE   In the circuit of Figure B.1, with the mesh currents assigned as shown, the mesh equations are

$$2I_1 + I_3 = E_1, \qquad 2I_2 + I_4 = E_2$$

$$I_1 + 3I_3 + I_4 = 0, \qquad I_2 + I_3 + 3I_4 = 0$$

These equations can be written in matrix form and partitioned as follows.

$$\begin{bmatrix} 2 & 0 & 1 & 0 \\ 0 & 2 & 0 & 1 \\ \hline 1 & 0 & 3 & 1 \\ 0 & 1 & 1 & 3 \end{bmatrix} \begin{bmatrix} I_1 \\ I_2 \\ \hline I_3 \\ I_4 \end{bmatrix} = \begin{bmatrix} E_1 \\ E_2 \\ \hline 0 \\ 0 \end{bmatrix}$$

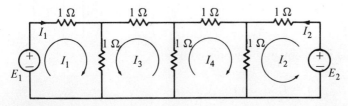

Figure B.1

Using (B.49) we get

$$\begin{bmatrix} E_1 \\ E_2 \end{bmatrix} = \left(\begin{bmatrix} 2 & 0 \\ 0 & 2 \end{bmatrix} - \begin{bmatrix} 1 & 0 \\ 0 & 1 \end{bmatrix} \begin{bmatrix} 3 & 1 \\ 1 & 3 \end{bmatrix}^{-1} \begin{bmatrix} 1 & 0 \\ 0 & 1 \end{bmatrix} \right) \begin{bmatrix} I_1 \\ I_2 \end{bmatrix}$$

$$= \left(\begin{bmatrix} 2 & 0 \\ 0 & 2 \end{bmatrix} - \frac{1}{8} \begin{bmatrix} 3 & -1 \\ -1 & 3 \end{bmatrix} \right) \begin{bmatrix} I_1 \\ I_2 \end{bmatrix}$$

$$= \begin{bmatrix} \frac{13}{8} & \frac{1}{8} \\ \frac{1}{8} & \frac{13}{8} \end{bmatrix} \begin{bmatrix} I_1 \\ I_2 \end{bmatrix}$$

which is the terminal relationship of the ladder as a two-port.

Problems

B.1 Given

$$[A] = \begin{bmatrix} 5 & 2 & 3 \\ 1 & -3 & 2 \\ 3 & -1 & -1 \end{bmatrix} \quad \text{and} \quad [B] = \begin{bmatrix} 1 & 4 & 8 \\ -1 & 2 & 12 \\ 2 & 3 & -5 \end{bmatrix}$$

find $[A] + [B]$, $|[A] + [B]|$, $|[A]|$, $|[B]|$, $[A][B]$, $[B][A]$, and $|[A][B]|$.

B.2 Evaluate

$$\begin{bmatrix} -1 & 5 \\ 2 & -2 \\ 0 & -7 \\ 3 & 8 \end{bmatrix} \times \begin{bmatrix} 3 & -7 & 1 \\ 5 & -2 & 1 \end{bmatrix}$$

B.3 Evaluate the following matrix products.

(a) $\begin{bmatrix} 1 & 0 & 0 \\ 0 & 1 & 0 \\ 0 & 0 & 1 \end{bmatrix} \times \begin{bmatrix} 5 & 3 \\ 6 & 2+j7 \\ 8 & 85 \end{bmatrix}$ (d) $\begin{bmatrix} 2 & 0 & 0 \\ 0 & 5 & 0 \\ 0 & 0 & 1 \end{bmatrix} \times \begin{bmatrix} 2 & -1 \\ 5 & -2 \\ 6 & 7 \end{bmatrix}$

(b) $\begin{bmatrix} 5 & 3 \\ 6 & 2+j7 \\ 8 & 85 \end{bmatrix} \times \begin{bmatrix} 1 & 0 \\ 0 & 1 \end{bmatrix}$ (e) $\begin{bmatrix} 2 & 5 & 6 \\ -1 & -2 & 7 \end{bmatrix} \times \begin{bmatrix} 2 & 0 & 0 \\ 0 & 5 & 0 \\ 0 & 0 & 1 \end{bmatrix}$

(c) $\begin{bmatrix} 0 & 0 & 0 \\ 0 & 0 & 0 \\ 1 & 1 & 1 \end{bmatrix} \times \begin{bmatrix} 1 & 1 & 0 \\ -1 & 0 & 1 \\ 0 & -1 & -1 \end{bmatrix}$ (f) $\begin{bmatrix} 2 & 3 & 2 \\ 2 & 5 & 0 \\ 2 & 7 & 6 \end{bmatrix} \times \begin{bmatrix} x \\ y \\ z \end{bmatrix}$

B.4 Given the set of equations expressed by

$$e_s = \sum_{k=1}^{n} Z_{sk} i_k, \qquad s = 1, 2, \ldots, n$$

(a) write out these equations for $n = 5$; (b) write this set of equations in matrix form.

B.5 Given

$$[1\ 5\ 2\ 4] \begin{bmatrix} 2 \\ 3 \\ 4 \\ 6x \end{bmatrix} = 0$$

find x.

B.6 Find $[A]^3$, given

$$[A] = \begin{bmatrix} 1 & -2 & 3 \\ 0 & 0 & 0 \\ 2 & 1 & -5 \end{bmatrix}$$

B.7 Find $[A][A]_t$ and $[A]_t[A]$ for $[A]$ as given in Problem B.6.

B.8 Given

$$\begin{bmatrix} 2 & 5 & 0 \\ 3 & 2 & 0 \\ 0 & 0 & 8 \end{bmatrix} \begin{bmatrix} x \\ y \\ z \end{bmatrix} = \begin{bmatrix} 10 \\ 20 \\ 1 \end{bmatrix}$$

find x, y, and z.

B.9 Given

$$[A] = \begin{bmatrix} 3 & 5 & 0 \\ 5 & 1 & 2 \\ 0 & 2 & 0 \end{bmatrix}$$

find $[A]^{-1}$.

B.10 Given the set of simultaneous equations

$$5x + 4y + z = a$$
$$y + 2z = b$$
$$x + 2y - 5z = c$$

express x, y, and z in terms of a, b, and c by matrix manipulation.

B.11 Given

$$[A] = \begin{bmatrix} 2 & a \\ b & c \end{bmatrix} \quad \text{and} \quad [A]_t^{-1} = [A]$$

find a, b, and c.

B.12 Given

$$a_1 = 2b_1 - 3b_2 + b_3 \qquad \text{and} \qquad b_1 = c_1 - c_2$$

$$a_2 = 3b_1 \qquad\quad - b_3 \qquad\qquad\qquad b_2 = 2c_1 - c_3$$

$$b_3 = 3c_2 + c_3$$

Express a's in terms of c's by (a) direct substitution, and (b) matrix manipulation.

B.13 Given

$$2X + Y + 4Z = a$$

$$4X + 2Y + Z = b$$

$$-X \qquad\quad + Z = c$$

express X, Y, and Z in terms of a, b, and c.

B.14 Show that $([A][B])^{-1} = [B]^{-1}[A]^{-1}$.

B.15 Show that $([A][B])_t = [B]_t[A]_t$.

B.16 Show that $([A]_t)^{-1} = ([A]^{-1})_t$.

B.17 Show that, if $[A]$ and $[B]$ are both symmetric or both skew-symmetric, then $[A][B] = ([B][A])_t$.

B.18 Given

$$[C] = \begin{bmatrix} a_{11} & a_{12} & x_1 \\ a_{21} & a_{22} & x_2 \\ y_1 & y_2 & 0 \end{bmatrix} = \begin{bmatrix} [A] & [X] \\ [Y] & 0 \end{bmatrix}$$

prove that

$$[C]^2 = \begin{bmatrix} [A]^2 + [X][Y] & [A][X] \\ [Y][A] & [Y][X] \end{bmatrix}$$

where

$$[A] = \begin{bmatrix} a_{11} & a_{12} \\ a_{21} & a_{22} \end{bmatrix} \qquad [X] = \begin{bmatrix} x_1 \\ x_2 \end{bmatrix} \qquad \text{and} \qquad [Y] = [y_1 \ y_2]$$

Do not use the rule of multiplication of matrices by submatrices.

B.19 Suppose that

$$\begin{bmatrix} 3 & 2 & 2 & -2 & 3 \\ 2 & 3 & 4 & 0 & 5 \\ -1 & 2 & 4 & -1 & 0 \\ -2 & 0 & -1 & 1 & 2 \\ 3 & 5 & 0 & 2 & 2 \end{bmatrix} \begin{bmatrix} I_1 \\ I_2 \\ I_3 \\ I_4 \\ I_5 \end{bmatrix} = \begin{bmatrix} E_1 \\ E_2 \\ 0 \\ 0 \\ 0 \end{bmatrix}$$

Find

$$\begin{bmatrix} I_1 \\ I_2 \end{bmatrix} \text{ in terms of } \begin{bmatrix} E_1 \\ E_2 \end{bmatrix}$$

B.20 Express E_1, E_2, and E_3 in terms of I_1, I_2, and I_3, for the network shown in Figure PB.20. Use matrix notations.

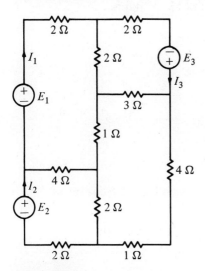

Figure PB.20

B.21 Let $E_3 = 0$ for the circuit of Figure PB.20. Then express

$$\begin{bmatrix} E_1 \\ E_2 \end{bmatrix} \text{ in terms of } \begin{bmatrix} I_1 \\ I_2 \end{bmatrix}$$

and vice versa.

C | ANSWERS TO SELECTED PROBLEMS

Chapter 1

1.2 (b) $v(t) = 1 + \sin 3t + 0.5 \cos 10t + \sin 13t - 0.5 \cos 16t$

1.14 $i(t) = 0.2 \cos t + 0.01 \sin 2t$

1.15 $v(t) = 100 \cos 10t(t + \tanh t) + 10(1 + \mathrm{sech}^2 t) \sin 10t$

1.16 (a) 0.8278 J   (b) 4.3480 J

Chapter 2

2.1 -25 V, 33 V, 13 V, -35 V, -2 V, 3 V, -2 A

2.2 -1 V, -1 V, 7 V, -9 V, 4 V, -2 V, -2 V

2.3 $I_6 = -1$ A, $I_7 = -1$ A, $I_8 = 7$ A, $I_9 = -9$ A,
$I_{10} = 4$ A, $I_{11} = -2$ A, $I_{12} = 2$ A

2.4 $I = 9$ A

2.7 $e_1 = 2$ V, $e_2 = 22$ V, $e_3 = 3$ V, $e_4 = -24$ V,
$e_5 = 1$ V, $e_6 = 25$ V

2.8 6 V, 3 V, -9 V, 3 A, -1 A, -2 A

2.9 8 V, 1 V, 17 V

2.10 $I_1 = -7$ A, $I_3 = 5$ A

2.11 1.25 A,   2.5 V

2.12 (a) $2\frac{5}{16}\,\Omega$ (b) $\frac{1}{3}\,\Omega$

2.13 4 A, 16 V

2.14 44 V, 45 V

2.15 6 V

2.17 0.625 V, 1.25 V, −1.875 V

2.18 1.25 V, −0.625 A

2.22 $v_1 = \dfrac{R_1}{R_1+R_2+R_3}v, \qquad v_2 = \dfrac{R_2}{R_1+R_2+R_3}v,$

$v_3 = \dfrac{R_3}{R_1+R_2+R_3}v$

2.23 $i_1 = \dfrac{G_1}{G_1+G_2+G_3}i = \dfrac{R_2 R_3}{R_1 R_2+R_2 R_3+R_3 R_1}i$

$i_2 = \dfrac{G_2}{G_1+G_2+G_3}i = \dfrac{R_3 R_1}{R_1 R_2+R_2 R_3+R_3 R_1}i$

$i_3 = \dfrac{G_3}{G_1+G_2+G_3}i = \dfrac{R_1 R_2}{R_1 R_2+R_2 R_3+R_3 R_1}i$

2.25 $e_5 = e_1 + e_2$ $\qquad\qquad i_1 = i_8 - i_5$

$e_6 = e_4 + e_3 - e_2 \qquad\quad i_2 = i_6 - i_5$

$e_7 = e_4 + E_s \qquad\qquad\quad i_3 = i_8 + I_{s1} - I_{s2} - i_6$

$e_8 = -(e_1 + e_3) + E_s \qquad i_4 = I_{s1} - i_6 - i_7$

2.27 $11e_1 + 9e_2 + 5e_3 = 7, \qquad e_2 + 5e_3 + 8e_4 = 5$

$9e_1 + 18e_2 + 6e_3 + e_4 = 17, \qquad 5e_1 + 6e_2 + 12e_3 + 5e_4 = 17$

2.28 $I = \frac{40}{769}$ A

2.29 $I_1 = \frac{440}{481}$ A, $\qquad I_2 = -\frac{549}{481}$ A, $\qquad I_3 = \frac{207}{481}$ A

2.30 $4i_1 + 5 \sin 10t + 2(i_1 - i_2) + 5\dfrac{d}{dt}(i_1 + i_3 - i_2)$

$\qquad + 2(i_1 + i_3) + 10\epsilon^{-t} = 0$

$3i_2 - 5\dfrac{d}{dt}(i_1 + i_3 - i_2) - 2(i_1 - i_2) - 5 \sin 10t = 0$

$3i_3 + 5\dfrac{d}{dt}(i_1 + i_3 - i_2) + 2(i_1 + i_3) + 10\epsilon^{-t} = 0$

2.31 $I_1 = -\frac{27}{13}$ A, $\qquad I_2 = \frac{6}{13}$ A

2.32 (b) $E_1 = \frac{197}{158}$ V, $\qquad E_2 = \frac{139}{158}$ V, $\qquad E_3 = \frac{405}{316}$ V

2.33 6.2 V

2.34 12 A, 7 V

2.35 $9E_1 - 11E_2 + 6E_3 - 2E_4 - 2E_5 = 0,$

$5E_1 - 17E_2 + 5E_3 + 3E_5 = -3$

$E_2 + 4E_3 = 8, \qquad 2E_1 - 15E_4 + 6E_5 = 3,$

$2E_1 + 3E_2 + 6E_4 - 13E_5 = 8$

2.36 $I_1 = 0.6$ A

2.37 $9I_1 - 4I_2 - 2I_3 = 10,$ $-4I_1 + 7I_2 - 2I_3 = 0,$
$-2I_1 - 2I_2 + 10I_3 = 5$

2.38 $\frac{960}{353}$ A, $3\frac{65}{96}$ Ω

2.40 -2.6 A

Chapter 3

3.1 3.5 A

3.2 -2.25 V

3.3 0.375 A

3.4 -2 A

3.5 $\frac{140}{29} \cos t$ V, $\frac{161}{58}$ Ω

3.6 13 V, 4 Ω

3.7 -7.5 V

3.8 -1.5 A

3.9 -3.2 A

3.10 1 A

3.11 $-\frac{980}{13}$ A

3.12 $-\frac{11}{13}$ A

3.13 -207 V

3.14 $\frac{15}{11}$ A

3.19 $-\frac{1}{120}$ A

3.20 2.5 Ω

Chapter 4

4.2 $f_1(t) = 2u_{-2}(t) - 2u_{-2}(t-1) + 2u_{-2}(t-2) - 2u_{-2}(t-3)$
$- 4u_{-2}(t-4) + 4u_{-2}(t-5)$
$f_2(t) = 5u_{-1}(t-1) - 5u_{-2}(t-1) + 5u_{-2}(t-2)$
$f_3(t) = \frac{1}{2}u_{-2}(t) - \frac{1}{2}u_{-2}(t-2) + 2u_{-1}(t-2) - 5u_{-1}(t-4)$
$+ 2u_{-1}(t-5)$

4.4 (a) $2(1-\epsilon^{-t})u_{-1}(t) - 2[1-\epsilon^{-(t-1)}]u_{-1}(t-1)$
$+ 2[1-\epsilon^{-(t-2)}]u_{-1}(t-2) - 2[1-\epsilon^{-(t-3)}]u_{-1}(t-3)$
$- 4[1-\epsilon^{-(t-4)}]u_{-1}(t-4) + 4[1-\epsilon^{-(t-5)}]u_{-1}(t-5)$

(b) $5\epsilon^{-(t-1)}u_{-1}(t-1) - 5[1-\epsilon^{-(t-1)}]u_{-1}(t-1)$
$\quad + 5[1-\epsilon^{-(t-2)}]u_{-1}(t-2)$

(c) $\frac{1}{2}(1-\epsilon^{-t})u_{-1}(t) - \frac{1}{2}[1-\epsilon^{-(t-2)}]u_{-1}(t-2) + 2\epsilon^{-(t-2)}u_{-1}(t-2)$
$\quad - 5\epsilon^{-(t-4)}u_{-1}(t-4) + 2\epsilon^{-(t-5)}u_{-1}(t-5)$

(d) $5u_0(t-1) - 5\epsilon^{-(t-1)}u_{-1}(t-1) - 5\epsilon^{-(t-1)}u_{-1}(t-1)$
$\quad + 5\epsilon^{-(t-2)}u_{-1}(t-2)$

4.5 $i(t) = 1.5(1-\epsilon^{-(1/3)t})u_{-1}(t)$

4.6 (a) $i(t) = \dfrac{R_1}{L}\epsilon^{-[(R_1+R_2)/L]t}u_{-1}(t)$

$\quad e(t) = R_1 u_0(t) - \dfrac{R_1(R_1+R_2)}{L}\epsilon^{-[(R_1+R_2)/L]t}u_{-1}(t)$

(b) $i(t) = \dfrac{R_1}{R_1+R_2}[1-\epsilon^{-[(R_1+R_2)/L]t}]u_{-1}(t)$

$\quad e(t) = R_1\epsilon^{-[(R_1+R_2)/L]t}u_{-1}(t)$

4.7 $\left[\dfrac{t}{R} - \dfrac{L}{R^2}(1-\epsilon^{-(R/L)t})\right]u_{-1}(t)$

4.8 $i(t) = \left[\dfrac{1}{R_2}\epsilon^{-(1/RC)t} + \dfrac{1}{R_1+R_2}(\epsilon^{-(1/RC)t}-1)\right]u_{-1}(t)$

$\quad e_2(t) = \left[\epsilon^{-t/RC} - \dfrac{R_2}{R_1+R_2}(\epsilon^{-t/RC}-1)\right]u_{-1}(t)$

4.9 $e_1 = \left[1 - \dfrac{R}{R_1}(1-\epsilon^{-(1/RC)t}) - \dfrac{C_1}{C}\epsilon^{-(1/RC)t}\right]u_{-1}(t)$

$\quad i = \left[\dfrac{1}{R_1+R_2} + \left(\dfrac{C_1}{CR_2} + \dfrac{C_2}{CR_1} - \dfrac{1}{R_1+R_2} - \dfrac{C_1C_2}{RC^2}\right)\epsilon^{-(1/RC)t}\right]u_{-1}(t)$
$\quad + \dfrac{C_1C_2}{C_1+C_2}u_0(t)$

4.10 $4.5(1+\epsilon^{-3t})u_{-1}(t)$

4.11 (a) $\dfrac{E}{1000}[\epsilon^{-1000(t-t_1)}u_{-1}(t-t_1) - \epsilon^{-1000(t-t_2)}u_{-1}(t-t_2)]$

(b) $4\times10^{-6}\{[1-\epsilon^{-1000(t-1)}]u_{-1}(t-1)$
$\quad -[1-\epsilon^{-1000(t-2)}]u_{-1}(t-2)\}$

4.12 $20(1-\epsilon^{-5t})u_{-1}(t) - 12(1-\epsilon^{-5(t-7)})u_{-1}(t-7)$

4.13 $5(1-\epsilon^{-2t})u_{-1}(t) - 2.5(1-\epsilon^{-2(t-5)})u_{-1}(t-5)$

4.14 $5(1-\epsilon^{-2(t-1)}) + 10\epsilon^{-2(t-1)}$

4.15 $5 - 3\epsilon^{-2t}$

4.16 $-100\epsilon^{-11t}u_{-1}(t)$

4.17 $\dfrac{1}{2\sqrt{2}} [\epsilon^{-(2-\sqrt{2})t} - \epsilon^{-(2+\sqrt{2})t}]$

4.18 $(\cosh \sqrt{2}t - \sqrt{2} \sinh \sqrt{2}t) \epsilon^{-2t}$

4.19 $-0.1 \cos t + 0.0101 \sin t + 0.1\epsilon^{-0.05t} \cos 0.0866t - 0.0589 \sin 0.0866t$

4.20 $(t/L)\epsilon^{-zt}$

4.21 $1.1547\epsilon^{-0.5t} \sin 0.866t$

4.22 $(0.28 \sin 7.14t - \cos 7.14t)\epsilon^{-7t}$

Chapter 5

5.1 $16.8 \underline{/13.77°}$ (b) $45.47 \underline{/17.96°}$ (c) $2136.1 \underline{/77.5°}$
(d) $47.31 \underline{/-15°}$

5.2 (a) 2.75   (b) 3.42   (c) $10 \cos(\omega t + 50°)$
(d) $|E| \sin(\omega t + \theta)$

5.3 (a) $23.32 \cos(\omega t - 59°)$ (b) $12.96 \cos(\omega t - 53.9°)$
(c) $13.94 \cos(\omega t - 14.42°)$

5.4 $4.92 \underline{/-63.4°}$, $4.92 \underline{/-18.5°}$, $12.8 \underline{/50°}$, $248.6 \underline{/78.7°}$,
$85.1 \underline{/206.1°}$, $46.22 \underline{/84°}$, $10.72 \underline{/69.6°}$

5.5 $i(t) = 0.4 \cos(500t - 36.9°)$
$e_L(t) = 12 \cos(500t + 53.1°)$

5.6 $16.14 \cos(\omega t + 38.3°)$

5.7 $I = 2.25 \underline{/-54.4°}$, $I_1 = 3.43 \underline{/-96.7°}$, $I_2 = 2.32 \underline{/42.7°}$

5.8 $I_1 = 0.667$, $I = 0.333$, $E = 0.667$, $E_C = 1 \underline{/-90°}$

5.9 $E = 4 \underline{/30°}$ V, $I = 1 \underline{/30°}$ A

5.10 (a) $R = 21.6 \ \Omega$, $X = 12.5 \ \Omega$ (inductive)
(b) $R = 28.9 \ \Omega$, $X = 50 \ \Omega$ (inductive)

5.11 $I_C = 2.5 + j7.5$ A, $I_L = 2.5 - j7.5$ A

5.12 $Z = 4 \underline{/0°} \ \Omega$, $Y = 0.25 \underline{/0°} \ \mho$

5.13 $0.666 \underline{/0°}$ A

5.14 $E = 2.236 \underline{/63.42°}$ V, $I = 0.527 \underline{/108.42°}$ A

5.15 $I_1 = 8.51 \underline{/-27.6°}$, $I_2 = 4.52 \underline{/177.7°}$, $I_3 = 4.84 \underline{/-51.3°}$

5.16 $I = 3 + j3$ A, $E = 11.66 \underline{/89°}$ V, $I_e = 1.268 + j2$ A,
$E_i = 16.9 \underline{/43.7°}$ V

5.17 $E_1 = 2.5$ V, $E_2 = j2.5$ V

5.18 $P = 1679.5$ W, $Q = 655.2$ VAR (L)

5.19 $R = 16.795\,\Omega,\ X = 6.552\,\Omega$

5.20 $G = 0.05168\,\mho,\ B = -0.02016\,\mho$

5.21 (a) $E_s = 70.71\,\underline{/-30°},\ I = 3.922\,\underline{/26.3°}$ A, $E_R = 39.22\,\underline{/26.3°}$ V,

$\qquad$ $E_L = 19.61\,\underline{/116.3°}$ V, $E_C = 78.44\,\underline{/-63.7°}$ V

$\qquad$ (b) $i(t) = 5.547\cos(10t + 26.3°),\qquad e_R(t) = 55.47$

$\qquad\qquad e_L(t) = 27.73\cos(10t + 116.3°),$

$\qquad\qquad e_C(t) = 110.93\cos(10t - 63.7°)$

$\qquad$ (c) 153.82 W

$\qquad$ (d) 76.91 VAR (L), 307.64 VAR (C)

$\qquad$ (e) 277.32 VA, 153.83 W, 230.74 VAR (C)

5.22 (a) $0.993\,\underline{/13.2°},\ 3.152\,\underline{/66.35°},\ 3.831\,\underline{/54.38°}$

$\qquad$ (b) 29.01 W, 6.81 VAR, 62.65 W, 6.97 VAR

$\qquad$ (c) (8Ω) 7.89 W; 39.74 W, 59.61 VAR $(4+j6\ \Omega)$;

$\qquad\qquad$ 44.03 W, 73.38 VAR $(3-j5\ \Omega)$

5.23 106.1 μF

5.24 1240 W, 1280.6 VA, 0.968

5.25 129.5 Ω, 120.7 Ω

5.26 0.04 Ω

5.27 8 Ω

5.28 80 W

5.29 $R_L = \sqrt{R_s^2 + X_s^2}$

5.30 $X_L = -X_s$

Chapter 6

6.2 58.17

6.3 0.641 V, 68 mA

6.4 58 mA

6.5 (a) 9.96 mA, 0 $\qquad$ (b) 53.75 mA, 45 mA

6.7 (a) 0.3025 V, 4.494 mA $\qquad$ (b) $1.538 \times 10^{-4}\sin \omega t$ V

6.8 (a) 0.3301 V, 9.667 mA $\qquad$ (b) $3.531\cos(2\pi \times 10^8 t + 8.73°)$ mV

6.11 $\frac{4}{30}$ A

6.12 400 V

6.13 29 mA

6.14 $3 < r_s < 10/3\ \Omega$

Chapter 7

7.1 $z_{11} = z_{22} = \frac{11}{5}\,\Omega, \qquad z_{12} = z_{21} = \frac{4}{5}\,\Omega$

7.2 $y_{11} = y_{22} = 1.2 + j1.6\,\mho, \qquad y_{12} = y_{21} = -0.8 - j1.4\,\mho$

7.3 $z_{11} = z_{22} = 3.75 + j1.5\,\Omega, \qquad z_{12} = z_{21} = -1.25 - j4.5\,\Omega$

7.4 $y_{11} = -j0.75\,\mho, \qquad y_{12} = y_{21} = j0.25\,\mho, \qquad y_{22} = j0.25\,\mho$

7.5 $z_{11} = R_1(R_2 + R_3)/(R_3 + R_2 + R_1 + AR_1),$

$z_{21} = R_1(R_2 - AR_3)/(R_3 + R_2 + R_1 + AR_1)$

7.9 $y_{21}\, Y_s/[y_{12}\, y_{21} - (y_{11} + Y_s)(Y_L + y_{22})]$

7.10 $y_1 = \dfrac{y_b\, y_c}{y_a + y_b + y_c}, \qquad y_2 = \dfrac{y_a\, y_c}{y_a + y_b + y_c}, \qquad y_3 = \dfrac{y_a\, y_b}{y_a + y_b + y_c}$

7.11 $z_a = \dfrac{z_2\, z_3}{z_1 + z_2 + z_3}, \qquad z_b = \dfrac{z_1\, z_3}{z_1 + z_2 + z_3}, \qquad z_c = \dfrac{z_1\, z_2}{z_1 + z_2 + z_3}$

7.12 $\begin{bmatrix} y_a & y_b \\ y_c & y_d \end{bmatrix}$

7.13 (a) $\begin{bmatrix} 5+j10 & -j3 \\ -j3 & 5+j5 \end{bmatrix}\Omega$ (b) $\begin{bmatrix} 0 & j \\ -j & j2 \end{bmatrix}\Omega$

7.14 $13.2 + j11.6\,\Omega$

7.15 $I_1 = I_2 + I_3, \qquad 10I_1 + (10+j16)I_2 - j12I_3 = 100,$

$10I_1 - j12I_2 + (3+j24)I_3 = 100, \qquad (-10-j28)I_2 + (3+j36)I_3 = 0$

7.16 $\begin{bmatrix} \dfrac{z_{11}}{n^2} & \dfrac{z_{12}}{n} \\[2ex] \dfrac{z_{21}}{n} & z_{22} \end{bmatrix}$

7.17 $\begin{bmatrix} 0.3 & -0.3 \\ -0.3 & 0.3 \end{bmatrix}\Omega$

7.18 $\begin{bmatrix} n^2 & 0 \\[1ex] 0 & \dfrac{1}{n^2} \end{bmatrix}$

7.19 $\frac{1}{26}\begin{bmatrix} 53 & 28 \\ 28 & 75.5 \end{bmatrix}\Omega$

7.20 $y_{11} = y_{22} = \dfrac{2R^2C^2s^2 + 4RCs + 1}{R(RCs + 2)(1 + RCs)}$

$y_{12} = y_{21} = -\dfrac{R^2C^2s^2 + 3RCs + 1}{R(RCs + 2)(1 + RCs)}$

7.21
$$\begin{bmatrix} g_b & -g_b & 0 \\ g_m-g_b & g_b-g_m+g_s & -g_s \\ -g_m & g_m-g_s & g_s \end{bmatrix}$$

7.22
$$\begin{bmatrix} j\omega(C_1+C_2) & -j\omega C_2 & -j\omega C_1 \\ g_m-j\omega C_2 & G+j\omega C_2 & -g_m-G \\ -g_m-j\omega C_1 & -G & g_m+G+j\omega C_1 \end{bmatrix}$$

7.23
$$\text{IAM} = \begin{bmatrix} 0.75 & -0.25 & -0.5 & 0 \\ -0.25 & 0.45 & 0 & -0.2 \\ -0.5 & 0 & 1.5 & -1 \\ 0 & -0.2 & -1 & 1.2 \end{bmatrix} \mho$$

$$[Y] = \begin{bmatrix} \frac{3}{4} & -\frac{1}{4} \\ -\frac{1}{4} & \frac{5}{12} \end{bmatrix} \mho$$

7.24
$$\begin{bmatrix} y_{11}+\dfrac{(y_{11}+y_{41})(y_{11}+y_{14})}{(y_{21}+y_{24})+(y_{31}+y_{34})} & y_{12}+\dfrac{(y_{21}+y_{24})(y_{11}+y_{14})}{(y_{21}+y_{24})+(y_{31}+y_{34})} \\ y_{21}+\dfrac{(y_{11}+y_{14})(y_{21}+y_{24})}{(y_{21}+y_{24})+(y_{31}+y_{34})} & y_{22}+\dfrac{(y_{12}+y_{42})(y_{21}+y_{24})}{(y_{21}+y_{24})+(y_{31}+y_{34})} \end{bmatrix}$$
(There are many other equivalent answers.)

Chapter 8

8.1 $3.4 \text{ k}\Omega$

8.2 $I_D = 4 \text{ mA}$, $\quad R_d = 4.5 \text{ k}\Omega$

8.3 $I_D = -5.07 \text{ mA}$, $\quad V_{DS} = -8.269 \text{ V}$

8.4 $I_D = -2.3 \text{ mA}$, $\quad V_{DS} = -21 \text{ V}$

8.6 $g_m = 5.5 \times 10^{-3} \mho$, $\quad r_d = 800 \text{ k}\Omega$, $\quad \mu = 4400$

8.7 $g_m = 2.5 \times 10^{-3} \mho$, $\quad r_d = \infty$, $\quad \mu = \infty$

8.8 $g_m = 3.12 \times 10^{-3} \mho$, $\quad r_d = \infty$, $\quad \mu = \infty$

8.9 -8.5

8.10 -10.3

8.11 (a) $V_{DS} = -16 \text{ V}$, $\quad I_D = -1.45 \text{ mA}$, $\quad V_{GS} = 0.58 \text{ V}$

8.12 (a) -0.38 $\quad$ (b) $-0.396 \, \underline{/\, 3.26°}$ $\quad$ (c) -0.4114

8.13 $-0.488 \, \underline{/\, 0.58°}$

8.14 -15.48

8.15 (b) -25 $\quad$ (c) $5 \text{ k}\Omega$

8.16 2.95 V, 6 kΩ

8.17 (a) 1.5 kΩ   (b) 0.66 V

8.18 −9

8.19 2 kΩ

8.20 $I_D = -2.25$ mA, $V_{GS} = 1$ V, $V_{DS} = -10.5$ V

8.21 −18.69

8.22 $-10.57 \underline{/42.29°}$

8.24 6.26 kΩ

8.25 (a) $V_{GS} = 0.95$ V, $I_D = 2.9$ mA

   (b) $r_d = 80$ kΩ, $g_m = 1.65$ m℧, $\mu = 132$ (c) −0.761

Chapter 9

9.2 $I_E = 0.502$ μA, $I_C = -5.51$ μA

9.3 $I_{CO} = 50$ μA, $\beta_0 = 30$

9.5 7.234 V

9.6 $V_{CE} = 12$ V, $I_C = 4.5$ mA

9.7 $I_C = -3.96$ mA, $V_{CB} = -3.051$ V

9.8 $I_B = 38.3$ μA, $I_C = 1.915$ mA, $V_{CE} = 8.28$ V

9.9 1.279 V

9.10 5.96 V

9.11 $I_B = 0.47$ mA, $V_{CE} = 3$ V, $I_C = 32.5$ mA, $V_{BE} = 0.58$ V

9.12 $I_B = -38.2$ μA, $V_{CE} = -4$ V, $I_C = -1.65$ mA

9.13 $V_{CE} = -10$ V, $I_C = -5$ mA, $I_B = -0.188$ mA,
   $V_{BE} = -0.68$ V

9.14 $V_{CE} = -3.7$ V, $I_C = -32$ mA, $I_B = -0.33$ mA,
   $V_{BE} = -0.38$ V

9.15 $I_C = 33$ mA, $V_{CE} = 5.2$ V, $I_B = 0.46$ mA, $V_{BE} = 0.6$ V

9.16 $[h_b] = \dfrac{1}{1+h_{fe}+|h_e|-h_{re}} \begin{bmatrix} h_{ie} & -h_{re}+|h_e| \\ -h_{fe}-|h_e| & h_{oe} \end{bmatrix}$

9.17 $[h_c] = \begin{bmatrix} h_{ie} & 1-h_{re} \\ -1-h_{fe} & h_{oe} \end{bmatrix}$

9.18 $A_v = \dfrac{(1+h_{fe})/(R_s+h_{ie})}{G_L+h_{oe}+[(1-h_{re})(1+h_{fe})]/(R_s+h_{ie})}$

   $A_i = \dfrac{1+h_{fe}}{1+R_L h_{oe}}$

$$Z_i = h_{ie} + \frac{(1-h_{re})(1+h_{fe})}{G_L + h_{oe}}$$

$$Z_o = \frac{R_s + h_{ie}}{h_{oe}(R_s + h_{ie}) + (1-h_{re})(1+h_{fe})}$$

9.19 $A_v = \dfrac{G_L h_{ie} + |h_e|}{G_L h_{ie} + |h_e| + G_L R_s D + h_{oe} R_s}$

$$A_i = \frac{h_{fe} + |h_e|}{D + h_{oe} R_L}$$

$$Z_i = \frac{G_L h_{ie} + |h_e|}{G_L D + h_{oe}}$$

$$Z_o = \frac{h_{ie} + D R_s}{|h_e| + h_{oe} R_s}$$

where $D = 1 + |h_e| + h_{fe} - h_{re}$

9.20 139 kΩ

9.21 $h_{fe} = 50,\quad h_{oe} = 0.04$ m$\mho$

9.22 $h_{ie} = 0.68$ k$\Omega,\quad h_{fe} = 38,\quad h_{re} = 10^{-5},\quad h_{oe} = 0.125$ m$\mho$

9.23 $h_{ie} = 160\ \Omega,\quad h_{fe} = 65,\quad h_{re} = 0,\quad h_{oe} = 1.1$ m$\mho$

9.24 $h_{ie} = 420\ \Omega,\quad h_{fe} = 70,\quad h_{re} = 0.007,\quad h_{oe} = 0.6$ m$\mho$

9.27 $h_{ie} = 50.99$ k$\Omega,\quad h_{fe} = 2549,\quad h_{re} = 0.02,\quad h_{oe} = 1.02$ m$\mho$

9.28 $\dfrac{V_o}{V_i} = -18.93,\quad Z_i = 954.5\ \Omega,\quad Z_o = 54.75$ kΩ

9.29 $A_v = 0.241,\quad Z_i = 43.72\ \Omega,\quad Z_o = 10.61\ \Omega$

9.30 $\dfrac{V_o}{V_i} = -2.06,\quad 7.578$ kΩ

9.31 -11.265

Chapter 10

10.1 $V_P = 230$ V, $\quad I_P = 3.5$ mA, $\quad V_{GK} = -7$ V

10.2 48.2 V

10.3 $(1+\mu) R_L/(R_L + r_p)$

10.4 (b) -25 (c) 5 kΩ

10.5 -18.2

10.6 $V_{o1} = 0.512$ V, 180° out; $\quad V_{o2} = 0.488$ V, in phase

10.7 0.9615

10.8 $0.477 V_1 + 0.161 V_2$

10.9 0.05 cm

10.10 6 pF

10.11 $R_3 + R_2 R_3/R_1$

10.14 $v_o = \dfrac{R_4(R_1+R_2)}{R_1(R_3+R_4)} v_2 - \dfrac{R_2}{R_1} v_1$

10.15 $v_o = \dfrac{R_2 R_5}{R_1 R_3} v_1 - \dfrac{R_5}{R_4} v_2$

Chapter 11

11.1 $Z(s) = \dfrac{4s^2+4s+3}{2s^2+s+1}$; zeros, $-\dfrac{1}{2} \pm j\dfrac{\sqrt{2}}{2}$; poles, $-\dfrac{1}{4} \pm j\dfrac{\sqrt{7}}{4}$

11.2 $\dfrac{s^2+2s+2}{s^2+4s+2}$

11.3 $\dfrac{5s+4}{3(s+1)}$

11.4 (a) $\begin{bmatrix} 5+10s & -3s \\ -3s & 5+5s \end{bmatrix}$ (b) $\begin{bmatrix} s+\dfrac{1}{s} & s \\ -s & 2s \end{bmatrix}$

11.5 $\dfrac{0.02(s+1358.2)(s+70.92+j48.31)(s+70.92-j48.31)}{(s+100+j100)(s+100-j100)}$

11.6 $\dfrac{2s}{3s^2+4s+2}$

11.7 $\dfrac{3}{7} \times \dfrac{s-1.333 \times 10^9}{s+5.714 \times 10^7}$

11.8 (b) $\dfrac{-25s}{s+12.5 \times 10^3}$, (c) $\dfrac{5(s+50\text{ k})}{s+12.5\text{ k}} \times 10^3 \ \Omega$

11.9 $\dfrac{80s(s+550)}{6.04s^2+3342s+111 \times 10^3}$

11.10 $\dfrac{10^8 s}{(s+2.7667 \times 10^6)(s+963.95)}$

11.11 $\dfrac{0.2744s}{s+20.126}$

11.12 (a) 159.15 kHz, (b) 100, (c) 1.005×10^6, 0.995×10^6

11.13 70.36 μF, 4.193 Ω

11.14 (a) $\dfrac{1}{R}\sqrt{\dfrac{L}{C}}$, (b) $\dfrac{1}{R\omega_0 C}$, (c) $\dfrac{\omega_0 L}{R}$

11.15 1.414 Ω, 70.7 mH, 354 μF

11.16 $\pm\dfrac{\omega_0\sqrt{1-a^2}}{2aQ} + \sqrt{\dfrac{\omega_0^2(1-a^2)}{4a^2Q^2} + \omega_0^2}$, $BW = \dfrac{\sqrt{1-a^2}}{aQ}\omega_0$

11.20 $\dfrac{10(s+1)}{(s+0.01)(s+10)}$

Chapter 12

12.1 (a) $y_1(t) = \frac{1}{2}u_0(t) - \frac{1}{4}\epsilon^{-t/2}$, $y_2(t) = \frac{1}{2}\epsilon^{-t/2}$;
(b) $y(t) = \frac{1}{3}\epsilon^{-(2/3)t}$

12.2 (a) $y_1(t) = \frac{1}{2}\epsilon^{-t/2}$, $y_2(t) = 1 - \epsilon^{-t/2}$;
(b) $y(t) = \frac{1}{2}(1 - \epsilon^{-(2/3)t})$

12.3 (a) $y_1(t) = \epsilon^{-t} - \frac{1}{2}\epsilon^{-t/2}$, $y_2(t) = \epsilon^{-t/2} - \epsilon^{-t}$;
(b) $y(t) = \epsilon^{-(2/3)t} - \epsilon^{-t}$

12.4 $-\frac{1}{6}t^3 + t^2 - t + \frac{1}{3}$

12.5 $\frac{1}{2}(\epsilon^{-3t} - \epsilon^{-5t})$

12.6 $\epsilon^{-1}(1 - \epsilon^{-(t-3)})u_{-1}(t-3)$

12.7 $f(t) = 0$, $t < 0$
$f(t) = 2t$, $0 < t < 1$
$f(t) = t + 1$, $1 < t < 2$
$f(t) = -2t + 7$, $2 < t < 3$
$f(t) = -t + 4$, $3 < t < 4$
$f(t) = 0$, $4 < t$

12.8 $y = 0$, $t < 1$
$y = (t-1)^2$, $1 < t < 3$
$y = -2t^2 + 14t - 20$, $3 < t < 4$
$y = -4t + 20$, $4 < t < 5$
$y = 0$, $5 < t$

12.9 $y = 0$, $t < 2$
$y = \frac{1}{4}(t^2 - 4)$, $2 < t < 3$
$y = \frac{1}{4}(2t - 1)$, $3 < t < 4$,
$y = \frac{1}{4}(15 + 2t - t^2)$, $4 < t < 5$
$y = 0$, $5 < t$

12.10 $y = 0, \quad t < 0$

$\quad\quad y = \tfrac{1}{2}t^2, \quad\quad 0 < t < 1$

$\quad\quad y = \tfrac{1}{2}, \quad\quad 1 < t < 2$

$\quad\quad y = \tfrac{1}{2} + 2t - \tfrac{1}{2}t^2, \quad\quad 2 < t < 3$

$\quad\quad y = 2, \quad\quad 3 < t < 4$

$\quad\quad y = 0, \quad\quad 4 < t$

Chapter 13

13.1 $\dfrac{1}{2} + \dfrac{2}{\pi}\sin t + \dfrac{2}{3\pi}\sin 3t + \dfrac{2}{5\pi}\sin 5t + \cdots$

13.2 (a) $\dfrac{\pi}{2} - \dfrac{4}{\pi}\left(\cos x + \dfrac{1}{3^2}\cos 3x + \dfrac{1}{5^2}\cos 5x + \cdots\right)$

13.3 $\dfrac{A}{T} + \dfrac{2A}{T}(\cos \omega_0 t + \cos 2\omega_0 t + \cos 3\omega_0 t + \cdots), \quad\quad \omega_0 = 2\pi/T$

13.4 $\dfrac{\pi^2}{3} + 4\displaystyle\sum_{n=1}^{\infty}\dfrac{(-1)^n}{n^2}\cos nx$

13.5 $\dfrac{2}{\pi} - \dfrac{4}{\pi}\displaystyle\sum_{n=1}^{\infty}\dfrac{\cos 2nx}{4n^2 - 1}$

13.6 $\dfrac{\pi}{4} - \dfrac{2}{\pi}\displaystyle\sum_{n=1}^{\infty}\dfrac{\cos(2n+1)x}{(2n+1)^2} - \displaystyle\sum_{n=1}^{\infty}\dfrac{(-1)^n \sin nx}{n}$

13.7 $\dfrac{20}{\pi}\displaystyle\sum_{n=1}^{\infty}\dfrac{\sin(2n+1)\pi t}{2n+1}$

13.8 $f(x) = \dfrac{1}{\pi} + \dfrac{1}{2}\sin x - \dfrac{2}{\pi}\displaystyle\sum_{n=1}^{\infty}\dfrac{\cos 2nx}{4n^2 - 1}$

13.10 $g(t) = \dfrac{8}{\pi^2}\left[\sin\left(t - \dfrac{5\pi}{6}\right) - \dfrac{1}{3^2}\sin 3\left(t - \dfrac{5\pi}{6}\right)\right.$

$\quad\quad\quad\quad\quad \left. + \dfrac{1}{5^2}\sin 5\left(t - \dfrac{5\pi}{6}\right) - \cdots\right]$

13.11 $g(t) = 2 + 11.46\sin(0.785t - 135°) - 3.820\sin(2.356t - 45°) + \cdots$

13.12 $g(t) = 5 + \dfrac{60}{\pi}\left[\cos\left(t - \dfrac{7\pi}{6}\right) - \tfrac{1}{3}\cos 3\left(t - \dfrac{7\pi}{6}\right)\right.$

$\quad\quad\quad\quad\quad \left. + \tfrac{1}{5}\cos 5\left(t - \dfrac{7\pi}{6}\right) - \cdots\right]$

13.13 $\displaystyle\sum_{\substack{n=-\infty \\ n\neq 0}}^{\infty}\dfrac{jE}{n\pi}e^{jn\omega_0 t}, \quad\quad \omega_0 = 2\pi/T$

13.14 $\quad\cdots -\dfrac{2jE}{5\pi}\epsilon^{-j5\omega_0 t}-\dfrac{2jE}{3\pi}\epsilon^{-j3\omega_0 t}-\dfrac{2jE}{\pi}\epsilon^{-j\omega_0 t}+\dfrac{2jE}{\pi}\epsilon^{j\omega_0 t}+\dfrac{2jE}{3\pi}\epsilon^{j3\omega_0 t}$

$\qquad +\dfrac{2jE}{5\pi}\epsilon^{j5\omega_0 t}+\cdots$

13.15 $\quad\dfrac{A}{T}\left(\cdots+\epsilon^{-j(5\pi t/T)}+\epsilon^{-j(3\pi t/T)}+\epsilon^{-j(\pi t/T)}+\epsilon^{j(\pi t/T)}+\epsilon^{j(3\pi t/T)}+\epsilon^{j(5\pi t/T)}+\cdots\right)$

13.16 $\quad\dfrac{1}{2}+\dfrac{3}{\pi}\left(\cdots+\frac{1}{5}\epsilon^{-j5\pi t}-\frac{1}{3}\epsilon^{-j3\pi t}+\epsilon^{-j\pi t}+\epsilon^{j\pi t}-\frac{1}{3}\epsilon^{j3\pi t}+\frac{1}{5}\epsilon^{j5\pi t}-\cdots\right)$

$\qquad +\dfrac{4}{j\pi}\left(\cdots-\frac{1}{5}\epsilon^{-j10\pi t}-\frac{1}{3}\epsilon^{-j6\pi t}-\epsilon^{-j2\pi t}+\epsilon^{j2\pi t}+\frac{1}{3}\epsilon^{j6\pi t}+\frac{1}{5}\epsilon^{j10\pi t}+\cdots\right)$

13.17 $\quad i_1 = 102.7\sin(377t-48.2°)+2.96\sin(3\times377t-84.5°)$

$\qquad\qquad +1.53\sin(5\times377t+93.1°)$

$\qquad i_2 = 41.2\sin(377t+66.3°)+7.44\sin(3\times377t-68.9°)$

$\qquad\qquad +3.30\sin(5\times377t+100.2°)$

$\qquad i = 93.5\sin(377t-24.5°)+10.3\sin(3\times377t-73.3°)$

$\qquad\qquad +4.82\sin(5\times377t+97.9°)$

13.18 $\quad$ 52.8 kW, $\qquad$ 13.3 kW, $\qquad$ 66.1 kW

13.19 $\quad$ $24.76 - 0.726\sin(377t-59.22°)+0.0385\cos(2\times377t-74.76°)$ V

Chapter 14

14.1

(a) $\quad\dfrac{A}{b\omega^2}[(j\omega b+1)\epsilon^{-j\omega b}-1]$

(b) $\quad\dfrac{2\omega_0\cos(\pi\omega/2\omega_0)}{\omega_0^2-\omega^2}$

(c) $\quad\dfrac{2}{j\omega}\dfrac{\sin(\omega T/2)}{\omega T/2}-\dfrac{2}{j\omega}\cos\dfrac{\omega T}{2}$

(d) $\quad\dfrac{2v}{P\omega^2}(\cos\omega P-\cos2\omega P)$

(e) $\quad\dfrac{2\sin2\omega}{\omega}-\dfrac{2\sin\omega}{\omega}$

14.2 (a) $\quad\dfrac{2a}{a^2+\omega^2}$

(b) $\quad\dfrac{1}{(a+j\omega)^2}$

(c) $\quad-\dfrac{2j\omega}{a^2+\omega^2}$

(d) $\quad\dfrac{\pi}{a}\epsilon^{-a|\omega|}$

14.3 $a_1 = 0.11188$; $\quad b_1 = 0.15399$

14.5 $\dfrac{E}{R}[1-\epsilon^{-(R/L)(t+a)}]\,u_{-1}(t+a) - \dfrac{E}{R}[1+\epsilon^{-(R/L)(t-a)}u_{-1}(t-a)]$

14.8 (a) $\dfrac{2}{1+(2\pi t)^2}$ $\quad$ (b) $\quad -\dfrac{4\pi t}{1+(2\pi t)^2}$

14.12 $\dfrac{j2\omega}{(a+j\omega)(2j\omega+2+1/j\omega)}$

14.13 $\sqrt{2\pi/\omega}$

14.14 $\dfrac{1}{2j}[G(\omega-\omega_c)-G(\omega+\omega_c)]$

14.16 0.447 m

14.17 $\dfrac{1}{\pi}s(t)$

14.18 (a) $-j\pi[u_0(\omega-\omega_0)-u_0(\omega+\omega_0)]$

$\quad$ (b) $\dfrac{\pi}{2}[u_0(\omega-\omega_0)+u_0(\omega+\omega_0)] + \dfrac{j\omega}{\omega_0^2-\omega^2}$

$\quad$ (c) $\dfrac{\pi}{2j}[u_0(\omega-\omega_0)-u_0(\omega+\omega_0)] + \dfrac{\omega_0}{\omega_0^2-\omega^2}$

$\quad$ (d) $\sqrt{2\pi}\sigma\epsilon^{-\omega^2\sigma^2/2}$

$\quad$ (e) $\dfrac{\pi}{2}[u_0(\omega-\omega_1-\omega_2)+u_0(\omega+\omega_1+\omega_2)+u_0(\omega-\omega_1+\omega_2)$

$\qquad +u_0(\omega+\omega_1-\omega_2)]$

$\quad$ (f) $\dfrac{\pi}{4}[u_0(\omega-\omega_1-\omega_2)+u_0(\omega+\omega_1+\omega_2)$

$\qquad + u_0(\omega-\omega_1+\omega_2)+u_0(\omega+\omega_1-\omega_2)]$

$\qquad +\dfrac{1}{2}\left[\dfrac{j\omega}{(\omega_1+\omega_2)^2-\omega^2} + \dfrac{j\omega}{(\omega_1-\omega_2)^2-\omega^2}\right]$

Chapter 15

15.1 (a) $\dfrac{1}{s+a} - \dfrac{1}{s+b}$, $\quad -a < \sigma < -b$

$\quad$ (b) $\dfrac{1}{s+a} - \dfrac{1}{s+b}$, $\quad -b < \sigma < -a$

15.2 (a) $\epsilon^{-t}u_{-1}(-t) - 2\epsilon^{-2t}u_{-1}(-t)$

$\quad$ (b) $\epsilon^{-t}u_{-1}(-t) + 2\epsilon^{-2t}u_{-1}(t)$

$\quad$ (c) $-\epsilon^{-t}u_{-1}(t) + 2\epsilon^{-2t}u_{-1}(t)$

15.3 (a) Does not exist. (b) $-1 < \sigma < 0$

15.4 (a) $\dfrac{2}{(s+1)^3}$, $\sigma > -1$; (b) $\dfrac{2\beta}{(s^2+\beta^2)^2}$, $\sigma > 0$

15.5 (a) $(2/s^2)(1-\epsilon^{-s}-2\epsilon^{-2s}+2\epsilon^{-3s}) + (2/s)\epsilon^{-3s}$

(b) $(2/s)(1-\epsilon^{-s}-\epsilon^{-2s}+\epsilon^{-3s})$

(c) $\dfrac{1}{s(1+\epsilon^{-s})}$

(d) $(1+\epsilon^{-\pi s})/(s^2+1)$

(e) $(1-\epsilon^{-2\pi s})/(s^2+1)$

(f) $\epsilon^{-\pi s}/(s^2+1)$

15.6 (a) $\dfrac{1}{s(1-\epsilon^{-s})}$ (b) $\dfrac{1-\epsilon^{-(s+2)}}{(s+2)(1-\epsilon^{-s})}$

15.8 (a) $t - 2 + 3\epsilon^{-t}$

(b) $2u_0(t) - \tfrac{1}{2}(\epsilon^{-t}+\epsilon^{-t/2})$

(c) $u_0(t) - 2\epsilon^{-t}\sin t$

(d) $t^2 + t - 2 + 2\cos t - \sin t$

(e) $\tfrac{1}{5} + \tfrac{1}{10}\epsilon^{t}(-2\cos 2t + \sin 2t)$

(f) $-1 - \dfrac{t^2}{2} + \cosh t$

(g) $2[u_{-1}(t-1)-u_{-1}(t-3)+u_{-1}(t-5)-u_{-1}(t-7)+\cdots]$

(h) $2[u_{-1}(t-1)+u_{-1}(t-3)+u_{-1}(t-5)+u_{-1}(t-7)+\cdots]$

(i) $(1-\epsilon^{-t})^n$

15.9 (a) $y(x) = \epsilon^{-x}$

(b) $y(x) = 1 + \tfrac{3}{2}(\epsilon^{-x}-\epsilon^{-3x})$

(c) $y(x) = \tfrac{1}{3}x^3 + 2\epsilon^{-x} + 2$

15.10 $i(t) = 2t\epsilon^{-t}$

15.11 $e_o(t) = \tfrac{1}{2}(t-1)\epsilon^{-t}$

15.12 $i_L(t) = 2 - \epsilon^{-t/2}$

15.13 $i_2(t) = \tfrac{1}{2} - \tfrac{1}{10}\epsilon^{-2t} - \tfrac{2}{5}\epsilon^{-(1/3)t}$

15.14 $i_1(t) = 3.33 + 1.22\epsilon^{-6.34t} - 4.55\epsilon^{-23.66t}$

15.15 $e_2(t) = -1020(\epsilon^{-0.155t}-\epsilon^{-0.645t})$

15.16 $i_2(t) = 2 + \epsilon^{-2t}(\cos 2t - \sin 2t)$

15.17 $i_1(t) = \epsilon^{-t}\left[\cos\dfrac{t}{\sqrt{3}} + \dfrac{1}{\sqrt{3}}\sin\dfrac{t}{\sqrt{3}}\right]$

15.18 $e_2(t) = \epsilon^{-(3/2)t}\left[2\cos\dfrac{\sqrt{15}}{2}t + \dfrac{2}{\sqrt{15}}\sin\dfrac{\sqrt{15}}{2}t\right]$

15.19 (a) $f(0) = 7$, $\qquad f(\infty) = 0$

(b) $f(0) = 1$, $\qquad f(\infty) = \frac{3}{8}$

(c) $f(0) = 0$, $\qquad f(\infty) = 0$

(d) $f(0) = 1$, $\qquad f(\infty) = 1$

15.20 $-\dfrac{1}{s(s+1)}$

15.21 (b) $f(t) = 2\epsilon^{-2t}u_{-1}(t) + \epsilon^{-t}u_{-1}(t)$

Chapter 16

16.1 (a)

$$
\begin{bmatrix} \dfrac{dv_C}{dt} \\ \dfrac{di_L}{dt} \end{bmatrix} = \begin{bmatrix} -\dfrac{1}{RC} & -\dfrac{1}{C} \\ \dfrac{1}{L} & 0 \end{bmatrix} \begin{bmatrix} v_C \\ i_L \end{bmatrix} + \begin{bmatrix} \dfrac{1}{RC} \\ 0 \end{bmatrix} e_s
$$

(b)

$$
\begin{bmatrix} \dfrac{dv_C}{dt} \\ \dfrac{di_L}{dt} \end{bmatrix} = \begin{bmatrix} -\dfrac{1}{CR_1} & -\dfrac{1}{C} \\ \dfrac{1}{L} & -\dfrac{R_2}{L} \end{bmatrix} \begin{bmatrix} v_C \\ i_L \end{bmatrix} + \begin{bmatrix} \dfrac{1}{C} \\ 0 \end{bmatrix} i_s
$$

(c)

$$
\begin{bmatrix} \dfrac{di_1}{dt} \\ \dfrac{dv_2}{dt} \\ \dfrac{dv_3}{dt} \end{bmatrix} = \begin{bmatrix} 0 & 1 & -1 \\ -\frac{1}{2} & -\frac{1}{2} & 0 \\ \frac{1}{2} & 0 & 0 \end{bmatrix} \begin{bmatrix} i_1 \\ v_2 \\ v_3 \end{bmatrix} + \begin{bmatrix} 0 \\ \frac{1}{2} \\ 0 \end{bmatrix} e_s
$$

16.2 (a)

$$
\begin{bmatrix} \dfrac{dv_1}{dt} \\ \dfrac{di_2}{dt} \end{bmatrix} = \begin{bmatrix} -\dfrac{R_1+R_2+R_3}{CR_1(R_2+R_3)} & \dfrac{R_3}{C(R_2+R_3)} \\ -\dfrac{R_3}{L(R_2+R_3)} & -\dfrac{R_2R_3}{L(R_2+R_3)} \end{bmatrix} \begin{bmatrix} v_1 \\ i_2 \end{bmatrix}
$$

$$
+ \begin{bmatrix} \dfrac{1}{CR_1} \\ \dfrac{1}{L} \end{bmatrix} e_s
$$

(b)
$$
\begin{bmatrix} \dfrac{dv_1}{dt} \\[2ex] \dfrac{di_2}{dt} \\[2ex] \dfrac{di_3}{dt} \end{bmatrix}
=
\begin{bmatrix}
-\dfrac{1}{C(R_1+R_3)} & -\dfrac{R_1}{C(R_1+R_3)} & -\dfrac{1}{C} \\[3ex]
\dfrac{R_1}{L_1(R_1+R_3)} & -\dfrac{R_1 R_3}{L_1(R_1+R_3)} & 0 \\[3ex]
\dfrac{1}{L_2} & 0 & 0
\end{bmatrix}
\begin{bmatrix} v_1 \\ i_2 \\ i_3 \end{bmatrix}
$$

$$
+
\begin{bmatrix}
\dfrac{1}{C(R_1+R_3)} \\[3ex]
\dfrac{R_3}{L_1(R_1+R_3)} \\[3ex]
0
\end{bmatrix}
e_s
$$

16.3
$$
\begin{bmatrix} \dfrac{dv_1}{dt} \\[2ex] \dfrac{dv_2}{dt} \\[2ex] \dfrac{di_3}{dt} \end{bmatrix}
=
\begin{bmatrix}
-1 & 0 & -1 \\
0 & 0 & 1 \\
\frac{1}{2} & -\frac{1}{2} & 0
\end{bmatrix}
\begin{bmatrix} v_1 \\ v_2 \\ i_3 \end{bmatrix}
+
\begin{bmatrix}
1 & 0 \\
0 & 1 \\
0 & 0
\end{bmatrix}
\begin{bmatrix} e_s \\ i_s \end{bmatrix}
$$

16.4 (a)
$$
\begin{bmatrix} \dfrac{dv_1}{dt} \\[2ex] \dfrac{dv_2}{dt} \\[2ex] \dfrac{di_3}{dt} \\[2ex] \dfrac{di_4}{dt} \end{bmatrix}
=
\begin{bmatrix}
0 & 0 & -\dfrac{1}{C_1} & 0 \\[3ex]
0 & 0 & 0 & \dfrac{1}{C_2} \\[3ex]
\dfrac{L_4}{|L|} & \dfrac{M}{|L|} & -\dfrac{R_5 L_4}{|L|} & \dfrac{R_6 M}{|L|} \\[3ex]
-\dfrac{M}{|L|} & -\dfrac{L_3}{|L|} & \dfrac{R_5 M}{|L|} & -\dfrac{R_6 L_3}{|L|}
\end{bmatrix}
\begin{bmatrix} v_1 \\ v_2 \\ i_3 \\ i_4 \end{bmatrix}
$$

$$
+
\begin{bmatrix}
0 \\[2ex]
0 \\[2ex]
\dfrac{R_5 L_4}{|L|} \\[2ex]
-\dfrac{R_5 M}{|L|}
\end{bmatrix}
i_s
$$

where $|L| = L_3 L_4 - M^2$.

$$\begin{bmatrix} \dfrac{dv_1}{dt} \\[2ex] \dfrac{dv_2}{dt} \\[2ex] \dfrac{di_3}{dt} \\[2ex] \dfrac{di_4}{dt} \\[2ex] \dfrac{di_5}{dt} \end{bmatrix} = \begin{bmatrix} -\frac{3}{4} & \frac{3}{4} & -\frac{3}{4} & -\frac{3}{2} & -\frac{1}{4} \\[1ex] \frac{3}{8} & -\frac{3}{8} & -\frac{1}{8} & \frac{1}{4} & -\frac{3}{8} \\[1ex] \frac{1}{12} & \frac{1}{4} & -\frac{1}{4} & -\frac{1}{6} & -\frac{1}{12} \\[1ex] \frac{1}{8} & \frac{1}{8} & -\frac{1}{8} & -\frac{1}{4} & -\frac{1}{8} \\[1ex] \frac{3}{20} & \frac{1}{20} & -\frac{1}{20} & -\frac{1}{10} & -\frac{3}{20} \end{bmatrix} \begin{bmatrix} v_1 \\[1ex] v_2 \\[1ex] i_3 \\[1ex] i_4 \\[1ex] i_5 \end{bmatrix}$$

$$+ \begin{bmatrix} -\frac{3}{4} & 0 \\[1ex] \frac{3}{8} & \frac{1}{2} \\[1ex] \frac{1}{12} & 0 \\[1ex] \frac{1}{8} & 0 \\[1ex] \frac{3}{20} & 0 \end{bmatrix} \begin{bmatrix} e_s \\[1ex] i_s \end{bmatrix}$$

(c) $$\begin{bmatrix} \dfrac{dv_1}{dt} \\[2ex] \dfrac{di_2}{dt} \\[2ex] \dfrac{di_3}{dt} \\[2ex] \dfrac{di_4}{dt} \end{bmatrix} = \begin{bmatrix} 0 & -\frac{1}{2} & 0 & \frac{3}{4} \\[1ex] \frac{1}{2} & -1 & 1 & 0 \\[1ex] 0 & \frac{2}{3} & -\frac{4}{3} & \frac{2}{3} \\[1ex] 0 & 0 & 2 & -1 \end{bmatrix} \begin{bmatrix} v_1 \\[1ex] i_2 \\[1ex] i_3 \\[1ex] i_4 \end{bmatrix} + \begin{bmatrix} \frac{1}{2} \\[1ex] 0 \\[1ex] 0 \\[1ex] 0 \end{bmatrix} i_s$$

16.5 (a) $\begin{bmatrix} 0.5 & -0.864 \\ -0.288 & 0.5 \end{bmatrix} \epsilon^{-0.268t} + \begin{bmatrix} 0.5 & 0.864 \\ 0.288 & 0.5 \end{bmatrix} \epsilon^{-3.732t}$

(b) $\begin{bmatrix} 3 & 2.5 & 0.5 \\ -3 & -2.5 & -0.5 \\ 3 & 2.5 & 0.5 \end{bmatrix} \epsilon^{-t} + \begin{bmatrix} -3 & -4 & -1 \\ 6 & 8 & 2 \\ -12 & -16 & -4 \end{bmatrix} \epsilon^{-2t}$

$+ \begin{bmatrix} 1 & 1.5 & 0.5 \\ -3 & -4.5 & -1.5 \\ 9 & 13.5 & 4.5 \end{bmatrix} \epsilon^{-3t}$

16.6 (a) $\begin{bmatrix} \cos 0.4t + 1.04 \sin 0.4t & -0.834 \sin 0.4t \\ 2.5 \sin 0.4t & \cos 0.4t - 1.04 \sin 0.4t \end{bmatrix} \epsilon^{-7/12t}$

(b) $\begin{bmatrix} 0.4918 & 0.5077 & 0.1249 \\ 0.5077 & 0.5240 & 0.1289 \\ -0.06245 & -0.06447 & -0.01587 \end{bmatrix} \epsilon^{-3.9375t}$

$+ \begin{bmatrix} 0.5082 & -0.5077 & -0.1249 \\ -0.5077 & 0.4760 & -0.1289 \\ 0.06245 & 0.06447 & 1.0159 \end{bmatrix} \epsilon^{-0.03124t} \cos 0.50298t$

$+ \begin{bmatrix} -0.09463 & -0.03358 & -1.0181 \\ -0.03358 & 0.1557 & 1.0013 \\ 0.5091 & -0.5006 & -0.0611 \end{bmatrix} \epsilon^{-0.03124t} \sin 0.50298t$

16.7 (a) $\begin{bmatrix} \dfrac{dv_1}{dt} \\[2ex] \dfrac{dv_2}{dt} \\[2ex] \dfrac{di_3}{dt} \end{bmatrix} = \begin{bmatrix} -\dfrac{1}{C_1 R_7} & \dfrac{1}{C_1 R_7} & -\dfrac{1}{C_1} \\[2ex] \dfrac{1}{C_2 R_7} & -\dfrac{1}{C_2 R_7} & 0 \\[2ex] \dfrac{1}{L_3 + L_4} & 0 & -\dfrac{R_5 + R_6}{L_3 + L_4} \end{bmatrix} \begin{bmatrix} v_1 \\[2ex] v_2 \\[2ex] i_3 \end{bmatrix}$

$+ \begin{bmatrix} \dfrac{1}{C_1} \\[2ex] 0 \\[2ex] \dfrac{L_4}{L_3 + L_4} \times \dfrac{d}{dt} + \dfrac{R_5}{L_3 + L_4} \end{bmatrix} i_s$

(b) $\begin{bmatrix} \dfrac{dv_1}{dt} \\[2ex] \dfrac{dv_2}{dt} \\[2ex] \dfrac{di_3}{dt} \end{bmatrix} = \begin{bmatrix} -\dfrac{C_2 + C_4}{R_5 |C|} & -\dfrac{C_4}{R_6 |C|} & -\dfrac{C_2}{|C|} \\[2ex] -\dfrac{C_4}{R_5 |C|} & -\dfrac{C_1 + C_4}{R_6 |C|} & \dfrac{C_1}{|C|} \\[2ex] \dfrac{1}{L_3} & -\dfrac{1}{L_3} & 0 \end{bmatrix} \begin{bmatrix} v_1 \\[2ex] v_2 \\[2ex] i_3 \end{bmatrix}$

$+ \begin{bmatrix} \dfrac{C_2 + C_4}{R_5 |C|} \\[2ex] \dfrac{C_4}{R_5 |C|} \\[2ex] 0 \end{bmatrix} e_s$

where $|C| = C_1 C_2 + C_1 C_4 + C_2 C_4$.

Chapter 17

17.2 (a) $F = A + C$;   (b) $F = A + \bar{B} + C$

17.4 (a) $AC + \bar{A}B$;   (b) $A(B + \bar{C})$;   (c) $B(A + D)$

17.7 10110

17.8 1001101

17.11 (a) and (b) EXCLUSIVE-OR

Appendix B

B.1 $[A] + [B] = \begin{bmatrix} 6 & 6 & 11 \\ 0 & -1 & 14 \\ 5 & 2 & -6 \end{bmatrix}$; $|[A] + [B]| = 343$;

$|[A]| = 63$; $|[B]| = -26$; $[A][B] = \begin{bmatrix} 9 & 33 & 49 \\ 8 & 4 & -38 \\ 2 & 7 & 17 \end{bmatrix}$;

$[B][A] = \begin{bmatrix} 33 & -18 & 3 \\ 33 & -20 & -11 \\ -2 & 0 & 17 \end{bmatrix}$; $|[A][B]| = -1638$

B.2 $\begin{bmatrix} 22 & -3 & 4 \\ -4 & -10 & 0 \\ -35 & 14 & -7 \\ 49 & -37 & 11 \end{bmatrix}$

B.3 $\begin{bmatrix} 5 & 3 \\ 6 & 2+j7 \\ 8 & 85 \end{bmatrix}, \begin{bmatrix} 5 & 3 \\ 6 & 2+j7 \\ 8 & 85 \end{bmatrix}, \begin{bmatrix} 0 & 0 & 0 \\ 0 & 0 & 0 \\ 0 & 0 & 0 \end{bmatrix},$

$\begin{bmatrix} 4 & -2 \\ 25 & -10 \\ 6 & 7 \end{bmatrix} \begin{bmatrix} 4 & 25 & 6 \\ -2 & -10 & 7 \end{bmatrix}, \begin{bmatrix} 2x + 3y + 2z \\ 2x + 5y \\ 2x + 7y + 6z \end{bmatrix}$

B.5 $-\frac{25}{24}$

B.6 $\begin{bmatrix} -17 & -26 & 81 \\ 0 & 0 & 0 \\ 54 & 47 & -179 \end{bmatrix}$

B.7 $\begin{bmatrix} 14 & 0 & -15 \\ 0 & 0 & 0 \\ -15 & 0 & 30 \end{bmatrix}$

B.8 $\quad x = \frac{80}{11}, \qquad y = -\frac{10}{11}, \qquad z = \frac{1}{8}$

B.9 $\quad \begin{bmatrix} \frac{1}{3} & 0 & -\frac{5}{6} \\ 0 & 0 & \frac{1}{2} \\ -\frac{5}{6} & \frac{1}{2} & \frac{11}{6} \end{bmatrix}$

B.10 $\quad x = \frac{9}{38}a - \frac{11}{19}b - \frac{7}{38}c$

$\qquad y = -\frac{1}{19}a + \frac{13}{19}b + \frac{5}{19}c$

$\qquad z = \frac{1}{38}a + \frac{3}{19}b - \frac{5}{38}c$

B.11 $\quad a = \pm j\sqrt{3}, \qquad b = \pm j\sqrt{3}, \qquad c = -2$

$\qquad a = \pm j\sqrt{3}, \qquad b = \mp j\sqrt{3}, \qquad c = 2$

B.19 $\quad \begin{bmatrix} I_1 \\ I_2 \end{bmatrix} = \begin{bmatrix} -\frac{29}{674} & \frac{97}{674} \\ \frac{123}{674} & -\frac{179}{674} \end{bmatrix} \begin{bmatrix} E_1 \\ E_2 \end{bmatrix}$

B.20 $\quad \begin{bmatrix} E_1 \\ E_2 \\ E_3 \end{bmatrix} = \frac{1}{11} \begin{bmatrix} 98 & -46 & -25 \\ -46 & 84 & -6 \\ -25 & -6 & 68 \end{bmatrix} \begin{bmatrix} I_1 \\ I_2 \\ I_3 \end{bmatrix}$

B.21 $\quad \begin{bmatrix} E_1 \\ E_2 \end{bmatrix} = \frac{1}{68} \begin{bmatrix} 549 & -298 \\ -298 & 516 \end{bmatrix} \begin{bmatrix} I_1 \\ I_2 \end{bmatrix}$

INDEX